VOLUME 95

VECTOR MEASURES

VECTOR MEASURES

by

N. DINCULEANU

Bucharest

PERGAMON PRESS

OXFORD · LONDON · EDINBURGH · NEW YORK
TORONTO · SYDNEY · PARIS · BRAUNSCHWEIG

VEB DEUTSCHER VERLAG DER WISSENSCHAFTEN

BERLIN

Pergamon Press Ltd., Headington Hill Hall, Oxford
4 & 5 Fitzroy Square, London W.1
Pergamon Press (Scotland) Ltd., 2 & 3 Teviot Place, Edinburgh 1
Pergamon Press Inc., 44–01 21st Street, Long Island City, New York 11101
Pergamon of Canada, Ltd., 6 Adelaide Street East, Toronto, Ontario
Pergamon Press (Aust.) Pty. Ltd., 20–22 Margaret Street, Sydney, N.S.W.
Pergamon Press S.A.R.L., 24 rue des Écoles, Paris 5e
Vieweg & Sohn GmbH, Burgplatz 1, Braunschweig

Hochschulbücher für Mathematik, Band 64
Herausgegeben von H. Grell, K. Maruhn und W. Rinow

First English edition 1967

The Library of Congress Catalog Card No. 66-28055

3115/67

PREFACE

This book contains the material of a special course of Measure Theory delivered at the University of Bucharest. As the title shows, the book is devoted especially to the study of measures with values in a Banach space. However, the positive measures (with finite or infinite values) are also treated in detail, for most of the properties of a vector measure are derived from the corresponding properties of its variation, which is a positive measure.

Prerequisites for reading the book are a familiarity with general topology and elementary properties of Banach spaces.

The first chapter contains: classes of sets, set functions, variation and semi-variation of set functions, and extension of set functions from a certain class to a wider one.

It appears that the semi-tribe is the natural domain of definition of a vector measure. In fact, even for a positive measure which takes also the value ∞, in the definition of the integral are used only the sets of finite measure, which form a semi-tribe. The extension of a positive measure is made from a clan to a tribe which contains always the whole space. This tribe contains all the Borel sets in case the initial clan is generated by the compact parts of a locally compact space.

The second chapter is devoted to the integration of vector functions with respect to vector measures. Beside the study of the measurable functions (with respect to a tribe or to a measure) and of the integrable functions, this chapter contains: the spaces $\mathscr{L}^p$ and the integral representation of the linear operations on the spaces $\mathscr{L}^p$ or on the spaces of totally measurable functions, vector measures defined by densities, absolutely continuous measures and the Lebesgue–Nikodym theorem (for vector measures), conditional expectations, martingales and the recent results concerning the existence of a lifting of the space $\mathscr{L}^\infty$. The existence of the lifting made it possible to drop the countability hypotheses on the Banach spaces involved in the Lebesgue–Nikodym theorem and in the integral representation of the linear operations on $\mathscr{L}^p$.

The last chapter is devoted to the regular measures on a locally compact space and to the integral representation of the dominated operations on the space of continuous functions with compact carrier.

Many important topics, as, for example, product measures and the Lebesgue–Fubini theorem, are not included in the present book.

The book is greatly influenced by many excellent monographs on Measure Theory, especially by those of Halmos [1], Bourbaki [3], Dunford and Schwartz [1], and M. Nicolescu [3].

N. Dinculeanu

CONTENTS

Chapter I. Vector measures

Chapter II. Integration

CHAPTER I

VECTOR MEASURES

§ 1. CLASSES OF SETS

1. CLANS

Let T be a set. A set of subsets of T will be called a *class* of subsets of T.

Definition 1. *A nonvoid class $\mathscr{C}$ of subsets of T is called a clan*[1]) *if:*

1. $A - B \in \mathscr{C}$, *for* $A, B \in \mathscr{C}$;

2. $A \cup B \in \mathscr{C}$, *for* $A, B \in \mathscr{C}$.

From this definition we deduce that a clan $\mathscr{C}$ has also the following properties:

3. $\emptyset \in \mathscr{C}$.

As $\mathscr{C}$ is nonvoid, there is a set $A \in \mathscr{C}$. Then, by property 1, we have

$$\emptyset = A - A \in \mathscr{C}.$$

4. $A \cap B \in \mathscr{C}$, *for* $A, B \in \mathscr{C}$.

For $A, B \in \mathscr{C}$ we have, by property 1, $A - B \in \mathscr{C}$, therefore

$$A \cap B = A - (A - B) \in \mathscr{C}.$$

5. $\bigcup_{i=1}^{n} A_i \in \mathscr{C}$ *and* $\bigcap_{i=1}^{n} A_i \in \mathscr{C}$ *for every finite family* $(A_i)_{1 \leqq i \leqq n}$ *of sets of* $\mathscr{C}$.

The proof is made by complete induction, using only the properties 2 and 4.

Examples of clans: $\{\emptyset\}$; the set $\mathscr{P}(T)$ of all the subsets of T; $\{\emptyset, A, B, B - A\}$ if $A \subset B$.

We deduce easily that the intersection of an arbitrary family $(\mathscr{C}_\alpha)_{\alpha \in I}$ of clans is also a clan.

The union of a family of clans is not necessarily a clan. However, if $(\mathscr{C}_\alpha)_{\alpha \in I}$ is a *filtering* family of clans (i.e. for every $\alpha, \beta \in I$ there exists $\gamma \in I$ such that $\mathscr{C}_\alpha \subset \mathscr{C}_\gamma$ and $\mathscr{C}_\beta \subset \mathscr{C}_\gamma$), then the union of this family is also a clan.

---

[1]) The clan is also called a *ring* (Halmos [1]).

Proposition 1. *For every class $\mathscr{A}$ of subsets of T there exists a smallest clan containing $\mathscr{A}$.*

The set of the clans which contain $\mathscr{A}$ is nonvoid, because $\mathscr{P}(T)$ is a clan containing $\mathscr{A}$. The intersection $\mathscr{C}$ of all the clans containing $\mathscr{A}$ is also a clan containing $\mathscr{A}$. For every clan $\mathscr{C}' \supset \mathscr{A}$ we have $\mathscr{C} \subset \mathscr{C}'$, therefore $\mathscr{C}$ is the smallest clan containing $\mathscr{A}$.

The smallest clan containing $\mathscr{A}$ is called the *clan generated by* $\mathscr{A}$ and is denoted by $\mathscr{C}(\mathscr{A})$.

The clan generated by the void class is $\{\emptyset\}$.

Proposition 2. *If $\mathscr{A}$ is a countable class, then the clan $\mathscr{C}$ generated by $\mathscr{A}$ is also countable.*

Let $\mathscr{C}_1$ be the class of the finite unions of sets of $\mathscr{A}$, $\mathscr{D}_1$ the class of the differences of sets of $\mathscr{C}_1$, $\mathscr{C}_2$ the class of the finite unions of sets of $\mathscr{D}_1$, $\mathscr{D}_2$ the class of the differences of sets of $\mathscr{C}_2$, etc. It is clear that every class $\mathscr{C}_n$ is countable, therefore the class $\mathscr{C} = \bigcup_{n=1}^{\infty} \mathscr{C}_n$ is also countable If $A, B \in \mathscr{C}$ there exists an index n such that $A, B \in \mathscr{C}_n$. Then $A \cup B \in \mathscr{C}_n$ and $A - B \in \mathscr{D}_n \subset \mathscr{C}_{n+1}$ therefore $A \cup B \in \mathscr{C}$ and $A - B \in \mathscr{C}$, consequently $\mathscr{C}$ is a clan.

We verify easily that $\mathscr{C}$ is the smallest clan containing $\mathscr{A}$, i.e. $\mathscr{C} = \mathscr{C}(\mathscr{A})$.

2. TRIBES

Definition 2. *A nonvoid class $\mathscr{T}$ of subsets of T is called a tribe*[1]) *if:*

1. $A - B \in \mathscr{T}$, *for* $A, B \in \mathscr{T}$;

2. $\bigcup_{i=1}^{\infty} A_i \in \mathscr{T}$, *for every sequence* (A_i) *of sets of* $\mathscr{T}$.

From this definition it follows that a tribe $\mathscr{T}$ of subsets of T has also the following properties:

3. $\emptyset \in \mathscr{T}$;

4. $\bigcap_{i=1}^{\infty} A_i \in \mathscr{T}$ *for every sequence* (A_i) *of sets of* $\mathscr{T}$;

We have $A = \bigcup_{i=1}^{\infty} A_i \in \mathscr{T}$ and $A - A_i \in \mathscr{T}$ for every i, therefore

$$\bigcap_{i=1}^{\infty} A_i = A - \bigcup_{i=1}^{\infty} (A - A_i) \in \mathscr{T}.$$

5. $A \cup B \in \mathscr{T}$, *for* $A, B \in \mathscr{T}$.

---

[1]) The tribe is also called σ-ring (Halmos [1]), or *borelian clan* (M. Nicolescu [3]).

We take $A_1 = A$ and $A_i = B$ for $i \geqq 2$, and we have

$$A \cup B = \bigcup_{i=1}^{\infty} A_i \in \mathscr{T}.$$

From properties 1 and 5 it follows that we can also define a tribe to be a clan having in addition the property 2 to contain the countable unions.

The classes: $\{\emptyset\}$; $\mathscr{P}(T)$; $\{\emptyset, A\}$; $\{\emptyset, A, B, B - A\}$ if $A \subset B$, are tribes.

The intersection of an arbitrary family of tribes is also a tribe.

The union of a family of tribes is not necessarily a tribe, even if this family is filtering.

However, if $(\mathscr{T}_\alpha)_{\alpha \in I}$ is a family of tribes having the property that every sequence of tribes of the family is contained in a tribe of the family, then the union of this family is also a tribe.

Proposition 3. *For every class $\mathscr{A}$ of subsets of T there exists a smallest tribe $\mathscr{T}$ containing $\mathscr{A}$.*

The proof is analogous to that of proposition 1.

The smallest tribe containing $\mathscr{A}$ is called the *tribe generated by the class* $\mathscr{A}$ and is denoted by $\mathscr{T}(\mathscr{A})$.

Proposition 4. *Let $\mathscr{A}$ be a class of subsets of T and $\mathscr{T}$ the tribe generated by $\mathscr{A}$. For every set $E \in \mathscr{T}$ there exists a sequence (A_n) of sets of $\mathscr{A}$ such that* $E \subset \bigcup_{n=1}^{\infty} A_n$.

Let us denote by $\mathscr{H}$ the class of all the subsets $E \subset T$ which can be covered by countable unions of sets of $\mathscr{A}$. It is easy to verify that $\mathscr{H}$ is a *tribe* containing $\mathscr{A}$. Then $\mathscr{T} \subset \mathscr{H}$, therefore every set $E \in \mathscr{T}$ can be covered by the union of a sequence (A_n) of sets of $\mathscr{A}$.

Proposition 5. *Let A be a class of subsets of T and $\mathscr{T}$ the tribe generated by $\mathscr{A}$. For every $E \in \mathscr{T}$ there exists a sequence (A_n) of sets of $\mathscr{A}$ such that E belongs to the tribe generated by the sets A_n.*

Let us consider all the tribes generated by sequences of sets of $\mathscr{A}$. Every sequence of such tribes is contained in a tribe of the same kind. We deduce that the union of all these tribes is a tribe containing $\mathscr{A}$, therefore containing $\mathscr{T}$. It follows that every set $E \in \mathscr{T}$ belongs to a tribe generated by a sequence of sets of $\mathscr{A}$.

3. SEMI-TRIBES

Definition 3. *A nonvoid class $\mathscr{S}$ of subsets of T is called a semi-tribe*[1]) *if:*

1. $A - B \in \mathscr{S}$, *for* $A, B \in \mathscr{S}$;

2. $A \cup B \in \mathscr{S}$, *for* $A, B \in \mathscr{S}$;

[1]) The semi-tribe is also called a δ-*clan* or a δ-*ring*.

3. $\bigcap_{i=1}^{\infty} A_i \in \mathcal{S}$, *for every sequence* (A_i) *of sets of* $\mathcal{S}$.

From this definition we deduce that a semi-tribe $\mathcal{S}$ is a clan having in addition the property 3.

A semi-tribe $\mathcal{S}$ has all the properties of a clan: $\emptyset \in \mathcal{S}$, $\bigcup_{i=1}^{n} A_i \in \mathcal{S}$ and $\bigcup_{i=1}^{n} A_i \in \mathcal{S}$ for every finite family $(A_i)_{1 \leq i \leq n}$ of sets of $\mathcal{S}$.

Every tribe is a semi-tribe, but a semi-tribe does not necessarily contain all the countable unions. However, a semi-tribe $\mathcal{S}$ has the following property:

4. *For every sequence* (A_i) *of sets of* $\mathcal{S}$ *contained in a set* $A \in \mathcal{S}$ *we have* $\bigcup_{i=1}^{\infty} A_i \in \mathcal{S}$.

In fact, for every i we have $A - A_i \in \mathcal{S}$, therefore

$$\bigcap_{i=1}^{\infty} (A - A_i) \in \mathcal{S}.$$

It follows that

$$\bigcup_{i=1}^{\infty} A_i = A - \bigcap_{i=1}^{\infty} (A - A_i) \in \mathcal{S}.$$

We see easily that the intersection of an arbitrary family of semi-tribes is also a semi-tribe.

Proposition 6. *For every class* $\mathcal{A}$ *of subsets of* T *there exists a smallest semi-tribe* $\mathcal{S}$ *containing* $\mathcal{A}$.

The proof is analogous to that of the proposition 1.

The smallest semi-tribe containing $\mathcal{A}$ is called the *semi-tribe generated by* $\mathcal{A}$ and is denoted by $\mathcal{S}(\mathcal{A})$.

Proposition 7. *Let* $(\mathcal{S}_\alpha)$ *be a filtering family of semi-tribes and put* $\mathcal{S} = \bigcup_\alpha \mathcal{S}_\alpha$. *If* $A, B \in \mathcal{S}$, $A \subset B$ *and* $B \in \mathcal{S}_\alpha$ *imply* $A \in \mathcal{S}_\alpha$, *then* $\mathcal{S}$ *is a semi-tribe.*

First we see that $\mathcal{S}$ is a clan. We have only to verify condition 3 in the definition of a semi-tribe.

Let (A_i) be a sequence of sets of $\mathcal{S}$. For each n put $B_n = \bigcap_{i=1}^{n} A_i$. We have $B_n \in \mathcal{S}$ for each n, and

$$\bigcap_{n=1}^{\infty} B_n = \bigcap_{i=1}^{\infty} A_i.$$

Let $\mathcal{S}_\alpha$ be a semi-tribe of the family such that $B_1 \in \mathcal{S}_\alpha$. As $B_n \subset B_1$ for each n, we have $B_n \in \mathcal{S}_\alpha$ and therefore

$$\bigcap_{i=1}^{\infty} A_i = \bigcap_{n=1}^{\infty} B_n \in \mathcal{S}_\alpha \subset \mathcal{S}.$$

Proposition 8. *A clan $\mathscr{C}$ is a semi-tribe, if and only if for every sequence (A_i) of sets of $\mathscr{C}$, contained in a set $A \in \mathscr{C}$, we have* $\bigcup_{i=1}^{\infty} A_i \in \mathscr{C}$.

We have already seen that every semi-tribe is a clan having the property 4. Conversely, suppose that $\mathscr{C}$ is a clan having the property 4. We have to prove that $\mathscr{C}$ has also the property 3 in the definition of a semi-tribe.

Let (A_i) be a sequence of sets of $\mathscr{C}$. For every n we have $A_1 - A_n \in \mathscr{C}$ and $A_1 - A_n \subset A_1$, therefore

$$\bigcup_{n=1}^{\infty} (A_1 - A_n) \in \mathscr{C}.$$

Then

$$\bigcap_{n=1}^{\infty} A_n = A_1 - \bigcup_{n=1}^{\infty} (A_1 - A_n)$$

hence

$$\bigcap_{n=1}^{\infty} A_n \in \mathscr{C}.$$

Remark. It follows that for a clan $\mathscr{C}$ conditions 3 and 4 are equivalent.

Proposition 9. *If $\mathscr{S}$ is a semi-tribe, then the class of all the countable unions of sets of $\mathscr{S}$ is equal to the tribe generated by $\mathscr{S}$.*

Let us denote by Φ the class of all the countable unions of sets of $\mathscr{S}$. If $A \in \mathscr{S}$, then taking $A_i = A$ for $i = 1, 2, \ldots$, we have $A = \bigcup_{i=1}^{\infty} A_i \in \Phi$, whence $\mathscr{S} \subset \Phi$.

Let $A, B \in \Phi$:

$$A = \bigcup_{i=1}^{\infty} A_i, \quad B = \bigcup_{j=1}^{\infty} B_j, \quad A_i, B_j \in \mathscr{S}.$$

Then $A_i - B_j \in \mathscr{S}$ for every i and j, therefore

$$\bigcap_{j=1}^{\infty} (A_i - B_j) \in \mathscr{S}$$

for each i, hence

$$A - B = A \cap \complement B = \left(\bigcup_{i=1}^{\infty} A_i\right) \cap \left(\bigcap_{j=1}^{\infty} \complement B_j\right) = \bigcup_{i=1}^{\infty} \left(\bigcap_{j=1}^{\infty} (A_i - B_j)\right) \in \Phi.$$

Let now (A_i) be a sequence of sets of Φ:

$$A_i = \bigcup_{j=1}^{\infty} A_{ij}, \quad A_{ij} \in \mathscr{S}.$$

Then

$$\bigcup_{i=1}^{\infty} A_i = \bigcup_{i,j=1}^{\infty} A_{ij} \in \Phi$$

therefore Φ is a tribe containing $\mathscr{S}$. It follows that $\mathscr{T}(\mathscr{S}) \subset \Phi$. On the other hand, every set $E \in \Phi$ is contained in $\mathscr{T}(\mathscr{S})$; hence $\Phi \subset \mathscr{T}(\mathscr{S})$ and therefore $\Phi = \mathscr{T}(\mathscr{S})$.

Corollary 1. *If $\mathscr{S}$ is a semi-tribe and $\mathscr{T}$ is the tribe generated by $\mathscr{S}$, then every set of $\mathscr{T}$ is the union of a sequence of disjoint sets of $\mathscr{S}$.*

Let $A \in \mathscr{T}$ and let (A_i) be a sequence of $\mathscr{S}$ with union A. We take $B_1 = A_1$ and $B_n = A_n - \bigcup_{i<n} A_i$ for $n \geqq 2$. Then $B_n \in \mathscr{S}$ for every n, the sets B_n are disjoint and

$$\bigcup_{n=1}^{\infty} B_n = \bigcup_{n=1}^{\infty} A_n = A.$$

Corollary 2. *Let $\mathscr{S}$ be a semi-tribe and $\mathscr{T}$ the tribe generated by $\mathscr{S}$. If a set $A \in \mathscr{T}$ is contained in a set $B \in \mathscr{S}$ then $A \in \mathscr{S}$.*

Let (A_n) be a sequence of sets of $\mathscr{S}$ with union A. Then $A_n \subset B$ for every n, hence, according to the proposition 8, $A \in \mathscr{S}$.

Corollary 3. *If $\mathscr{S}$ is a semi-tribe and $\mathscr{T}$ is the tribe generated by $\mathscr{S}$, then for every $E \in \mathscr{T}$ and $A \in \mathscr{S}$ we have $E \cap A \in \mathscr{S}$.*

Proposition 10. *Let $\mathscr{A}$ be a class of subsets of T and $\mathscr{S}$ the semi-tribe generated by $\mathscr{A}$. For every set $E \in \mathscr{S}$ there exists a finite family $(A_i)_{1 \leqq i \leqq n}$ of sets of $\mathscr{A}$ such that $E \subset \bigcup_{i=1}^{n} A_i$.*

The class $\mathscr{H}$ of all the subsets of T which can be covered by finite families of sets of $\mathscr{A}$, is a semi-tribe containing $\mathscr{A}$, therefore containing $\mathscr{S}$.

Corollary. *Let $\mathscr{C}$ be a clan and $\mathscr{S}$ the semi-tribe generated by $\mathscr{C}$. Every set of $\mathscr{S}$ is contained in a set of $\mathscr{C}$.*

Remark. The corollary remains valid if we suppose that $\mathscr{C}$ is a class having only the property to contain the union $A \cup B$ of every pair of sets $A, B \in \mathscr{C}$.

Proposition 11. *Let $\mathscr{A}$ be a class of subsets of T and $\mathscr{S}$ the semi-tribe generated by $\mathscr{A}$. Every set $E \in \mathscr{S}$ is contained in a semi-tribe generated by a sequence of sets of $\mathscr{A}$.*

The proof is similar to that of proposition 5, putting "semi-tribe" instead of "tribe".

4. SEMI-CLANS AND LATTICES

Definition 4. *A nonvoid class $\mathscr{P}$ of subsets of T is called a semi-clan*[1]) *if:*

1. $A \cap B \in \mathscr{P}$, *for* $A, B \in \mathscr{P}$;

2. *for every pair* (A, B) *of sets of* $\mathscr{P}$ *such that* $A \subset B$, *there exists a finite family* $(C_i)_{0 \leqq i \leqq n}$ *of sets of* $\mathscr{P}$, *such that*

$$A = C_0 \subset C_1 \subset \cdots \subset C_n = B \quad \text{ad n} \; C_i - C_{i-1} \in \mathscr{P} \quad \textit{for} \quad i = 1, 2, \ldots, n.$$

A semi-clan $\mathscr{P}$ of subsets of T has also the following property:

3. $\emptyset \in \mathscr{P}$.

We have only to take $A = B$ in the property 2, and we have $\emptyset = B - A \in \mathscr{P}$.

Every clan $\mathscr{C}$ is also a semi-clan, because if for every pair (A, B) of sets of $\mathscr{C}$ with $A \subset B$, we take $C_0 = A$ and $C_1 = B$, then $C_0, C_1 \in \mathscr{C}$ and $C_1 - C_0 = B - A \in \mathscr{C}$.

The class of all the intervals of the real line R of the form $[a, b)$ is a semi-clan.

In fact, the intersection of two such intervals is an interval of the same kind. On the other hand, if $[a, b) \subset [a', b')$, we take $C_0 = [a, b)$, $C_1 = [a', b)$ and $C_2 = [a', b')$ and the condition 2 in the definition of the semi-clan is fulfilled.

Definition 5. *A nonvoid class $\mathscr{L}$ of subsets of T is called a lattice, if:*

a) $A \cup B \in \mathscr{L}$, *for* $A, B \in \mathscr{L}$;

b) $A \cap B \in \mathscr{L}$, *for* $A, B \in \mathscr{L}$;

c) $\emptyset \in \mathscr{L}$.

Every clan is a lattice.

If T is a topological space, the class $\mathscr{G}$ of the open subsets of T, the class $\mathscr{F}$ of the closed subsets of T and the class $\mathscr{K}$ of the compact subsets of T, are lattices.

Proposition 12. *If $\mathscr{L}$ is a lattice of subsets of T, then the class $\mathscr{P}$ of the differences $A - B$ of sets $A, B \in \mathscr{L}$ is a semi-clan.*

We remark first that every set of $\mathscr{P}$ can be written in the form $A - B$ with $A, B \in \mathscr{L}$ and $B \subset A$. In fact, if $A, E \in \mathscr{L}$, then $B = A \cap E \in \mathscr{L}$, $B \subset A$ and $A - E = A - B$.

Let $E_1 = A_1 - B_1$ and $E_2 = A_2 - B_2$ with $A_1, A_2, B_1, B_2 \in \mathscr{L}$. Then $A_1 \cap A_2 \in \mathscr{L}$ and $B_1 \cup B_2 \in \mathscr{L}$, therefore

$$E_1 \cap E_2 = (A_1 - B_1) \cap (A_2 - B_2) = (A_1 \cap A_2) - (B_1 \cup B_2) \in \mathscr{P}$$

and thus the condition 1 in the definition of the semi-clan is verified.

---

[1]) The semi-clan is called also *semi-ring* (Halmos [1]).

Suppose now that $E_1 \subset E_2$ and that $B_i \subset A_i$, $i = 1, 2$. Then $A_1 \cap A_2 \in \mathscr{L}$ and $A_1 \cap B_2 \in \mathscr{L}$, therefore

$$F = (A_1 \cap A_2) - B_2 \in \mathscr{P}.$$

It is easy to see that $E_1 \subset F \subset E_2$ and

$$E_2 - F = A_2 - (A_1 \cup B_2) \in \mathscr{P},$$
$$F - E_1 = (A_2 \cap B_1) - B_2 \in \mathscr{P}$$

and thus the condition 2 in the definition of the semi-clan is also verified. It follows that $\mathscr{P}$ is a semi-clan.

From this proposition we deduce that if T is a topological space, the following classes of subsets of T are semi-clans:

the class of the differences $G_1 - G_2$ of open sets,
the class of the differences $F_1 - F_2$ of closed sets,
the class of the differences $K_1 - K_2$ of compact sets.

Proposition 13. *If $\mathscr{P}$ is a semi-clan, then the class of all the finite unions of disjoint sets of $\mathscr{P}$ is equal to the clan $\mathscr{C}$ generated by $\mathscr{P}$.*

Denote by Φ the class of all the finite unions of disjoint sets of $\mathscr{P}$. We have $\mathscr{P} \subset \Phi \subset \mathscr{C}$.

To prove the equality $\Phi = \mathscr{C}$, it is sufficient to show that Φ is a clan.

Let $E, F \in \Phi$:

$$E = \bigcup_{i=1}^{n} A_i, \quad F = \bigcup_{j=1}^{m} B_j$$

where each of the families $(A_i)_{1 \leqq i \leqq n}$ and $(B_j)_{1 \leqq j \leqq m}$ consists of mutually disjoint sets of $\mathscr{P}$.

We have to prove that $E - F \in \Phi$ and $E \cup F \in \Phi$. This will be made in several steps:

a) $E \cap F \in \Phi$.

In fact the sets $A_i \cap B_j$ are mutually disjoint and belong to $\mathscr{P}$, therefore

$$E \cap F = \bigcup_{i,j} (A_i \cap B_j) \in \Phi.$$

b) If E and F are disjoint, then $E \cup F \in \Phi$.

In fact, in this case, the family $A_1, \ldots, A_n, B_1, \ldots, B_m$ consists of mutually disjoint sets of $\mathscr{P}$, therefore

$$E \cup F = \left(\bigcup_{i=1}^{n} A_i\right) \cup \left(\bigcup_{j=1}^{m} B_j\right) \in \Phi.$$

c) If $A, B \in \mathscr{P}$, then $A - B \in \Phi$.

In fact, $\mathscr{P}$ is a semi-clan: we have $A \cap B \in \mathscr{P}$ and $A \cap B \subset A$; then, there exists a finite family $(C_i)_{1 \leqq i \leqq n}$ of sets of $\mathscr{P}$ such that

$$A \cap B = C_0 \subset C_1 \subset \cdots \subset C_n = A \quad \text{and} \quad C_i - C_{i-1} \in \mathscr{P}, \quad i = 1, 2, \ldots, n.$$

The sets $C_{i+1} - C_i$ are mutually disjoint, hence

$$A - B = A - (A \cap B) = \bigcup_{i=1}^{n} (C_i - C_{i-1}) \in \Phi.$$

d) $E - F \in \Phi$.

In fact,

$$E - F = \bigcup_{i=1}^{n} \left(\bigcap_{j=1}^{m} (A_i - B_j) \right) = \bigcap_{j=1}^{m} \left(\bigcup_{i=1}^{n} (A_i - B_j) \right).$$

For every j, the family $(A_i - B_j)_{1 \leqq i \leqq n}$ consists of mutually disjoint sets $A_i - B_j \in \Phi$ (see c)), whence, by b),

$$\bigcup_{i=1}^{n} (A_i - B_j) \in \Phi.$$

By a), we deduce that $E - F \in \Phi$.

e) $E \cup F \in \Phi$.

In fact

$$E \cup F = (E - F) \cup (E \cap F) \cup (F - E).$$

The sets $E - F$, $E \cap F$ and $F - E$ are disjoint and contained in Φ, by a) and d). By a) we deduce that $E \cup F \in \Phi$.

It follows that Φ is a clan containing $\mathscr{P}$ and contained in $\mathscr{C}$, therefore $\Phi = \mathscr{C}$.

Corollary. *If $\mathscr{L}$ is a lattice of subsets of T, then the class of all the finite unions $\bigcup_{i=1}^{n} (A_i - B_i)$ of disjoint differences $A_i - B_i$ with $A_i, B_i \in \mathscr{L}$, is equal to the clan generated by $\mathscr{L}$.*

5. MONOTONE CLASSES

Definition 6. *A nonvoid class $\mathscr{M}$ of subsets of T is said to be monotone, if for every monotone sequence (A_n) of sets of $\mathscr{M}$ we have*[1]) $\lim_n A_n \in \mathscr{M}$.

We say that $\mathscr{M}$ is an *increasing monotone class* if for every increasing sequence (A_n) of sets of $\mathscr{M}$ we have $\bigcup_{n=1}^{\infty} A_n \in \mathscr{M}$.

---

[1]) If the sequence (A_n) is increasing, we have $\lim_n A_n = \bigcup_{n=1}^{\infty} A_n$; if (A_n) is decreasing, we have $\lim_n A_n = \bigcap_{n=1}^{\infty} A_n$.

We say that $\mathscr{M}$ is a *decreasing monotone class* if for every decreasing sequence (A_n) o sets of $\mathscr{M}$ we have $\bigcap_{n=1}^{\infty} A_n \in \mathscr{M}$.

The class $\mathscr{M}$ is monotone if and only if it is increasing and decreasing monotone. Every tribe is a monotone class. Every semi-tribe is a decreasing monotone class.

Proposition 14. *An increasing monotone clan is a tribe. A decreasing monotone clan is a semi-tribe.*

If $\mathscr{C}$ is an increasing monotone clan, for every sequence (A_i) of sets of $\mathscr{C}$ we have $B_n = \bigcup_{i=1}^{n} A_i \in \mathscr{C}$ for each n, and (B_n) is an increasing sequence, therefore,

$$\bigcup_{i=1}^{\infty} A_i = \bigcup_{n=1}^{\infty} B_n \in \mathscr{C},$$

hence $\mathscr{C}$ is a tribe.

If $\mathscr{C}$ is a decreasing monotone clan, then it is a semi-tribe, as for every sequence (A_n) of sets of $\mathscr{C}$ we have $C_n = \bigcap_{i=1}^{n} A_i \in \mathscr{C}$ for each n, and (C_n) is a decreasing sequence, therefore

$$\bigcap_{i=1}^{\infty} A_i = \bigcap_{n=1}^{\infty} C_n \in \mathscr{C}.$$

Definition 7. *Let $\mathscr{A}$ and $\mathscr{M}$ be nonvoid classes of sets of T. We say that the class $\mathscr{M}$ is monotone with respect to the class $\mathscr{A}$, if for every monotone sequence (A_n) of sets of $\mathscr{M}$ such that* $\lim_n A_n \in \mathscr{A}$ *we have* $\lim_n A_n \in \mathscr{M}$.

Every class $\mathscr{M}$ is monotone with respect to itself, or with respect to any class $\mathscr{A} \subset \mathscr{M}$.

A monotone class $\mathscr{M}$ is monotone with respect to any class $\mathscr{A}$.

A class $\mathscr{M}$, monotone with respect to a *tribe $\mathscr{T}$ containing $\mathscr{M}$*, is monotone.

We define in the same manner *increasing monotone* and *decreasing monotone* classes with respect to a class $\mathscr{A}$.

A class $\mathscr{M}$ which is decreasing monotone with respect to a *semi-tribe $\mathscr{S}$ containing $\mathscr{M}$*, is decreasing monotone.

Proposition 15. *For every class $\mathscr{B} \subset \mathscr{A}$, there exists a smallest class $\mathscr{M}$, monotone with respect to $\mathscr{A}$ and containing $\mathscr{B}$.*

In fact, $\mathscr{A}$ is monotone with respect to $\mathscr{A}$ and contains $\mathscr{B}$. The intersection of all the classes which are monotone with respect to $\mathscr{A}$ and contains $\mathscr{B}$, is also monotone with respect to $\mathscr{A}$ and contains $\mathscr{B}$.

The smallest class which is monotone with respect to $\mathscr{A}$ and contains $\mathscr{B}$ is called the *monotone class with respect to $\mathscr{A}$ generated by $\mathscr{B}$*, and is included in $\mathscr{A}$.

Proposition 16. *Let $\mathscr{C}$ be a clan of subsets of T and $\mathscr{S}$ the semi-tribe generated by $\mathscr{C}$. The monotone class with respect to $\mathscr{S}$, generated by $\mathscr{C}$, is equal to $\mathscr{S}$.*

First, we remark that a class $\mathscr{M} \subset \mathscr{S}$ is monotone with respect to the semi-tribe $\mathscr{S}$ if and only if, for every *decreasing* sequence (A_n) of sets of $\mathscr{M}$ we have $\bigcap_{n=1}^{\infty} A_n \in \mathscr{M}$ and for every *increasing* sequence (A_n) of sets of $\mathscr{M}$, contained in a set $A \in \mathscr{S}$, we have $\bigcup_{n=1}^{\infty} A_n \in \mathscr{M}$.

We have $\mathscr{C} \subset \mathscr{M} \subset \mathscr{S}$. In order to prove that $\mathscr{M} = \mathscr{S}$ it is sufficient to show that $\mathscr{M}$ is a *semi-tribe*.

For every set $F \in \mathscr{S}$ put

$$\mathscr{M}(F) = \{E \mid E \in \mathscr{S};\ E - F,\ F - E,\ E \cup F \in \mathscr{M}\}.$$

We see that $E \in \mathscr{M}(F)$ if and only if $F \in \mathscr{M}(E)$.

We shall show that the class $\mathscr{M}(F)$ is monotone with respect to $\mathscr{S}$.

Let (E_n) be a monotone sequence of sets of $\mathscr{M}(F)$ such that $\lim_n E_n \in \mathscr{S}$. This means that for every n we have $E_n - F,\ F - E_n,\ E_n \cup F \in \mathscr{M}$.

The sequences $(E_n - F)$, $(F - E_n)$ and $(E_n \cup F)$ are monotone and their limits belong to $\mathscr{S}$. As $\mathscr{M}$ is monotone with respect to $\mathscr{S}$ these limits belong to $\mathscr{M}$, therefore

$$\lim_n E_n - F = \lim_n (E_n - F) \in \mathscr{M},$$

$$F - \lim_n E_n = \lim_n (F - E_n) \in \mathscr{M},$$

$$F \cup \lim_n E_n = \lim_n (F \cup E_n) \in \mathscr{M}.$$

It follows that $\lim_n E_n \in \mathscr{M}(F)$, hence $\mathscr{M}(F)$ is monotone with respect to $\mathscr{S}$.

If $E \in \mathscr{C}$ and $F \in \mathscr{C}$, then $E - F,\ F - E,\ E \cup F \in \mathscr{C} \subset \mathscr{M}$, therefore $E \in \mathscr{M}(F)$. It follows that for every set $F \in \mathscr{C}$ we have $\mathscr{C} \subset \mathscr{M}(F)$. But $\mathscr{M}$ is the smallest monotone class with respect to $\mathscr{S}$ containing $\mathscr{C}$, therefore $\mathscr{M} \subset \mathscr{M}(F)$ for every $F \in \mathscr{C}$.

Consequently, if $E \in \mathscr{M}$ and $F \in \mathscr{C}$, then $E \in \mathscr{M}(F)$, therefore $F \in \mathscr{M}(E)$. It follows that $\mathscr{C} \subset \mathscr{M}(E)$, hence

$$\mathscr{M} \subset \mathscr{M}(E), \quad \text{for} \quad E \in \mathscr{M}.$$

We conclude that if $E \in \mathscr{M}$ and $F \in \mathscr{M}$, then $F \in \mathscr{M}(E)$, i.e. $E - F \in \mathscr{M}$ and $E \cup F \in \mathscr{M}$, and thus we proved that $\mathscr{M}$ is a *clan*.

Since for every decreasing sequence (E_n) of sets of $\mathscr{M}$ we have $\bigcap_{n=1}^{\infty} E_n \in \mathscr{S}$, we deduce that $\bigcap_{n=1}^{\infty} E_n \in \mathscr{M}$, consequently $\mathscr{M}$ is a *semi-tribe* containing $\mathscr{C}$ and contained in $\mathscr{S}$, therefore $\mathscr{M} = \mathscr{S}$.

Proposition 17. *Let $\mathscr{C}$ be a clan of subsets of T. The monotone class $\mathscr{M}$ generated by $\mathscr{C}$ is equal to the tribe $\mathscr{T}$ generated by $\mathscr{C}$.*

As the tribe $\mathscr{T}$ generated by $\mathscr{C}$ is a monotone class, we have $\mathscr{M} \subset \mathscr{T}$. As in proposition 16, we prove that $\mathscr{M}$ is a *clan, monotone with respect* to the *tribe* $\mathscr{T}$, therefore $\mathscr{M}$ is a *monotone clan,* i.e. a tribe, consequently $\mathscr{M} = \mathscr{T}$.

6. THE CLASSES $\mathfrak{T}(\mathscr{A})$

Let $\mathscr{A}$ be a nonvoid class of subsets of T. We shall denote by $\mathfrak{T}(\mathscr{A})$ the class of all the subsets $E \subset T$ which have the property that $A \cap E \in \mathscr{A}$ for every $A \in \mathscr{A}$.

The class $\mathfrak{T}(\mathscr{A})$ has the following properties:

1. $T \in \mathfrak{T}(\mathscr{A})$.

In fact, for every set $A \in \mathscr{A}$ we have $A \cap T = A \in \mathscr{A}$, therefore $T \in \mathfrak{T}(\mathscr{A})$.

2. *If* $\emptyset \in \mathscr{A}$, *then* $\emptyset \in \mathfrak{T}(\mathscr{A})$.

For every set $A \in \mathscr{A}$ we have $A \cap \emptyset = \emptyset \in \mathscr{A}$, therefore $\emptyset \in \mathfrak{T}(\mathscr{A})$.

3. $E \cap F \in \mathfrak{T}(\mathscr{A})$ *for* $E, F \in \mathfrak{T}(\mathscr{A})$.

For every $A \in \mathscr{A}$ we have $A \cap E \in \mathscr{A}$ and $(A \cap E) \cap F \in \mathscr{A}$, i.e. $A \cap (E \cap F) \in \mathscr{A}$, consequently $E \cap F \in \mathfrak{T}(\mathscr{A})$.

4. *If* $E \in \mathfrak{T}(\mathscr{A})$ *and if* $E \subset A \in \mathscr{A}$, *then* $E \in \mathscr{A}$.

In fact, $E = A \cap E \in \mathscr{A}$.

5. *If* $T \in \mathscr{A}$ *then* $\mathfrak{T}(\mathscr{A}) \subset \mathscr{A}$.

For every set $E \in \mathfrak{T}(\mathscr{A})$ we have $E = T \cap E \in \mathscr{A}$.

6. *If* $A \cap B \in \mathscr{A}$ *for* $A, B \in \mathscr{A}$, *then* $\mathscr{A} \subset \mathfrak{T}(\mathscr{A})$.

In fact, if $E \in \mathscr{A}$, then $A \cap E \in \mathscr{A}$ for every $A \in \mathscr{A}$, therefore $E \in \mathfrak{T}(\mathscr{A})$.

From properties 5 and 6 we deduce that if $T \in \mathscr{A}$ and if $A \cap B \in \mathscr{A}$ for $A, B \in \mathscr{A}$, then $\mathfrak{T}(\mathscr{A}) = \mathscr{A}$.

7. *If* $A \cup B \in \mathscr{A}$ *for* $A, B \in \mathscr{A}$, *then* $E \cup F \in \mathfrak{T}(\mathscr{A})$ *for* $E, F \in \mathfrak{T}(\mathscr{A})$.

In fact, for every set $A \in \mathscr{A}$ we have $A \cap E \in \mathscr{A}$ and $A \cap F \in \mathscr{A}$, therefore

$$A \cap (E \cup F) = (A \cap E) \cup (A \cap F) \in \mathscr{A}$$

whence $E \cup F \in \mathfrak{T}(\mathscr{A})$.

Proposition 18. *If $\mathscr{C}$ is a clan then $\mathfrak{T}(\mathscr{C})$ is a clan containing $\mathscr{C}$ and T.*

The relations $T \in \mathfrak{T}(\mathscr{C})$ and $\mathscr{C} \subset \mathfrak{T}(\mathscr{C})$ follow from the properties 1 and 6. Let now $E, F \in \mathfrak{T}(\mathscr{C})$. From the property 7 we deduce that $E \cup F \in \mathfrak{T}(\mathscr{C})$. For every set $A \in \mathscr{C}$

we have $A \cap E \in \mathscr{C}$ and $A \cap F \in \mathscr{C}$, therefore, $\mathscr{C}$ being a clan,

$$A \cap (E - F) = (A \cap E) - (A \cap F) \in \mathscr{C};$$

hence $E - F \in \mathfrak{T}(\mathscr{C})$, therefore $\mathfrak{T}(\mathscr{C})$ is a clan.

Remark. $\mathfrak{T}(\mathscr{C})$ is not necessarily the smallest clan containing $\mathscr{C}$ and T. For example: if $\mathscr{C} = \{\emptyset\}$, the smallest clan containing $\mathscr{C}$ and T is $\{\emptyset, T\}$ and $\mathfrak{T}(\mathscr{C}) = \mathscr{P}(T)$; if $\mathscr{C} = \{\emptyset, A\}$, the smallest clan containing $\mathscr{C}$ and T is $\{\emptyset, A, T - A, T\}$ and $\mathfrak{T}(\mathscr{C})$ consists of $\emptyset$, A, the sets containing A and the sets disjoint of A.

Proposition 19. *If $\mathscr{S}$ is a semi-tribe, then $\mathfrak{T}(\mathscr{S})$ is a tribe containing $\mathscr{S}$ and T.*

Since $\mathscr{S}$ is a clan, $\mathfrak{T}(\mathscr{S})$ is a clan containing $\mathscr{S}$ and T. Let (E_n) be a sequence of $\mathfrak{T}(\mathscr{S})$. For every set $A \in \mathscr{S}$ and for every n we have $A \cap E_n \in \mathscr{S}$ and $A \cap E_n \subset A$. From the property 4 of the semi-tribes we deduce that

$$A \cap \left(\bigcup_{n=1}^{\infty} E_n \right) = \bigcup_{n=1}^{\infty} (A \cap E_n) \in \mathscr{S},$$

therefore $\bigcup_{n=1}^{\infty} E_n \in \mathfrak{T}(\mathscr{S})$; hence $\mathfrak{T}(\mathscr{S})$ is a tribe.

Proposition 20. *Let $\mathscr{C}$ be a clan and $\mathscr{A} \subset \mathscr{C}$ be a class such that every set of $\mathscr{C}$ is covered by a finite family of sets of $\mathscr{A}$. Then $\mathfrak{T}(\mathscr{A}) \subset \mathfrak{T}(\mathscr{C})$ and we have $E \in \mathfrak{T}(\mathscr{C})$ if and only if $E \cap A \in \mathscr{C}$ for every $A \in \mathscr{A}$.*

If $E \in \mathfrak{T}(\mathscr{C})$ we have $E \cap A \in \mathscr{C}$ for every $A \in \mathscr{C}$, in particular for every $A \in \mathscr{A}$.

Conversely suppose that $E \cap A \in \mathscr{C}$ for every $A \in \mathscr{A}$. Let $A \in \mathscr{C}$ and let (A_i) be a finite family of sets of $\mathscr{A}$ such that $A \subset \bigcup A_i$. For every i we have $E \cap A_i \in \mathscr{C}$; hence

$$E \cap (\bigcup A_i) = \bigcup (E \cap A_i) \in \mathscr{C}.$$

Then

$$E \cap A = [E \cap (\bigcup A_i)] \cap A \in \mathscr{C},$$

therefore $E \in \mathfrak{T}(\mathscr{C})$.

If now $E \in \mathfrak{T}(\mathscr{A})$, then $E \cap A \in \mathscr{A} \subset \mathscr{C}$ for every $A \in \mathscr{A}$, whence $E \in \mathfrak{T}(\mathscr{C})$.

Corollary. *Let $\mathscr{L}$ be a clan or a lattice, $\mathscr{C}$ the clan generated by $\mathscr{L}$ and $\mathscr{S}$ the semi-tribe generated by $\mathscr{L}$. Then $\mathfrak{T}(\mathscr{L}) \subset \mathfrak{T}(\mathscr{C}) \subset \mathfrak{T}(\mathscr{S})$ and we have $E \in \mathfrak{T}(\mathscr{S})$ (respectively $E \in \mathfrak{T}(\mathscr{C})$) if and only if $E \cap A \in \mathscr{S}$ (respectively $E \cap A \in \mathscr{C}$) for every $A \in \mathscr{L}$.*

In fact every set of $\mathscr{S}$ is contained in a set of $\mathscr{C}$ and every set of $\mathscr{C}$ is covered by a finite family of sets of $\mathscr{L}$ (proposition 12 and its corollary).

Proposition 21. *Let $\mathscr{T}$ be a tribe and $\mathscr{A} \subset \mathscr{T}$ a class such that every set of $\mathscr{T}$ is covered by a sequence of sets of $\mathscr{A}$. Then $\mathfrak{T}(\mathscr{A}) \subset \mathfrak{T}(\mathscr{T})$ and we have $E \in \mathscr{T}$ if and only if $E \cap A \in \mathscr{T}$ for every $A \in \mathscr{A}$.*

The proof is similar to that of the proposition 20, taking a countable family (A_i) instead of a finite one.

Corollary. *If $\mathscr{S}$ is a semi-tribe and $\mathscr{T}$ is the tribe generated by $\mathscr{S}$, then $\mathfrak{T}(\mathscr{S}) = \mathfrak{T}(\mathscr{T})$.*

We have first $\mathfrak{T}(\mathscr{S}) \subset \mathfrak{T}(\mathscr{T})$. If $E \in \mathfrak{T}(\mathscr{T})$ and $A \in \mathscr{S}$, we have $E \cap A \in \mathscr{T}$ and $E \cap A \subset A$; hence $E \cap A \in \mathscr{S}$, therefore $E \in \mathfrak{T}(\mathscr{S})$, consequently $\mathfrak{T}(\mathscr{T}) \subset \mathfrak{T}(\mathscr{S})$.

§ 2. SET FUNCTIONS

Let T be a set and X a vector space. In particular, X can be the space C of the complex numbers or the space R of the real numbers.

We denote by R_+ the set $[0, +\infty)$ of the *finite positive* numbers, and by $\bar{R}_+$ the set $[0, +\infty]$ of the (finite or $+\infty$) *positive* numbers.

In the sequel we shall consider *set functions*, i.e. functions defined on a nonvoid class $\mathscr{A}$ of sets of T, with values in X or in $\bar{R}_+$.

The set functions with values in $\bar{R}_+$ *having at least one finite value* will be called *positive set functions.* A positive set function μ is *finite on* $\mathscr{A}$ if $\mu(A) < \infty$ for every $A \in \mathscr{A}$, and is *σ-finite on* $\mathscr{A}$ if every set $A \in \mathscr{A}$ is the union of a sequence (A_n) of sets of $\mathscr{A}$ such that $\mu(A_n) < \infty$ for every n.

Throughout the book we shall do the convention $0 \cdot \infty = 0$.

1. ADDITIVE SET FUNCTIONS

Definition 1. *A set function $\boldsymbol{m}$ defined on a nonvoid class $\mathscr{A}$ of subsets of T, with values in X or in $\bar{R}_+$ is said to be additive if*

1. $\boldsymbol{m}(A \cup B) = \boldsymbol{m}(A) + \boldsymbol{m}(B)$

for every pair of disjoint sets $A, B \in \mathscr{A}$ such that $A \cup B \in \mathscr{A}$.

An *additive* set function $\boldsymbol{m}$ defined on $\mathscr{A}$ has also the following properties:

2. *If $\emptyset \in \mathscr{A}$, then $\boldsymbol{m}(\emptyset) = 0$.*

Let $A \in \mathscr{A}$ be such that $\boldsymbol{m}(A) < +\infty$ (in case $\boldsymbol{m}$ is positive). Then A and $\emptyset$ are disjoint sets of $\mathscr{A}$ and $A \cup \emptyset = A \in \mathscr{A}$, therefore

$$\boldsymbol{m}(A) = \boldsymbol{m}(A \cup \emptyset) = \boldsymbol{m}(A) + \boldsymbol{m}(\emptyset)$$

hence $\boldsymbol{m}(\emptyset) = 0$.

3. *$\boldsymbol{m}$ is subtractive:*

$$\boldsymbol{m}(B - A) = \boldsymbol{m}(B) - \boldsymbol{m}(A)$$

for every pair of sets $A, B \in \mathscr{A}$ such that $A \subset B$, $B - A \in \mathscr{A}$ and $\boldsymbol{m}(A) < +\infty$ (in case $\boldsymbol{m}$ is positive).

We have $B = (B - A) \cup A$ and $(B - A) \cap A = \emptyset$, therefore

$$\boldsymbol{m}(B) = \boldsymbol{m}(B - A) + \boldsymbol{m}(A)$$

hence ($\boldsymbol{m}(A)$ being finite, in case $\boldsymbol{m}$ is positive)

$$\boldsymbol{m}(B) - \boldsymbol{m}(A) = \boldsymbol{m}(B - A).$$

4. *If $A \cup B \in \mathscr{A}$ for every $A, B \in \mathscr{A}$ then $\boldsymbol{m}$ is finitely additive:*

$$\boldsymbol{m}\left(\bigcup_{i=1}^{n} A_i\right) = \sum_{i=1}^{n} \boldsymbol{m}(A_i)$$

for every finite family $(A_i)_{1 \leqq i \leqq n}$ of (mutually) disjoint sets of $\mathscr{A}$.

We deduce first by induction, that for every finite family $(A_i)_{i \in I}$ of sets of $\mathscr{A}$ we have $\bigcup_{i \in I} A_i \in \mathscr{A}$.

Then, again by induction, we deduce that $\boldsymbol{m}$ is finitely additive.

Remarks.

1°. The property 4 remains valid if we suppose that for every finite family $(A_i)_{i \in I}$ of sets of $\mathscr{A}$ such that $\bigcup_{i \in I} A_i \in \mathscr{A}$ there exists $i' \in I$ such that $\bigcup_{\substack{i \neq i' \\ i \in I}} A_i \in \mathscr{A}$.

2°. Without any restriction on $\mathscr{A}$, if $\boldsymbol{m}$ is finitely additive then it is additive.

5. *If $\boldsymbol{m}$ and $\boldsymbol{n}$ are (finitely) additive set functions defined on $\mathscr{A}$ with values in X and α is a scalar, then $\boldsymbol{m} + \boldsymbol{n}$ and $\alpha\boldsymbol{m}$ are (finitely) additive.*

If μ and ν are (finitely) additive positive set functions defined on $\mathscr{A}$ and $\alpha \geqq 0$, then $\mu + \nu$ and $\alpha\mu$ are (finitely) additive positive set functions.

Remark. According to the convention $0 \cdot \infty = 0$, we have $0\mu = 0$ for every positive set function μ.

From the preceding properties we deduce the following.

Proposition 1. *If $\boldsymbol{m}$ is an additive set function defined on a clan $\mathscr{C}$, with values in X or in $\bar{R}_+$, then $\boldsymbol{m}$ is finitely additive, subtractive and $\boldsymbol{m}(\emptyset) = 0$.*

2. POSITIVE ADDITIVE SET FUNCTIONS ON A CLAN

A *positive additive* set function μ defined on a *clan* $\mathscr{C}$ has additional properties:

6. *μ is increasing:*

$$\mu(A) \leqq \mu(B) \quad \text{if} \quad A \subset B.$$

If $A, B \in \mathscr{C}$ and $A \subset B$ we have $B = (B - A) \cup A$, $(B - A) \cap A = \emptyset$ and $\mu(B - A) \geqq 0$, therefore

$$\mu(B) = \mu(B - A) + \mu(A) \geqq \mu(A).$$

7. *μ is finitely subadditive:*

$$\mu\left(\bigcup_{i=1}^{n} A_i\right) \leqq \sum_{i=1}^{n} \mu(A_i)$$

for every finite family $(A_i)_{1 \leqq i \leqq n}$ of (not necessarily disjoint) sets of $\mathscr{C}$.

Put $B_1 = A$ and $B_k = A_k - \bigcup_{i<k} A_i$ for $2 \leqq k \leqq n$. The sets B_k belong to $\mathscr{C}$, are mutually disjoint and

$$\bigcup_{i=1}^{n} B_i = \bigcup_{i=1}^{n} A_i.$$

On the other hand we have $B_i \subset A_i$; hence $\mu(B_i) \leqq \mu(A_i)$ for each i, therefore

$$\mu\left(\bigcup_{i=1}^{n} A_i\right) = \mu\left(\bigcup_{i=1}^{n} B_i\right) = \sum_{i=1}^{n} \mu(B_i) \leqq \sum_{i=1}^{n} \mu(A_i).$$

From the property 7 we deduce in particular that

7′. $\mu(A \cup B) \leqq \mu(A) + \mu(B)$

or every pair of (not necessarily disjoint) sets $A, B \in \mathscr{C}$.

8. *μ is superadditive:*

$$\mu\left(\bigcup_{i \in I} A_i\right) \geqq \sum_{i \in I} \mu(A_i)$$

for every (not necessarily countable) family $(A_i)_{i \in I}$ of (mutually) disjoint sets of $\mathscr{C}$ such that $\bigcup_{i \in I} A_i \in \mathscr{C}$.

For every *finite* subset $J \subset I$ we have

$$\sum_{i \in J} \mu(A_i) = \mu\left(\bigcup_{i \in J} A_i\right) \leqq \mu\left(\bigcup_{i \in I} A_i\right),$$

therefore

$$\sum_{i \in I} \mu(A_i) = \sup_{J \subset I} \sum_{i \in J} \mu(A_i) \leqq \mu\left(\bigcup_{i \in I} A_i\right).$$

Remark. The property 8 remains valid if we suppose that $\mathscr{A}$ is a class such that $A \cup B \in \mathscr{A}$ for $A, B \in \mathscr{A}$ and that the set function $\mu: \mathscr{A} \to \bar{R}_+$ is *increasing* and *finitely superadditive:*

$$\mu\left(\bigcup_{i=1}^{n} A_i\right) \geqq \sum_{i=1}^{n} \mu(A_i)$$

for every finite family $(A_i)_{1 \leqq i \leqq n}$ of disjoint sets of $\mathscr{A}$.

3. COUNTABLY ADDITIVE SET FUNCTIONS

We suppose now that X is a *separated topological* vector space.

Definition 2. *A set function $\boldsymbol{m}$ defined on a nonvoid class $\mathscr{A}$ of sets of T, with values in X or in $\bar{R}_+$ is said to be countably additive, if:*

1. $\boldsymbol{m}\left(\bigcup_{i=1}^{\infty} A_i\right) = \sum_{i=1}^{\infty} \boldsymbol{m}(A_i)$

for every sequence (A_i) of mutually disjoint sets of $\mathscr{A}$ such that $\bigcup_{i=1}^{\infty} A_i \in \mathscr{A}$.

A *countably additive* set function $\boldsymbol{m}$ defined on the class $\mathscr{A}$ with values in X or in $\bar{R}_+$ has also the following properties:

2. *If $\emptyset \in \mathscr{A}$, then $\boldsymbol{m}(\emptyset) = 0$.*

We take $A \in \mathscr{A}$ such that $\boldsymbol{m}(A) < +\infty$ (in case $\boldsymbol{m}$ is *positive*) and put $A_1 = A$ and $A_i = \emptyset$ for $i \geqq 2$. Then $\bigcup_{i=1}^{\infty} A_i = A \in \mathscr{A}$, therefore

$$\boldsymbol{m}(A) = \boldsymbol{m}(A) + \boldsymbol{m}(\emptyset) + \boldsymbol{m}(\emptyset) + \cdots,$$

hence

$$0 = \boldsymbol{m}(\emptyset) + \boldsymbol{m}(\emptyset) + \cdots.$$

As X is separated, from the last equality we deduce that $\boldsymbol{m}(\emptyset) = 0$.

Remark. If X is not separated, from the last equality we cannot deduce that $\boldsymbol{m}(\emptyset) = 0$. However, the following properties remain valid even if X is not separated, for a countably additive set function $\boldsymbol{m}$ such that $\boldsymbol{m}(\emptyset) = 0$.

3. *If $\emptyset \in \mathscr{A}$, then $\boldsymbol{m}$ is finitely additive.*

Let $(A_i)_{1 \leqq i \leqq n}$ be a finite family of sets of $\mathscr{A}$ such that $\bigcup_{i=1}^{n} A_i \in \mathscr{A}$. Taking $A_i = \emptyset$ for $i > n$, we have $A_i \in \mathscr{A}$ for $1 \leqq i < \infty$,

$$\bigcup_{i=1}^{\infty} A_i = \bigcup_{i=1}^{n} A_i \in \mathscr{A}$$

and the sets A_i, $1 \leqq i < +\infty$, are mutually disjoint, therefore

$$\boldsymbol{m}\left(\bigcup_{i=1}^{n} A_i\right) = \boldsymbol{m}\left(\bigcup_{i=1}^{\infty} A_i\right) = \sum_{i=1}^{\infty} \boldsymbol{m}(A_i) = \sum_{i=1}^{n} \boldsymbol{m}(A_i)$$

because for $i > n$ we have $\boldsymbol{m}(A_i) = \boldsymbol{m}(\emptyset) = 0$.

In particular, we deduce that

3'. *If $\emptyset \in \mathscr{A}$, then $\boldsymbol{m}$ is additive.*

It follows then that

4. *If $\emptyset \in \mathscr{A}$, then $\boldsymbol{m}$ is subtractive.*

5. *If $\boldsymbol{m}$ and $\boldsymbol{n}$ are countably additive set functions defined on $\mathscr{A}$ with values in X and α is a scalar, then $\boldsymbol{m} + \boldsymbol{n}$ and $\alpha\boldsymbol{m}$ are countably additive.*

If μ and ν are countably additive positive set functions defined on $\mathscr{A}$ and $\alpha \geqq 0$, then $\mu + \nu$ and $\alpha\mu$ are countably additive positive set functions.

4. MEASURES

Definition 3. *Let $\mathscr{C}$ be a clan and X a normed space. A countably additive set function defined on $\mathscr{C}$ with values in X or in $\bar{R}_+$ is called a measure. A measure with values in $\bar{R}_+$ is called a positive measure.*

If μ is a *positive measure* on $\mathscr{C}$, we say that a set $A \in \mathscr{A}$ has *finite measure* if $\mu(A) < \infty$, and that A has *σ-finite measure* if A is the union of a sequence (A_n) of $\mathscr{C}$ with finite measure.

If $\mu(A) < \infty$ for every set $A \in \mathscr{C}$ we say that μ is a *finite measure*.

If every set $A \in \mathscr{C}$ has σ-finite measure we say that μ is a *σ-finite measure*.

From the preceding properties we deduce that a *measure* $\boldsymbol{m}$ defined on a *clan* $\mathscr{C}$, with values in X or in $\bar{R}_+$ is *finitely additive, subtractive* and $\boldsymbol{m}(\emptyset) = 0$; the set of the measures with values in X is a *vector space*; if μ and ν are positive measures and $\alpha \geqq 0$, then $\mu + \nu$ and $\alpha\mu$ are positive measures. A measure $\boldsymbol{m}$ defined on $\mathscr{C}$ with values in X or in $\bar{R}_+$ has also the following properties:

6. *For every increasing sequence (A_n) of sets of $\mathscr{C}$ such that $\bigcup_{n=1}^{\infty} A_n \in \mathscr{C}$, we have*

$$\boldsymbol{m}\left(\bigcup_{n=1}^{\infty} A_n\right) = \lim_{n\to\infty} \boldsymbol{m}(A_n).$$

Put $A_0 = \emptyset$. The sets $A_i - A_{i-1}$, $i = 1, 2, \ldots$, are mutually disjoint, belong to $\mathscr{C}$ and

$$\bigcup_{i=1}^{\infty} (A_i - A_{i-1}) = \bigcup_{n=1}^{\infty} A_n \in \mathscr{C},$$

therefore

$$\begin{aligned}\boldsymbol{m}\left(\bigcup_{n=1}^{\infty} A_n\right) &= \boldsymbol{m}\left(\bigcup_{i=1}^{\infty} (A_i - A_{i-1})\right) = \sum_{i=1}^{\infty} \boldsymbol{m}(A_i - A_{i-1}) \\ &= \lim_{n\to\infty} \sum_{i=1}^{n} \boldsymbol{m}(A_i - A_{i-1}) = \lim_{n\to\infty} \boldsymbol{m}\left(\bigcup_{i=1}^{n} (A_i - A_{i-1})\right) \\ &= \lim_{n\to\infty} \boldsymbol{m}(A_n).\end{aligned}$$

7. *For every decreasing sequence $A_1 \supset A_2 \supset \cdots \supset A_n \supset \cdots$ of sets of $\mathscr{C}$ such that $\bigcap_{n=1}^{\infty} A_n \in \mathscr{C}$ and such that $\boldsymbol{m}(A_1) < +\infty$ (in case $\boldsymbol{m}$ is positive), we have*

$$\boldsymbol{m}\left(\bigcap_{n=1}^{\infty} A_n\right) = \lim_{n\to\infty} \boldsymbol{m}(A_n).$$

(We remark that, in case $\boldsymbol{m}$ is positive, we have $\boldsymbol{m}(A_n) \leqq \boldsymbol{m}(A_1) < \infty$ for every n.)

The sequence $(A_1 - A_n)$ is increasing and

$$\bigcup_{n=1}^{\infty} (A_1 - A_n) = A_1 - \bigcap_{n=1}^{\infty} A_n \in \mathscr{C},$$

therefore, by the property 6, we have

$$\begin{aligned}\boldsymbol{m}(A_1) - \boldsymbol{m}\left(\bigcap_{n=1}^{\infty} A_n\right) &= \boldsymbol{m}\left(A_1 - \bigcap_{n=1}^{\infty} A_n\right) = \boldsymbol{m}\left(\bigcup_{n=1}^{\infty} (A_1 - A_n)\right)\\ &= \lim_{n\to\infty} \boldsymbol{m}(A_1 - A_n) = \lim_{n\to\infty} [\boldsymbol{m}(A_1) - \boldsymbol{m}(A_n)]\\ &= \boldsymbol{m}(A_1) - \lim_{n\to\infty} \boldsymbol{m}(A_n),\end{aligned}$$

hence ($\boldsymbol{m}(A_1)$ being finite, in case $\boldsymbol{m}$ is positive)

$$\boldsymbol{m}\left(\bigcap_{n=1}^{\infty} A_n\right) = \lim_{n\to\infty} \boldsymbol{m}(A_n).$$

R e m a r k. The properties 6 and 7 can be stated together as follows:

If (A_n) is a monotone sequence of sets of $\mathscr{C}$ such that $\lim_n A_n \in \mathscr{C}$ *(and if $\boldsymbol{m}(A_1) < \infty$, in case $\boldsymbol{m}$ is positive and (A_n) is decreasing) then* $\boldsymbol{m}\left(\lim_{n\to\infty} A_n\right) = \lim_{n\to\infty} \boldsymbol{m}(A_n)$.

The *additive* set functions have properties which are converse to the properties 6 and 7:

8. *Let $\boldsymbol{m}$ be an additive set function defined on the clan $\mathscr{C}$ with values in X or in $\bar{R}_+$. If for every increasing sequence (A_n) of sets of $\mathscr{C}$ such that $\bigcup_{n=1}^{\infty} A_n \in \mathscr{C}$ we have*

$$\boldsymbol{m}\left(\bigcup_{n=1}^{\infty} A_n\right) = \lim_{n\to\infty} \boldsymbol{m}(A_n)$$

then $\boldsymbol{m}$ is countably additive.

Let (B_n) be a sequence of mutually disjoint sets of $\mathscr{C}$ such that $\bigcup_{n=1}^{\infty} B_n \in \mathscr{C}$. For each n put

$$A_n = \bigcup_{i=1}^{n} B_i \in \mathscr{C}.$$

The sequence (A_n) is increasing and

$$\bigcup_{n=1}^{\infty} A_n = \bigcup_{n=1}^{\infty} B_n \in \mathscr{C},$$

therefore

$$m\left(\bigcup_{n=1}^{\infty} B_n\right) = m\left(\bigcup_{n=1}^{\infty} A_n\right) = \lim_{n\to\infty} m(A_n) = \lim_{n\to\infty} m\left(\bigcup_{i=1}^{n} B_i\right)$$

$$= \lim_{n\to\infty} \sum_{i=1}^{n} m(B_i) = \sum_{i=1}^{\infty} m(B_i),$$

i.e. $\boldsymbol{m}$ is countably additive.

9. *Let* $\boldsymbol{m}$ *be an additive set function defined on the clan* $\mathscr{C}$ *with values in* X *(*$\boldsymbol{m}$ *is finite if it is positive).*

If for every decreasing sequence (A_n) *of sets of* $\mathscr{C}$ *such that* $\bigcap_{n=1}^{\infty} A_n = \emptyset$ *we have*

$$\lim_{n\to\infty} m(A_n) = 0$$

then $\boldsymbol{m}$ *is countably additive.*

Let (B_n) be a sequence of mutually disjoint sets of $\mathscr{C}$ such that $B = \bigcup_{n=1}^{\infty} B_n \in \mathscr{C}$. For each n put

$$A_n = B - \bigcup_{i=1}^{n} B_i \in \mathscr{C}.$$

The sequence (A_n) is decreasing and $\bigcap_{n=1}^{\infty} A_n = \emptyset$, therefore

$$0 = \lim_{n\to\infty} m(A_n) = \lim_{n\to\infty} m\left(B - \bigcup_{i=1}^{n} B_i\right) = m(B) - \lim_{n\to\infty} m\left(\bigcup_{i=1}^{n} B_i\right)$$

$$= m(B) - \lim_{n\to\infty} \sum_{i=1}^{n} m(B_i) = m(B) - \sum_{i=1}^{\infty} m(B_i),$$

hence

$$m(B) = \sum_{i=1}^{\infty} m(B_i).$$

5. POSITIVE MEASURES

A *positive* measure μ defined on a *clan* $\mathscr{C}$ has, in addition, the following properties:

10. μ *is increasing;*

11. μ *is finitely subadditive;*

12. μ *is superadditive.*

In fact, μ is additive.

13. *μ is countably subadditive:*

$$\mu\left(\bigcup_{n=1}^{\infty} A_n\right) \leqq \sum_{n=1}^{\infty} \mu(A_n)$$

for every sequence (A_n) of (not necessarily disjoint) sets of $\mathscr{C}$ such that $\bigcup_{n=1}^{\infty} A_n \in \mathscr{C}$.

Put $B_1 = A_1$ and $B_n = A_n - \bigcup_{i<n} A_i$ for $n \geqq 2$. The sets B_n are mutually disjoint, belong to $\mathscr{C}$ and

$$\bigcup_{n=1}^{\infty} B_n = \bigcup_{n=1}^{\infty} A_n \in \mathscr{C}.$$

We have $B_i \subset A_i$; hence $\mu(B_i) \leqq \mu(A_i)$ for each i, therefore

$$\mu\left(\bigcup_{n=1}^{\infty} A_n\right) = \mu\left(\bigcup_{n=1}^{\infty} B_n\right) = \sum_{n=1}^{\infty} \mu(B_n) \leqq \sum_{n=1}^{\infty} \mu(A_n).$$

Conversely

14. *If μ is additive, countably subadditive and finite, then μ is countably additive.*

Let (A_n) be a sequence of disjoint sets of $\mathscr{C}$ with $A = \bigcup_{n=1}^{\infty} A_n \in \mathscr{C}$. For every n we have

$$\sum_{i=1}^{n} \mu(A_i) = \mu\left(\bigcup_{i=1}^{n} A_i\right) \leqq \mu(A) < \infty,$$

hence $\sum_{i=1}^{\infty} \mu(A_i) < \infty$, therefore $\lim_{n\to\infty} \sum_{i=n}^{\infty} \mu(A_i) = 0$. Then we have

$$\mu(A) - \sum_{i=1}^{n} \mu(A_i) = \mu(A) - \mu\left(\bigcup_{i=1}^{n} A_i\right) = \mu\left(\bigcup_{i=n}^{\infty} A_i\right) \leqq \sum_{i=n}^{\infty} \mu(A_i),$$

hence

$$\mu(A) = \lim_{n\to\infty} \sum_{i=1}^{n} \mu(A_i) = \sum_{i=1}^{\infty} \mu(A_i).$$

The properties 6 and 7 are now stated in the following form:

15. *For every increasing sequence (A_n) of sets of $\mathscr{C}$ such that $\bigcup_{n=1}^{\infty} A_n \in \mathscr{C}$ we have*

$$\mu\left(\bigcup_{n=1}^{\infty} A_n\right) = \lim_{n\to\infty} \mu(A_n) = \sup_{n\in N} \mu(A_n).$$

In fact, μ is increasing, therefore the sequence of numbers $(\mu(A_n))$ is increasing, hence

$$\lim_{n\to\infty} \mu(A_n) = \sup_{n\in N} \mu(A_n).$$

16. *For every decreasing sequence* (A_n) *of sets of* $\mathscr{C}$ *such that* $\bigcap_{n=1}^{\infty} A_n \in \mathscr{C}$ *and* $\mu(A_1) < \infty$, *we have*

$$\mu\left(\bigcap_{n=1}^{\infty} A_n\right) = \lim_{n\to\infty} \mu(A_n) = \inf_{n\in N} \mu(A_n).$$

In fact, in this case the sequence $(\mu(A_n))$ is decreasing.

6. OPERATOR SET FUNCTIONS

Let E and F be two *normed* spaces, such that $X \subset \mathscr{L}(E, F)$[1]) and let $\boldsymbol{m}$ be a set function defined on a nonvoid class $\mathscr{A}$, with values in X.

For every $x \in E$ we define the set function $\boldsymbol{m}_x$ on $\mathscr{A}$ with values in F, by the equality

$$\boldsymbol{m}_x(A) = \boldsymbol{m}(A)\,x, \quad \text{for} \quad A \in \mathscr{A}.$$

It is easy to verify that for every $x, y \in E$ and for every scalar α we have

$$\boldsymbol{m}_{x+y} = \boldsymbol{m}_x + \boldsymbol{m}_y \quad \text{and} \quad \boldsymbol{m}_{\alpha x} = \alpha \boldsymbol{m}_x.$$

Proposition 2. *If* $\boldsymbol{m}$ *is additive (respectively countably additive) then* $\boldsymbol{m}_x$ *is additive (respectively countably additive) for every* $x \in E$.

The part concerning the additivity is evident.

We shall prove the part concerning the countable additivity. Let (A_i) be a sequence of mutually disjoint sets of $\mathscr{A}$ such that $A = \bigcup_{i=1}^{\infty} A_i \in \mathscr{A}$. For each n we have[2])

$$\left|\boldsymbol{m}_x(A) - \sum_{i=1}^{n} \boldsymbol{m}_x(A_i)\right| \leqq \left|\boldsymbol{m}(A) - \sum_{i=1}^{n} \boldsymbol{m}(A_i)\right| |x|.$$

But

$$\lim_{n\to\infty} \left|\boldsymbol{m}(A) - \sum_{i=1}^{n} \boldsymbol{m}(A_i)\right| = 0$$

therefore

$$\lim_{n\to\infty} \left|\boldsymbol{m}_x(A) - \sum_{i=1}^{n} \boldsymbol{m}_x(A_i)\right| = 0,$$

i.e.

$$\boldsymbol{m}_x(A) = \sum_{i=1}^{\infty} \boldsymbol{m}_x(A_i).$$

Corollary. *If* $\boldsymbol{m}$ *is additive (respectively countably additive) then for every* $x \in E$ *and* $z \in F'$[3]), *the set function* $\boldsymbol{m}_{x,z}$ *defined on* $\mathscr{A}$ *by the equality*

$$\boldsymbol{m}_{x,z}(A) = \langle \boldsymbol{m}(A)\,x, z\rangle, \quad \textit{for} \quad A \in \mathscr{A}$$

is additive (respectively countably additive).

---

[1]) $\mathscr{L}(E, F)$ is the vector space of the linear continuous operations $U\colon E \to F$, equipped with the norm $|U| = \sup\{|Ux|;\ |x| \leqq 1,\ x \in E\}$.

[2]) The norm of an element z in a normed space Z will be denoted by $|z|$.

[3]) F' is the conjugate (or dual) space of F.

In fact $\boldsymbol{m}_x$ is a set function defined on $\mathscr{A}$ with values in $F \subset \mathscr{L}(F', C)$, and we apply the proposition 2 to the set function $(\boldsymbol{m}_x)_z = \boldsymbol{m}_{x,z}$.

Remark. The part concerning the additivity remains valid if E and F are arbitrary (non topological) vector spaces, and X a space of linear mappings of E into F.

7. COMPLEX SET FUNCTIONS

A complex set function m defined on a class $\mathscr{A}$ can be written uniquely in the form

$$m = m_1 + im_2$$

where m_1 and m_2 are real set functions defined on $\mathscr{A}$; namely, for every set $A \in \mathscr{A}$ we define $m_1(A)$ and $m_2(A)$ to be respectively the real part and the imaginary part of the complex number $m(A)$, and we have

$$m(A) = m_1(A) + im_2(A).$$

Proposition 3. *A complex set function $m = m_1 + im_2$ defined on $\mathscr{A}$ is additive (countably additive) if and only if m_1 and m_2 are additive (countably additive).*

The part concerning the additivity is evident.

Let (A_n) be a sequence of mutually disjoint sets of $\mathscr{A}$ such that $A = \bigcup_{n=1}^{\infty} A_n \in \mathscr{A}$. We have

$$m(A) = \sum_{n=1}^{\infty} m(A_n)$$

if and only if

$$m_1(A) = \sum_{n=1}^{\infty} m_1(A_n) \quad \text{and} \quad m_2(A) = \sum_{n=1}^{\infty} m_2(A_n).$$

Remark. For every set $A \in \mathscr{A}$ we have

$$|m_i(A)| \leqq |m(A)| \leqq |m_1(A)| + |m_2(A)|, \quad i = 1, 2.$$

8. UNIQUENESS OF THE SET FUNCTIONS

The next two propositions show that an *additive* set function on *clan* $\mathscr{C}$ is uniquely determined by its values on a lattice or on a semi-clan which generates $\mathscr{C}$.

Proposition 4. *Let $\mathscr{L}$ be a lattice of subsets of T, $\mathscr{C}$ the clan generated by $\mathscr{L}$, $\boldsymbol{m}$ and $\boldsymbol{n}$ two additive set functions defined on $\mathscr{C}$ with values in X.*

If $\boldsymbol{m}(A) = \boldsymbol{n}(A)$ for every $A \in \mathscr{L}$, then $\boldsymbol{m} = \boldsymbol{n}$.

In fact, every set $E \in \mathscr{C}$ is of the form

$$E = \bigcup_{i=1}^{n} (A_i - B_i)$$

where A_i and B_i are sets of $\mathscr{L}$ such that $B_i \subset A_i$ for every i, and the differences $A_i - B_i$ are mutually disjoint (§ 1, corollary of proposition 13). Then

$$\boldsymbol{m}(E) = \sum_{i=1}^{n} [\boldsymbol{m}(A_i) - \boldsymbol{m}(B_i)] = \sum_{i=1}^{n} [\boldsymbol{n}(A_i) - \boldsymbol{n}(B_i)] = \boldsymbol{n}(E).$$

Remark. If μ and ν are two *positive* additive set functions taking *infinite* values, then from the equality $\mu(A) = \nu(A)$ for $A \in \mathscr{L}$, we can not conclude that $\mu = \nu$, because, if $\mu(A) = +\infty$ and $B \subset A$ then the equality $\mu(A - B) = \mu(A) - \mu(B)$ may be false.

Proposition 5. *Let $\mathscr{P}$ be a semi-clan, $\mathscr{C}$ the clan generated by $\mathscr{P}$, $\boldsymbol{m}$ and $\boldsymbol{n}$ two additive set functions defined on $\mathscr{C}$ with values in X or in $\bar{R}_+$.*

If $\boldsymbol{m}(A) = \boldsymbol{n}(A)$ for every $A \in \mathscr{P}$, then $\boldsymbol{m} = \boldsymbol{n}$.

In this case every set $E \in \mathscr{C}$ can be written in the form

$$E = \bigcup_{i=1}^{n} A_i$$

where A_i are mutually disjoint sets of $\mathscr{P}$ (§ 1, proposition 13), therefore

$$\boldsymbol{m}(E) = \sum_{i=1}^{n} \boldsymbol{m}(A_i) = \sum_{i=1}^{n} \boldsymbol{n}(A_i) = \boldsymbol{n}(E),$$

hence $\boldsymbol{m} = \boldsymbol{n}$.

We show now that a *countably additive* set function defined on a tribe or on a semi-tribe is uniquely determined by its values taken on a *clan* generating the semi-tribe or the tribe.

Proposition 6. *Let $\mathscr{C}$ be a clan, $\mathscr{S}$ the semi-tribe generated by $\mathscr{C}$, $\mathscr{T}$ the tribe generated by $\mathscr{C}$, $\boldsymbol{m}$ and $\boldsymbol{n}$ two countably additive set functions defined on $\mathscr{S}$ or on $\mathscr{T}$ with values in X or in $\bar{R}_+$.*

If $\boldsymbol{m}(A) = \boldsymbol{n}(A)$ for every $A \in \mathscr{C}$ and if $\boldsymbol{m}$ and $\boldsymbol{n}$ are σ-finite on $\mathscr{C}$ (in case $\boldsymbol{m}$ and $\boldsymbol{n}$ are positive), then $\boldsymbol{m} = \boldsymbol{n}$.

Suppose first that $\boldsymbol{m}$ and $\boldsymbol{n}$ are finite on $\mathscr{C}$.

Denote by Φ the class of all the sets $A \in \mathscr{S}$ such that $\boldsymbol{m}(A) = \boldsymbol{n}(A)$. Then, by hypothesis, $\mathscr{C} \subset \Phi \subset \mathscr{S}$.

If (A_n) is a monotone sequence of sets of Φ such that $\lim A_n \in \mathscr{S}$, then (properties 6 and 7 of the countably additive set functions on a clan)

$$\boldsymbol{m}(\lim A_n) = \lim \boldsymbol{m}(A_n) = \lim \boldsymbol{n}(A_n) = \boldsymbol{n}(\lim A_n),$$

therefore $\lim A_n \in \Phi$. It follows that Φ is monotone with respect to $\mathscr{S}$, hence (§ 1, proposition 16) $\Phi = \mathscr{S}$. It follows that $\boldsymbol{m}(A) = \boldsymbol{n}(A)$ for every $A \in \mathscr{S}$.

If $\boldsymbol{m}$ and $\boldsymbol{n}$ are defined on $\mathscr{T}$, then every set $E \in \mathscr{T}$ is the union of a sequence (E_n) of disjoint sets of $\mathscr{S}$, therefore

$$\boldsymbol{m}(E) = \sum \boldsymbol{m}(E_n) = \sum \boldsymbol{n}(E_n) = \boldsymbol{n}(E),$$

consequently $\boldsymbol{m} = \boldsymbol{n}$.

Suppose now that $\boldsymbol{m}$ and $\boldsymbol{n}$ are σ-finite on $\mathscr{C}$ and consider the clan $\mathscr{C}_0 \subset \mathscr{C}$ on which $\boldsymbol{m}$ and $\boldsymbol{n}$ are finite. Every set of $\mathscr{C}$ is the union of a sequence of sets of $\mathscr{C}_0$. By the preceding proof, $\boldsymbol{m}$ and $\boldsymbol{n}$ are equal on the semi-tribe $\mathscr{S}_0$ generated by $\mathscr{C}_0$. If $\boldsymbol{m}$ and $\boldsymbol{n}$ are defined on $\mathscr{T}$, then $\boldsymbol{m}$ and $\boldsymbol{n}$ are equal on the tribe $\mathscr{T}_0$ generated by $\mathscr{C}_0$.

We remark that the union of a sequence of sets of $\mathscr{C}_0$ belongs to $\mathscr{T}_0$; hence $\mathscr{C} \subset \mathscr{T}_0$, therefore $\mathscr{T}_0 = \mathscr{T}$. It follows that if $\boldsymbol{m}$ and $\boldsymbol{n}$ are defined on $\mathscr{T}$, then $\boldsymbol{m} = \boldsymbol{n}$.

On the other hand, every set of $\mathscr{S}$ belongs to $\mathscr{T} = \mathscr{T}_0$; hence it is the union of a sequence of disjoint sets of $\mathscr{S}_0$, therefore $\boldsymbol{m}$ and $\boldsymbol{n}$ are equal on $\mathscr{S}$.

Corollary. *Let $\mathscr{L}$ be a lattice or a semi-clan, $\mathscr{S}$ the semi-tribe generated by $\mathscr{L}$, $\mathscr{T}$ the tribe generated by $\mathscr{L}$, $\boldsymbol{m}$ and $\boldsymbol{n}$ two countably additive set functions defined on $\mathscr{S}$ or on $\mathscr{T}$, with values in X or in $\bar{R}_+$.*

If $\boldsymbol{m}(A) = \boldsymbol{n}(A)$ for every $A \in \mathscr{L}$ and if $\boldsymbol{m}$ and $\boldsymbol{n}$ are finite on $\mathscr{L}$ (in case $\boldsymbol{m}$ and $\boldsymbol{n}$ are positive) then $\boldsymbol{m} = \boldsymbol{n}$.

In fact by propositions 4 and 5, $\boldsymbol{m}$ and $\boldsymbol{n}$ are equal (and finite in case $\boldsymbol{m}$ and $\boldsymbol{n}$ are positive) on the clan $\mathscr{C}$ generated by $\mathscr{L}$. On the other hand, $\mathscr{S}$ is also the semi-tribe generated by $\mathscr{C}$ and $\mathscr{T}$ is the tribe generated by $\mathscr{C}$, therefore $\boldsymbol{m} = \boldsymbol{n}$.

Remark. If $\mathscr{L}$ is a semi-clan, $\boldsymbol{m}$ and $\boldsymbol{n}$ can be supposed σ-finite on $\mathscr{L}$.

9. ATOMIC MEASURES

Let $\mathscr{C}$ be a clan and μ a positive (finite or infinite) set function defined on $\mathscr{C}$.

Definition 4. *We say that a set $E \in \mathscr{C}$ is an atom (with respect to μ) if $\mu(E) > 0$ and if for every set $A \in \mathscr{C}$ with $A \subset E$ we have either $\mu(A) = 0$ or $\mu(A) = \mu(E)$.*

We say that a set $E \in \mathscr{C}$ has the Darboux property (with respect to μ) if for every number α such that $0 \leqq \alpha \leqq \mu(E)$ there exists a set $A \in \mathscr{C}$ with $A \subset E$ and $\mu(A) = \alpha$.

We say that μ has the Darboux property if every set $E \in \mathscr{C}$ has the Darboux property.

We say that μ is atomic if there exists at least one atom in $\mathscr{C}$, and that μ is non-atomic if there exists no atom in $\mathscr{C}$.

Examples.

1°. Let $t_0 \in T$ and $0 < a \leqq \infty$ and for every set $A \in \mathscr{C}$ put $\mu(A) = a$ if $t_0 \in A$ and $\mu(A) = 0$ if $t_0 \notin A$. Then every set $E \in \mathscr{C}$ such that $t_0 \in E$ is an atom.

2°. Suppose that $\mathscr{C}$ contains every set $\{t\}$ with $t \in T$. For every $t \in T$ let $\alpha(t) \geqq 0$ and for every $A \in \mathscr{C}$ put

$$\mu(A) = \sum_{t \in A} \alpha(t).$$

Then μ is a positive measure on $\mathscr{C}$ and every set $\{t\}$ with $\alpha(t) > 0$ is an atom.

3°. The Lebesgue measure on the real line has the Darboux property and is non-atomic.

We shall show that every *σ-finite non-atomic measure* on a *semi-tribe* has the Darboux property (corollary of the proposition 7) but the converse is not true (proposition 10).

We remark that if μ is a *measure*, then a set $E \in \mathscr{C}$ with $\mu(E) < \infty$ can have at most a countable family of disjoint atoms, and the same property has every set with σ-finite measure.

Proposition 7. *Let μ be a positive measure on a semi-tribe $\mathscr{S}$. If $E \in \mathscr{S}$ has σ-finite measure and if E has no atom, then E has the Darboux property.*

Suppose first that $\mu(E) < \infty$ and let $0 < \alpha < \mu(E)$. We shall find by recurrence two sequences (A_n) and (B_n) of sets of $\mathscr{S}$ having the following properties:

1. $A_0 \subset A_1 \subset \cdots \subset A_n \subset \cdots \subset B_n \subset \cdots \subset B_1 \subset B_0 \subset E$.

2. If we put

$$\begin{aligned} a_n &= \sup\{\mu(A);\ A_{n-1} \subset A \subset B_{n-1},\ \mu(A) \leqq \alpha\}, \\ b_n &= \inf\{\mu(B);\ A_n \subset B \subset B_{n-1},\ \mu(B) \geqq \alpha\} \end{aligned}$$

the sequence (a_n) is decreasing, the sequence (b_n) is increasing and we have

$$a_n \leqq \alpha \leqq b_n, \quad \text{for} \quad n = 1, 2, \ldots$$

3. There exists two sequences $\varepsilon_n \searrow 0$ and $\eta_n \searrow 0$ such that

$$a_n - \varepsilon_n < \mu(A_n) \leqq a_n, \quad b_n \leqq \mu(B_n) < b_n + \eta_n.$$

In fact, let $r_n \searrow 0$. Put

$$a_0 = \sup\{\mu(A);\ A \subset E,\ \mu(A) \leqq \alpha\}.$$

Then $0 \leqq a_0 \leqq \alpha$ and for $\varepsilon_0 > 0$ there exists a set $A_0 \in \mathscr{S}$ with $A_0 \subset E$ and

$$a_0 - \varepsilon_0 < \mu(A_0) \leqq a_0.$$

Put

$$b_0 = \inf\{\mu(B);\ A_0 \subset B \subset E,\ \mu(B) \geqq \alpha\}.$$

Then $\alpha \leqq b_0 \leqq \mu(E)$ and for $\eta_0 > 0$ there exists a set $B_0 \in \mathscr{S}$ with $A_0 \subset B_0 \subset E$ and

$$b_0 \leqq \mu(B_0) < b_0 + \eta_0.$$

Put then

$$a_1 = \sup\{\mu(A);\ A_0 \subset A \subset B_0,\ \mu(A) \leqq \alpha\}.$$

Then $a_0 - \varepsilon_0 < a_1 \leqq a_0$ and if we take $0 < \varepsilon_1 \leqq r_1$ such that $a_0 - \varepsilon_0 < a_1 - \varepsilon_1$, there exists a set $A_1 \in \mathscr{S}$ with

$$A_0 \subset A_1 \subset B \quad \text{and} \quad a_1 - \varepsilon_1 < \mu(A_1) \leqq a_1.$$

Put

$$b_1 = \inf\{\mu(B);\ A_1 \subset B \subset B_0,\ \mu(B) \geqq \alpha\}.$$

Then $b_0 \leqq b_1 < b_0 + \eta_0$ and if we take $0 < \eta_1 < r_1$ such that $b_1 + \eta_1 < b_0 + \eta_0$, there exists a set $B_1 \in \mathscr{S}$ with

$$A_1 \subset B_1 \subset B_0 \quad \text{and} \quad b_1 \leqq \mu(A_1) < b_1 + \eta_1.$$

Suppose that we have found $A_1, \ldots, A_n, B_1, \ldots, B_n, \varepsilon_1, \ldots, \varepsilon_n, \eta_1, \ldots, \eta_n$ verifying the preceding three conditions. Put

$$a_{n+1} = \sup\{\mu(A);\ A_n \subset A \subset B_n,\ \mu(A) \leqq \alpha\}.$$

Then $a_n - \varepsilon_n < a_{n+1} \leqq a_n$ and if we take $0 < \varepsilon_{n+1} < r_{n+1}$ such that the inequality $a_n - \varepsilon_n < a_{n+1} - \varepsilon_{n+1}$ holds, there exists a set $A_{n+1} \in \mathscr{S}$ with

$$A_n \subset A_{n+1} \subset B_n \quad \text{and} \quad a_{n+1} - \varepsilon_{n+1} < \mu(A_{n+1}) \leqq a_{n+1}.$$

Put

$$b_{n+1} = \inf\{\mu(B);\ A_{n+1} \subset B \subset B_n,\ \mu(B) \geqq \alpha\}.$$

Then $b_n \leqq b_{n+1} < b_n + \eta_n$ and if we take $0 < \eta_{n+1} < r_{n+1}$ such that $b_{n+1} + \eta_{n+1} < b_n + \eta_n$, there exists a set $B_{n+1} \in \mathscr{S}$ with

$$A_{n+1} \subset B_{n+1} \subset B_n \quad \text{and} \quad b_{n+1} \leqq \mu(B_{n+1}) < b_{n+1} + \eta_{n+1}.$$

Since $\varepsilon_n \leqq r_n$ and $\eta_n \leqq r_n$ it follows that $\varepsilon_n \to 0$ and $\eta_n \to 0$.

The sequences (a_n) and (b_n) are monotone, therefore they have limits a respectively b and we have

$$0 \leqq a \leqq \alpha \leqq b \leqq \mu(E) < \infty.$$

The sets

$$A = \bigcup_{n=1}^{\infty} A_n \quad \text{and} \quad B = \bigcap_{n=1}^{\infty} B_n$$

belong to $\mathscr{S}$ and we have

$$A_n \subset A \subset B \subset B_n \subset E.$$

From the condition 3 we deduce that

$$\mu(A) = \lim_{n\to\infty} \mu(A_n) = a \leqq \alpha.$$

Since $\mu(B_n) < \infty$, we deduce also that

$$\mu(B) = \lim_{n\to\infty} \mu(B_n) = b \geqq \alpha.$$

Let $C \in \mathscr{S}$ be such that $C \subset B - A$. Then $A_n \subset A \subset A \cup C \subset B \subset B_n$, for every n. If $\mu(A \cup C) \leqq \alpha$ from the conditions 2 and 3 we deduce that $a_n - \varepsilon_n \leqq \mu(A \cup C) \leqq a_{n+1}$, for every n, consequently $\mu(A \cup C) = a$. It follows that

$$\mu(C) = \mu(A \cup C) - \mu(A) = 0.$$

If $\mu(A \cup C) \geqq \alpha$, from the conditions 2 and 3 we deduce that $b_{n+1} \leqq \mu(A \cup C) \leqq b_n + \eta_n$ for every n, consequently $\mu(A \cup C) = b$, therefore $\mu(C) = \mu(A \cup C) - \mu(A) = b - a = \mu(B - A)$. Since E has no atom we deduce that $\mu(B - A) = 0$, consequently $a = \mu(A) = \mu(B) = b$, therefore $\alpha = a = b$, and finally

$$\mu(A) = \alpha.$$

Suppose now that E has σ-finite measure and put $E = \bigcup_{n=1}^{\infty} E_n$ where E_n are sets of $\mathscr{S}$ with finite measure. We can consider the sets E_n disjoint and $\mu(E_n) > 0$ for every n. If $0 < \alpha < \mu(E)$, we can find a sequence (α_n) with $0 < \alpha_n < \mu(E_n)$ and $\sum_{n=1}^{\infty} \alpha_n = \alpha$. For each n we find a set $A_n \in \mathscr{S}$ with $A_n \subset E_n$ and $\mu(A_n) = \alpha_n$. The sets A_n are disjoint, the set $A = \bigcup_{n=1}^{\infty} A_n$ belongs to $\mathscr{S}$ and we have $A \subset E$ and

$$\mu(A) = \sum_{n=1}^{\infty} \mu(A_n) = \alpha.$$

Corollary. *A σ-finite non-atomic positive measure on a semi-tribe has the Darboux property.*

We shall give now equivalent conditions for a set to have the Darboux property.

We shall consider first the case of a set containing only a finite number of disjoint atoms.

Proposition 8. *Let μ be a positive measure on a semi-tribe $\mathscr{S}$ and let $E \in \mathscr{S}$ be a set with $\mu(E) < \infty$ containing finitely many disjoint atoms. Let $\alpha_1 > \alpha_2 > \cdots > \alpha_n$ be such that $\alpha_i \mu(E)$ are the distinct values of μ on the atoms of E. Let $A_i^1, A_i^2, \ldots, A_i^{s_i}$ be the atoms of E having the same measure $\alpha_i \mu(E)$, let $\alpha = \sum_{i=1}^{n} s_i \alpha_i$, $A_i = A_i^1 \cup A_i^2 \cup \cdots \cup A_i^{s_i}$, $A = \bigcup_{i=1}^{n} A_i$, $\beta = \mu(E)$ and $\beta_p = \sum_{i=p+1}^{n} s_i \alpha_i$.*

Then E has the Darboux property if and only if

$$\alpha_n \leqq 1 - \alpha$$

and

$$\alpha_p \leqq 1 - \alpha - \beta_p, \quad \text{for each} \quad p \leqq n - 1.$$

Suppose first that E has the Darboux property. Assume that $\alpha_n > 1 - \alpha$ and select a number ξ such that $1 - \alpha < \xi < \alpha_n$. There exists then a set $F \subset E$ of $\mathscr{S}$ such that $\mu(F) = \xi\beta$. Since $\xi > 1 - \alpha$ it follows that F contains at least an atom. On the other hand, since $\xi < \alpha_n$ and since there does not exist an atom having measure $\alpha_i\beta$ with $\alpha_i < \alpha_n$, it follows that F contains no atom. This contradiction shows that $\alpha_n \leqq 1 - \alpha$.

Assume now that there exists $p \leqq n - 1$ such that $1 - \alpha - \beta_p < \alpha_p$ and choose a number ξ such that $1 - \alpha - \beta_p < \xi < \alpha_p$. There exists then a set $F \subset E$ of $\mathscr{S}$ such that $\mu(F) = \xi\beta$. From the first inequality above it follows that F contains an atom having measure $\alpha_i\beta$ with $\alpha_i > \alpha_{p+1}$. On the other hand, since $\xi < \alpha_p$ it follows that each atom contained in F has measure $\alpha_i\beta$ with $\alpha_i < \alpha_p$. But this is a contradiction, since E contains no atom having measure $\alpha_i\beta$ with $\alpha_{p+1} < \alpha_i < \alpha_p$. Thus we have

$$\alpha_p \leqq 1 - \alpha + \beta_n, \quad \text{for each} \quad p \leqq n - 1.$$

Conversely, suppose that the inequalities of the statement are verified and prove that E has the Darboux property.

Suppose first that $0 \leqq \xi \leqq 1 - \alpha$. The set $E - A$ is of measure $(1 - \alpha)\beta$ and contains no atom, therefore, by the proposition 7, there exists a set $F \subset E - A$ of $\mathscr{S}$ such that $\mu(F) = \xi\beta$.

Now suppose that $1 - \alpha \leqq \xi \leqq 1 - \alpha + s_n\alpha_n$. Let j be the least integer satisfying $\xi \leqq 1 - \alpha + j\alpha_n$. Let $\gamma = \xi - j\alpha_n$. Then we have

$$\begin{aligned} 0 \leqq 1 - \alpha - \alpha_n &= (1 - \alpha + (j - 1)\,\alpha_n) - j\alpha_n < \gamma \\ &\leqq (1 - \alpha + j\alpha_n) - j\alpha_n = 1 - \alpha. \end{aligned}$$

By the proposition 7 there exists a set $G \subset E - A$ of $\mathscr{S}$ such that $\mu(G) = \gamma\beta$. Putting $F = G \cup A_n^1 \cup A_n^2 \cup \cdots \cup A_n^j$ we obtain $\mu(F) = (\gamma + j\alpha_n)\,\beta_n = \xi\beta$.

Let us admit that we have proved, for each ξ satisfying $0 \leqq \xi \leqq 1 - \alpha + \beta_p$, the existence of a set $F \subset E - (A_1 \cup \cdots \cup A_p)$ of $\mathscr{S}$ such that $\mu(F) = \xi\beta$. Now consider a number ξ with $1 - \alpha + \beta_p < \xi \leqq 1 - \alpha + \beta_{p-1}$. We shall show that there exists a set $F \subset E - (A_1 \cup \cdots \cup A_{p-1})$ so that $\mu(F) = \xi\beta$.

Let k be the least integer satisfying $\xi \leqq 1 - \alpha + \beta_p + k\alpha_p$. Setting $\gamma = \xi - k\alpha_p$, we obtain

$$\begin{aligned} 0 \leqq 1 - \alpha + \beta_p - \alpha_p &= 1 - \alpha + \beta_p + (k - 1)\,\alpha_p - k\alpha_p < \gamma \\ &\leqq (1 - \alpha + \beta_p + k\alpha_p) - k\alpha_p = 1 - \alpha + \beta_p. \end{aligned}$$

For such a γ there exists, by our induction hypothesis, a set $G \subset E - (A_1 \cup \cdots \cup A_p)$ of $\mathscr{S}$ such that $\mu(G) = \gamma\beta$. Putting $F = G \cup A_p^1 \cup \cdots \cup A_p^k$ we obtain $\mu(F) = (\gamma + k\alpha_p)\,\beta = \xi\beta$.

Since for each ξ satisfying $1 - \alpha + s_n\alpha_n < \xi \leqq 1$ there exists an integer $p \leqq n - 1$ such that $1 - \alpha + \beta_p < \gamma \leqq 1 - \alpha + \beta_{p-1}$, it follows that E has the Darboux property and the proposition 8 is proved.

Corollary. *If E has n atoms each of them of measure $\delta\beta$, then E has the Darboux property if and only if* $(n + 1)\,\delta \leqq 1$.

We remark that $\alpha_n = \delta$, $\alpha = n\delta$ and we apply the preceding proposition.

We consider now the case of a set containing countably many disjoint atoms.

Proposition 9. *Let μ be a positive measure on a semi-tribe $\mathcal{S}$ and let $E \in \mathcal{S}$ be a set with $\mu(E) < \infty$ containing countably many disjoint atoms. Let $\alpha_1 > \alpha_2 > \cdots > \alpha_i > \alpha_{i+1} > \cdots$ be such that $\alpha_i\mu(E)$ are the distinct values of μ on the atoms of E. Let $A_i^1, A_i^2, \ldots, A_i^{s_i}$ be the atoms of E having the same measure $\alpha_i\mu(E)$, let $\alpha = \sum_{i=1}^{\infty} s_i\alpha_i \leqq 1$, $A_i = A_i^1 \cup \cdots \cup A_i^{s_i}$, $A = \bigcup_{i=1}^{\infty} A_i$, $\mu(E) = \beta$ and $\beta_p = \sum_{i=p+1}^{\infty} s_i\alpha_i$.*

Then E has the Darboux property if and only if

$$\alpha_p \leqq 1 - \alpha + \beta_p, \quad \textit{for} \quad p = 1, 2, \ldots$$

If E has the Darboux property, then we prove like in the proposition 8 that we have $\alpha_p \leqq 1 - \alpha + \beta_p$ for every p.

Conversely, suppose these inequalities verified and prove that E has the Darboux property.

We consider first the case $\alpha < 1$. If $0 \leqq \xi \leqq 1 - \alpha$, we proceed as in the corresponding case of the proposition 8 and find a set $F \subset E - A$ of $\mathcal{S}$ such that $\mu(F) = \xi\beta$.

Let m be an integer satisfying $\beta_m < 1 - \alpha$. Such an integer exists, since the series $\sum s_i\alpha_i$ converges and $1 - \alpha > 0$.

Consider a number ξ satisfying $1 - \alpha < \xi \leqq 1 - \alpha + \beta_m$. Let $\gamma = \xi - \beta_m$. We have $0 \leqq \gamma \leqq 1 - \alpha$ and so, by the proposition 7 there exists a set $G \subset E - A$ of $\mathcal{S}$ such that $\mu(G) = \gamma\beta$. If we put $F = G \cup A_{m+1} \cup A_{m+2} \cup \cdots$ we have $\mu(F) = (\gamma + \beta_m)\,\beta = \xi\beta$.

Now suppose that $1 - \alpha + \beta_m < \xi \leqq 1 - \alpha + \beta_{m-1}$. Let j be the least integer satisfying $\xi \leqq 1 - \alpha + \beta_m + j\alpha_m$. Let $\gamma = \xi - j\alpha_m$.

We have $\gamma \leqq 1 - \alpha + \beta_m$ and

$$\gamma > (1 - \alpha + \beta_m + (j - 1)\,\alpha_m) - j\alpha_m = 1 - \alpha + \beta_m - \alpha_m \geqq 0.$$

Thus, as we have proved above, there exists a set $F \subset E - A$ of $\mathcal{S}$ such that, putting $H = G \cup A_{m+1} \cup A_{m+2} \cup \cdots$ we have $\mu(H) = \gamma\beta$. Next, putting $F = H \cup A_m^1 \cup A_m^2 \cup \cdots \cup A_m^j$ we obtain $\mu(F) = (\gamma + j\alpha_m)\,\beta = \xi\beta$.

Let us admit that we have proved, for every real ξ satisfying $0 \leqq \xi \leqq 1 - \alpha + \beta_p$ with $p + 1 < m$, the existence of a measurable subset $F \subset E - (A_1 \cup A_2 \cup \cdots \cup A_p)$ such that $\mu(F) = \xi\beta$. Now consider a real ξ satisfying $1 - \alpha + \beta_p < \xi \leqq 1 - \alpha + \beta_{p-1}$. By proceeding as in the last part of the proof of the proposition 8 we find a measurable subset $F \subset E - (A_1 \cup \cdots \cup A_{p-1})$ such that $\mu(F) = \xi\beta$.

Since for each real ξ satisfying $1 - \alpha + \beta_m < \xi \leqq 1$ there exists an integer p such that $1 \leqq p \leqq m$ and $1 - \alpha + \beta_p < \xi \leqq 1 - \alpha + \beta_{p-1}$ it follows that E has the Darboux property.

Consider now the case $\alpha = 1$. Let ξ be a real number such that $0 < \xi < 1$. Denote by p_1 the greatest integer p for which $p \leqq s_1$ and $p\alpha_1 \leqq \xi$. If $p_1\alpha_1 = \xi$, the theorem is proved; putting $F = A_1^1 \cup \cdots \cup A_1^{p_1}$, we have $\mu(F) = \xi\beta$. If $p_1\alpha_1 < \xi$ let p_2 be the greatest integer p for which $p \leqq s_2$ and $p_1\alpha_1 + p\alpha_2 \leqq \xi$. If $p_1\alpha_1 + p_2\alpha_2 = \xi$, the theorem is proved; putting $F = A_1^1 \cup \cdots \cup A_1^{p_1} \cup A_2^1 \cup \cdots \cup A_2^{p_2}$, we have $\mu(F) = \xi\beta$.

Let us suppose that we have defined, for each positive integer $j < i$ the greatest p_j for which $p_j \leqq s_j$ and $\sum_{k=1}^{j} p_k\alpha_k \leqq \xi$.

If, for some $j < i$, we have $\sum_{k=1}^{j} p_k\alpha_k = \xi$, the theorem is proved; if not, let p_i be the greatest integer for which $p_i \leqq s_i$ and $\sum_{k=1}^{i} p_k\alpha_k \leqq \xi$. If $\sum_{k=1}^{i} p_k\alpha_k = \xi$ we put $F = \bigcup_{k=1}^{i} (A_k^1 \cup \cdots \cup A_k^{p_k})$ and we have $\mu(F) = \xi\beta$. If the equality does not hold for any positive integer i, then we put $F = \bigcup_{i=1}^{\infty} (A_i^1 \cup \cdots \cup A_i^{p_i})$. We shall prove that $\mu(F) = \xi\beta$.

We reason by contradiction. Suppose that $\mu(F) \neq \xi\beta$. Since, for each n, $\mu\left(\bigcup_{i=1}^{n} (A_i^1 \cup \cdots \cup A_i^{p_i})\right) = \lambda_n\beta$ with $\lambda_n < \xi$, it follows that $\mu(F) = \lambda\beta$, where $\lambda < \xi$.

Since the series $\sum_{i=1}^{\infty} s_i\alpha_i$ converges, we have $\lim_{i\to\infty} \alpha_i = 0$. Hence, there is an integer m' such that, for $i > m'$, we have $\alpha_i \leqq \xi - \lambda$. It follows that for each $i > m'$ we have $p_i = s_i$. Denote by m the least m' for which $i > m'$ implies $p_i = s_i$. Since $\xi < \alpha$, we have $m > 0$. It follows that $p_m < s_m$ and

$$\sum_{i=1}^{m} p_i\alpha_i + \beta_m = \lambda < \xi.$$

But $\alpha = 1$ and $\alpha_m \leqq \beta_m$, therefore

$$\sum_{i=1}^{m-1} p_i\alpha_i + (1 + p_m)\,\alpha_m \leqq \lambda < \xi.$$

This inequality contradicts the fact that p_m is the greatest integer with $p_m \leqq s_m$ and $\sum_{i=1}^{m} p_i\alpha_i \leqq \xi$. It follows that $\mu(F) = \xi\beta$, and the proposition is completely proved.

The last two propositions are included in the following:

Proposition 10. *A set $E \in \mathscr{S}$ has the Darboux property if and only if*

$$\alpha_p \leqq 1 - \sum_{i=1}^{p} s_i\alpha_i, \quad \textit{for} \quad p = 1, 2, \ldots$$

§ 3. VARIATION OF SET FUNCTIONS

Let T be a set, $\mathscr{A}$ an arbitrary class of subsets of T with $\emptyset \in \mathscr{A}$, and X a *normed* space.

In particular $\mathscr{A}$ can be a clan, a semi-tribe or a tribe, and X can be the space of the reals or the space of the complex numbers.

1. DEFINITION OF THE VARIATION

Let $\boldsymbol{m}$ be a set function defined on $\mathscr{A}$ with values in X or in $\overline{R}_+$ with

$$\boldsymbol{m}(\emptyset) = 0.$$

For every set $A \subset T$ we put

$$\overline{\boldsymbol{m}}(A) = \sup_I \sum_{i \in I} |\boldsymbol{m}(A_i)|$$

where the supremum is taken for all the families $(A_i)_{i \in I}$ of mutually disjoint sets of $\mathscr{A}$ *contained* in A.

(There exist always such families, for instance the family consisting of the void set only).

The number $\overline{\boldsymbol{m}}(A)$ is called the *variation of the set function* $\boldsymbol{m}$ *on the set* A. The set function $\overline{\boldsymbol{m}}$ is called the *variation* of $\boldsymbol{m}$.

Proposition 1. *For every set* $A \subset T$ *we have*

$$\overline{\boldsymbol{m}}(A) = \sup_J \sum_{i \in J} |\boldsymbol{m}(A_i)|$$

where the supremum is taken for all the finite families $(A_i)_{i \in J}$ *of disjoint sets of* $\mathscr{A}$ *contained in* A.

We have only to remark that for an arbitrary family $(A_i)_{i \in I}$ of sets of $\mathscr{A}$ we have

$$\sum_{i \in I} |\boldsymbol{m}(A_i)| = \sup_J \sum_{i \in J} |\boldsymbol{m}(A_i)|$$

where the supremum is taken for all the *finite* subsets $J \subset I$.

Corollary. *In the definition of* $\overline{\boldsymbol{m}}(A)$, *the supremum can be taken for all the sequences* (A_i) *of disjoint sets of* $\mathscr{A}$ *contained in* A.

Proposition 2. *If* $\mathscr{A}$ *is a clan, then for every set* $A \in \mathscr{A}$ *we have*

$$\overline{\boldsymbol{m}}(A) = \sup_J \sum_{i \in J} |\boldsymbol{m}(A_i)|$$

where the supremum is taken for all the finite families $(A_i)_{i \in J}$ *of disjoint sets of* $\mathscr{A}$ *such that* $\bigcup_{i \in J} A_i = A$.

In fact, if $A_1, A_2, \ldots, A_n$ are disjoint sets of $\mathscr{A}$ *contained* in A, then taking $A_{n+1} = A - \bigcup_{i=1}^{n} A_i$, the sets $A_1, \ldots, A_n, A_{n+1}$ belong to $\mathscr{A}$, are mutually disjoint, their union is *equal* to A and

$$\sum_{i=1}^{n} |\boldsymbol{m}(A_i)| \leqq \sum_{i=1}^{n+1} |\boldsymbol{m}(A_i)|.$$

Proposition 3. *If $\mathscr{A}$ is a semi-tribe, then for every set $A \in \mathscr{A}$, we have*

$$\bar{\boldsymbol{m}}(A) = \sup_{I} \sum_{i \in I} |\boldsymbol{m}(A_i)|$$

where the supremum is taken for all the countable families $(A_i)_{i \in I}$ of disjoint sets of $\mathscr{A}$ such that $\bigcup_{i \in I} A_i = A$.

In fact, if $(A_i)_{1 \leqq i < \infty}$ is a sequence of disjoint sets of $\mathscr{A}$ contained in A, then taking $A_0 = A - \bigcup_{i=1}^{\infty} A_i$ the sequence $(A_i)_{0 \leqq i < \infty}$ consists of disjoint sets of $\mathscr{A}$, the union of which is *equal* to A and

$$\sum_{i=1}^{\infty} |\boldsymbol{m}(A_i)| \leqq \sum_{i=0}^{\infty} |\boldsymbol{m}(A_i)|.$$

2. PROPERTIES OF THE VARIATION

Let $\boldsymbol{m}$ be a set function defined on $\mathscr{A}$ with values in X or in $\bar{R}_+$ with $\boldsymbol{m}(\emptyset) = 0$. The variation $\bar{\boldsymbol{m}}$ of $\boldsymbol{m}$ has the following properties:

1. $0 \leqq \bar{\boldsymbol{m}}(A) \leqq +\infty$, *for every* $A \subset T$;

2. $\bar{\boldsymbol{m}}(\emptyset) = 0$.

Every family of disjoint sets of $\mathscr{A}$ contained in $\emptyset$ consists only of void sets, therefore $\bar{\boldsymbol{m}}(\emptyset) = \sup \sum |\boldsymbol{m}(\emptyset)| = 0$.

3. $|\boldsymbol{m}(A)| \leqq \bar{\boldsymbol{m}}(A)$, *for* $A \in \mathscr{A}$.

In fact, one of the families of disjoint sets of $\mathscr{A}$ contained in A is the family consisting of the set A only.

4. $\bar{\boldsymbol{m}}$ *is increasing:*

$$\bar{\boldsymbol{m}}(A) \leqq \bar{\boldsymbol{m}}(B), \quad \textit{if} \quad A \subset B.$$

If (A_i) is a family of disjoint sets of $\mathscr{A}$ contained in A, they are contained in B too, therefore

$$\sum |\boldsymbol{m}(A_i)| \leqq \bar{\boldsymbol{m}}(B),$$

hence

$$\bar{m}(A) \leqq \bar{m}(B).$$

5. $\bar{m}(A) \geqq \sup_{\substack{B \subset A \\ B \in \mathscr{A}}} |m(B)|$.

In fact, for every set $B \subset A$ of $\mathscr{A}$ we have

$$\bar{m}(A) \geqq \bar{m}(B) \geqq |m(B)|.$$

6. $\bar{m}(A) = 0$ *if and only if* $m(B) = 0$ *for every set* $B \subset A$ *of* $\mathscr{A}$.

If $\bar{m}(A) = 0$, then for every set $B \subset A$ of $\mathscr{A}$ we have

$$|m(B)| \leqq \bar{m}(B) \leqq \bar{m}(A) = 0,$$

hence $m(B) = 0$.

Conversely, if $m(B) = 0$ for every set $B \subset A$ of $\mathscr{A}$ then for every family (A_i) of sets of $\mathscr{A}$ contained in A we have

$$\sum |m(A_i)| = 0,$$

hence $\bar{m}(A) = 0$.

Remark. If the mapping $x \to |x|$ is a *semi-norm* on X, then the property 6 is replaced by the following one:

$\bar{m}(A) = 0$ if and only if $|m(B)| = 0$ for every set $B \subset A$ of $\mathscr{A}$.

7. $\bar{m}$ is *superadditive:*

$$\bar{m}\left(\bigcup_{i \in I} A_i\right) \geqq \sum_{i \in I} \bar{m}(A_i)$$

for every family $(A_i)_{i \in I}$ *of disjoint sets of* T.

Let A and B be two *disjoint* subsets of T and choose an arbitrary number θ with $\theta < \bar{m}(A) + \bar{m}(B)$. There are two numbers α and β such that

$$\alpha < \bar{m}(A), \quad \beta < \bar{m}(B), \quad \text{and} \quad \alpha + \beta = \theta.$$

We find a *finite* family $(A_i)_{1 \leqq i \leqq n}$ of disjoint sets of $\mathscr{A}$ contained in A such that

$$\alpha < \sum_{i=1}^{n} |m(A_i)|$$

and a *finite* family $(B_j)_{1 \leqq j \leqq m}$ of disjoint sets of $\mathscr{A}$ contained in B such that

$$\beta < \sum_{j=1}^{m} |m(B_j)|.$$

The sets $A_1, A_2, \ldots, A_n, B_1, B_2, \ldots, B_m$ are disjoint, belong to $\mathscr{A}$ and are contained in $A \cup B$, therefore

$$\theta = \alpha + \beta < \sum_{i=1}^{n} |\boldsymbol{m}(A_i)| + \sum_{j=1}^{m} |\boldsymbol{m}(B_j)| \leqq \bar{\boldsymbol{m}}(A \cup B).$$

It follows that

$$\bar{\boldsymbol{m}}(A) + \bar{\boldsymbol{m}}(B) \leqq \bar{\boldsymbol{m}}(A \cup B).$$

By induction we deduce that for every finite family $(A_i)_{i \in J}$ of disjoint subsets of T we have

$$\sum_{i \in J} \bar{\boldsymbol{m}}(A_i) \leqq \bar{\boldsymbol{m}}\left(\bigcup_{i \in J} A_i\right).$$

If $(A_i)_{i \in I}$ is an arbitrary family of disjoint subsets of T, then for every finite subset $J \subset I$ we have

$$\sum_{i \in J} \bar{\boldsymbol{m}}(A_i) \leqq \bar{\boldsymbol{m}}\left(\bigcup_{i \in J} A_i\right) \leqq \bar{\boldsymbol{m}}\left(\bigcup_{i \in I} A_i\right),$$

hence

$$\sum_{i \in I} \bar{\boldsymbol{m}}(A_i) \leqq \bar{\boldsymbol{m}}\left(\bigcup_{i \in I} A_i\right).$$

8. *$\bar{\boldsymbol{m}}$ is the smallest of all the positive set functions ν defined on $\mathscr{P}(T)$ which are increasing, superadditive and verify the inequality*

$$|\boldsymbol{m}(A)| \leqq \nu(A), \quad \textit{for every} \quad A \in \mathscr{A}.$$

In fact, if ν is positive, increasing, superadditive and verifies the preceding inequality, then for every subset $A \subset T$ and for every family $(A_i)_{i \in I}$ of disjoint sets of $\mathscr{A}$ contained in A we have

$$\sum_{i \in I} |\boldsymbol{m}(A_i)| \leqq \sum_{i \in I} \nu(A_i) \leqq \nu\left(\bigcup_{i \in I} A_i\right) \leqq \nu(A),$$

hence

$$\bar{\boldsymbol{m}}(A) \leqq \nu(A).$$

9. *If $\boldsymbol{m}$ is finitely additive on $\mathscr{A}$, then for every finite family $(A_i)_{1 \leqq i \leqq n}$ of disjoint sets of $\mathcal{C}(\mathscr{A})$ we have*

$$\bar{\boldsymbol{m}}\left(\bigcup_{i=1}^{n} A_i\right) = \sum_{i=1}^{n} \bar{\boldsymbol{m}}(A_i).$$

If $\boldsymbol{m}$ is countably additive on $\mathscr{A}$, then for every sequence (A_i) of disjoint sets of $\mathcal{C}(\mathscr{A})$ we have

$$\bar{\boldsymbol{m}}\left(\bigcup_{i=1}^{\infty} A_i\right) = \sum_{i=1}^{\infty} \bar{\boldsymbol{m}}(A_i).$$

Let $(A_i)_{i \in I}$ be a family of disjoint sets of $\mathcal{C}(\mathscr{A})$ (whose union does not necessarily belong to $\mathcal{C}(\mathscr{A})$).

We suppose that this family is finite if $\boldsymbol{m}$ is finitely additive, and countable if $\boldsymbol{m}$ is countably additive.

Let $(B_j)_{1 \leqq j \leqq m}$ be a *finite* family of disjoint sets of $\mathscr{A}$ contained in $\bigcup_{i \in I} A_i$. For every $i \in I$, the family $(A_i \cap B_j)_{1 \leqq j \leqq m}$ consists of disjoint sets of $\mathscr{A}$ contained in A_i.

On the other hand, for each j, the family $(A_i \cap B_j)_{i \in I}$ consists of disjoint sets of $\mathscr{A}$, and its union is $B_j \in \mathscr{A}$. Then

$$\sum_{j=1}^{m} |\boldsymbol{m}(B_j)| = \sum_{j=1}^{m} \left|\boldsymbol{m}\left(\bigcup_{i \in I}(A_i \cap B_j)\right)\right| = \sum_{j=1}^{m} \left|\sum_{i \in I} \boldsymbol{m}(A_i \cap B_j)\right|$$
$$\leqq \sum_{j=1}^{m} \sum_{i \in I} |\boldsymbol{m}(A_i \cap B_j)| = \sum_{i \in I} \sum_{j=1}^{m} |\boldsymbol{m}(A_i \cap B_j)|$$
$$\leqq \sum_{i \in I} \overline{\boldsymbol{m}}(A_i).$$

The finite family (B_j) being arbitrary $\left(\text{with } B_j \subset \bigcup_{i \in I} A_i\right)$ we deduce

$$\overline{\boldsymbol{m}}\left(\bigcup_{i \in I} A_i\right) \leqq \sum_{i \in I} \overline{\boldsymbol{m}}(A_i).$$

The other inequality is also true, because $\overline{\boldsymbol{m}}$ is superadditive, hence

$$\overline{\boldsymbol{m}}\left(\bigcup_{i \in I} A_i\right) = \sum_{i \in I} \overline{\boldsymbol{m}}(A_i).$$

Remark. From the proof of the preceding property we deduce that if μ is a *positive* set function, finitely (or countably) *subadditive* on $\mathscr{A}$, then its variation $\bar{\mu}$ is finitely (or countably) *additive* on $\mathcal{C}(\mathscr{A})$.

10. *If* $\boldsymbol{m}$ *and* $\boldsymbol{n}$ *are two set functions defined on* $\mathscr{A}$ *and* α *is a scalar, then*

$$\overline{\boldsymbol{m} + \boldsymbol{n}} \leqq \overline{\boldsymbol{m}} + \overline{\boldsymbol{n}} \quad \textit{and} \quad \overline{\alpha \boldsymbol{m}} = |\alpha|\, \overline{\boldsymbol{m}}.$$

For every set $A \subset T$ and for every family (A_i) of disjoint sets of $\mathscr{A}$ contained in A, we have

$$\sum |(\boldsymbol{m} + \boldsymbol{n})(A_i)| = \sum |\boldsymbol{m}(A_i) + \boldsymbol{n}(A_i)|$$
$$\leqq \sum |\boldsymbol{m}(A_i)| + \sum |\boldsymbol{n}(A_i)| \leqq \overline{\boldsymbol{m}}(A) + \overline{\boldsymbol{n}}(A),$$

therefore

$$\overline{\boldsymbol{m} + \boldsymbol{n}}(A) \leqq \overline{\boldsymbol{m}}(A) + \overline{\boldsymbol{n}}(A).$$

On the other hand

$$\overline{\alpha \boldsymbol{m}}(A) = \sup \sum |\alpha \boldsymbol{m}(A_i)| = |\alpha| \sup \sum |\boldsymbol{m}(A_i)| = |\alpha|\, \overline{\boldsymbol{m}}(A).$$

11. *Let* $\boldsymbol{m}$ *be a set function defined on* $\mathscr{A}$, *and* $\boldsymbol{m}_{\mathscr{B}}$ *the restriction of* $\boldsymbol{m}$ *to a subclass* $\mathscr{B} \subset \mathscr{A}$ *such that* $\emptyset \in \mathscr{B}$. *Then*

$$\overline{\boldsymbol{m}}_{\mathscr{B}} \leqq \overline{\boldsymbol{m}}.$$

In fact, for every $A \subset T$ we have

$$\overline{\boldsymbol{m}}_{\mathscr{B}}(A) = \sup_{A_i \in \mathscr{B}} \sum |\boldsymbol{m}_{\mathscr{B}}(A_i)| \leqq \sup_{A_i \in \mathscr{A}} \sum |\boldsymbol{m}(A_i)| = \overline{\boldsymbol{m}}(A),$$

the supremum being taken for families (A_i) of disjoint sets contained in A.

Proposition 4. *Let* $\boldsymbol{m}$ *be a set function defined on* $\mathscr{A}$ *and* $\boldsymbol{m}_{\mathscr{B}}$ *the restriction of* $\boldsymbol{m}$ *to a subclass* $\mathscr{B} \subset \mathscr{A}$ *with* $\emptyset \in \mathscr{B}$.

If every set of $\mathscr{A}$ *is the union of a finite (respectively countable) family of disjoint sets of* $\mathscr{B}$, *and if* $\boldsymbol{m}$ *is finitely (respectively countably) additive, then*

$$\overline{\boldsymbol{m}}_{\mathscr{B}} = \overline{\boldsymbol{m}}.$$

Let $A \in \mathscr{A}$ and $(A_i)_{i \in I}$ be a family of disjoint sets of $\mathscr{B}$ such that $A = \bigcup_{i \in I} A_i$.

We suppose that the family is finite if $\boldsymbol{m}$ is finitely additive, and countable if $\boldsymbol{m}$ is countably additive. Then

$$|\boldsymbol{m}(A)| = \left|\sum_{i \in I} \boldsymbol{m}(A_i)\right| \leqq \sum_{i \in I} |\boldsymbol{m}(A_i)| = \sum_{i \in I} |\boldsymbol{m}_{\mathscr{B}}(A_i)| \leqq \overline{\boldsymbol{m}}_{\mathscr{B}}(A).$$

But $\overline{\boldsymbol{m}}$ is the smallest increasing and superadditive set function defined on $\mathscr{P}(T)$ which verifies $|m(A)| \leqq \overline{m}(A)$ for $A \in \mathscr{A}$, therefore $\overline{\boldsymbol{m}} \leqq \overline{\boldsymbol{m}}_{\mathscr{B}}$.

On the other hand, from the property 11 we have $\overline{\boldsymbol{m}}_{\mathscr{B}} \leqq \overline{\boldsymbol{m}}$, therefore $\overline{\boldsymbol{m}}_{\mathscr{B}} = \overline{\boldsymbol{m}}$.

Corollary 1. *Let* $\mathscr{P}$ *be a semi-clan,* $\mathscr{C}$ *the clan generated by* $\mathscr{P}$ *and* $\boldsymbol{m}$ *an additive set function defined on* $\mathscr{C}$ *(with values in* X *or in* $\bar{R}_+$*). Then*

$$\overline{\boldsymbol{m}} = \overline{\boldsymbol{m}}_{\mathscr{P}}.$$

In fact, every set of $\mathscr{C}$ is the union of a finite family of disjoint sets of $\mathscr{P}$ (§ 1, proposition 13).

Corollary 2. *Let* $\mathscr{S}$ *be a semi-tribe,* $\mathscr{T}$ *the tribe generated by* $\mathscr{S}$ *and* $\overline{\boldsymbol{m}}$ *a measure defined on* $\mathscr{T}$. *Then*

$$\overline{\boldsymbol{m}}_{\mathscr{S}} = \overline{\boldsymbol{m}}.$$

In fact, every set of $\mathscr{T}$ is the union of a sequence of disjoint sets of $\mathscr{S}$ (§ 1, proposition 9).

Remark. If $\mathscr{C}$ is a clan, $\mathscr{S}$ the semi-tribe generated by $\mathscr{C}$ and $\boldsymbol{m}$ a measure on $\mathscr{S}$, then we have not in general $\overline{\boldsymbol{m}}_{\mathscr{C}} = \overline{\boldsymbol{m}}$.

We shall see in § 5 (theorem 3), that if $\boldsymbol{m}$ is a measure with finite variation on $\mathscr{S}$, then we have

$$\overline{\boldsymbol{m}}_{\mathscr{C}}(A) = \overline{\boldsymbol{m}}(A), \quad \text{for} \quad A \in \mathscr{C}$$

(but not for every set $A \subset T$).

The following proposition gives sufficient conditions to have $\bar{\boldsymbol{m}}_{\mathscr{C}} = \bar{\boldsymbol{m}}$. In particular, these conditions are verified for the Borel or Baire regular measures (§ 15).

Proposition 5. *Let* $\boldsymbol{m}$ *be a set function defined on* $\mathscr{A}$ *and* $\mathscr{B}$ *a subclass of* $\mathscr{A}$ *with* $\emptyset \in \mathscr{B}$. *If for every set* $A \in \mathscr{A}$ *we have*

$$|\boldsymbol{m}(A)| \leqq \sup_{\substack{B \subset A \\ B \in \mathscr{B}}} |\boldsymbol{m}(B)|,$$

then $\bar{\boldsymbol{m}}_{\mathscr{B}} = \bar{\boldsymbol{m}}$.

Let $A \subset T$ and $(A_i)_{1 \leqq i \leqq n}$ a family of disjoint sets of $\mathscr{A}$ contained in A. Let $\varepsilon > 0$. For each i there exists a set $B_i \subset A_i$ of $\mathscr{B}$ such that $|\boldsymbol{m}(A_i)| \leqq |\boldsymbol{m}(B_i)| + \frac{\varepsilon}{2^i}$. Then

$$\sum_{i=1}^{n} |\boldsymbol{m}(A_i)| \leqq \sum_{i=1}^{n} |\boldsymbol{m}(B_i)| + \varepsilon \leqq \bar{\boldsymbol{m}}_{\mathscr{B}}(A) + \varepsilon,$$

therefore

$$\bar{\boldsymbol{m}}(A) \leqq \bar{\boldsymbol{m}}_{\mathscr{B}}(A) + \varepsilon,$$

consequently

$$\bar{\boldsymbol{m}}(A) = \bar{\boldsymbol{m}}_{\mathscr{B}}(A).$$

3. VARIATION OF THE SCALAR ADDITIVE SET FUNCTIONS

Let μ be a *scalar* set function defined on $\mathscr{A}$ such that $\mu(\emptyset) = 0$. If μ is *positive*, then μ can take also the value $+\infty$.

Proposition 6. *If* $A \cup B \in \mathscr{A}$ *for every disjoint sets* $A, B \in \mathscr{A}$ *and if* μ *is positive and additive, then for every set* $A \subset T$ *we have*

$$\bar{\mu}(A) = \sup_{\substack{B \subset A \\ B \in \mathscr{A}}} \mu(B) = \sup_{B \in \mathscr{A}} \bar{\mu}(A \cap B).$$

We remark first that μ is finitely additive on $\mathscr{A}$. As μ is positive, we have $|\mu(B)| = \mu(B)$ for every set $B \in \mathscr{A}$. Let $A \subset T$, let (A_i) be a finite family of disjoint sets of $\mathscr{A}$ contained in A, and put $B = \bigcup A_i$. We have $B \subset A$, $B \in \mathscr{A}$ and

$$\sum |\mu(A_i)| = \sum \mu(A_i) = \mu(\bigcup A_i) = \mu(B) \leqq \sup_{\substack{B \subset A \\ B \in \mathscr{A}}} \mu(B),$$

hence

$$\bar{\mu}(A) \leqq \sup_{\substack{B \subset A \\ B \in \mathscr{A}}} \mu(B) \leqq \sup_{B \in \mathscr{A}} \bar{\mu}(A \cap B) \leqq \bar{\mu}(A).$$

Corollary 1. *If $A \cup B \in \mathscr{A}$ for every disjoint sets $A, B \in \mathscr{A}$ and if μ is positive, additive and increasing, then*

$$\bar{\mu}(A) = \mu(A), \quad \textit{for every} \quad A \in \mathscr{A}.$$

In fact, for every set $A \in \mathscr{A}$ we have

$$\mu(A) \leqq \bar{\mu}(A) = \sup_{\substack{B \subset A \\ B \in \mathscr{A}}} \mu(B) \leqq \mu(A).$$

Remark. Proposition 1 remains valid if μ is positive and superadditive, consequently, the corollary remains valid if μ is positive, superadditive and increasing.

Corollary 2. *If $\mathscr{A}$ is a clan and if μ is additive and positive, then*

$$\bar{\mu}(A) = \mu(A), \quad \textit{for} \quad A \in \mathscr{A}$$

and

$$\bar{\mu}(A) = \sup_{\substack{B \subset A \\ B \in \mathscr{A}}} \mu(B), \qquad \textit{for } A \subset T.$$

Proposition 7. *If $A \cup B \in \mathscr{A}$ for every disjoint sets $A, B \in \mathscr{A}$ and if μ is additive, then for every set $A \subset T$ we have*

$$\sup_{\substack{B \subset A \\ B \in \mathscr{A}}} |\mu(B)| \leqq \bar{\mu}(A) \leqq 4 \sup_{\substack{B \subset A \\ B \in \mathscr{A}}} |\mu(B)|.$$

The former inequality was proved for every set function (property 5 of the variation). To prove the latter inequality, we suppose first that μ is *real valued.*

Let $(A_i)_{i \in I}$ be a *finite* family of disjoint sets of $\mathscr{A}$ contained in A. If I' is the set of the indices $i \in I$ for which $\mu(A_i) > 0$ and I'' is the set of the indices $i \in I$ for which $\mu(A_i) \leqq 0$ and if we put

$$B' = \bigcup_{i \in I'} A_i \quad \text{and} \quad B'' = \bigcup_{i \in I''} A_i$$

then the sets B' and B'' belong to $\mathscr{A}$, are contained in A, and

$$\begin{aligned}\sum_{i \in I} |\mu(A_i)| &= \sum_{i \in I'} \mu(A_i) - \sum_{i \in I''} \mu(A_i) = \mu(B') - \mu(B'') \\ &= |\mu(B')| + |\mu(B'')| \leqq 2 \sup_{\substack{B \subset A \\ B \in \mathscr{A}}} |\mu(B)|,\end{aligned}$$

hence

$$\bar{\mu}(A) \leqq 2 \sup_{\substack{B \subset A \\ B \in \mathscr{A}}} |\mu(B)|.$$

Suppose now that μ is *complex valued* and put $\mu = \mu_1 + i\mu_2$ where μ_1 and μ_2 are additive *real valued* set functions defined on $\mathscr{A}$. We have

$$|\mu_1(B)| \leqq |\mu(B)| \quad \text{and} \quad |\mu_2(B)| \leqq |\mu(B)|, \quad \text{for every} \quad B \in \mathscr{A}$$

and

$$\bar{\mu} = \overline{\mu_1 + i\mu_2} \leqq \bar{\mu}_1 + \bar{\mu}_2,$$

therefore

$$\bar{\mu}(A) \leqq \bar{\mu}_1(A) + \bar{\mu}_2(A) \leqq 2 \sup_{\substack{B \subset A \\ B \in \mathscr{A}}} |\mu_1(B)| + 2 \sup_{\substack{B \subset A \\ B \in \mathscr{A}}} |\mu_2(B)| \leqq 4 \sup_{\substack{B \subset A \\ B \in \mathscr{A}}} |\mu(B)|$$

and thus, the latter inequality is proved.

4. SET FUNCTIONS WITH FINITE VARIATION

Let $\boldsymbol{m}: \mathscr{A} \to X$ be a set function with $\boldsymbol{m}(\emptyset) = 0$. We say that $\boldsymbol{m}$ is with *finite variation* (with respect to the class $\mathscr{A}$) if

$$\bar{\boldsymbol{m}}(A) < +\infty, \quad \text{for every} \quad A \in \mathscr{A}.$$

The restriction of the variation $\bar{\boldsymbol{m}}$ to the class $\mathscr{A}$ is called the *modulus* of $\boldsymbol{m}$ and is denoted by $|\boldsymbol{m}|$. Sometimes, we shall call $|\boldsymbol{m}|$ also the *variation* of $\boldsymbol{m}$. From the text it will be clear if by *variation* of $\boldsymbol{m}$ we mean $\bar{\boldsymbol{m}}$ or $|\boldsymbol{m}|$.

From the inequality $|\boldsymbol{m}(A)| \leqq \bar{\boldsymbol{m}}(A)$ we deduce that

$$|\boldsymbol{m}(A)| \leqq |\boldsymbol{m}|\,(A), \quad \text{for every} \quad A \in \mathscr{A}.$$

It is the same to say that $\boldsymbol{m}$ is with finite variation or that the positive set function $|\boldsymbol{m}|$ defined on $\mathscr{A}$ is *finite*.

From the relations $\overline{\boldsymbol{m} + \boldsymbol{n}} \leqq \bar{\boldsymbol{m}} + \bar{\boldsymbol{n}}$ and $\overline{\alpha\boldsymbol{m}} = |\alpha|\, \bar{\boldsymbol{m}}$ we deduce now

$$|\boldsymbol{m} + \boldsymbol{n}| \leqq |\boldsymbol{m}| + |\boldsymbol{n}| \quad \text{and} \quad |\alpha\boldsymbol{m}| = |\alpha|\, |\boldsymbol{m}|.$$

It follows that the set of the set functions $\boldsymbol{m}: \mathscr{A} \to X$ with finite variation, is a vector space.

There are set functions which are not with finite variation.

Example. Take X the space of the bounded real functions defined on T, with norm $\|f\| = \sup_{t \in T} |f(t)|$ and $\mathscr{C}$ the clan of the finite or countable subsets of T.

The set function $\boldsymbol{m}: \mathscr{C} \to X$ defined by the equality

$$\boldsymbol{m}(A) = \varphi_A, \quad \text{for} \quad A \in \mathscr{C}$$

is countably additive and $|\boldsymbol{m}(A)| = \|\varphi_A\| = 1$ for every $A \in \mathscr{C}$. It follows that $\bar{\boldsymbol{m}}(A) = k$ if A is finite and consists of k points, and $\bar{\boldsymbol{m}}(A) = +\infty$ if A is infinite.

Proposition 8. *If $A \cup B \in \mathscr{A}$ for every disjoint sets $A, B \in \mathscr{A}$ and if $\boldsymbol{m}$ is with finite variation, then $|\boldsymbol{m}|$ is the smallest of all the positive set functions ν defined on $\mathscr{A}$, which are finite, increasing and superadditive and verify the inequality*

$$|\boldsymbol{m}(A)| \leqq \nu(A), \quad \textit{for every} \quad A \in \mathscr{A}.$$

We remark first that for every finite family $(A_i)_{i \in I}$ of disjoint sets of $\mathscr{A}$ we have $\bigcup_{i \in I} A_i \in \mathscr{A}$.

If ν is a positive, increasing and superadditive set function on $\mathscr{A}$ verifying the preceding inequality, then for every set $A \in \mathscr{A}$ and for every family $(A_i)_{i \in I}$ of disjoint sets of $\mathscr{A}$ contained in A we have

$$\sum_{i \in I} |\boldsymbol{m}(A_i)| \leqq \sum_{i \in I} \nu(A_i) \leqq \nu\left(\bigcup_{i \in I} A_i\right) \leqq \nu(A),$$

hence

$$|\boldsymbol{m}|\,(A) \leqq \nu(A).$$

Proposition 9. *If $A \cup B \in \mathscr{A}$ for every disjoint sets $A, B \in \mathscr{A}$ and if $\boldsymbol{m}$ is with finite variation, then $\overline{|\boldsymbol{m}|} = \bar{\boldsymbol{m}}$.*

If we put $\mu = |\boldsymbol{m}|$ then μ is a *positive, finite, increasing* and *superadditive* set function defined on $\mathscr{A}$, and

$$|\boldsymbol{m}(A)| \leqq \mu(A), \quad \text{for every} \quad A \in \mathscr{A}.$$

We have to show that $\bar{\boldsymbol{m}} = \bar{\mu}$. Let $A \subset T$. For every finite family (A_i) of disjoint sets of $\mathscr{A}$ contained in A, we have

$$\sum |\boldsymbol{m}(A_i)| \leqq \sum \mu(A_i) \leqq \bar{\mu}(A),$$

hence

$$\bar{\boldsymbol{m}}(A) \leqq \bar{\mu}(A).$$

Conversely, if $B \subset A$, $B \in \mathscr{A}$, we have

$$\mu(B) = \bar{\boldsymbol{m}}(B) \leqq \bar{\boldsymbol{m}}(A).$$

As μ is positive and superadditive, we deduce from the remark following proposition 6 that

$$\bar{\mu}(A) = \sup_{\substack{B \subset A \\ B \in \mathscr{A}}} \mu(B) \leqq \bar{\boldsymbol{m}}(A),$$

consequently, $\bar{\mu}(A) = \bar{\boldsymbol{m}}(A)$ for every $A \subset T$, i.e. $\bar{\mu} = \bar{\boldsymbol{m}}$.

Proposition 10. *If $A \cap B \in \mathscr{A}$ for every $A, B \in \mathscr{A}$ and if $\boldsymbol{m}$ is finitely (or countably) additive then $|\boldsymbol{m}|$ is finitely (respectively countably) additive.*

In fact, if $A \cap B \in \mathscr{A}$ for $A, B \in \mathscr{A}$, we have $\mathscr{A} \subset \mathcal{C}(\mathscr{A})$ (§ 1, property 6 of the class $\mathcal{C}(\mathscr{A})$).

On the other hand from the property 9 of the variation we deduce that $\bar{m}$ is finitely (or countably) additive on $\mathcal{T}(\mathcal{A})$ hence on $\mathcal{A}$ too, therefore $|m|$ is finitely (respectively countably) additive on $\mathcal{A}$.

Conversely, we have

Proposition 11. *Let $\mathcal{C}$ be a clan and $m: \mathcal{C} \to X$ an additive set function with finite variation.*

If $|m|$ is countably additive, then m is also countably additive.

Let (A_i) be a sequence of disjoint sets of $\mathcal{C}$ such that $A = \bigcup_{i=1}^{\infty} A_i \in \mathcal{C}$. For every n we have

$$\left|m(A) - \sum_{i=1}^{n} m(A_i)\right| = \left|m(A) - m\left(\bigcup_{i \leq n} A_i\right)\right|$$

$$= \left|m\left(\bigcup_{i>n} A_i\right)\right| \leq |m|\left(\bigcup_{i>n} A_i\right).$$

As $|m|$ is countably additive, we have

$$\lim_{n\to\infty} |m|\left(\bigcup_{i>n} A_i\right) = \lim_{n\to\infty}\left(|m|(A) - \sum_{i=1}^{n} |m|(A_i)\right) = 0,$$

therefore

$$\lim_{n\to\infty}\left|m(A) - \sum_{i=1}^{n} m(A_i)\right| = 0,$$

hence

$$m(A) = \sum_{i=1}^{\infty} m(A_i).$$

5. LOCALLY BOUNDED SET FUNCTIONS

Let $m: \mathcal{A} \to X$ be a set function. We say that m is *bounded* if

$$\sup_{A \in \mathcal{A}} |m(A)| < \infty$$

and that m is *locally bounded* if for every set $A \in \mathcal{A}$ we have

$$\sup_{\substack{B \subset A \\ B \in \mathcal{A}}} |m(B)| < \infty.$$

Every *positive, finite* and *increasing* set function μ on $\mathcal{A}$ is locally bounded, since

$$\sup |\mu(B)| \leq \mu(A) < \infty, \quad \text{for} \quad B \in \mathcal{A} \quad \text{with} \quad B \subset A.$$

We shall see (proposition 17) that every *measure* defined on a *semi-tribe* is locally bounded.

If $\boldsymbol{m}$ is with finite variation, then $\boldsymbol{m}$ is locally bounded. In fact, if $A \in \mathscr{A}$, then for every $B \in \mathscr{A}$ with $B \subset A$ we have

$$|\boldsymbol{m}(B)| \leqq \bar{\boldsymbol{m}}(B) \leqq \bar{\boldsymbol{m}}(A) < \infty .$$

For the scalar additive set functions we have also a converse property:

Proposition 12. *Suppose that $A \cup B \in \mathscr{A}$ for every disjoint sets $A, B \in \mathscr{A}$. A scalar additive set function μ on $\mathscr{A}$ is locally bounded if and only if it is with finite variation.*

In fact, if μ is locally bounded, then from the inequality (proposition 7)

$$\bar{\mu}(A) \leqq 4 \sup_{\substack{B \subset A \\ B \in \mathscr{A}}} |\mu(B)|$$

we deduce that μ is with finite variation.

Remark. In particular, the proposition is true for a *scalar additive* set function on a *clan.*

The real additive set functions with finite variation are differences of positive additive set functions:

Proposition 13. *If μ is a real additive set function on $\mathscr{A}$, with finite variation $|\mu|$, then the set functions*

$$\mu^+ = \frac{1}{2}(|\mu| + \mu) \quad \textit{and} \quad \mu^- = \frac{1}{2}(|\mu| - \mu)$$

are positive and additive on $\mathscr{A}$ and we have

$$\mu = \mu^+ - \mu^- \quad \textit{and} \quad |\mu| = \mu^+ + \mu^- .$$

Since μ is additive, its variation $|\mu|$ is also additive, whence μ^+ and μ^- are additive. For every set $A \in \mathscr{A}$ we have

$$|\mu(A)| \leqq |\mu| (A),$$

whence

$$-|\mu| (A) \leqq \mu(A) \leqq |\mu| (A),$$

therefore $-|\mu| \leqq \mu \leqq |\mu|$. Then $|\mu| + \mu \geqq 0$ and $|\mu| - \mu \geqq 0$. It follows that μ^+ and μ^- are positive.

Remarks.

1°. The set functions μ^+ and μ^- are called, respectively, the *positive part* and the *negative part* of μ.

2°. The equality $\mu = \mu^+ - \mu^-$ is not the only way to write μ as a difference of two positive additive set functions. In fact if ν is a positive additive set function on $\mathscr{A}$, then $\mu^+ + \nu \geqq 0$ and $\mu^- + \nu \geqq 0$ and we have $\mu = (\mu^+ + \nu) - (\mu^- + \nu)$.

3°. The set functions μ^+ and μ^- are the only ones which verify in the same time the two equalities $\mu = \mu^+ - \mu^-$ and $|\mu| = \mu^+ + \mu^-$. In fact, if μ_1 and μ_2 are two positive additive set functions on $\mathscr{A}$ such that $\mu = \mu_1 - \mu_2$ and $|\mu| = \mu_1 + \mu_2$, then

$$\mu_1 = \frac{1}{2}(|\mu| + \mu) = \mu^+ \quad \text{and} \quad \mu_2 = \frac{1}{2}(|\mu| - \mu) = \mu^-.$$

Corollary. *Every complex additive set function μ on $\mathscr{A}$ with finite variation can be written in the form*

$$\mu = (\mu_1 - \mu_2) + i(\mu_3 - \mu_4)$$

where μ_i are positive additive set functions on $\mathscr{A}$.

In fact, $\mu = m_1 + im_2$, where m_1 and m_2 are real additive set functions. From the inequalities $|m_1(A)| \leqq |\mu(A)|$ and $|m_2(A)| \leqq |\mu(A)|$ we deduce that m_1 and m_2 are with finite variation. Then we take $\mu_1 = m_1^+$, $\mu_2 = m_1^-$, $\mu_3 = m_2^+$ and $\mu_4 = m_2^-$.

6. VARIATION OF THE SCALAR MEASURES ON A SEMI-TRIBE

We shall prove now that every (finite) *scalar* measure defined on a *semi-tribe* is with finite variation.

We shall consider, first, the case of the *real* measures.

Let $\mathscr{S}$ be a *semi-tribe* of subsets of T and $\mu: \mathscr{S} \to R$ a *real measure.*

A set $A \in \mathscr{S}$ is said to be *essentially positive* (with respect to μ) if $\mu(B) \geqq 0$ for every set $B \in \mathscr{S}$ such that $B \subset A$. The void set $\emptyset$ is, evidently, essentially positive. If $\mu(B) = 0$ for every set $B \subset A$ of $\mathscr{S}$, then A is essentially positive.

If A is essentially positive, then $\mu(A) \geqq 0$ and

$$\mu(B_1) \leqq \mu(B_2), \quad \text{for} \quad B_1 \subset B_2 \subset A.$$

In fact, if $B_1 \subset B_2 \subset A$ and $B_1, B_2 \in \mathscr{S}$, then $B_2 - B_1 \subset A$, therefore $\mu(B_2 - B_1) \geqq 0$; on the other hand

$$\mu(B_2) - \mu(B_1) = \mu(B_2 - B_1) \geqq 0,$$

hence

$$\mu(B_1) \leqq \mu(B_2).$$

If $A \in \mathscr{S}$ is essentially positive, then every set $A' \subset A$ of $\mathscr{S}$ is essentially positive.

In particular, if A is essentially positive and $A' \in \mathscr{S}$ then the difference $A - A'$ and the intersection $A \cap A'$ are essentially positive.

Lemma 1. *If (A_n) is a sequence of essentially positive sets of $\mathscr{S}$, and if their union A belongs to $\mathscr{S}$, then A is essentially positive.*

Suppose, first, that the sets A_n are mutually disjoint, and let $B \subset A$ be a set of $\mathscr{S}$. Then

$$B = A \cap B = \bigcup_{n=1}^{\infty} (A_n \cap B),$$

consequently

$$\mu(B) = \sum_{n=1}^{\infty} \mu(A_n \cap B) \geqq 0,$$

therefore, in this case, A is essentially positive.

Suppose now that (A_n) is an arbitrary sequence of essentially positive sets of $\mathscr{S}$ with $A = \bigcup_{i=1}^{\infty} A_i \in \mathscr{S}$. Put $B_1 = A_1$ and $B_n = A_n - \bigcup_{i<n} A_i$ for $n \geqq 2$. The sets B_n are essentially positive, mutually disjoint, belong to $\mathscr{S}$ and

$$\bigcup_{n=1}^{\infty} B_n = \bigcup_{i=1}^{\infty} A_i = A \in \mathscr{S}.$$

From the first part of the proof we deduce that A is essentially positive.

A set $A \in \mathscr{S}$ is said to be *essentially negative* if $\mu(B) \leqq 0$ for every set $B \subset A$ of $\mathscr{S}$. If A is essentially negative, then $\mu(A) \leqq 0$ and

$$\mu(B_1) \geqq \mu(B_2), \quad \text{for} \quad B_1 \subset B_2 \subset A.$$

The void set $\emptyset$ is essentially negative.

Theorem 1 (Hahn). *If μ is a real measure on the semi-tribe $\mathscr{S}$ then every set $A \in \mathscr{S}$ is the union of two disjoint sets A^+, $A^- \in \mathscr{S}$, such that A^+ is essentially positive and A^- is essentially negative.*

Let $A \in \mathscr{S}$ and put

$$a = \sup \mu(A'),$$

the supremum being taken for all the *essentially positive* sets $A' \subset A$. There exists then a sequence (A'_n) of essentially positive subsets of A such that

$$a = \lim_{n \to \infty} \mu(A'_n).$$

The set $A^+ = \bigcup_{n=1}^{\infty} A'_n$ belongs to $\mathscr{S}$, is contained in A and is essentially positive. We have $A'_n \subset A^+$ for every n, therefore

$$\mu(A'_n) \leqq \mu(A^+),$$

hence

$$a = \lim_{n \to \infty} \mu(A'_n) \leqq \mu(A^+) \leqq a,$$

consequently

$$\mu(A^+) = a.$$

It follows that

$$0 \leqq a < +\infty.$$

We remark that A contains no essentially positive subset A' such that $A' \cap A^+ = \emptyset$ and $\mu(A') > 0$.

In fact, if A' were an essentially positive subset of A such that $A' \cap A^+ = \emptyset$ and $\mu(A') > 0$, then $A' \cup A^+$ would be an essentially positive subset of A, therefore

$$\mu(A' \cup A^+) \leqq a;$$

on the other hand

$$\mu(A' \cup A^+) = \mu(A') + \mu(A^+) > \mu(A^+) = a,$$

hence $a < a$, which is absurd.

Put now $A^- = A - A^+$. We have $A = A^+ \cup A^-$ and $A^+ \cap A^- = \emptyset$. We have only to show that A is essentially negative, i.e. $\mu(B) \leqq 0$ for every set $B \subset A^-$ of $\mathscr{S}$.

Let $B \subset A^-$ be a set of $\mathscr{S}$. Suppose that we would have $\mu(B) > 0$. As $B \cap A^+ = \emptyset$, B is not essentially positive, therefore B contains subsets of strictly negative measure.

Let k_1 be the smallest natural number having the property that there exists a set $B_1 \subset B$ of $\mathscr{S}$ with

$$\mu(B_1) < -\frac{1}{k_1}.$$

We have

$$\mu(B - B_1) = \mu(B) - \mu(B_1) > \mu(B) + \frac{1}{k_1} > 0.$$

As $B - B_1$ is disjoint of A^+, it is not essentially positive, therefore it contains subsets of strictly negative measure.

Let k_2 be the smallest natural number having the property that there exists a set $B_2 \subset B - B_1$ of $\mathscr{S}$ with

$$\mu(B_2) < -\frac{1}{k_2}.$$

We have

$$\mu(B - (B_1 \cup B_2)) = \mu((B - B_1) - B_2) = \mu(B - B_1) - \mu(B_2)$$
$$> \mu(B - B_1) + \frac{1}{k_2} > 0.$$

In this manner, we find, by induction, a sequence (B_n) of disjoint sets of $\mathscr{S}$ and a sequence (k_n) of natural numbers, such that for every n we have

$$B_n \subset B - \bigcup_{i<n} B_i, \quad \mu(B_n) < -\frac{1}{k_n} \quad \text{and} \quad \mu\left(B - \bigcup_{i=1}^{n} B_i\right) > 0.$$

If we put $B_0 = \bigcup_{n=1}^{\infty} B_n$, we have $B_0 \subset B$, $B_0 \in \mathscr{S}$ and

$$-\infty < \mu(B_0) = \sum_{n=1}^{\infty} \mu(B_n) \leqq -\sum_{n=1}^{\infty} \frac{1}{k_n} < 0.$$

Consequently, the series $\sum_{n=1}^{\infty} \frac{1}{k_n}$ is convergent, hence $\lim_{n\to\infty} \frac{1}{k_n} = 0$. The set $B - B_0$ belongs to $\mathscr{S}$, the set $B - B_0$ and the set A^+ are disjoint, and

$$\mu(B - B_0) = \mu(B) - \mu(B_0) > 0,$$

therefore $B - B_0$ is not *essentially positive*.

Let now $C \subset B - B_0$ be an arbitrary set of $\mathscr{S}$. For every n we have

$$\mu(C) \geqq -\frac{1}{k_n},$$

hence $\mu(C) \geqq 0$, therefore $B - B_0$ is *essentially positive*, which is contradictory.

This contradiction is due to the supposition that there exists a set $B \subset A^-$ with $\mu(B) > 0$.

It follows that $\mu(B) \leqq 0$ for every set $B \subset A^-$ of $\mathscr{S}$, therefore A^- is essentially negative, and thus the theorem is completely proved.

Remark. If μ is a real measure on a *tribe* $\mathscr{T}$, then the whole space T can be written $T = T^+ \cup T^-$ with $T^+ \in \mathscr{T}$, $T^+ \cap T^- = \emptyset$ and $\mu(T^+ \cap A) \geqq 0$, $\mu(T^- \cap A) \leqq 0$ for every $A \in \mathscr{T}$.

Proposition 14. *If μ is a scalar measure defined on the semi-tribe $\mathscr{S}$, then μ is locally bounded:*

$$\sup_{\substack{B \subset A \\ B \in \mathscr{S}}} |\mu(B)| < +\infty, \quad \textit{for every} \quad A \in \mathscr{S}.$$

Let $A \in \mathscr{S}$. Suppose first that μ is *real-valued*. According to the preceding theorem, there exists an essentially positive set $A^+ \in \mathscr{S}$ and an essentially negative set $A^- \in \mathscr{S}$ such that $A = A^+ \cup A^-$ and $A^+ \cap A^- = \emptyset$. Put $a^+ = \mu(A^+)$ and $a^- = \mu(A^-)$. The numbers a^+ and a^- are finite and

$$a^- \leqq 0 \leqq a^+.$$

If $B \subset A$ is an arbitrary set of $\mathcal{S}$, then $B \cap A^+ \subset A^+$ and $B \cap A^- \subset A^-$, therefore

$$0 \leqq \mu(B \cap A^+) \leqq \mu(A^+) = a^+,$$

$$a^- = \mu(A^-) \leqq \mu(B \cap A^-) \leqq 0,$$

hence

$$a^- \leqq \mu(B \cap A^-) + \mu(B \cap A^+) \leqq a^+,$$

consequently

$$a^- \leqq \mu(B) \leqq a^+,$$

hence

$$|\mu(B)| \leqq a^+ - a^-.$$

It follows that

$$\sup_{\substack{B \subset A \\ B \in \mathcal{S}}} |\mu(B)| \leqq a^+ - a^- < +\infty.$$

Suppose now that μ is complexe and write $\mu = \mu_1 + i\mu_2$ where μ_1 and μ_2 are real measures on $\mathcal{S}$. For every set $B \subset A$ of $\mathcal{S}$ we have

$$|\mu(B)| \leqq |\mu_1(B)| + |\mu_2(B)|,$$

therefore

$$\sup_{\substack{B \subset A \\ B \in \mathcal{S}}} |\mu(B)| \leqq \sup_{\substack{B \subset A \\ B \in \mathcal{S}}} |\mu_1(B)| + \sup_{\substack{B \subset A \\ B \in \mathcal{S}}} |\mu_2(B)| < +\infty.$$

Corollary 1. *Every scalar measure μ on a semi-tribe $\mathcal{S}$ is with finite variation.*

We use the proposition 14.

Corollary 2. *If μ is a real measure on a semi-tribe $\mathcal{S}$, then the set functions*

$$\mu^+ = \frac{1}{2}(|\mu| + \mu) \quad \text{and} \quad \mu^- = \frac{1}{2}(|\mu| - \mu)$$

are positive measures on $\mathcal{S}$ and we have

$$\mu = \mu^+ - \mu^- \quad \textit{and} \quad |\mu| = \mu^+ + \mu^-.$$

In fact, $|\mu|$ is countably additive and finite, hence $|\mu|$ is a positive measure. Then μ^+ and μ^- are also countably additive. The other properties follow from the proposition 13.

Corollary 3. *A complex measure μ on a semi-tribe $\mathcal{S}$ can be written $\mu = (\mu_1 - \mu_2) + i(\mu_3 - \mu_4)$ where μ_i are positive measures on $\mathcal{S}$.*

We write first $\mu = m_1 + im_2$, where m_1 and m_2 are real measures on $\mathcal{S}$. Then we take $\mu_1 = m_1^+$, $\mu_2 = m_1^-$, $\mu_3 = m_2^+$ and $\mu_4 = m_2^-$.

The measures μ^+ and μ^- are characterized by the following two propositions.

Proposition 15. *If μ is a real measure on the semi-tribe $\mathscr{S}$ then for every $A \in \mathscr{S}$ we have*

$$\mu^+(A) = \mu(A^+) \quad \text{and} \quad \mu^-(A) = -\mu(A^-)$$

where A^+ is essentially positive and A^- is essentially negative such that $A^+ \cup A^- = A$ and $A^+ \cap A^- = \emptyset$.

Let $A \in \mathscr{S}$ and let $A = A^+ \cup A^-$ be a decomposition of A in the sense of the theorem 1. We have

$$\mu(A) = \mu(A^+) + \mu(A^-).$$

We shall prove that we have also

$$|\mu|(A) = \mu(A^+) - \mu(A^-).$$

It will then follow that

$$\mu^+(A) = \frac{1}{2}(|\mu|(A) + \mu(A)) = \mu(A^+)$$

and

$$\mu^-(A) = \frac{1}{2}(|\mu|(A) - \mu(A)) = -\mu(A^-).$$

Let (A_i) be a finite family of disjoint sets of $\mathscr{S}$, with union equal to A. For each i put $A_i^+ = A_i \cap A^+$ and $A_i^- = A_i \cap A^-$. The sets A_i^+ are essentially positive and disjoint, the sets A_i^- are essentially negative and disjoint and we have

$$A^+ = \bigcup A_i^+ \quad \text{and} \quad A^- = \bigcup A_i^-,$$

hence

$$\begin{aligned}\sum |\mu(A_i)| &= \sum \mu(A_i^+) - \sum \mu(A_i^-)\\ &= \mu(\bigcup A_i^+) - \mu(\bigcup A_i^-) = \mu(A^+) - \mu(A^-).\end{aligned}$$

Taking the supremum in the left hand we deduce

$$|\mu|(A) = \mu(A^+) - \mu(A^-).$$

Remark. For every set $A \in \mathscr{S}$ we have

$$\mu^+(A^-) = 0 \quad \text{and} \quad \mu^-(A^+) = 0.$$

Proposition 16. *Let μ be a real measure on the semi-tribe $\mathscr{S}$ and let μ_1, μ_2 be two positive measures on $\mathscr{S}$ such that $\mu = \mu_1 - \mu_2$. We have $\mu_1 = \mu^+$ and $\mu_2 = \mu^-$ if and only if for every positive measure λ on $\mathscr{S}$ such that $\lambda \leqq \mu_1$ and $\lambda \leqq \mu_2$ we have $\lambda = 0$.*

If $\lambda \geqq 0$, $\lambda \leqq \mu^+$ and $\lambda \leqq \mu^-$, then for every set $A \in \mathscr{S}$ we have

$$\lambda(A) = \lambda(A^+) + \lambda(A^-) \leqq \mu^-(A^+) + \mu^+(A^-) = 0,$$

hence $\lambda = 0$.

Conversely, suppose that $\lambda = 0$ for every positive measure λ such that $\lambda \leqq \mu_1$ and $\lambda \leqq \mu_2$. We have $\mu = \mu_1 - \mu_2 = \mu^+ - \mu^-$, hence $\mu_1 - \mu^+ = \mu_2 - \mu^-$. We show that $\mu_1 - \mu^+ \geqq 0$. For every $A \in \mathscr{S}$ we have

$$\mu_1(A^+) - \mu^+(A^+) = \mu_2(A^+) \geqq 0,$$

$$\mu_1(A^-) - \mu^+(A^-) = \mu_1(A^-) \geqq 0,$$

whence $\mu_1(A) - \mu^+(A) \geqq 0$. If we put $\lambda = \mu_1 - \mu^+ = \mu_2 - \mu^-$, then λ is a positive measure and we have $\lambda \leqq \mu_1$ and $\lambda \leqq \mu_2$. It follows that $\lambda = 0$, whence $\mu_1 = \mu^+$ and $\mu_2 = \mu^-$.

We can prove now that every measure on a semi-tribe is locally bounded. More generally:

Proposition 17. *Let $\mathscr{S}$ be a semi-tribe and $\boldsymbol{m}: \mathscr{S} \to \mathscr{L}(E, F)$ an additive set function. If for every $x \in E$ and every $z \in F'$ the scalar set function $\boldsymbol{m}_{x,z}$ defined on $\mathscr{S}$ by*

$$\boldsymbol{m}_{x,z}(A) = \langle \boldsymbol{m}(A)\, x, z \rangle \quad \textit{for} \quad A \in \mathscr{S}$$

is countably additive, then $\boldsymbol{m}$ is locally bounded:

$$\sup_{\substack{B \subset A \\ B \in \mathscr{S}}} |\boldsymbol{m}(B)| < \infty, \quad \textit{for every} \quad A \in \mathscr{S}.$$

In fact, since for each $x \in E$ and $z \in F'$, $\boldsymbol{m}_{x,z}$ is a scalar measure on the semi-tribe $\mathscr{S}$, we have

$$\sup_{B \subset A} \langle \boldsymbol{m}(B)\, x, z \rangle = \sup_{B \subset A} |\boldsymbol{m}_{x,z}(B)| < \infty, \quad \text{for every} \quad A \in \mathscr{S}.$$

By the Banach-Steinhaus theorem, for each $x \in E$ we have

$$\sup_{B \subset A} |\boldsymbol{m}(B)\, x| < \infty, \quad \text{for every} \quad A \in \mathscr{S}.$$

Then, again by the Banach-Steinhaus theorem, we deduce that

$$\sup_{B \subset A} |\boldsymbol{m}(B)| < \infty, \quad \text{for every} \quad A \in \mathscr{S}.$$

Remark. If $\mathscr{S}$ is a *tribe*, then m is *bounded*.

§ 4. SEMI-VARIATION OF SET FUNCTIONS

Let T be a set, $\mathscr{A}$ a class of subsets of T such that $\emptyset \in \mathscr{A}$, and X a normed space. Let E and F be two normed spaces such that X can be plunged isometrically in $\mathscr{L}(E, F)$. We can consider, for example, $X = \mathscr{L}(R, X)$ or $X \subset \mathscr{L}(X', R)$.

1. DEFINITION OF THE SEMI-VARIATION

Let $\boldsymbol{m}: \mathscr{A} \to X \subset \mathscr{L}(E, F)$ be a set function such that $\boldsymbol{m}(\emptyset) = 0$. For every set $A \subset T$ we put

$$\tilde{\boldsymbol{m}}(A) = \sup_I \left|\sum_{i \in I} \boldsymbol{m}(A_i)\, x_i\right|$$

where the supremum is taken for all the finite families $(A_i)_{i \in I}$ of *disjoint* sets of $\mathscr{A}$ *contained* in A and for all the finite families $(x_i)_{i \in I}$ of elements of E such that $|x_i| \leqq 1$ for each $i \in I$.

The number $\tilde{\boldsymbol{m}}(A)$ is called the *semi-variation* of the set function $\boldsymbol{m}$ on the set A.

The set function $\tilde{\boldsymbol{m}}$ defined on $\mathscr{P}(T)$ is called the *semi-variation* of $\boldsymbol{m}$ (relatively to the spaces E and F).

Remark. The semi-variation $\tilde{\boldsymbol{m}}$ of $\boldsymbol{m}$ depends essentially on the spaces E and F. If we want to emphasize this dependence we shall write $\tilde{\boldsymbol{m}}_{E,F}$ instead of $\tilde{\boldsymbol{m}}$.

Proposition 1. *We have*

$$\tilde{\boldsymbol{m}}_{R,X} \leqq \tilde{\boldsymbol{m}}_{E,F} \leqq \tilde{\boldsymbol{m}}_{X',R}.$$

In fact, let $A \subset T$. Let (A_i) be a finite family of disjoint sets of $\mathscr{A}$ contained in A, and (α_i) a family of numbers such that $|\alpha_i| \leqq 1$. Then

$$\left|\sum \boldsymbol{m}(A_i)\, \alpha_i\right| = \sup_{\substack{|x| \leqq 1 \\ x \in E}} \left|\sum \boldsymbol{m}(A_i)\, \alpha_i x\right| \leqq \tilde{\boldsymbol{m}}_{E,F}(A),$$

therefore

$$\tilde{\boldsymbol{m}}_{R,X}(A) \leqq \tilde{\boldsymbol{m}}_{E,F}(A).$$

We remark then that for every $e \in E$ and every $f' \in F'$, the mapping $x \to \langle xe, f' \rangle$ is a continuous linear functional $x' \in X'$:

$$\langle xe, f' \rangle = \langle x, x' \rangle, \quad \text{for} \quad x \in X$$

and we have $|x'| \leqq |e|\,|f|$.

Let now (A_i) be a finite family of disjoint sets of $\mathscr{A}$ contained in A, and (x_i) a family of elements of E such that $|x_i| \leqq 1$. Then

$$\left|\sum \boldsymbol{m}(A_i)\, x_i\right| = \sup_{\substack{|z| \leqq 1 \\ z \in F'}} \left|\sum \langle \boldsymbol{m}(A_i)\, x_i, z \rangle\right|$$

$$\leqq \sup_{\substack{|x_i'| \leqq 1 \\ x_i' \in X'}} \left|\sum \langle \boldsymbol{m}(A_i), x_i' \rangle\right| = \tilde{\boldsymbol{m}}_{X',R}(A)$$

therefore $\tilde{\boldsymbol{m}}_{E,F}(A) \leqq \tilde{\boldsymbol{m}}_{X',R}(A)$.

Proposition 2. *If $\mathscr{A}$ is a clan, then for every set $A \in \mathscr{A}$ we have*

$$\tilde{m}(A) = \sup_I \left| \sum_{i \in I} m(A_i)\, x_i \right|,$$

the supremum being taken for all the finite families $(A_i)_{i \in I}$ of disjoint sets of $\mathscr{A}$ such that $\bigcup_{i \in I} A_i = A$ and for all the finite families $(x_i)_{i \in I}$ of elements of E such that $|x_i| \leqq 1$ for each $i \in I$.

In fact, if $(A_i)_{1 \leqq i \leqq n}$ is a family of disjoint sets of $\mathscr{A}$ *contained* in A and if $(x_i)_{1 \leqq i \leqq n}$ is a family of elements of E such that $|x_i| \leqq 1$ for $i = 1, 2, \ldots, n$, then, taking $A_{n+1} = A - \bigcup_{i=1}^{n} A_i$ and $x_{n+1} = 0$, the family $(A_i)_{1 \leqq i \leqq n+1}$ consists of disjoint sets of $\mathscr{A}$, $\bigcup_{i=1}^{n+1} A_i = A$ and we have

$$\left| \sum_{i=1}^{n} m(A_i)\, x_i \right| = \left| \sum_{i=1}^{n+1} m(A_i)\, x_i \right|.$$

2. PROPERTIES OF THE SEMI-VARIATION

Let $m\colon \mathscr{A} \to X \subset \mathscr{L}(E, F)$ be a set function such that $m(\emptyset) = 0$.
The semi-variation $\tilde{m}$ of m has the following properties:

1. $0 \leqq \tilde{m}(A) \leqq +\infty$, *for every* $A \subset T$;

2. $\tilde{m}(\emptyset) = 0$.

In fact, every finite family of disjoint sets of $\mathscr{A}$ contained in $\emptyset$ consists of void sets only, therefore

$$\tilde{m}(\emptyset) = \sup_I \left| \sum_{i \in I} m(\emptyset)\, x_i \right| = 0.$$

3. $|m(A)| \leqq \tilde{m}(A) \leqq \bar{m}(A)$, *for every* $A \in \mathscr{A}$.

In fact,

$$|m(A)| = \sup_{\substack{|x| \leqq 1 \\ x \in E}} |m(A)\, x| \leqq \sup_I \left| \sum_{i \in I} m(A_i)\, x_i \right| = \tilde{m}(A).$$

On the other hand, if $|x_i| \leqq 1$, we have

$$\left| \sum_{i \in I} m(A_i)\, x_i \right| \leqq \sum_{i \in I} |m(A_i)| \leqq \bar{m}(A),$$

therefore

$$\tilde{m}(A) \leqq \bar{m}(A).$$

4. $\tilde{m}$ *is increasing:*

$$\tilde{m}(A) \leqq \tilde{m}(B) \quad \text{if} \quad A \subset B;$$

5. $\tilde{m}(A) \geqq \sup\limits_{\substack{B \subset A \\ B \in \mathscr{A}}} |m(B)|$.

In fact, if $B \subset A$ and $B \in \mathscr{A}$, then $\tilde{m}(A) \geqq \tilde{m}(B) \geqq |m(B)|$.

6. $\tilde{m}(A) = 0$ *if and only if* $\overline{m}(A) = 0$.

If $\tilde{m}(A) = 0$, then $\tilde{m}(B) = 0$; hence $|m(B)| = 0$ for every set $B \subset A$ of $\mathscr{A}$, therefore $\overline{m}(A) = 0$.

Conversely, $\tilde{m}(A) \leqq \overline{m}(A)$, therefore if $\overline{m}(A) = 0$ then $\tilde{m}(A) = 0$.

7. *If* m *and* n *are two set functions defined on* $\mathscr{A}$ *with values in* $X \subset \mathscr{L}(E, F)$ *such that* $m(\emptyset) = n(\emptyset) = 0$, *and* α *is a scalar, then*

$$\widetilde{m + n} \leqq \tilde{m} + \tilde{n} \quad \text{and} \quad \widetilde{\alpha m} = |\alpha|\, \tilde{m}.$$

8. *Let* $m\colon \mathscr{A} \to X \subset \mathscr{L}(E, F)$ *be a set function such that* $m(\emptyset) = 0$ *and* $m_{\mathscr{B}}$ *the restriction of* m *to a subclass* $\mathscr{B} \subset \mathscr{A}$ *with* $\emptyset \in \mathscr{B}$. *Then*

$$\tilde{m}_{\mathscr{B}} \leqq \tilde{m}.$$

Proposition 3. *Let* $\mathscr{C}$ *be a clan and* $m\colon \mathscr{C} \to X \subset \mathscr{L}(E, F)$ *a set function.*

If m *is additive on* $\mathscr{C}$, *then* $\tilde{m}$ *is subadditive on the clan* $\mathfrak{C}(\mathscr{C})$.

If m *is countably additive on* $\mathscr{C}$, *then* $\tilde{m}$ *is countably subadditive on the clan* $\mathfrak{C}(\mathscr{C})$.

We remark first that $\mathfrak{C}(\mathscr{C})$ is a clan, because $\mathscr{C}$ is a clan (§ 1, proposition 18).

Let (A_i) be a sequence of sets of $\mathfrak{C}(\mathscr{C})$. If m is only additive, we suppose that $A_i = \emptyset$ except for a finite set of indices. Put $A'_1 = A_1$ and $A'_n = A_n - \bigcup\limits_{i<n} A_i$. The sets A'_i are mutually disjoint, belong to $\mathfrak{C}(\mathscr{C})$ and $\bigcup\limits_{i=1}^{\infty} A'_i = \bigcup\limits_{i=1}^{\infty} A_i$.

We have $A'_i \subset A_i$, hence $\tilde{m}(A'_i) \leqq \tilde{m}(A_i)$ for each i.

Let $(B_j)_{1 \leqq j \leqq m}$ be a family of disjoint sets of $\mathscr{C}$ contained in $\bigcup\limits_{i=1}^{\infty} A_i$ and let $(x_j)_{1 \leqq j \leqq m}$ be a family of elements of E such that $|x_j| \leqq 1$ for each j.

For each i, the family $(A'_i \cap B_j)_{1 \leqq j \leqq m}$ consists of disjoint sets of $\mathscr{C}$, contained in A'_i. For each j the sequence $(A'_i \cap B_j)_{i \in N}$ consists of disjoint sets of $\mathscr{C}$, and their union is B_j. Then

$$\begin{aligned}
\left|\sum_{j=1}^{m} m(B_j)\, x_j\right| &= \left|\sum_{j=1}^{m} m\left(\bigcup_{i=1}^{\infty} (A'_i \cap B_j)\right) x_j\right| \\
&= \left|\sum_{j=1}^{m} \sum_{i=1}^{\infty} m(A'_i \cap B_j)\, x_j\right| = \left|\sum_{i=1}^{\infty} \sum_{j=1}^{m} m(A'_i \cap B_j)\, x_j\right| \\
&\leqq \sum_{i=1}^{\infty} \left|\sum_{j=1}^{m} m(A'_i \cap B_j)\, x_j\right| \leqq \sum_{i=1}^{\infty} \tilde{m}(A'_i) \leqq \sum_{i=1}^{\infty} \tilde{m}(A_i),
\end{aligned}$$

whence

$$\tilde{m}\left(\bigcup_{i=1}^{\infty} A_i\right) \leqq \sum_{i=1}^{\infty} \tilde{m}(A_i).$$

3. SEMI-VARIATION OF SET FUNCTIONS WITH VALUES IN A CONJUGATE SPACE

Let $\boldsymbol{m}: \mathscr{A} \to X$ be a set function such that $\boldsymbol{m}(\emptyset) = 0$.

We can choose the spaces E and F so that the semi-variation of $\boldsymbol{m}$ – relatively to these spaces – is equal to the variation of $\boldsymbol{m}$.

We can plunge the space X in a conjugate space, for example in X''.

We can therefore choose the space E such that $X \subset \mathscr{L}(E, C)$.

Proposition 4. *The semi-variation of the set function $\boldsymbol{m}: \mathscr{A} \to X \subset \mathscr{L}(E, C)$ – relatively to the spaces E and C – is equal to the variation of $\boldsymbol{m}$.*

As $\tilde{\boldsymbol{m}}(A) \leqq \bar{\boldsymbol{m}}(A)$ for every set $A \subset T$, it remains to prove the converse inequality. Let $A \subset T$ and $\varepsilon > 0$; let $(A_i)_{1 \leqq i \leqq n}$ be a finite family of disjoint sets of $\mathscr{A}$ contained in A. For each $i \leqq n$, there exists an element $x_i \in E$ with $|x_i| = 1$ such that

$$|\boldsymbol{m}(A_i)| \leqq \langle x_i, \boldsymbol{m}(A_i)\rangle + \frac{\varepsilon}{n}.$$

Then

$$\sum_{i=1}^{n} |\boldsymbol{m}(A_i)| \leqq \sum_{i=1}^{n} \langle x_i, \boldsymbol{m}(A_i)\rangle + \varepsilon$$

$$= \left|\sum_{i=1}^{n} \boldsymbol{m}(A_i)\, x_i\right| + \varepsilon \leqq \tilde{\boldsymbol{m}}(A) + \varepsilon.$$

It follows that $\bar{\boldsymbol{m}}(A) \leqq \tilde{\boldsymbol{m}}(A) + \varepsilon$. As ε is arbitrary we deduce that $\bar{\boldsymbol{m}}(A) \leqq \tilde{\boldsymbol{m}}(A)$, hence $\bar{\boldsymbol{m}}(A) = \tilde{\boldsymbol{m}}(A)$.

Corollary 1. *If μ is a scalar set function defined on $\mathscr{A}$ such that $\mu(\emptyset) = 0$, and if we consider μ with values in $\mathscr{L}(C, C)$ the variation and the semi-variation (with respect to the spaces C and C) of μ are equal.*

Corollary 2. *If $A \cup B \in \mathscr{A}$ for every $A, B \in \mathscr{A}$ and if μ is a positive increasing and additive set function defined on $\mathscr{A}$, then*

$$\tilde{\mu}(A) = \bar{\mu}(A) = \mu(A), \quad \textit{for every} \quad A \in \mathscr{A}.$$

We use the corollary 1 of the proposition 6, § 3, and the preceding corollary 1.

Now we can compute the semi-variation of a set function $\boldsymbol{m}: \mathscr{A} \to \mathscr{L}(E, F)$ with the aid of the variations of the set functions $\boldsymbol{m}_z: \mathscr{A} \to \mathscr{L}(E, C)$, for $z \in F'$, defined by the equality

$$\boldsymbol{m}_z(A)\, x = \langle \boldsymbol{m}(A)\, x, z\rangle, \quad \text{for} \quad A \in \mathscr{A} \quad \text{and} \quad x \in E.$$

Let $Z \subset F'$ be a norming subspace, i.e. such that $|x| = \sup_{z \in Z} \frac{|\langle x, z \rangle|}{|z|}$, for $x \in E$.

Proposition 5. *If $\boldsymbol{m}: \mathscr{A} \to \mathscr{L}(E, F)$ is a set function with $\boldsymbol{m}(\emptyset) = 0$, then for every $A \in \mathscr{A}$ we have*

$$\tilde{\boldsymbol{m}}(A) = \sup_{\substack{|z| \leqq 1 \\ z \in Z}} \overline{\boldsymbol{m}_z}(A).$$

Since for $z \in Z$, the set function $\boldsymbol{m}_z$ has values in $\mathscr{L}(E, C)$, we have $\tilde{\boldsymbol{m}}_z = \overline{\boldsymbol{m}_z}$.

Let $A \subset T$. For every finite family (A_i) of disjoint sets of $\mathscr{A}$ contained in A, and every finite family (x_i) of E with $|x_i| \leqq 1$ we have

$$\left|\sum \boldsymbol{m}(A_i)\, x_i\right| = \sup_{|z| \leqq 1} \left|\left\langle \sum \boldsymbol{m}(A_i)\, x_i, z \right\rangle\right| = \sup_{|z| \leqq 1} \left|\sum \langle \boldsymbol{m}(A_i)\, x_i, z \rangle\right|$$

$$= \sup_{|z| \leqq 1} \left|\sum \boldsymbol{m}_z(A_i)\, x_i\right| \leqq \sup_{|z| \leqq 1} \tilde{\boldsymbol{m}}_z(A) = \sup_{|z| \leqq 1} \overline{\boldsymbol{m}_z}(A),$$

therefore

$$\tilde{\boldsymbol{m}}(A) \leqq \sup_{|z| \leqq 1} \overline{\boldsymbol{m}_z}(A).$$

On the other hand, if $z \in Z$ and $|z| \leqq 1$, we have

$$\left|\sum \boldsymbol{m}_z(A_i)\, x_i\right| = \left|\left\langle \sum \boldsymbol{m}(A_i)\, x_i, z \right\rangle\right| \leqq \left|\sum \boldsymbol{m}(A_i)\, x_i\right| \leqq \tilde{\boldsymbol{m}}(A),$$

therefore

$$\tilde{\boldsymbol{m}}_z(A) \leqq \tilde{\boldsymbol{m}}(A),$$

whence

$$\sup_{|z| \leqq 1} \overline{\boldsymbol{m}_z}(A) = \sup_{|z| \leqq 1} \tilde{\boldsymbol{m}}_z(A) \leqq \tilde{\boldsymbol{m}}(A).$$

We can now precise the proposition 3:

Corollary. *If $\mathscr{C}$ is a clan and if $\boldsymbol{m}: \mathscr{C} \to \mathscr{L}(E, F)$ is an additive set function and if for every $z \in Z$, the set function $\boldsymbol{m}_z: \mathscr{C} \to \mathscr{L}(E, C)$ is countably additive, then the semi-variation is countably subadditive on $\mathcal{C}(\mathscr{C})$.*

In fact, $\overline{\boldsymbol{m}_z}$ is countably subadditive on $\mathcal{C}(\mathscr{C})$, therefore, for every sequence (A_n) of $\mathcal{C}(\mathscr{C})$ we have

$$\tilde{\boldsymbol{m}}\left(\bigcup A_n\right) = \sup_{|z| \leqq 1} \overline{\boldsymbol{m}_z}\left(\bigcup A_n\right) \leqq \sup_{|z| \leqq 1} \sum \overline{\boldsymbol{m}_z}(A_n) \leqq \sum \sup_{|z| \leqq 1} \overline{\boldsymbol{m}_z}(A_n) = \sum \tilde{\boldsymbol{m}}(A_n).$$

Proposition 6. *Let $\boldsymbol{m}: \mathscr{A} \to \mathscr{L}(E, F)$ be a set function with $\boldsymbol{m}(\emptyset) = 0$, let $\mathscr{B} \subset \mathscr{A}$ be a class with $\emptyset \in \mathscr{B}$ and let $Z \subset F'$ be a norming subspace.*

If for a set $A \in \mathscr{A}$ and for every $z \in Z$ we have

$$\overline{(\boldsymbol{m}_z)_{\mathscr{B}}}\,(A) = \overline{\boldsymbol{m}_z}(A),$$

then

$$\tilde{\boldsymbol{m}}_{\mathscr{B}} = \tilde{\boldsymbol{m}}.$$

We remark that $(\boldsymbol{m}_z)_{\mathscr{B}} = (\boldsymbol{m}_{\mathscr{B}})_z$ and apply the proposition 5.

Corollary. *Let $\boldsymbol{m}: \mathscr{A} \to \mathscr{L}(E, F)$ be a set function with $\boldsymbol{m}(\emptyset) = 0$ and $\mathscr{B} \subset \mathscr{A}$ a subclass with $\emptyset \in \mathscr{B}$. We have*

$$\tilde{\boldsymbol{m}}_{\mathscr{B}} = \tilde{\boldsymbol{m}}$$

in each of the following cases:

1. *$\boldsymbol{m}$ is finitely additive on $\mathscr{A}$ and every set of $\mathscr{A}$ is the union of a finite family of disjoint sets of $\mathscr{B}$; in particular $\mathscr{B}$ is a semi-clan and $\mathscr{A} = \mathscr{C}(\mathscr{B})$.*

2. *$\boldsymbol{m}$ is countably additive and every set of $\mathscr{A}$ is the union of a countable family of disjoint sets of $\mathscr{B}$; in particular $\mathscr{B}$ is a semi-tribe and $\mathscr{A} = \mathscr{T}(\mathscr{B})$.*

3. *For every set $A \in \mathscr{A}$ we have*

$$|\boldsymbol{m}(A)| \leq \sup_{\substack{B \subset A \\ B \in \mathscr{B}}} |\boldsymbol{m}(B)| .$$

In fact, in each of these cases, we have $\overline{(\boldsymbol{m}_z)_{\mathscr{B}}} = \overline{\boldsymbol{m}}_z$ for every $z \in Z$ (§ 3, propositions 4 and 5).

4. SET FUNCTIONS WITH FINITE SEMI-VARIATION

Let $\boldsymbol{m}: \mathscr{A} \to X$ be a set function such that $\boldsymbol{m}(\emptyset) = 0$, and consider $X \subset \mathscr{L}(E, F)$. We say that $\boldsymbol{m}$ is with finite semi-variation – relatively to the spaces E and F – if

$$\tilde{\boldsymbol{m}}(A) < \infty, \quad \text{for every set} \quad A \in \mathscr{A} .$$

If $\boldsymbol{m}$ is with finite variation, then it is with finite semi-variation, relatively to all the pairs of spaces E und F.

If $\boldsymbol{m}$ is not with finite variation, we can choose the spaces E and F such that $\boldsymbol{m}$ is not with finite semi-variation – relatively to these spaces. For example, we can choose E such that $X \subset \mathscr{L}(E, C)$ and then $\tilde{\boldsymbol{m}} = \overline{\boldsymbol{m}}$.

On the other hand, if $\boldsymbol{m}$ is a *measure* defined on a *semi-tribe*, we can choose the spaces E and F such that – relatively to these spaces – $\boldsymbol{m}$ is with finite semi-variation.

Proposition 7. *If $\mathscr{S}$ is a semi-tribe and if $\boldsymbol{m}: \mathscr{S} \to X \subset \mathscr{L}(R, X)$ is a measure, then $\boldsymbol{m}$ is with finite semi-variation – relatively to the spaces R and X.*

For every $z \in X'$, the set function $\boldsymbol{m}_z$ defined on $\mathscr{S}$ by the equality

$$\boldsymbol{m}_z(A) = \langle \boldsymbol{m}(A), z \rangle, \quad \text{for} \quad A \in \mathscr{S}$$

is a scalar measure on $\mathscr{S}$, therefore, for every set $A \in \mathscr{S}$ we have (§ 3, proposition 14)

$$\sup_{\substack{B \subset A \\ B \in \mathscr{S}}} |\langle \boldsymbol{m}(B), z \rangle| = \sup_{\substack{B \subset A \\ B \in \mathscr{S}}} |\boldsymbol{m}_z(B)| < +\infty .$$

According to the theorem of Banach–Steinhaus, it follows that

$$\sup_{\substack{B \subset A \\ B \in \mathscr{S}}} |\boldsymbol{m}(B)| < +\infty .$$

Then, for every set $A \in \mathscr{S}$ we have (proposition 5 and § 3, proposition 7)

$$\tilde{\boldsymbol{m}}(A) = \sup_{|z| \leq 1} \bar{\boldsymbol{m}}_z(A) \leq \sup_{|z| \leq 1} 4 \sup_{\substack{B \subset A \\ B \in \mathscr{S}}} |\boldsymbol{m}_z(B)|$$

$$= 4 \sup_{\substack{B \subset A \\ B \in \mathscr{S}}} \sup_{|z| \leq 1} |\langle \boldsymbol{m}(B), z \rangle| = 4 \sup_{\substack{B \subset A \\ B \in \mathscr{S}}} |\boldsymbol{m}(B)| < +\infty ,$$

therefore $\boldsymbol{m}$ is with finite semi-variation – relatively to the spaces R and X.

§ 5. EXTENSION OF SET FUNCTIONS

1. EXTENSION OF ADDITIVE SET FUNCTIONS

We consider here the extension of an additive set function from a semi-clan to a clan.

Proposition 1. *Let $\mathscr{P}$ be a semi-clan and $\mathscr{C}$ the clan generated by $\mathscr{P}$. Then every cnitely additive set function $\boldsymbol{m}$ defined on $\mathscr{P}$ with values in a vector space X or in $\bar{R}_+$ fian be uniquely extended to an additive set function $\boldsymbol{m}_1$ defined on $\mathscr{C}$. If, in addition, X is a normed space and $\boldsymbol{m}$ is countably additive, then $\boldsymbol{m}_1$ is countably additive.*

Let E be a set of $\mathscr{C}$, $(A_i)_{1 \leq i \leq n}$ and $(B_j)_{1 \leq j \leq m}$ two finite families of mutually disjoint sets of $\mathscr{P}$ such that

$$E = \bigcup_{i=1}^{n} A_i = \bigcup_{j=1}^{m} B_j .$$

For each i we have

$$A_i = \bigcup_{j=1}^{m} (A_i \cap B_j)$$

and $(A_i \cap B_j)_{1 \leq j \leq m}$ is a finite family of mutually disjoint sets of $\mathscr{P}$ with union $A_i \in \mathscr{P}$. As $\boldsymbol{m}$ is finitely additive on $\mathscr{P}$ we have

$$\boldsymbol{m}(A_i) = \sum_{j=1}^{m} \boldsymbol{m}(A_i \cap B_j),$$

whence

$$\sum_{i=1}^{n} \boldsymbol{m}(A_i) = \sum_{i=1}^{n} \sum_{j=1}^{m} \boldsymbol{m}(A_i \cap B_j).$$

In the same way we deduce that

$$\sum_{j=1}^{m} m(B_j) = \sum_{j=1}^{m} \sum_{i=1}^{n} m(A_i \cap B_j),$$

whence

$$\sum_{i=1}^{n} m(A_i) = \sum_{j=1}^{m} m(B_j).$$

If we define $m_1(E)$ by the equality

$$m_1(E) = \sum_{i=1}^{n} m(A_i),$$

then $m_1(E)$ is independent on the particular representation of E as finite union of disjoint sets of P.

For $E \in \mathscr{P}$ we have $m_1(E) = m(E)$, therefore m_1 is an extension of m from $\mathscr{P}$ to $\mathscr{C}$.

From the definition of m_1 it follows immediately that m_1 is additive. The uniqueness of m_1 follows from the proposition 5, § 2.

Suppose now that X is a normed space and m is countably additive and prove that m_1 is countably additive.

Let (E_i) be a sequence of mutually disjoint sets of $\mathscr{C}$. Every set E_i is of the form

$$E_i = \bigcup_j A_{ij}$$

where $(A_{ij})_j$ is a finite family of disjoint sets of $\mathscr{P}$, therefore

$$m_1(E_i) = \sum_j m(A_{ij}).$$

If E belongs to $\mathscr{P}$, then

$$E = \bigcup_i E_i = \bigcup_{i,j} A_{ij}$$

and the sets A_{ij} are mutually disjoint. As m is countably additive on $\mathscr{P}$ we have

$$m(E) = \sum_{i,j} m(A_{ij}) = \sum_{i=1}^{\infty} \sum_j m(A_{ij}) = \sum_{i=1}^{\infty} m_1(E_i).$$

If E does not belong to $\mathscr{P}$, then E can be written in the form

$$E = \bigcup_k B_k$$

where (B_k) is a finite family of disjoint sets of $\mathscr{P}$, therefore

$$m_1(E) = \sum_k m(B_k).$$

For each k we have

$$B_k = \bigcup_{i=1}^{\infty} (E_i \cap B_k)$$

where $(E_i \cap B_k)_i$ is a sequence of mutually disjoint sets of $\mathscr{C}$. It follows that

$$\boldsymbol{m}(B_k) = \sum_{i=1}^{\infty} \boldsymbol{m}_1(E_i \cap B_k).$$

Similarly, for each i we have

$$E_i = \bigcup_k (E_i \cap B_k)$$

and $(E_i \cap B_k)_k$ is a finite family of disjoint sets of $\mathscr{C}$. As $\boldsymbol{m}_1$ is finitely additive we have

$$\boldsymbol{m}_1(E_i) = \sum_k \boldsymbol{m}_1(E_i \cap B_k).$$

We deduce then that

$$\boldsymbol{m}_1(E) = \sum_k \boldsymbol{m}(B_k) = \sum_k \sum_{i=1}^{\infty} \boldsymbol{m}_1(E_i \cap B_k)$$

$$= \sum_{i=1}^{\infty} \sum_k \boldsymbol{m}_1(E_i \cap B_k) = \sum_{i=1}^{\infty} \boldsymbol{m}_1(E_i),$$

therefore $\boldsymbol{m}_1$ is countably additive.

2. COMPLETION OF AN ADDITIVE SET FUNCTION

Let $\mathscr{C}$ be a *clan*, X a vector space and $\boldsymbol{m}$ an *additive* set function defined on $\mathscr{C}$ with values in X or in R_+.

Definition 1. *A set $A \in \mathfrak{T}(\mathscr{C})$ is said to be essentially $\boldsymbol{m}$-null if $\boldsymbol{m}(B) = 0$ for every set $B \in \mathscr{C}$ with $B \subset A$.*

The set function $\boldsymbol{m}$ is said to be complete on $\mathscr{C}$ if $\mathscr{C}$ contains all the subsets of every essentially $\boldsymbol{m}$-null set of $\mathscr{C}$.

The class of the essentially $\boldsymbol{m}$-null sets is a *clan*. We denote by $\mathscr{N}(\boldsymbol{m})$ the *hereditary clan* generated by the essentially $\boldsymbol{m}$-null sets, i.e. the class of the sets contained in essentially $\boldsymbol{m}$-null sets.

If $\mathscr{C}$ is a *tribe* and $\boldsymbol{m}$ is a *measure* on $\mathscr{C}$, then $\mathscr{N}(\boldsymbol{m})$ is a *tribe*.

To say that $\boldsymbol{m}$ is complete means that $\mathscr{N}(\boldsymbol{m}) \cap \mathscr{C} \subset \mathscr{C}$.

We show now that every additive set function can be extended to a complete additive set function.

Proposition 2. *The class $\mathscr{K}$ of the sets of the form $A \cup N$ with $A \in \mathscr{C}$ and $N \in \mathscr{N}(\boldsymbol{m})$ is a clan containing $\mathscr{C}$ and $\mathscr{N}(\boldsymbol{m})$. The set function $\boldsymbol{m}$ can be extended uniquely to a complete additive set function $\boldsymbol{m}_1$ on $\mathscr{K}$, vanishing on $\mathscr{N}(\boldsymbol{m})$.*

Let $A_1 \cup N_1$ and $A_2 \cup N_2$ be two sets of $\mathscr{K}$ with $A_1, A_2 \in \mathscr{C}$ and $N_1, N_2 \in \mathscr{N}(\boldsymbol{m})$. Then $A_1 \cup A_2 \in \mathscr{C}$ and $N_1 \cup N_2 \in \mathscr{N}(\boldsymbol{m})$, therefore

$$(A_1 \cup N_1) \cup (A_2 \cup N_2) = (A_1 \cup A_2) \cup (N_1 \cup N_2) \in \mathscr{K}.$$

We remark that if $A \in \mathscr{C}$ and $N \in \mathscr{N}(\boldsymbol{m})$, then $A - N \in \mathscr{K}$, because N is contained in some essentially $\boldsymbol{m}$-null set $M \in \tilde{\mathscr{C}}(\mathscr{C})$; then $A - M \in \mathscr{C}$ and $(M - N) \cap A \subset M \in \mathscr{N}(\boldsymbol{m})$, therefore

$$A - N = (A - M) \cup [(M - N) \cap A] \in \mathscr{K}.$$

We have now

$$(A_1 \cup N_1) - (A_2 \cup N_2) = [(A_1 - A_2) - N_2] \cup [(N_1 - A_1) - N_2] \in \mathscr{K},$$

whence $\mathscr{K}$ is a clan.

We remark that if $A_1 \cup N_1 = A_2 \cup N_2$ then $\boldsymbol{m}(A_1) = \boldsymbol{m}(A_2)$. In fact, $A_1 \cap N_1$ is contained in an essentially $\boldsymbol{m}$-null set $N_1' \in \mathscr{C}$ such that $N_1' \subset A_1$, and $A_2 \cap N_2$ is contained in an essentially $\boldsymbol{m}$-null set $N_2' \in \mathscr{C}$ such that $N_2' \subset A_2$. Then the set $A = (A_1 \cup A_2) - (N_1' \cup N_2')$ belongs to $\mathscr{C}$ and we have $A_1 = A \cup N_1'$ and $A_2 = A \cup N_2'$. Since $\boldsymbol{m}(N_1') = 0$ and $A \cap N_1' = \emptyset$ we have $\boldsymbol{m}(A_1) = \boldsymbol{m}(A \cup N_1') = \boldsymbol{m}(A) + \boldsymbol{m}(N_1') = \boldsymbol{m}(A)$ and we prove in the same manner that $\boldsymbol{m}(A_2) = \boldsymbol{m}(A)$, therefore $\boldsymbol{m}(A_1) = \boldsymbol{m}(A_2)$.

For every set $E = A \cup N$ of $\mathscr{K}$ with $A \in \mathscr{C}$ and $N \in \mathscr{N}(\boldsymbol{m})$, we define $\boldsymbol{m}_1(E)$ by the equality

$$\boldsymbol{m}_1(E) = \boldsymbol{m}(A).$$

By the preceding remark, $\boldsymbol{m}_1(E)$ depends only on E. For every set $A \in \mathscr{C}$ we have $A = A \cup \emptyset$, whence $\boldsymbol{m}_1(A) = \boldsymbol{m}(A)$.

If $N \in \mathscr{N}(\boldsymbol{m})$ we have $N = \emptyset \cup N$, whence $\boldsymbol{m}_1(N) = \boldsymbol{m}(\emptyset) = 0$.

It is easy to verify then that $\boldsymbol{m}_1$ is additive on $\mathscr{K}$.

3. EXTENSION OF SET FUNCTIONS WITH FINITE VARIATION

Let $\mathscr{K}$ be a clan of subsets of T and μ a *positive*, *finite*, *subadditive* and *increasing* set function defined on $\mathscr{K}$.

We shall show that some additive set functions defined on a clan $\mathscr{C} \subset \mathscr{K}$ can be extended to $\mathscr{K}$.

We define on $\mathscr{K}$ a finite semi-distance $\varrho_\mu = \varrho$ by the equality

$$\varrho(A, B) = \mu(A - B) + \mu(B - A), \quad \text{for} \quad A, B \in \mathscr{K}.$$

We verify easily the following properties:

1. $0 \leqq \varrho(A, B) \leqq \infty; \varrho(A, A) = 0;$

2. $\varrho(A, B) = \varrho(B, A);$

3. $\varrho(A, B) \leqq \varrho(A, C) + \varrho(C, B).$

The last property follows from

$$A - B \subset (A - C) \cup (C - B).$$

The semi-distance ϱ defines on $\mathscr{K}$ a structure of uniform space, non separated in general.

We remark that if $\boldsymbol{n}$ is an *additive* set function defined on a clan $\mathscr{C} \subset \mathscr{K}$, then

$$\begin{aligned} \boldsymbol{n}(A) - \boldsymbol{n}(B) &= \boldsymbol{n}[(A - B) \cup (A \cap B)] - \boldsymbol{n}[(B - A) \cup (A \cap B)] \\ &= \boldsymbol{n}(A - B) - \boldsymbol{n}(B - A) \end{aligned}$$

and that if $\boldsymbol{n}$ is positive, subadditive and increasing, then

$$\begin{aligned} |\boldsymbol{n}(A) - \boldsymbol{n}(B)| &\leqq |\boldsymbol{n}(A) - \boldsymbol{n}(A \cap B)| + |\boldsymbol{n}(B) - \boldsymbol{n}(A \cap B)| \\ &\leqq \boldsymbol{n}(A - B) + \boldsymbol{n}(B - A). \end{aligned}$$

Lemma 1. *Let X be a Banach space, $\mathscr{C}$ a clan contained in $\mathscr{K}$ and $\boldsymbol{n}: \mathscr{C} \to X$ an additive set function. If*

$$|\boldsymbol{n}(A)| \leqq \mu(A), \quad \textit{for} \quad A \in \mathscr{C}$$

then $\boldsymbol{n}$ is uniformly continuous on $\mathscr{C}$.

In fact, for $A, B \in \mathscr{C}$ we have

$$\begin{aligned} |\boldsymbol{n}(A) - \boldsymbol{n}(B)| &\leqq |\boldsymbol{n}(A - B)| + |\boldsymbol{n}(B - A)| \\ &\leqq \mu(A - B) + \mu(B - A) = \varrho(A, B), \end{aligned}$$

whence $\boldsymbol{n}$ is uniformly continuous.

In particular, μ is uniformly continuous on $\mathscr{K}$.

Lemma 2. *The functions $f, g, h: \mathscr{K} \times \mathscr{K} \to \mathscr{K}$ defined by the equalities*

$$f(A, B) = A \cup B, \quad g(A, B) = A \cap B, \quad h(A, B) = A - B$$

are uniformly continuous.

Denote by $\circ$ one of the operations $\cup$, $\cap$, $-$. Then

$$\begin{aligned}\varrho(A_1 \circ B_1, A_2 \circ B_2) &= \mu[(A_1 \circ B_1) - (A_2 \circ B_2)] + \mu[(A_2 \circ B_2) - (A_1 \circ B_1)] \\ &\leqq \mu(A_1 - A_2) + \mu(A_2 - A_1) + \mu(B_1 - B_2) + \mu(B_2 - B_1) \\ &= \varrho(A_1, A_2) + \varrho(B_1, B_2),\end{aligned}$$

whence the function $(A, B) \to A \circ B$ is uniformly continuous.

Theorem 1. *Let $\mathscr{C}$ be a clan dense in $\mathscr{K}$ for the topology defined by ϱ, X a Banach space and $\boldsymbol{m}: \mathscr{C} \to X$ an additive set function such that*

$$|\boldsymbol{m}(A)| \leqq \mu(A), \quad \textit{for} \quad A \in \mathscr{C}.$$

Then $\boldsymbol{m}$ can be extended to an additive set function $\boldsymbol{m}_1 : \mathscr{K} \to X$ such that

$$|\boldsymbol{m}_1(A)| \leqq \mu(A), \quad \textit{for} \quad A \in \mathscr{K}.$$

If μ is additive, then $\boldsymbol{m}$ has finite variation $|\boldsymbol{m}|$ on $\mathscr{C}$, $\boldsymbol{m}_1$ has finite variation $|\boldsymbol{m}_1|$ on $\mathscr{K}$ and $|\boldsymbol{m}_1|$ is an extension of $|\boldsymbol{m}|$.

If μ is countably additive, then $\boldsymbol{m}_1$ is countably additive.

From the lemma 1 we deduce that $\boldsymbol{m}$ is uniformly continuous on the dense set $\mathscr{C}$, therefore $\boldsymbol{m}$ can be extended to a uniformly continuous function $\boldsymbol{m}_1 : \mathscr{K} \to X$. To prove that $\boldsymbol{m}_1$ is additive, let A, B be two disjoint sets of $\mathscr{K}$. There exist two sequences (A_n) and (B_n) of sets of $\mathscr{C}$, such that $\varrho(A, A_n) \to 0$ and $\varrho(B, B_n) \to 0$. Since the operations $A \cup B$, and $A - B$ are uniformly continuous, we deduce $\varrho(A_n \cup B_n, A \cup B) \to 0$ and $\varrho(A_n - B_n, A - B) \to 0$. Since A and B are disjoint we have $A - B = A$, whence $\varrho(A_n - B_n, A) \to 0$.

For the disjoint sets $A_n - B_n$ and B_n we have

$$\boldsymbol{m}(A_n \cup B_n) = \boldsymbol{m}((A_n - B_n) \cup B_n) = \boldsymbol{m}(A_n - B_n) + \boldsymbol{m}(B_n).$$

Passing to the limit we obtain

$$\boldsymbol{m}_1(A \cup B) = \boldsymbol{m}_1(A) + \boldsymbol{m}_1(B),$$

whence $\boldsymbol{m}_1$ is additive.

Let $A \in \mathscr{K}$ and let (A_n) be a sequence of $\mathscr{C}$ such that $\varrho(A_n, A) \to 0$. Since $\boldsymbol{m}$ and μ are continuous we have $\boldsymbol{m}(A_n) \to \boldsymbol{m}(A)$ and $\mu(A_n) \to \mu(A)$. For every n we have

$$|\boldsymbol{m}(A_n)| \leqq \mu(A_n)$$

whence, passing to the limit, $|\boldsymbol{m}_1(A)| \leqq \mu(A)$.

Suppose now that μ is additive.

From the inequality $|\boldsymbol{m}(A)| \leqq \mu(A)$ for $A \in \mathscr{C}$, we deduce that $\boldsymbol{m}$ has finite variation $|\boldsymbol{m}|$ and that

$$|\boldsymbol{m}|(A) \leqq \mu(A), \quad \text{for} \quad A \in \mathscr{C}.$$

From this inequality we deduce that $|\boldsymbol{m}|$ can be extended to an additive set function $|\boldsymbol{m}|_1$ on $\mathscr{K}$ such that $|\boldsymbol{m}|_1 \leqq \mu$.

From the inequality $|\boldsymbol{m}_1(A)| \leqq \mu(A)$ for $A \in \mathscr{K}$ it follows that $\boldsymbol{m}_1$ has finite variation $|\boldsymbol{m}_1|$ on $\mathscr{K}$ and that $|\boldsymbol{m}_1| \leqq \mu$.

We have

$$|\boldsymbol{m}(A)| = |\boldsymbol{m}_1(A)| \leqq |\boldsymbol{m}_1|(A), \quad \text{for} \quad A \in \mathscr{C},$$

therefore

$$|\boldsymbol{m}|(A) \leqq |\boldsymbol{m}_1|(A), \quad \text{for} \quad A \in \mathscr{C}.$$

On the other hand, considering the additive set function $\nu = |\boldsymbol{m}|_1$ and the semi-distance

$$\varrho_\nu(A, B) = \nu(A \,\Delta\, B),$$

from the inequality $\nu \leqq \mu$ we deduce that $\varrho_\nu \leqq \varrho$, whence the topology defined on $\mathscr{K}$ by ϱ_ν is weaker than the topology defined by ϱ. It follows that $\mathscr{C}$ is dense in $\mathscr{K}$ for the topology defined by ϱ_ν, and from $|\boldsymbol{m}(A)| \leqq \nu(A)$ for $A \in \mathscr{C}$ it follows that $\boldsymbol{m}$ is uniformly continuous on $\mathscr{C}$ for this topology, consequently it can be extended to an additive set function $\boldsymbol{m}_2 : \mathscr{K} \to X$ verifying

$$|\boldsymbol{m}_2(A)| \leqq \nu(A), \quad \text{for} \quad A \in \mathscr{K}.$$

We deduce that $\boldsymbol{m}_2$ is continuous on $\mathscr{K}$ for the semi-distance ϱ_ν whence $\boldsymbol{m}_2$ is continuous on $\mathscr{K}$ also for ϱ.

Since $\boldsymbol{m}_1$ and $\boldsymbol{m}_2$ are continuous on $\mathscr{K}$ for ϱ and are equal on the dense set $\mathscr{C}$, it follows that $\boldsymbol{m}_1 = \boldsymbol{m}_2$, whence

$$|\boldsymbol{m}_1(A)| \leqq \nu(A), \quad \text{for} \quad A \in \mathscr{K},$$

consequently $|\boldsymbol{m}_1| \leqq \nu = |\boldsymbol{m}|_1$. In particular

$$|\boldsymbol{m}_1|(A) = |\boldsymbol{m}|_1(A), \quad \text{for} \quad A \in \mathscr{C}.$$

Since $|\boldsymbol{m}_1|$ and $|\boldsymbol{m}|_1$ are continuous on $\mathscr{K}$ for ϱ and are equal on $\mathscr{C}$, it follows that $|\boldsymbol{m}_1| = |\boldsymbol{m}|_1$.

Finally, if μ is countably additive, from the inequality $|\boldsymbol{m}_1(A)| \leqq \mu(A)$ for $A \in \mathscr{K}$, we deduce that $\boldsymbol{m}_1$ is countably additive.

Corollary. *Let $\mathscr{C}$ be a clan, X a Banach space and $\boldsymbol{m} : \mathscr{C} \to X$ an additive set function with finite variation μ. If μ can be extended to a positive (finite) additive set function μ_1 on a clan $\mathscr{K} \supset \mathscr{C}$, and if $\mathscr{C}$ is dense in $\mathscr{K}$ for the semi-distance ϱ_{μ_1}, then $\boldsymbol{m}$ can be extended to an additive set function $\boldsymbol{m}_1 : \mathscr{K} \to X$ with finite variation $|\boldsymbol{m}_1|$ such that $|\boldsymbol{m}_1| = \mu_1$.*

This corollary shows that the extension of the set functions with finite variation reduces to the extension of the *positive* set functions. In the next section we shall study the extension of the countably additive positive set functions and the extension of the additive positive set functions.

4. EXTENSION OF POSITIVE MEASURES

Let $\mathscr{C}$ be a *clan* of subsets of T and $\mu: \mathscr{C} \to \bar{R}_+$ a countably additive set function. We shall realise the extension of μ in two steps. First we extend μ to an outer measure μ^* on the hereditary tribe $\mathscr{H}$ generated by $\mathscr{C}$ and we delimitate the tribe $\mathscr{T}(\mu)$ on which μ^* is countably additive. The second step is the extension of μ^* from $\mathscr{T}(\mu)$ to the tribe $\mathfrak{T}(\mu)$ of the sets $E \subset T$ which are locally in $\mathscr{T}(\mu)$, i.e. such that $E \cap A \in \mathscr{T}(\mu)$ for every $A \in \mathscr{T}(\mu)$. The set function μ^* is countably additive on $\mathfrak{T}(\mu)$.

If $\mathscr{C}$ is a tribe and μ is complete on $\mathscr{C}$, then $\mathscr{T}(\mu) = \mathscr{C}$ and the first step is superfluous; if T is a countable union of sets of $\mathscr{C}$, then the second step is superfluous.

The sets of $\mathfrak{T}(\mu)$ are called μ-measurable. The sets $E \in \mathfrak{T}(\mu)$ with $\mu^*(E) < \infty$ are called μ-integrable. The class $\Sigma(\mu)$ of the μ-integrable sets is a semi-tribe.

We denote by $\mathscr{H}(\mathscr{C})$ or $\mathscr{H}$ the class of the subsets $A \subset T$ which can be covered by a sequence of sets of $\mathscr{C}$. We have $\mathscr{C} \subset \mathscr{H}$ and $\mathscr{H}$ is a *hereditary class*, i.e. if $A \in \mathscr{H}$ then $\mathscr{H}$ contains all the subsets of A. It is easy to verify that $\mathscr{H}$ is a *tribe*, therefore $\mathscr{H}$ contains the tribe $\mathscr{T}$ generated by $\mathscr{C}$. We call $\mathscr{H}$ the hereditary tribe generated by $\mathscr{C}$.

Definition 2. *For every set $A \in \mathscr{H}$ we define the outer (or exterior) measure $\mu^*(A)$ of A, by the equality*

$$\mu^*(A) = \inf \sum_{n=1}^{\infty} \mu(A_n),$$

the infimum being taken for all the sequences (A_n) of sets of $\mathscr{C}$ such that $A \subset \bigcup_{n=1}^{\infty} A_n$.

The set function μ^* *defined* on $\mathscr{H}$ is called the *outer* (or *exterior*) *measure* induced by μ.

The outer measure μ^* has the following properties:

1. $0 \leqq \mu^*(A) \leqq +\infty$, *for* $A \in \mathscr{H}$;

2. μ^* *is increasing*

$$\mu^*(A) \leqq \mu^*(B), \quad \text{if} \quad A \subset B;$$

3. μ^* *is countably subadditive:*

$$\mu^*\left(\bigcup_{i=1}^{\infty} A_i\right) \leqq \sum_{i=1}^{\infty} \mu^*(A_i)$$

for every sequence (A_i) of sets of $\mathscr{H}$.

Let (A_i) be a sequence of sets of $\mathscr{H}$ and $\varepsilon > 0$. For each i there exists a sequence $(A_{ij})_j$ of sets of $\mathscr{C}$ such that

$$A_i \subset \bigcup_{j=1}^{\infty} A_{ij} \quad \text{and} \quad \sum_{j=1}^{\infty} \mu(A_{ij}) \leqq \mu^*(A_i) + \frac{\varepsilon}{2^i}.$$

Because $\bigcup_{i=1}^{\infty} A_i \subset \bigcup_{i,j=1}^{\infty} A_{ij}$, we have

$$\mu^*\left(\bigcup_{i=1}^{\infty} A_i\right) \leqq \sum_{i,j=1}^{\infty} \mu(A_{ij}) = \sum_{i=1}^{\infty}\left(\sum_{j=1}^{\infty} \mu(A_{ij})\right) \leqq \sum_{i=1}^{\infty} \mu^*(A_i) + \varepsilon,$$

consequently, ε being arbitrary,

$$\mu^*\left(\bigcup_{i=1}^{\infty} A_i\right) \leqq \sum_{i=1}^{\infty} \mu^*(A_i).$$

4. *For every set $A \in \mathscr{C}$ we have*

$$\mu^*(A) = \mu(A).$$

If $A \in \mathscr{C}$ and if (A_n) is a sequence of sets of $\mathscr{C}$ such that $A \subset \bigcup_{n=1}^{\infty} A_n$, then $A = \bigcup_{n=1}^{\infty} (A_n \cap A)$, therefore

$$\mu(A) = \mu\left(\bigcup_{n=1}^{\infty} (A_n \cap A)\right) \leqq \sum_{n=1}^{\infty} \mu(A_n \cap A) \leqq \sum_{n=1}^{\infty} \mu(A_n),$$

whence

$$\mu(A) \leqq \mu^*(A).$$

On the other hand, taking $A_1 = A$ and $A_i = \emptyset$ for $i \geqq 2$, we have

$$\mu^*(A) \leqq \sum_{i=1}^{\infty} \mu(A_i) = \mu(A),$$

whence

$$\mu^*(A) = \mu(A).$$

In particular, we deduce that $\mu^*(\emptyset) = 0$.

5. *If $\bar{\mu}$ is the variation of μ, then for every set $A \in \mathscr{H}$ we have*

$$\bar{\mu}(A) \leqq \mu^*(A).$$

Let $A \in \mathscr{H}$ and $\varepsilon > 0$. There exists a finite family $(A_i)_{1 \leqq i \leqq n}$ of disjoint sets of $\mathscr{C}$ such that

$$\bigcup_{i=1}^{n} A_i \subset A \quad \text{and} \quad \bar{\mu}(A) < \sum_{i=1}^{n} \mu(A_i) + \varepsilon.$$

Let (B_j) be an arbitrary sequence of sets of $\mathscr{C}$ with $A \subset \bigcup_{j=1}^{\infty} B_j$. We have $A_i \cap B_j \in \mathscr{C}$ for every i and j. For each i, we have

$$A_i = \bigcup_{j=1}^{\infty} (A_i \cap B_j), \quad \text{whence} \quad \mu(A_i) \leqq \sum_{j=1}^{\infty} \mu(A_i \cap B_j).$$

For each j, the family $(A_i \cap B_j)_i$ consists of disjoint sets of $\mathscr{C}$ and

$$\bigcup_{i=1}^{n} (A_i \cap B_j) \subset B_j.$$

It follows then that

$$\begin{aligned}\bar{\mu}(A) - \varepsilon < \sum_{i=1}^{n} \mu(A_i) &\leqq \sum_{i=1}^{n} \sum_{j=1}^{\infty} \mu(A_i \cap B_j)\\ &= \sum_{j=1}^{\infty} \sum_{i=1}^{n} \mu(A_i \cap B_j) = \sum_{j=1}^{\infty} \mu\left(\bigcup_{i=1}^{n} (A_i \cap B_j)\right)\\ &\leqq \sum_{j=1}^{\infty} \mu(B_j),\end{aligned}$$

therefore

$$\bar{\mu}(A) - \varepsilon \leqq \mu^*(A),$$

whence, ε being arbitrary,

$$\bar{\mu}(A) \leqq \mu^*(A).$$

Proposition 3. *If $\mathscr{T}$ is the tribe generated by $\mathscr{C}$, then for every set $A \in \mathscr{H}$ we have*

$$\mu^*(A) = \inf_{\substack{B \supset A\\ B \in \mathscr{T}}} \mu^*(B).$$

Let $A \in \mathscr{H}$. As μ^* is increasing on $\mathscr{H}$, we have

$$\mu^*(A) \leqq \inf\{\mu^*(B);\, B \supset A,\, B \in \mathscr{T}\}.$$

Conversely, let $\varepsilon > 0$. There exists a sequence (A_n) of sets of $\mathscr{C}$ such that $A \subset \bigcup_{n=1}^{\infty} A_n$ and

$$\sum_{n=1}^{\infty} \mu(A_n) \leqq \mu^*(A) + \varepsilon.$$

Putting $B_0 = \bigcup_{n=1}^{\infty} A_n$ we have $B_0 \in \mathscr{T}$ and $B_0 \supset A$. As μ^* is countably subadditive, we have

$$\mu^*(B_0) = \mu^*\left(\bigcup_{n=1}^{\infty} A_n\right) \leqq \sum_{n=1}^{\infty} \mu^*(A_n) \leqq \mu^*(A) + \varepsilon,$$

therefore

$$\inf\{\mu^*(B);\, B \supset A,\, B \in \mathscr{T}\} \leqq \mu^*(A) + \varepsilon,$$

whence, ε being arbitrary,

$$\inf\{\mu^*(B); B \supset A, B \in \mathscr{T}\} \leqq \mu^*(A).$$

Corollary. *If $\mathscr{C}$ is a tribe, then for every set $A \in \mathscr{H}$ we have*

$$\mu^*(A) = \inf_{\substack{B \supset A \\ B \in \mathscr{C}}} \mu(B).$$

In fact, in this case we have $\mu^*(B) = \mu(B)$ for $B \in \mathscr{C}$.

Proposition 4. *If $\mathscr{T}$ is the tribe generated by $\mathscr{C}$, then for every set $A \in \mathscr{H}$ there exists a set $B \in \mathscr{T}$ such that $B \supset A$ and*

$$\mu^*(A) = \mu^*(B).$$

In fact, for each n there exists (proposition 3) a set $B_n \supset A$ of $\mathscr{T}$ such that

$$\mu^*(B_n) \leqq \mu^*(A) + \frac{1}{n}.$$

The set $B = \bigcap_{n=1}^{\infty} B_n$ belongs to $\mathscr{T}$, contains A and

$$\mu^*(A) \leqq \mu^*(B) \leqq \mu^*(B_n) \leqq \mu^*(A) + \frac{1}{n},$$

whence, n being arbitrary,

$$\mu^*(A) = \mu^*(B).$$

Corollary. *Every set $A \in \mathscr{H}$ with $\mu^*(A) = 0$ is contained in a set $B \in \mathscr{T}$ with* $\mu^*(B) = 0$.

Definition 3. *We denote by $\mathscr{T}(\mu)$ the class of the sets $E \in \mathscr{H}$ having the property*

$$\mu^*(A) = \mu^*(A \cap E) + \mu^*(A - E), \quad \textit{for every} \quad A \in \mathscr{H}.$$

We denote by $\mathfrak{T}(\mu)$ the class of the sets $E \subset T$ having the property that $E \cap A \in \mathscr{T}(\mu)$ for every $A \in \mathscr{T}(\mu)$.

The sets of $\mathfrak{T}(\mu)$ are called μ-measurable (or measurable with respect to μ).

If no confusion may occur, we shall say, simply, *measurable sets* instead of *μ-measurable sets.*

We shall study first the measurable sets of $\mathscr{T}(\mu)$. Since μ^* is subadditive on $\mathscr{H}$ and $A = (A \cap E) \cup (A - E)$, we have always

$$\mu^*(A) \leqq \mu^*(A \cap E) + \mu^*(A - E), \quad \text{for} \quad A, E \in \mathscr{H}.$$

Therefore, a set $E \in \mathscr{H}$ belongs to $\mathscr{T}(\mu)$ if and only if

$$\mu^*(A) \geqq \mu^*(A \cap E) + \mu^*(A - E), \quad \text{for every} \quad A \in \mathscr{H}.$$

We remark that every set $E \in \mathscr{H}$ with $\mu^*(E) = 0$ belongs to $\mathscr{T}(\mu)$ and in this case every subset of E belongs to $\mathscr{T}(\mu)$.

Theorem 2. *The class $\mathscr{T}(\mu)$ is a tribe containing the clan $\mathscr{C}$ and μ^* is countably additive on $\mathscr{T}(\mu)$.*

Let E and F be two sets of $\mathscr{T}(\mu)$, and let $A \in \mathscr{H}$. We have successively:

$$\mu^*(A) = \mu^*(A \cap E) + \mu^*(A - E), \tag{1}$$

$$\mu^*(A \cap E) = \mu^*(A \cap E \cap F) + \mu^*((A \cap E) - F), \tag{2}$$

$$\mu^*(A - E) = \mu^*((A - E) \cap F) + \mu^*((A - E) - F). \tag{3}$$

Using the equalities (2) and (3) in the equality (1) we obtain

$$\mu^*(A) = \mu^*(A \cap E \cap F) + \mu^*((A \cap E) - F) + \mu^*((A - E) \cap F) + \mu^*((A - E) - F) \tag{4}$$

for every set $A \in \mathscr{H}$. Writing the last equality for the set $A \cap (E \cup F)$ instead of A, we obtain

$$\mu^*(A \cap (E \cup F)) = \mu^*(A \cap E \cap F) + \mu^*((A \cap E) - F) + \mu^*((A - E) \cap F) \tag{5}$$

because $(A \cap (E \cup F)) - E - F = \emptyset$. Using the equality (5) in the equality (4), we deduce

$$\mu^*(A) = \mu^*(A \cap (E \cup F)) + \mu^*(A - (E \cup F))$$

for every set $A \in \mathscr{H}$, therefore

$$E \cup F \in \mathscr{T}(\mu).$$

Writing now the equality for the set $A - (E - F)$ instead of A, we receive

$$\mu^*(A - (E - F)) = \mu^*(A \cap E \cap F) + \mu^*((A - E) \cap F) + \mu^*((A - E) - F) \tag{6}$$

because $[(A - (E - F) \cap E] - F = \emptyset$. Using the equality (6) in the equality (4) we obtain

$$\mu^*(A) = \mu^*(A - (E - F)) + \mu^*(A \cap (E - F))$$

for every set $A \in \mathscr{H}$, therefore

$$E - F \in \mathscr{T}(\mu).$$

We proved, thus, that $\mathscr{T}(\mu)$ is a *clan*.

Let now (E_i) be a sequence of *disjoint* sets of $\mathscr{T}(\mu)$ and put $E = \bigcup_{i=1}^{\infty} E_i$. Writing the equality (5) for the disjoint sets E_1 and E_2 of $\mathscr{T}(\mu)$ instead of E and F we obtain

$$\mu^*(A \cap (E_1 \cup E_2)) = \mu^*(A \cap E_1) + \mu^*(A \cap E_2).$$

By induction, we deduce that for every n we have

$$\mu^*\left(A \cap \left(\bigcup_{i=1}^{n} E_i\right)\right) = \sum_{i=1}^{n} \mu^*(A \cap E_i). \tag{7}$$

Because $\bigcup_{i=1}^{n} E_i \in \mathscr{T}(\mu)$ and μ^* is increasing, using the equalities (1) and (7) we obtain

$$\begin{aligned}\mu^*(A) &= \mu^*\left(A \cap \left(\bigcup_{i=1}^{n} E_i\right)\right) + \mu^*\left(A - \left(\bigcup_{i=1}^{n} E_i\right)\right)\\ &= \sum_{i=1}^{n} \mu^*(A \cap E_i) + \mu^*\left(A - \left(\bigcup_{i=1}^{n} E_i\right)\right)\\ &\geqq \sum_{i=1}^{n} \mu^*(A \cap E_i) + \mu^*(A - E).\end{aligned}$$

Because the inequality

$$\mu^*(A) \geqq \sum_{i=1}^{n} \mu^*(A \cap E_i) + \mu^*(A - E)$$

is true for every n, we deduce

$$\begin{aligned}\mu^*(A) &\geqq \sum_{i=1}^{\infty} \mu^*(A \cap E_i) + \mu^*(A - E)\\ &\geqq \mu^*\left(\bigcup_{i=1}^{\infty} (A \cap E_i)\right) + \mu^*(A - E)\\ &= \mu^*(A \cap E) + \mu^*(A - E).\end{aligned} \tag{8}$$

It follows that E is μ-measurable.

Let now (E_i) be an *arbitrary* sequence of sets of $\mathscr{T}(\mu)$. Putting $F_1 = E_1$ and $F_n = E_n - \bigcup_{i<n} F_i$ for $n \geqq 2$, the sets F_n are mutually disjoint, belong to $\mathscr{T}(\mu)$ and

$$\bigcup_{i=1}^{n} E_i = \bigcup_{i=1}^{\infty} F_i \in \mathscr{T}(\mu),$$

therefore $\mathscr{T}(\mu)$ is a *tribe*.

If in (8) we use the inequality

$$\mu^*(A \cap E) + \mu^*(A - E) \leqq \mu^*(A)$$

we deduce that

$$\sum_{i=1}^{\infty} \mu^*(A \cap E_i) + \mu^*(A - E) = \mu^*(A \cap E) + \mu^*(A - E)$$

for every sequence (E_i) of disjoint sets of $\mathscr{T}(\mu)$ and for every set $A \in \mathscr{H}$. Writing this last equality for $A = E = \bigcup_{i=1}^{\infty} E_i$ we obtain

$$\sum_{i=1}^{\infty} \mu^*(E_i) = \mu^*(E),$$

therefore μ^* is *countably additive* on $\mathcal{T}(\mu)$.

It remains to prove that $\mathscr{C} \subset \mathcal{T}(\mu)$. Let $E \in \mathscr{C}$, $A \in \mathscr{H}$ and $\varepsilon > 0$. There exists a sequence (E_n) of sets of $\mathscr{C}$ such that

$$A \subset \bigcup_{n=1}^{\infty} E_n \quad \text{and} \quad \mu^*(A) + \varepsilon \geqq \sum_{n=1}^{\infty} \mu(E_n).$$

Because $A \cap E \subset \bigcup_{n=1}^{\infty} (E_n \cap E)$ and $A - E \subset \bigcup_{n=1}^{\infty} (E_n - E)$ and because $E_n \cap E$ and $E_n - E$ are disjoint sets of $\mathscr{C}$ with union E_n, we have

$$\begin{aligned}\mu^*(A \cap E) + \mu^*(A - E) &\leqq \sum_{n=1}^{\infty} \mu(E_n \cap E) + \sum_{n=1}^{\infty} \mu(E_n - E)\\ &= \sum_{n=1}^{\infty} [\mu(E_n \cap E) + \mu(E_n - E)]\\ &\leqq \sum_{n=1}^{\infty} \mu(E_n) \leqq \mu^*(A) + \varepsilon;\end{aligned}$$

ε being arbitrary, we deduce

$$\mu^*(A) \geqq \mu^*(A \cap E) + \mu^*(A - E)$$

for every $A \in \mathscr{H}$, therefore E is μ-measurable, whence $\mathscr{C} \subset \mathcal{T}(\mu)$.

Corollary 1. *The class $\mathfrak{T}(\mu)$ of the μ-measurable sets is a tribe containing $\mathcal{T}(\mu)$ and T.*

Corollary 2. *We have $E \in \mathfrak{T}(\mu)$ if and only if $E \cap A \in \mathcal{T}(\mu)$ for every set $A \in \mathscr{C}$.*

Suppose that $E \cap A \in \mathcal{T}(\mu)$ for every set $A \in \mathscr{C}$ and let $A \in \mathcal{T}(\mu)$. Then $A \in \mathscr{H}$, whence A can be covered by a sequence (A_n) of sets of $\mathscr{C}$. For each n we have $E \cap A_n \in \mathcal{T}(\mu)$, whence

$$\bigcup_{n=1}^{\infty} (E \cap A_n) \in \mathcal{T}(\mu).$$

Then

$$E \cap A = \left[\bigcup_{n=1}^{\infty} (E \cap A_n)\right] \cap A \in \mathcal{T}(\mu),$$

consequently $E \in \mathfrak{T}(\mu)$. The converse implication is evident.

Corollary 3. *The class $\mathscr{S}(\mu)$ of the sets $A \in \mathcal{T}(\mu)$ with $\mu^*(A) < \infty$ is a semi-tribe.*

We remark that if a set $E \in \mathcal{T}(\mu)$ is contained in some set $A \in \mathscr{S}(\mu)$, then $E \in \mathscr{S}(\mu)$.

Corollary 4. *If μ is σ-finite on $\mathscr{C}$, then $E \in \mathfrak{T}(\mu)$ if and only if $E \cap A \in \mathscr{S}(\mu)$ for every $A \in \mathscr{S}(\mu)$.*

Suppose first that $E \in \mathfrak{T}(\mu)$ and let $A \in \mathscr{S}(\mu)$. Then $A \in \mathscr{T}(\mu)$, whence $E \cap A \in \mathscr{T}(\mu)$. But $E \cap A \subset A \in \mathscr{S}(\mu)$, whence $E \cap A \in \mathscr{S}(\mu)$. (We remark that the first implication does not need μ to be σ-finite.)

Conversely suppose that $E \cap A \in \mathscr{S}(\mu)$ for every $A \in \mathscr{S}(\mu)$ and let $A \in \mathscr{T}(\mu)$. Since A can be covered by a sequence of sets of $\mathscr{C}$ and since every set of $\mathscr{C}$ is the union of a sequence of sets of $\mathscr{C}$ on which μ is finite, A can be covered by a sequence (A_n) of sets of $\mathscr{S}(\mu)$. For each n we have $E \cap A_n \in \mathscr{S}(\mu) \subset \mathscr{T}(\mu)$ and we prove as in corollary 2 that $E \cap A \in \mathscr{T}(\mu)$.

We shall show now that if μ is σ-finite on $\mathscr{C}$, the tribe $\mathscr{T}(\mu)$ can be obtained from the tribe $\mathscr{T}$ generated by $\mathscr{C}$, by completion, i.e. by adding the subsets of the sets $N \in \mathscr{T}$ with $\mu^*(N) = 0$.

Proposition 5. *Suppose that μ is σ-finite on $\mathscr{C}$. A set $E \subset T$ belongs to $\mathscr{T}(\mu)$ if and only if it is of the form $E = A - N$ with A in the tribe $\mathscr{T}$ generated by $\mathscr{C}$ and $\mu^*(N) = 0$.*

If $E = A - N$ with $A \in \mathscr{T}$ and $\mu^*(N) = 0$, then $A \in \mathscr{T}(\mu)$ and $N \in \mathscr{T}(\mu)$, therefore $E \in \mathscr{T}(\mu)$.

Conversely, suppose that $E \in \mathscr{T}(\mu)$. There exists then a sequence (B_n) of sets of $\mathscr{C}$ such that $E \subset \bigcup_{n=1}^{\infty} B_n$ and $\mu(B_n) < \infty$.

The sets $E_n = E \cap B_n$ belong to $\mathscr{T}(\mu)$, $\mu^*(E_n) \leqq \mu(B_n) < \infty$ and $E = \bigcup_{n=1}^{\infty} E_n$. For each n there exists a set $A_n \in \mathscr{T}$ with $E_n \subset A_n$ and $\mu^*(E_n) = \mu^*(A_n)$.

If we put $A = \bigcup_{n=1}^{\infty} A_n$, we have $A \in \mathscr{T}$, $E \subset A$ and

$$A - E = \bigcup_{n=1}^{\infty} A_n - \left(\bigcup_{m=1}^{\infty} E_m\right) \subset \bigcup_{n=1}^{\infty} (A_n - E_n),$$

hence

$$\begin{aligned} \mu^*(A - E) &\leqq \mu^*\left(\bigcup_{n=1}^{\infty} (A_n - E_n)\right) \\ &\leqq \sum_{n=1}^{\infty} \mu^*(A_n - E_n) = \sum_{n=1}^{\infty} (\mu^*(A_n) - \mu^*(E_n)) = 0. \end{aligned}$$

If we take $N = A - E$, we have $\mu^*(N) = 0$ and $E = A - N$.

Corollary 1. *Suppose that μ is σ-finite on $\mathscr{C}$. A set $E \subset T$ belongs to $\mathscr{T}(\mu)$ if and only if it is of the form $E = A \cup N$ with $A \in \mathscr{T}$ and $\mu^*(N) = 0$.*

If $E = A \cup N$ with $A \in \mathscr{T}$ and $\mu^*(N) = 0$, then $E \in \mathscr{T}(\mu)$. Conversely, if $E \in \mathscr{T}(\mu)$, then E is of the form $E = A' - N'$ with $A' \in \mathscr{T}$ and $\mu^*(N') = 0$. There exists then a set $M \in \mathscr{T}$ with $N' \subset M$ and $\mu^*(M) = 0$. Taking $A = A' - M$ and $N = E - A$, we have $A \in \mathscr{T}$, $\mu^*(N) = 0$ and $E = A \cup N$.

Corollary 2. *Suppose that μ is σ-finite on $\mathscr{C}$. A set $E \subset T$ belongs to $\mathscr{T}(\mu)$ if and only if it is the union of a sequence (A_n) of disjoint sets of the semi-tribe $\mathscr{S}$ generated by $\mathscr{C}$, and a set N with $\mu^*(N) = 0$.*

In fact, every set of $\mathscr{T}$ is the union of a sequence of disjoint sets of $\mathscr{S}$.

Corollary 3. *Suppose that μ is σ-finite on $\mathscr{C}$. A set $E \subset T$ belongs to $\mathscr{T}(\mu)$ if and only if there exist two sets $A, B \in \mathscr{T}$ with $A \subset E \subset B$ and $\mu^*(B - A) = 0$.*

Corollary 4. *If μ is σ-finite on $\mathscr{C}$, then μ^* is the only countably additive positive extension of μ from $\mathscr{C}$ to $\mathscr{T}(\mu)$.*

Let μ' be a countably additive positive set function defined on $\mathscr{T}(\mu)$, such that $\mu'(A) = \mu(A)$ for $A \in \mathscr{C}$. From proposition 6, § 2, we deduce that $\mu'(A) = \mu^*(A)$ for every set $A \in \mathscr{T}$. From the corollary of the proposition 4, we deduce that for every set $N \in \mathscr{T}(\mu)$ with $\mu^*(N) = 0$ we have also $\mu'(N) = 0$. Then, every set $E \in \mathscr{T}(\mu)$ can be written $E = A \cup N$ with $A \in \mathscr{T}$ and $\mu^*(N) = 0$; hence $\mu'(E) = \mu^*(E)$, therefore $\mu' = \mu^*$.

Corollary 5. *Let ν be a countably additive positive set function defined on $\mathscr{T}$ and μ its restriction to $\mathscr{C}$. If μ is σ-finite on $\mathscr{C}$, then $\nu(E) = \mu^*(E)$ for every $E \in \mathscr{T}$.*

We extend now μ^* from $\mathscr{T}(\mu)$ to $\mathfrak{T}(\mu)$. Since the restriction ν of μ^* to $\mathscr{T}(\mu)$ is countably additive, its variation $\bar{\nu}$ is countably additive on $\mathfrak{T}(\mu)$ and verifies the following equalities (corollary 2 of the proposition 6, § 3):

$$\bar{\nu}(E) = \mu^*(E), \quad \text{for} \quad E \in \mathscr{T}(\mu),$$

$$\bar{\nu}(E) = \sup_{\substack{A \subset E \\ A \in \mathscr{T}(\mu)}} \mu^*(A).$$

We are led to the following:

Definition 4. *For every set $E \in \mathfrak{T}(\mu)$ we define the outer measure $\mu^*(E)$ by the equality*

$$\mu^*(E) = \sup_{\substack{A \subset E \\ A \in \mathscr{T}(\mu)}} \mu^*(A).$$

From the properties of the variation $\bar{\nu}$ we deduce the following.

Proposition 6. *The outer measure μ^* is positive and countably additive on the tribe $\mathfrak{T}(\mu)$.*

The outer measure can be defined starting from the tribe $\mathscr{T}$ generated by $\mathscr{C}$, or from the semi-tribe $\mathscr{S}$ generated by $\mathscr{C}$.

Proposition 7. *For every set* $E \in \mathfrak{C}(\mu)$ *we have*

$$\mu^*(E) = \sup_{\substack{A \subset E \\ A \in \mathscr{S}}} \mu^*(A) = \sup_{\substack{A \subset E \\ A \in \mathscr{T}}} \mu^*(A)$$

and

$$\mu^*(E) = \sup_{A \in \mathscr{C}} \mu^*(E \cap A) = \sup_{A \in \mathscr{S}} \mu^*(E \cap A)$$

$$= \sup_{A \in \mathscr{T}} \mu^*(E \cap A) = \sup_{A \in \mathscr{T}(\mu)} \mu^*(E \cap A).$$

We have first

$$\mu^*(E) = \sup_{\substack{A \subset E \\ A \in \mathscr{T}(\mu)}} \mu^*(A) = \sup_{\substack{A \subset E \\ A \in \mathscr{T}(\mu)}} \sup_{\substack{B \subset A \\ B \in \mathscr{T}}} \mu^*(B) = \sup_{\substack{B \subset E \\ B \in \mathscr{T}}} \mu^*(B)$$

$$= \sup_{\substack{B \subset E \\ B \in \mathscr{T}}} \sup_{\substack{C \subset B \\ C \in \mathscr{S}}} \mu^*(C) = \sup_{\substack{C \subset E \\ C \in \mathscr{S}}} \mu^*(C).$$

Since $\mathscr{C} \subset \mathscr{S} \subset \mathscr{T} \subset \mathscr{T}(\mu)$ we have

$$\sup_{A \in \mathscr{C}} \mu^*(E \cap A) \leqq \sup_{A \in \mathscr{S}} \mu^*(E \cap A) \leqq \sup_{A \in \mathscr{T}} \mu^*(E \cap A)$$

$$\leqq \sup_{A \in \mathscr{T}(\mu)} \mu^*(E \cap A) \leqq \mu^*(E).$$

It remains to prove that

$$\mu^*(E) \leqq \sup_{A \in \mathscr{C}} \mu^*(E \cap A).$$

Let $B \in \mathscr{T}(\mu)$ with $B \subset E$. Then B can be covered by an increasing sequence (A_n) of sets of $\mathscr{C}$.

If A is the union of the sequence (A_n), then $E \cap A$ is the union of the increasing sequence $(E \cap A_n)$, therefore

$$\mu^*(B) \leqq \mu^*(E \cap A) = \sup_n \mu^*(E \cap A_n) \leqq \sup_{A \in \mathscr{C}} \mu^*(E \cap A),$$

consequently

$$\mu^*(E) \leqq \sup_{A \in \mathscr{C}} \mu^*(E \cap A).$$

Corollary 1. *For every set* $E \in \mathfrak{C}(\mu)$, *there exists a set* $A \in \mathscr{T}$ *with* $A \subset E$ *and* $\mu^*(A) = \mu^*(E)$.

In fact, there exists an increasing sequence (A_n) of sets of $\mathscr{T}$ with $A_n \subset E$ and

$$\mu^*(E) = \sup_n \mu^*(A_n).$$

The union A of the sequence (A_n) belongs to $\mathscr{T}$, is contained in E and

$$\mu^*(A) = \sup_n \mu^*(A_n) = \mu^*(E).$$

Corollary 2. *If μ is a positive measure defined on a semi-tribe $\mathscr{S}$, then for every μ-measurable set $A \in \mathfrak{T}(\mu)$ we have*

$$\mu^*(A) = \bar{\mu}(A).$$

In fact (corollary 1 of the proposition 6, § 3) we have

$$\bar{\mu}(A) = \sup_{\substack{B \subset A \\ B \in \mathscr{S}}} \mu(B), \quad \text{for every } A \subset T.$$

Since for $B \in \mathscr{S}$ we have $\mu^*(B) = \mu(B)$, by the preceding proposition we deduce that

$$\mu^*(A) = \bar{\mu}(A), \quad \text{for} \quad A \in \mathfrak{T}(\mu).$$

Proposition 8. *Let $\mathscr{S}(\mu)$ be the semi-tribe of the sets $A \in \mathscr{T}(\mu)$ with $\mu^*(A) < \infty$. If μ is σ-finite on $\mathscr{C}$, then for every set $E \in \mathfrak{T}(\mu)$ we have*

$$\mu^*(E) = \sup_{\substack{A \subset E \\ A \in \mathscr{S}(\mu)}} \mu^*(A) = \sup_{A \in \mathscr{S}(\mu)} \mu^*(E \cap A).$$

From the corollary 4 of the theorem 2 we deduce that

$$\sup_{A \in \mathscr{S}(\mu)} \mu^*(E \cap A) = \sup\{\mu^*(A);\ A \subset E,\ A \in \mathscr{S}(\mu)\} \leqq \mu^*(E).$$

Let now $B \in \mathscr{T}(\mu)$ with $B \subset E$. The set B can be covered by an increasing sequence (B_n) of sets of $\mathscr{C}$ with $\mu(B_n) < \infty$. Then the sets $A_n = B \cap B_n$ belong to $\mathscr{S}(\mu)$, the sequence (A_n) is increasing and its union is equal to A, therefore

$$\mu^*(B) = \sup_n \mu^*(A_n) \leqq \sup\{\mu^*(A);\ A \subset E,\ A \in \mathscr{S}(\mu)\},$$

therefore

$$\mu^*(E) \leqq \sup\{\mu^*(A);\ A \subset E,\ A \in \mathscr{S}(\mu)\}.$$

Definition 5. *The sets $E \in \mathfrak{T}(\mu)$ with $\mu^*(E) = 0$ are called μ-negligible.*

If a property $P(t)$ defined for the points $t \in T$ is true for all the points of T except for a μ-negligible set, we say that the property $P(t)$ is true μ-almost everywhere.

Every set $A \in \mathscr{H}$ with $\mu^*(A) = 0$ is μ-negligible.

Proposition 9. *A set $E \in \mathfrak{T}(\mu)$ is μ-negligible if and only if every set $A \in \mathscr{T}(\mu)$ with $A \subset E$ is μ-negligible.*

If $E \cap A$ is μ-negligible for every set $A \in \mathscr{C}$, then E is μ-negligible.

In fact, we use the equalities

$$\mu^*(E) = \sup_{A \in \mathscr{C}} \mu^*(E \cap A) = \sup \{\mu^*(A);\, A \subset E,\, A \in \mathscr{T}(\mu)\}.$$

Proposition 10. *Every subset of a μ-negligible set is μ-negligible. The union of a sequence of μ-negligible sets is μ-negligible.*

Let $E \in \mathfrak{T}(\mu)$ with $\mu^*(E) = 0$ and let $F \subset E$. For every $A \in \mathscr{C}$, the set $A \cap E$ is μ-negligible and belongs to $\mathscr{T}(\mu)$. Then $A \cap F \subset A \cap E$; hence $A \cap F \in \mathscr{T}(\mu)$ and $A \cap F$ is μ-negligible, therefore F is μ-negligible.

The second part of the proposition follows from the countable subadditivity of μ^*.

Proposition 11. *Let μ and ν be two countably additive, positive, σ-finite set functions on $\mathscr{C}$. If $\mu \leqq \nu$ then $\mathfrak{T}(\mu) \supset \mathfrak{T}(\nu)$ and*

$$\mu^*(A) \leqq \nu^*(A), \quad \textit{for} \quad A \in \mathfrak{T}(\nu).$$

It is evident that

$$\mu^*(A) \leqq \nu^*(A), \quad \text{for} \quad A \in \mathscr{H}.$$

It follows that every ν-negligible set of $\mathscr{H}$ is also μ-negligible. From the corollary 1 of the proposition 5 we deduce that $\mathscr{T}(\mu) \supset \mathscr{T}(\nu)$. From the corollary 2 of the theorem 2 we deduce that $\mathfrak{T}(\mu) \supset \mathfrak{T}(\nu)$. Then, from the definition of the outer measure we deduce that $\mu^*(E) \leqq \nu^*(E)$ for $E \in \mathfrak{T}(\nu)$.

Definition 6. *The μ-measurable sets $E \in \mathfrak{T}(\mu)$ with $\mu^*(E) < \infty$ are called μ-integrable. For every μ-integrable set $E \subset T$ we define the measure $\mu(E)$ by the equality*

$$\mu(E) = \mu^*(E).$$

We say that a set $E \in \mathfrak{T}(\mu)$ has σ-finite measure, if E is the union of a sequence of μ-integrable sets.

Every μ-negligible set is μ-integrable.

The class of the μ-integrable sets is a *semi-tribe*. It will be denoted by $\Sigma(\mu)$. Then μ is a finite complete measure on $\Sigma(\mu)$.

Corollaries 1 and 2 of the proposition 5 can now be extended.

Proposition 12. *Every set $E \in \mathfrak{T}(\mu)$ with σ-finite measure is of the form $E = A \cup N$ with $A \in \mathscr{T}$ and N negligible.*

Let $E \in \mathfrak{T}(\mu)$ be the union of a sequence (E_n) of μ-integrable sets. From the corollary 1 of the proposition 7 we deduce that for every n there exists a set $A_n \in \mathscr{T}$ contained in E_n with $\mu^*(A_n) = \mu^*(E_n)$.

The set $N_n = E_n - A_n$ is negligible, therefore the union $N = \bigcup_{n=1}^{\infty} N_n$ is negligible, the set $A = \bigcup_{n=1}^{\infty} A_n$ belongs to $\mathscr{T}$ and we have $E = A \cup N$.

Corollary. *Every set $E \in \mathcal{T}(\mu)$ with σ-finite measure is the union of a sequence (A_n) of disjoint sets of the semi-tribe $\mathcal{S}$ generated by $\mathcal{C}$, and a μ-negligible set N.*

In fact, every set A of $\mathcal{T}$ is the union of a sequence of disjoint sets of $\mathcal{S}$.

Proposition 13. *For every μ-integrable set $E \in \Sigma(\mu)$ and for every $\varepsilon > 0$, there exists a set $A \in \mathcal{C}$ such that*

$$\mu(A \,\Delta\, E) < \varepsilon.$$

Let $E \in \Sigma(\mu)$ and $\varepsilon > 0$ and write $E = B \cup N$ with $B \in \mathcal{T}$ and N negligible. There exists a sequence (A_i) of sets of $\mathcal{C}$ such that

$$B \subset \bigcup_{i=1}^{\infty} A_i \quad \text{and} \quad \sum_{i=1}^{\infty} \mu(A_i) < \mu(B) + \frac{\varepsilon}{2}.$$

There exists a number n such that

$$\sum_{i>n} \mu(A_i) < \frac{\varepsilon}{2}.$$

The set $A = \bigcup_{i \leq n} A_i$ belongs to $\mathcal{C}$ and we have

$$\mu(E - A) = \mu(B - A) \leq \mu^*\left(\bigcup_{i=1}^{\infty} A_i - A\right) = \mu^*\left(\bigcup_{i>n} A_i\right) \leq \sum_{i>n} \mu(A_i) < \frac{\varepsilon}{2}$$

and

$$\mu(A - E) = \mu(A - B) \leq \mu^*\left(\bigcup_{i=1}^{\infty} A_i - B\right) = \mu^*\left(\bigcup_{i=1}^{\infty} A_i\right) - \mu(B) \leq \sum_{i=1}^{\infty} \mu(A_i) - \mu(B) < \frac{\varepsilon}{2},$$

whence

$$\mu(E \,\Delta\, A) = \mu(E - A) + \mu(A - E) < \varepsilon.$$

Theorem 3. *Let X be a Banach space, $\mathcal{C}$ a clan, $\boldsymbol{m}: \mathcal{C} \to X$ a measure with finite variation μ and $\mathcal{K}$ a clan such that $\mathcal{C} \subset \mathcal{K} \subset \Sigma(\mu)$. Then $\boldsymbol{m}$ can be extended to a measure $\boldsymbol{m}_1: \mathcal{K} \to X$ with finite variation μ_1 such that $\mathcal{T}(\mu_1) = \mathcal{T}(\mu)$ and $\mu_1^* = \mu^*$.*

The outer measure μ^* is finite and countably additive on $\Sigma(\mu)$. Then the restriction μ_1 of μ^* is a finite measure on $\mathcal{K}$ which extends μ. From the proposition 13 we deduce that $\mathcal{C}$ is dense in $\mathcal{K}$ for the semi-distance ϱ_{μ_1}, therefore we can apply the corollary of the theorem 1 and obtain a measure $\boldsymbol{m}_1: \mathcal{K} \to X$ with finite variation and $|\boldsymbol{m}_1| = \mu_1$.

The proof of the equalities $\mathcal{T}(\mu_1) = \mathcal{T}(\mu)$ and $\mu_1^* = \mu^*$ is devided in several parts:

a) $\mathcal{T}(\mu_1) \subset \mathcal{T}(\mu)$ and $\mu_1^*(A) = \mu^*(A)$ for $A \in \mathcal{T}(\mu_1)$. In fact, we remark that $\mathcal{S}(\mathcal{K}) \subset \Sigma(\mu)$, therefore $\mathcal{T}(\mathcal{K}) \subset \mathcal{T}(\mu)$. Since μ_1^* and μ^* are finite and equal on $\mathcal{K}$, then μ_1^* and μ^* are equal on $\mathcal{T}(\mathcal{K})$ (§ 2, proposition 6).

If $N \in \mathcal{T}(\mu_1)$ is μ_1-negligible, there exists a μ_1-negligible set $N' \in \mathcal{T}(\mathcal{K})$ such that $N \subset N'$. By the preceding remark we deduce that $N' \in \mathfrak{T}(\mu)$ and N' is μ-negligible, therefore $N \in \mathfrak{T}(\mu)$ and is μ-negligible.

Let now $A \in \mathcal{T}(\mu_1)$. Then $A = B \cup N$ with $B \in \mathcal{T}(\mathcal{K})$, $N \in \mathcal{T}(\mu_1)$ and $\mu_1^*(N) = 0$. It follows that $B, N \in \mathfrak{T}(\mu)$, whence $A \in \mathfrak{T}(\mu)$, and $\mu_1^*(A) = \mu_1^*(B) = \mu^*(B) = \mu^*(A)$.

b) $\mathfrak{T}(\mu_1) \subset \mathfrak{T}(\mu)$ and $\mu_1^*(E) = \mu^*(E)$ for $E \in \mathfrak{T}(\mu_1)$. Let $E \in \mathfrak{T}(\mu_1)$ and $A \in \mathscr{C}$. Then $A \in \mathcal{K}$, therefore $E \cap A \in \mathcal{T}(\mu_1) \subset \mathfrak{T}(\mu)$. We have also $E \cap A \subset A \in \mathscr{C}$, therefore $E \cap A \in \mathcal{T}(\mu)$. It follows that $E \in \mathfrak{T}(\mu)$. On the other hand (proposition 7)

$$\mu^*(E) = \sup_{A \in \mathscr{C}} \mu^*(E \cap A) = \sup_{A \in \mathscr{C}} \mu_1^*(E \cap A) \leqq \mu_1^*(E).$$

Since for $B \in \mathcal{K}$ we have $E \cap B \in \mathcal{T}(\mu_1) \subset \mathfrak{T}(\mu)$, we have also

$$\mu_1^*(E) = \sup_{B \in \mathcal{K}} \mu_1^*(E \cap B) = \sup_{B \in \mathcal{K}} \mu^*(E \cap B) \leqq \mu^*(E),$$

therefore $\mu_1^*(E) = \mu^*(E)$.

c) $\mathcal{T}(\mu) \subset \mathcal{T}(\mu_1)$. In fact, since $\mathscr{C} \subset \mathcal{K} \subset \mathcal{T}(\mu_1)$, we deduce that $\mathcal{T}(\mathscr{C}) \subset \mathcal{T}(\mu_1)$.

If $N \in \mathcal{T}(\mu)$ is μ-negligible, there exists a μ-negligible set $N' \in \mathcal{T}(\mathscr{C})$ with $N \subset N'$. Then $N' \in \mathcal{T}(\mu_1)$ and N' is μ_1-negligible, therefore $N \in \mathcal{T}(\mu_1)$ and $\mu_1^*(N) = 0$.

Let now $A \in \mathcal{T}(\mu)$. Then $A = B \cup N$ with $B \in \mathcal{T}$, $N \in \mathcal{T}(\mu)$ and $\mu^*(N) = 0$. It follows that $B, N \in \mathcal{T}(\mu_1)$, therefore $A \in \mathcal{T}(\mu_1)$.

d) $\mathfrak{T}(\mu) \subset \mathfrak{T}(\mu_1)$. In fact, let $E \in \mathfrak{T}(\mu)$ and $A \in \mathcal{K}$. Then $A \in \Sigma(\mu)$, therefore $A = B \cup N$ with $B \in \mathcal{T}(\mathscr{C})$ and N μ-negligible. Since $A \in \mathcal{T}(\mu_1)$ and $B \in \mathcal{T}(\mu_1)$ we deduce that $N = A - B \in \mathcal{T}(\mu_1)$ and that $\mu_1^*(N) = 0$. Then $E \cap B \in \mathcal{T}(\mu) \subset \mathcal{T}(\mu_1)$ and $E \cap N$ is μ_1-negligible and contained in the set A of $\mathcal{T}(\mu_1)$, therefore $E \cap N \in \mathcal{T}(\mu_1)$. It follows that $E \cap A = (E \cap B) \cup (E \cap N) \in \mathcal{T}(\mu_1)$, consequently $E \in \mathfrak{T}(\mu_1)$.

e) From b) and d) we deduce that $\mathfrak{T}(\mu_1) = \mathfrak{T}(\mu)$ and $\mu_1^* = \mu^*$.

Remark.

The preceding theorem shows that if we repeat the method of construction of the outer measure, starting from an arbitrary clan of integrable sets, we obtain no new measurable sets.

However, the tribe $\mathfrak{T}(\mu)$ of the measurable sets is not generally, the greatest clan on which μ can be extended as a measure, even if $\mathfrak{T}(\mu) = \mathcal{T}(\mu)$.

At the end of the § 14 is given an example of Baire measure μ for which a compact set is not measurable. But in the proposition 1, § 16, we shall see that a Baire measure can be extended to a Borel measure defined on a semi-tribe which contains all the compact sets.

5. JORDAN MEASURE

Let $\mathscr{C}$ be a clan and μ a positive (finite or infinite) *additive* set function defined on $\mathscr{C}$. In this section we shall extend μ to a larger *clan* containing $\mathscr{C}$ and the whole space T.

Consider the *hereditary clan* $\mathscr{K} = \mathscr{K}(\mathscr{C})$ generated by $\mathscr{C}$, i.e. the class of all the subsets of the sets of $\mathscr{C}$. Since every set of the semi-tribe $\mathscr{S}$ generated by $\mathscr{C}$ is contained in some set of $\mathscr{C}$, we deduce that $\mathscr{S} \subset \mathscr{K}$. For every set $E \in \mathscr{K}$ we put

$$\tau_\mu^*(E) = \tau^*(E) = \inf_{\substack{A \supset E \\ A \in \mathscr{C}}} \mu(A).$$

The set function $\tau^*: \mathscr{C} \to \bar{R}_+$ is called the *Jordan outer measure* induced by μ. We have the following properties:

1. $0 \leqq \tau^*(E) \leqq \infty$ *for* $E \in \mathscr{K}$.

If μ is finite on $\mathscr{C}$ then μ^* is finite on $\mathscr{K}$.

2. τ^* *is increasing:*

$$\tau^*(E) \leqq \tau^*(F), \quad \textit{if} \quad E \subset F;$$

3. τ^* *is subadditive:*

$$\tau^*(A \cup B) \leqq \tau^*(A) + \tau^*(B), \quad \textit{for} \quad A, B \in \mathscr{K};$$

4. *For every set* $A \in \mathscr{C}$ *we have*

$$\tau^*(A) = \mu(A).$$

5. *If* $\bar{\mu}$ *is the variation of* μ, *for every set* $E \in \mathscr{K}$ *we have*

$$\bar{\mu}(E) \leqq \tau^*(E).$$

From the corollary of the proposition 3 we deduce that if $\mathscr{C}$ is a tribe and μ is countably additive, then the outer measure and the Jordan outer measure induced by μ are equal.

Definition 7. *We denote by* $\mathscr{J}_0(\mu)$ *the class of the sets* $E \in \mathscr{K}$ *having the property*

$$\tau^*(A) = \tau^*(A \cap E) + \tau^*(A - E), \quad \textit{for every} \quad A \in \mathscr{K}.$$

We denote by $\mathscr{J}(\mu)$ *the class of the sets* $E \subset T$ *having the property that* $E \cap A \in \mathscr{J}_0(\mu)$ *for every* $A \in \mathscr{J}_0(\mu)$.

The sets of $\mathscr{J}(\mu)$ *are called* μ*-measurable in the sense of Jordan, or Jordan* μ*-measurable.*

We remark that a set $E \in \mathscr{K}$ belongs to $\mathscr{J}_0(\mu)$ if and only if

$$\tau^*(A) \geqq \tau^*(A \cap E) + \tau^*(A - E) \quad \text{for every} \quad A \in \mathscr{K}$$

and every set $E \in \mathscr{K}$ with $\tau^*(E) = 0$ belongs to $\mathscr{J}_0(\mu)$.

Theorem 4. *The class $\mathscr{J}_0(\mu)$ is a clan containing $\mathscr{C}$ and τ^* is additive on $\mathscr{J}_0(\mu)$.*

We prove like in the theorem 2 that $\mathscr{J}_0(\mu)$ is a clan. If E and F are disjoint sets of $\mathscr{J}_0(\mu)$ and $A \in \mathscr{K}$ we deduce from the equality 5 in the proof of the theorem 2 that

$$\tau^*(A \cap (E \cup F)) = \tau^*(E \cap E) + \tau^*(E \cap F),$$

therefore, taking $A = E \cup F$ we deduce that

$$\tau^*(E \cup F) = \tau^*(E) + \tau^*(F),$$

whence τ^* is additive on $\mathscr{J}_0(\mu)$.

It remains to prove that $\mathscr{C} \subset \mathscr{J}_0(\mu)$. Let $E \in \mathscr{C}$, $A \in \mathscr{K}$ and $\varepsilon > 0$. There exists a set $F \in \mathscr{C}$ with $A \subset F$ and $\mu(F) \leqq \tau^*(A) + \varepsilon$. We have $A \cap E \subset F \cap E$ and $A - E \subset F - E$. On the other hand the set $F \cap E$ and $F - E$ are disjoint sets of $\mathscr{C}$, therefore

$$\tau^*(A \cap E) + \tau^*(A - E) \leqq \mu(F \cap E) + \mu(F - E) = \mu(F) \leqq \tau^*(A) + \varepsilon.$$

ε being arbitrary, we deduce that

$$\tau^*(A) \geqq \tau^*(A \cap E) + \tau^*(A - E),$$

whence $E \in \mathscr{J}_0(\mu)$.

Corollary 1. *The class $\mathscr{J}(\mu)$ of the Jordan μ-measurable sets is a clan containing $\mathscr{J}_0(\mu)$ and T.*

Corollary 2. *We have $E \in \mathscr{J}(\mu)$ if and only if $E \cap A \in \mathscr{J}_0(\mu)$ for every $A \in \mathscr{C}$.*

Consider now the variation $\overline{\tau^*}$ of the restriction of τ^* to $\mathscr{J}_0(\mu)$. Since the restriction of τ^* to $\mathscr{J}_0(\mu)$ is additive and positive we have (§ 3, corollary 2 of the proposition 6)

$$\overline{\tau^*}(A) = \tau^*(A), \quad \text{for} \quad A \in \mathscr{J}_0(\mu)$$

and

$$\overline{\tau^*}(E) = \sup_{\substack{A \subset E \\ A \in \mathscr{J}_0(\mu)}} \tau^*(A), \quad \text{for} \quad E \subset T.$$

Definition 8. *For every Jordan μ-measurable set $E \in \mathscr{J}(\mu)$ we define the Jordan outer measure $\tau^*_\mu(E) = \tau^*(E)$ by the equality*

$$\tau^*(E) = \overline{\tau^*}(E).$$

Proposition 14. *The set function τ^* is positive and additive on $\mathscr{J}(\mu)$.*

We use the property 9 of the variation, § 3.

Corollary. *The class $\mathscr{I}(\mu)$ of the sets $E \in \mathscr{J}(\mu)$ with $\tau^*(E) < \infty$ is a clan.*

Proposition 15. *For every set* $E \in \mathcal{J}(\mu)$ *we have*

$$\tau^*(E) = \sup_{\substack{A \subset E \\ A \in \mathcal{J}_0(\mu)}} \tau^*(A) = \sup_{A \in \mathcal{J}_0(\mu)} \tau^*(E \cap A) = \sup_{A \in \mathscr{C}} \tau^*(E \cap A).$$

In fact we have $E \in \mathcal{J}(\mu)$ if and only if $E \cap A \in \mathcal{J}_0(\mu)$ for every $A \in \mathscr{C}$ (§ 1, proposition 20).

Corollary. *If* $E \in \mathcal{J}(\mu)$ *we have* $\tau^*(E) = 0$ *if and only if* $\tau^*(E \cap A) = 0$ *for every* $A \in \mathscr{C}$.

The sets $E \in \mathcal{J}(\mu)$ with $\tau^*(E) = 0$ are called Jordan μ-negligible sets. If E is Jordan μ-negligible, then every subset $F \subset E$ is Jordan μ-negligible; a finite union of Jordan μ-negligible sets is Jordan μ-negligible.

Proposition 16. *For every set* $E \in \mathcal{J}(\mu)$ *with* $\tau^*(E) < \infty$ *and for every* $\varepsilon > 0$ *there exists a set* $A \in \mathscr{C}$ *with* $\tau^*(E \,\Delta\, A) < \varepsilon$. *Moreover, if* $E \in \mathcal{J}_0(\mu)$, *we can take* $A \supset E$.

In fact, there exists a set $B \in \mathcal{J}_0(\mu)$ such that $B \subset E$ and $\tau^*(E) - \tau^*(B) < \frac{\varepsilon}{2}$. There exists then a set $A \in \mathscr{C}$ such that $B \subset A$ and $\tau^*(A) - \tau^*(B) < \frac{\varepsilon}{2}$. Since τ^* is additive we deduce $\tau^*(E - B) < \frac{\varepsilon}{2}$ and $\tau^*(A - B) < \frac{\varepsilon}{2}$. Then $E - A \subset E - B$ and $A - E \subset A - B$, whence $\tau^*(E \,\Delta\, A) = \tau^*(E - A) + \tau^*(A - E) < \varepsilon$. If $E \in \mathcal{J}_0(\mu)$, we take $B = E$ and then $E \subset A$.

Proposition 17. *If* μ *is finite on* $\mathscr{C}$, *then* τ^* *is the only positive additive extension of* μ *from* $\mathscr{C}$ *to* $\mathcal{J}_0(\mu)$.

From the preceding proposition we deduce that $\mathscr{C}$ is dense in $\mathcal{J}_0(\mu)$ for the semi-distance $\varrho(A, B) = \tau^*(A \,\Delta\, B)$.

Let λ be an additive positive set function on $\mathcal{J}_0(\mu)$ such that

$$\lambda(A) = \mu(A), \quad \text{for} \quad A \in \mathscr{C}.$$

Then we deduce that

$$\lambda(A) \leqq \tau^*(A), \quad \text{for} \quad A \in \mathcal{J}_0(\mu).$$

It follows that λ is uniformly continuous on $\mathcal{J}_0(\mu)$. Since τ^* is also uniformly continuous on $\mathcal{J}_0(\mu)$ and since λ and τ^* coincide on the dense set $\mathscr{C}$, we deduce that

$$\lambda(A) = \tau^*(A), \quad \text{for} \quad A \in \mathcal{J}_0(\mu).$$

Proposition 18. *If* μ *is a positive measure on* $\mathscr{C}$ *then* $\mathcal{J}_0(\mu) \subset \mathcal{T}(\mu)$ *and* $\mathcal{J}(\mu) \subset \mathcal{C}(\mu)$ *and we have*

$$\mu^*(E) = \tau^*_\mu(E), \quad \textit{for} \quad E \in \mathcal{J}(\mu).$$

We remark first that the hereditary clan $\mathscr{K}$ generated by $\mathscr{C}$ is contained in the hereditary tribe $\mathscr{H}$ generated by $\mathscr{C}$ and that

$$\mu^*(E) \leqq \tau_\mu^*(E), \quad \text{for} \quad E \in \mathscr{K}.$$

Let $E \in \mathscr{J}_0(\mu)$ and prove that $E \in \mathscr{T}(\mu)$. For every n we can find a set $A_n \in \mathscr{C}$ with $E \subset A_n$ and $\tau^*(A_n - E) < \frac{1}{n}$; then $\mu^*(A_n - E) < \frac{1}{n}$. The set $A = \bigcap_{n=1}^{\infty} A_n$ belongs to the tribe $\mathscr{T}$ generated by $\mathscr{C}$ and we have $\mu^*(A - E) \leqq \mu^*(A_n - E) < \frac{1}{n}$ for every n, consequently $\mu^*(A - E) = 0$. It follows that the set $N = A - E$ is μ-negligible, and $E = A - N$, therefore $E \in \mathscr{T}(\mu)$.

We deduce that μ^* and τ_μ^* are additive on $\mathscr{J}_0(\mu)$ and coincide on $\mathscr{C}$. From the proposition 17 it follows that μ^* and τ_μ^* coincide on $\mathscr{J}_0(\mu)$, therefore τ_μ^* is countably additive on $\mathscr{J}_0(\mu)$; then τ_μ^* is countably additive also on $\mathscr{J}(\mu)$ (§ 3, property 9 of the variation).

Let now $E \in \mathscr{J}(\mu)$ and prove that $E \in \mathfrak{C}(\mu)$. For every set $A \in \mathscr{C}$ we have $E \cap A \in \mathscr{J}_0(\mu) \subset \mathscr{T}(\mu)$, therefore $E \in \mathfrak{C}(\mu)$. Then (propositions 7 and 15)

$$\tau_\mu^*(E) = \sup_{A \in \mathscr{C}} \tau_\mu^*(E \cap A) = \sup_{A \in \mathscr{C}} \mu^*(E \cap A) = \mu^*(E).$$

Theorem 5. *Let X be a Banach space, $\boldsymbol{m}: \mathscr{C} \to X$ an additive set function with finite variation μ and $\mathscr{K}$ a clan such that $\mathscr{C} \subset \mathscr{K} \subset \mathscr{I}(\mu)$. Then $\boldsymbol{m}$ can be extended to an additive set function $\boldsymbol{m}_1 : \mathscr{K} \to X$ with finite variation μ_1 such that*

$$\mu_1(E) = \tau_\mu^*(E), \quad \textit{for} \quad E \in \mathscr{K}.$$

If $\boldsymbol{m}$ is countably additive, then $\boldsymbol{m}_1$ is also countably additive.

The Jordan outer measure τ_μ^* is finite and additive on $\mathscr{I}(\mu)$. The restriction μ_1 of τ_μ^* to $\mathscr{K}$ is finite, additive and extends μ. From the proposition 16 we deduce that $\mathscr{C}$ is dense in $\mathscr{K}$ for the semi-distance $\varrho(A, B) = \mu_1(A \,\Delta\, B)$, therefore we can apply the corollary of the theorem 1 and obtain an additive set function $\boldsymbol{m}_1 : \mathscr{K} \to X$ with finite variation and $|\boldsymbol{m}_1| = \mu_1$.

If $\boldsymbol{m}$ is countably additive, then μ is countably additive and from the proposition 18 it follows that τ_μ^* is countably additive, since $\tau_\mu^* = \mu^*$ on $\mathscr{J}(\mu)$. We deduce that μ_1 is countably additive, whence $\boldsymbol{m}_1$ is also countably additive.

CHAPTER II

INTEGRATION

§ 6. MEASURABLE FUNCTIONS

1. STEP FUNCTIONS

Let $\mathscr{A}$ be a nonvoid class of subsets of T and X a *vector space*.

Definition 1. *A function $f: T \to E$ is called a step function with respect to the class $\mathscr{A}$, or an $\mathscr{A}$-step function if it is of the form*

$$f = \sum_{i \in I} \varphi_{A_i} x_i$$

where I is a finite set, $A_i \in \mathscr{A}$ and $x_i \in E$ for every $i \in I$.

The set of the $\mathscr{A}$-step functions $f: T \to E$ will be denoted by $\mathscr{E}_E(\mathscr{A})$. If $E = R$ we shall write $\mathscr{E}(\mathscr{A})$ instead of $\mathscr{E}_R(\mathscr{A})$.

The set $\mathscr{E}_E(\mathscr{A})$ is a *vector space*.

The most important case is that of the step functions with respect to a *clan*.

Lemma 1. *Let $\mathscr{C}$ be a clan. For every finite family $(A_i)_{i \in I}$ of sets of $\mathscr{C}$ there exists a finite family $(B_j)_{j \in J}$ of disjoint sets of $\mathscr{C}$ such that each A_i is the union of a certain number of sets B_j.*

Consider all the sets of the form $\bigcap_{i \in I} C_i$, where $C_i = A_i$ for at least one index i, and if $C_i \neq A_i$ then $C_i = T - A_i$.

Let $(B_j)_{j \in J}$ be the family of these sets $\bigcap_{i \in I} C_i$. The sets B_j are disjoint and belong to $\mathscr{C}$, because

$$\Big(\bigcap_{i \in I'} A_i\Big) \cap \Big(\bigcap_{i \in I''} \complement A_i\Big) = \Big(\bigcap_{i \in I'} A_i\Big) - \Big(\bigcup_{i \in I''} A_i\Big)$$

where $I' \cup I'' = I, I' \cap I'' = \emptyset$ and $I' \neq \emptyset$. Each set A_k is the union of the sets $\bigcap_{i \in I} C_i$ with $C_k = A_k$.

Proposition 1. *Let $\mathscr{C}$ be a clan. Every step function $f = \sum \varphi_{A_i} x_i$ with $A_i \in \mathscr{C}$ and $x_i \in E$ can be written in the form $f = \sum \varphi_{B_j} y_j$ with B_j disjoint sets of $\mathscr{C}$ and $y_j \in E$.*

Let (B_j) be a finite family of disjoint sets of $\mathscr{C}$ such that each A_i is the union of a certain number of sets B_j. For each B_k let I_k be the set of the indices i such that

$B_k \subset A_i$ and put $y_k = \sum_{i \in I_k} x_i$. Then $f = \sum \varphi_{B_j} y_j$. In fact, let $t \in \bigcup A_i$. There is a single set B_k containing t. Then $t \in A_i$ if and only if $i \in I_k$; hence

$$f(t) = \sum \varphi_{A_i}(t) x_i = \sum_{i \in I_k} \varphi_{A_i}(t) x_i = \sum_{i \in I_k} x_i = y_k = \sum \varphi_{B_j}(t) y_j.$$

Remarks.

1°. If the function $\sum \varphi_{A_i} x_i$ is not identically null, we can write it uniquely in the form $\sum \varphi_{B_j} y_j$ with B_j disjoint sets of $\mathscr{C}$ such that the elements y_j are different from each other and from 0.

2°. If E is an arbitrary set, a function $f: T \to E$ is called a step function if the set of the values $f(E)$ is finite.

2. TOTALLY MEASURABLE FUNCTIONS

Let $\mathscr{C}$ be a *clan* and E a *Banach* space.

Definition 2. *A function $f: T \to E$ is called totally measurable with respect to $\mathscr{C}$, or totally $\mathscr{C}$-measurable, if it vanishes outside a set $A \in \mathscr{C}$ and if there exists a sequence (f_n) of step functions of $\mathscr{E}_E(\mathscr{C})$ converging uniformly to f.*

If $T \in \mathscr{C}$, the condition that f vanishes outside a set $A \in \mathscr{C}$ is superfluous.

The set of the totally $\mathscr{C}$-measurable functions $f: T \to E$ is denoted by $\mathscr{M}_E(\mathscr{C})$. If $E = R$ we write $\mathscr{M}(\mathscr{C})$ instead of $\mathscr{M}_R(\mathscr{C})$.

From the definition we deduce that $\mathscr{M}_E(\mathscr{C})$ is a vector space containing $\mathscr{E}_E(\mathscr{C})$. If E is an algebra then $\mathscr{M}_E(\mathscr{C})$ is an algebra. If $f \in \mathscr{M}_E(\mathscr{C})$ and $\varphi \in \mathscr{M}(\mathscr{C})$ then $f\varphi \in \mathscr{M}_E(\mathscr{C})$. Every function of $\mathscr{M}_E(\mathscr{C})$ is bounded.

For every set $A \subset T$ we design with $\mathscr{M}_E(\mathscr{C}, A)$ the subspace of the functions of $\mathscr{M}_E(\mathscr{C})$ vanishing outside A. The space $\mathscr{M}_E(\mathscr{C})$ is the union of the subspaces $\mathscr{M}_E(\mathscr{C}, A)$ with $A \in \mathscr{C}$.

On the spaces $\mathscr{M}_E(\mathscr{C})$ and $\mathscr{M}_E(\mathscr{C}, A)$ we shall consider the topology of the uniform convergence defined by the norm

$$\|f\| = \sup_{t \in T} |f(t)|.$$

Every space $\mathscr{M}_E(\mathscr{C}, A)$ with $A \in \mathscr{C}$ is a Banach space containing $\mathscr{E}_E(\mathscr{C}, A)$ as a dense subspace.

3. REAL FUNCTIONS MEASURABLE WITH RESPECT TO A TRIBE

Let $\mathscr{T}$ be a *tribe* of subsets of T with $T \in \mathscr{T}$. The sets of $\mathscr{T}$ are said to be $\mathscr{T}$-measurable or simply, measurable, if no confusion is possible. An important example of such a tribe is the tribe $\mathfrak{T}(\mu)$ of all the sets $A \subset T$ which are measurable with respect to a positive measure μ.

We denote with $\mathscr{T}(\mathscr{B})$ the tribe of the subsets of the real line R, generated by the open sets. The sets of $\mathscr{T}(\mathscr{B})$ are called *Borel sets* of the real line. We design with $\mathscr{T}(\overline{\mathscr{B}})$ the tribe of the subsets of the extended real line $\bar{R} = [-\infty, +\infty]$, generated by the open sets of $\bar{R}$. The sets of the tribe $\mathscr{T}(\overline{\mathscr{B}})$ are of one of the forms: A, $A \cup \{-\infty\}$, $A \cup \{+\infty\}$, $A \cup \{-\infty, +\infty\}$ with $A \in \mathscr{T}(\mathscr{B})$.

Definition 3. *A function $f: T \to \bar{R}$ is said to be measurable with respect to the tribe $\mathscr{T}$, or $\mathscr{T}$-measurable if $\overset{-1}{f}(A) \in \mathscr{T}$ for every $A \in \mathscr{T}(\overline{\mathscr{B}})$.*

A function $f: T \to R$, with finite values is $\mathscr{T}$-measurable if and only if $\overset{-1}{f}(A) \in \mathscr{T}$ for every set $A \in \mathscr{T}(\mathscr{B})$.

Remarks.

1^0. We can define the $\mathscr{T}$-measurability of a complex (or with values in R^n) function f by the condition that $\overset{-1}{f}(A) \in \mathscr{T}$ for every Borel set A of the tribe $\mathscr{T}(\mathscr{B})$ generated by the open sets of the plane (or of R^n).

2^0. We can give a general definition of the measurability. Let $\mathscr{A}$ be a nonvoid class of subsets of T and $\mathscr{A}'$ a nonvoid class of subsets of another set T'. We say that a function $f: T \to T'$ is measurable with respect to the classes $\mathscr{A}$ and $\mathscr{A}'$, if $\overset{-1}{f}(A') \in \mathscr{A}$ for every $A' \in \mathscr{A}'$.

If, for example, T and T' are topological spaces, and $\mathscr{A}$, $\mathscr{A}'$ are the classes of the open sets, then a function f is measurable with respect to $\mathscr{A}$ and $\mathscr{A}'$ if and only if f is continuous.

According to this general definition, to say that a function $f: T \to \bar{R}$ is $\mathscr{T}$-measurable (in the sense of the definition 3) means that f is measurable with respect to the tribes $\mathscr{T}$ and $\mathscr{T}(\overline{\mathscr{B}})$.

In the sequel we shall study real functions with finite or infinite values, measurable with respect to a tribe $\mathscr{T}$ such that $T \in \mathscr{T}$. We shall say also "measurable functions" instead of "$\mathscr{T}$-measurable functions" if the tribe $\mathscr{T}$ is understood.

Examples.

1. Every constant function $f(t) \equiv \alpha$ is $\mathscr{T}$-measurable, since $\overset{-1}{f}(A) = \emptyset$ if $\alpha \notin A$ and $\overset{-1}{f}(A) = T$ if $\alpha \in A$. From this example we deduce the importance of the condition $T \in \mathscr{T}$.

2. A characteristic function φ_A is $\mathscr{T}$-measurable if and only if $A \in \mathscr{T}$.

3. Every $\mathscr{T}$-step function

$$f = \sum_{i=1}^{n} \varphi_{A_i} \alpha_i, \quad \text{with} \quad A_i \in \mathscr{T} \quad \text{and} \quad \alpha_i \in R$$

is measurable. In fact we can consider the sets A_i disjoint and the numbers α_i different form each other. Then $\overset{-1}{f}(B)$ is equal to $\emptyset$, T or to the union of some sets A_i.

4. More generally, if f takes only a countable set of different values $\alpha_1, \alpha_2, \ldots, \alpha_n, \ldots$ and if each value α_n is taken on a set A_n of $\mathscr{T}$, then f is $\mathscr{T}$-measurable.

5. We shall see further that the totally $\mathscr{T}$-measurable functions are $\mathscr{T}$-measurable.

Proposition 2. *If the function $f: T \to \bar{R}$ is $\mathscr{T}$-measurable and if $-\infty \leqq a \leqq b \leqq +\infty$, then the following sets are $\mathscr{T}$-measurable:*

1. $\{t; f(t) > a\}$,
2. $\{t; f(t) \geqq a\}$,
3. $\{t; f(t) < b\}$,
4. $\{t; f(t) \leqq b\}$,
5. $\{t; a < f(t) < b\}$,
6. $\{t; a \leqq f(t) \leqq b\}$,
7. $\{t; a \leqq f(t) < b\}$,
8. $\{t; a < f(t) \leqq b\}$,
9. $\{t; f(t) = a\}$.

In fact each of these sets is of the form $\overset{-1}{f}(A)$ with $A \in \mathscr{T}(\bar{\mathscr{B}})$. In particular, if f is $\mathscr{T}$-measurable, then the following sets are $\mathscr{T}$-measurable:

$$\{t; f(t) = -\infty\}, \quad \{t; f(t) = +\infty\},$$
$$\{t; f(t) \geqq -\infty\}, \quad \{t; f(t) > -\infty\},$$
$$\{t; f(t) \leqq +\infty\}, \quad \{t; f(t) < +\infty\}.$$

Proposition 3. *If $f, g: T \to \bar{R}$ are $\mathscr{T}$-measurable functions, then the following sets are $\mathscr{T}$-measurable:*

$$\{t; f(t) < g(t)\}, \quad \{t; f(t) \leqq g(t)\}, \quad \{t; f(t) = g(t)\}.$$

We use the following relations:

$$\{t; f(t) < g(t)\} = \bigcup_{r \in Q} (\{t; f(t) < r\} \cap \{t; r < g(t)\}),$$

Q being the set of the rational numbers,

$$\{t; f(t) \leqq g(t)\} = \complement \{t; f(t) > g(t)\}$$

and

$$\{t; f(t) = g(t)\} = \{t; f(t) \leqq g(t)\} - \{t; f(t) < g(t)\}.$$

We shall show now that if the sets of proposition 2 are $\mathscr{T}$-measurable, then f is itself $\mathscr{T}$-measurable. More generally

Proposition 4. *Let $f: T \to \bar{R}$ be a function and let $\mathscr{A}$ be a class of subsets of $\bar{R}$, generating the tribe $\mathscr{T}(\bar{\mathscr{B}})$. If $\overset{-1}{f}(A) = \{t; f(t) \in A\}$ is $\mathscr{T}$-measurable for every set $A \in \mathscr{A}$, then f is $\mathscr{T}$-measurable.*

Denote by Φ the class of the sets $A \subset \bar{R}$ such that $\overset{-1}{f}(A) \in \mathscr{T}$. From the hypothesis we deduce that Φ is a tribe containing $\mathscr{A}$, hence containing $\mathscr{T}(\bar{\mathscr{B}})$.

Corollary. *Let D be a countable set dense in R and let $f: T \to \bar{R}$ be a function. If one of the following equivalent conditions is fulfilled:*

1. $\{t; f(t) > a\} \in \mathscr{T}$, *for* $a \in D$;
2. $\{t; f(t) \geqq a\} \in \mathscr{T}$, *for* $a \in D$;
3. $\{t; f(t) < b\} \in \mathscr{T}$, *for* $b \in D$;
4. $\{t; f(t) \leqq b\} \in \mathscr{T}$, *for* $b \in D$;
5. $\{t; a < f(t) < b\} \in \mathscr{T}$, *for* $a, b \in D$, *and* $\{t; f(t) = \infty\} \in \mathscr{T}$;
6. $\{t; a \leqq f(t) \leqq b\} \in \mathscr{T}$, *for* $a \in D$ *and* $b \in D \cup \{+\infty\}$;
7. $\{t; a \leqq f(t) < b\} \in \mathscr{T}$, *for* $a \in D$ *and* $b \in D \cup \{+\infty\}$;
8. $\{t; a < f(t) \leqq b\} \in \mathscr{T}$, *for* $a \in D$ *and* $b \in D \cup \{+\infty\}$,

then f is $\mathscr{T}$-measurable.

In fact, in each of these conditions, we have sets of the form $\overset{-1}{f}(A)$ where A belongs to a class $\mathscr{A}$ of sets of $\bar{R}$, such that the tribe generated by $\mathscr{A}$ contains all the countable unions of intervals of the form (a, b), $[-\infty, \infty)$ and $(-\infty, \infty]$; we deduce that the tribe generated by $\mathscr{A}$ contains all the open subsets of $\bar{R}$, hence it is equal to $\mathscr{T}(\bar{\mathscr{B}})$.

Remark. If f takes only finite values, then the value $+\infty$ must be dropped in the preceding conditions.

Proposition 5. *Let $f: T \to \bar{R}$ be a $\mathscr{T}$-measurable function and $E \in \mathscr{T}$. If a function $g: T \to \bar{R}$ is equal to f on E and constant on $T - E$ then g is $\mathscr{T}$-measurable.*

In fact if $g(t) = \alpha$ for $t \in T - E$, then

$$\{t; g(t) < c\} = \{t; f(t) < c\} \cap E, \quad \text{if} \quad c \leqq \alpha$$

and

$$\{t; g(t) < c\} = \{t; f(t) < c\} \cup \complement E, \quad \text{if} \quad \alpha < c.$$

4. SEQUENCES OF MEASURABLE REAL FUNCTIONS

Let $\mathscr{T}$ be a tribe of subsets of T with $T \in \mathscr{T}$. We shall show that the property of measurability is conserved by passing to the limit.

Proposition 6. *If* (f_n) *is a sequence of real (finite or infinite)* $\mathscr{T}$*-measurable functions, then the functions*

$$\sup_n f_n, \quad \inf_n f_n, \quad \limsup_{n\to\infty} f_n, \quad \liminf_{n\to\infty} f_n$$

are $\mathscr{T}$*-measurable.*

We remark first that if f is measurable, then $-f$ is measurable, since $\{t; -f(t) < c\} = \{t; f(t) > -c\}$. The proposition follows from the following relations:

$$\{t; \inf_n f_n(t) < c\} = \bigcup_{n=1}^{\infty} \{t; f_n(t) < c\};$$

$$\sup_n f_n = -\inf_n (-f_n),$$

$$\limsup_{n\to\infty} f_n(t) = \inf_{n\geqq 1} \sup_{m\geqq n} f_m(t),$$

$$\liminf_{n\to\infty} f_n(t) = \sup_{n\geqq 1} \inf_{m\geqq n} f_m(t).$$

Corollary 1. *If the function* $f_1, f_2\colon T \to \bar{R}$ *are* $\mathscr{T}$*-measurable, then the functions* $\sup(f_1, f_2)$ *and* $\inf(f_1, f_2)$ *are* $\mathscr{T}$*-measurable.*

We take $f_n = f_2$ for $n \geqq 2$, hence $\sup(f_1, f_2) = \sup_n f_n$ and $\inf(f_1, f_2) = \inf_n f_n$.

Corollary 2. *Let* (f_n) *be a sequence of (finite or infinite)* $\mathscr{T}$*-measurable functions and let* E *be the set of the points* $t \in T$ *such that* $\lim_{n\to\infty} f_n(t)$ *exists. Then the function* f *equal to the limit of* (f_n) *on the set* E *and constant on* $T - E$ *is* $\mathscr{T}$*-measurable.*

We remark that the set

$$E = \left\{t; \liminf_{n\to\infty} f_n(t) = \limsup_{n\to\infty} f_n(t)\right\}$$

is $\mathscr{T}$-measurable and is equal on E to the $\mathscr{T}$-measurable function $\limsup_{n\to\infty} f_n$ and constant on $T - E$. We can apply then the proposition 5.

Corollary 3. *If* (f_n) *is a sequence of (finite or infinite)* $\mathscr{T}$*-measurable functions having a limit* $f(t)$ *in every point* $t \in T$ *then the limit* f *is* $\mathscr{T}$*-measurable.*

Corollary 4. *Every totally* $\mathscr{T}$*-measurable function* $f\colon T \to R$ *is* $\mathscr{T}$*-measurable.*

We shall show now that every measurable function can be obtained from step functions by passing to the limit:

Proposition 7. *Every $\mathcal{T}$-measurable function $f: T \to \bar{R}$ is the limit of a sequence (f_n) of $\mathcal{T}$-measurable step functions.*

If $f \geqq 0$, we can choose $0 \leqq f_1 \leqq f_2 \leqq \cdots \leqq f_n \leqq \cdots$.
If f is bounded, we can choose the sequence (f_n) uniformly convergent to f.

Suppose first that $f \geqq 0$. For every natural number n put

$$f_n(t) = \begin{cases} \dfrac{i-1}{2^n}, & \text{if } \dfrac{i-1}{2^n} \leqq f(t) < \dfrac{i}{2^n}, \quad i = 1, 2, \ldots, 2^n n, \\ n, & \text{if } f(t) \geqq n. \end{cases}$$

Then f_n is a positive $\mathcal{T}$-step function and the sequence (f_n) is increasing. If $f(t) < \infty$, then for $n > f(t)$ we have $0 \leqq f(t) - f_n(t) \leqq \frac{1}{2^n}$; if $f(t) = \infty$, then $f_n(t) = n$; hence in both cases we have $\lim_{n\to\infty} f_n(t) = f(t)$. If f is bounded by a certain number M, then for every $n > M$ we have $0 \leqq f(t) - f_n(t) \leqq \frac{1}{2^n}$, hence the sequence (f_n) converges uniformly to f.

If f is not positive, then the functions $f^+ = \sup(f, 0)$ and $f^- = -\inf(f, 0)$ are $\mathcal{T}$-measurable and positive and we have $f = f^+ - f^-$. Let (f_n^+) and (f_n^-) be two sequences of positive $\mathcal{T}$-step functions tending respectively to f^+ and f^-. Then $f_n = f_n^+ - f_n^-$ are $\mathcal{T}$-step functions tending to f. If, in addition f is bounded, then f^+ and f^- are bounded; hence we can take f_n^+ and f_n^- uniformly convergent respectively to f^+ and f^-, therefore f_n converges uniformly to f.

Corollary. *A function $f: T \to R$ is totally $\mathcal{T}$-measurable if and only if it is bounded and $\mathcal{T}$-measurable.*

Proposition 8. *Let $f, g: T \to \bar{R}$ be two $\mathcal{T}$-measurable functions and $\alpha \in R$. Then the functions αf and fg are $\mathcal{T}$-measurable; the function h equal to $f(t) + g(t)$ in the points $t \in T$ where the sum is defined, and constant elsewhere is $\mathcal{T}$-measurable; the function h' equal to $\dfrac{1}{f(t)}$ in the point $t \in T$ where $f(t) \neq 0$ and constant elsewhere, is $\mathcal{T}$-measurable.*

Let (f_n) and (g_n) be two sequences of $\mathcal{T}$-step functions tending respectively to f and g. The sequence (αf_n) tends to αf, whence αf is $\mathcal{T}$-measurable. The set $E \subset T$ on which the product $f(t)\, g(t)$ is of the form $0 \cdot \infty$ is $\mathcal{T}$-measurable, as union of the $\mathcal{T}$-measurable sets

$$\{f(t) = 0\} \cap [\{g(t) = -\infty\} \cup \{g(t) = +\infty\}]$$

and

$$\{g(t) = 0\} \cap [\{f(t) = -\infty\} \cup \{f(t) = +\infty\}].$$

On the set E we have $f(t)\,g(t) = 0$ according to the convention $0 \cdot \infty = 0$. On the set $T - E$ the sequence $f_n g_n$ tends to fg. From the corollary 2 of the proposition 6 we deduce that fg is $\mathcal{T}$-measurable.

The set E' on which $f(t) + g(t)$ is of the form $\infty - \infty$ is $\mathcal{T}$-measurable. The function h is constant on E' and equal to the limit of the sequence $(f_n + g_n)$ on the set $T - E'$, whence h is $\mathcal{T}$-measurable.

We define now the function

$$f'(t) = \begin{cases} f(t), & \text{if } f(t) \neq 0, \\ 1, & \text{if } f(t) = 0. \end{cases}$$

The function f' is $\mathcal{T}$-measurable. In fact the functions

$$f_n'(t) = \begin{cases} f_n(t), & \text{if } f_n(t) \neq 0, \\ 1, & \text{if } f_n(t) = 0 \end{cases}$$

are $\mathcal{T}$-step functions tending to f'. Then

$$\frac{1}{f_n'(t)} \to \frac{1}{f'(t)}, \quad \text{for every} \quad t \in T$$

and $\dfrac{1}{f_n'}$ are $\mathcal{T}$-step functions. It follows that $\dfrac{1}{f'}$ is $\mathcal{T}$-measurable. Then the function h' is also $\mathcal{T}$-measurable.

Corollary 1. *The set of the $\mathcal{T}$-measurable finite real functions is an algebra.*

Corollary 2. *A function $f\colon T \to \bar{R}$ is $\mathcal{T}$-measurable if and only if f^+ and f^- are $\mathcal{T}$-measurable.*

In fact, we have $f^+ = \sup(f, 0)$, $f^- = -\sup(-f, 0)$, and $f = f^+ - f^-$.

Corollary 3. *If the function $f\colon T \to \bar{R}$ is $\mathcal{T}$-measurable, then the function $|f|$ is $\mathcal{T}$-measurable.*

In fact, we have $|f| = f^+ + f^-$.

5. MEASURABLE FUNCTIONS WITH RESPECT TO A MEASURE

Let $\mathscr{C}$ be a *clan* of subsets of T, μ a *positive measure* on $\mathscr{C}$, $\mathfrak{T}(\mu)$ the tribe of the μ-measurable subsets of T and E a separated topological space.

Definition 4. *A function $f\colon T \to E$ is said to be measurable with respect to the measure μ, or μ-measurable, if the following two conditions are fulfilled:*

1. *For every open set $G \subset E$, the set $\overset{-1}{f}(G)$ is μ-measurable;*

2. *for every μ-integrable set $A \subset T$ there exists a μ-negligible set $N \subset A$ and a countable set $H \subset E$ such that $f(A - N) \subset \bar{H}$.*

We remark that in this definition only the value 0 of the measure is taken into consideration.

We denote by $\mathscr{T}(\mathscr{B})$ the tribe generated by the open subsets of E. The sets of $\mathscr{T}(\mathscr{B})$ are called Borel subsets of E. The tribe $\mathscr{T}(\mathscr{B})$ is also generated by the closed subsets of E.

Condition 1 in the preceding definition can be replaced by each of the following equivalent conditions:

1′. *For every closed set* $F \subset E$, *the set* $\overset{-1}{f}(F)$ *is* μ-*measurable.*

1″. *for every Borel set* $B \in \mathscr{T}(\mathscr{B})$, *the set* $\overset{-1}{f}(B)$ *is* μ-*measurable.*

The implication $1 \Rightarrow 1''$ is true since the class of the sets $B \subset E$ with $\overset{-1}{f}(B)$ μ-measurable is a tribe. The other implications are evident.

Condition 2 in the preceding definition can be replaced by each of the following equivalent conditions:

2′. *For every set* $A \in \mathscr{C}$ *there exists a* μ-*negligible set* $N \subset A$ *and a countable set* $H \subset E$ *such that* $f(A - N) \subset \bar{H}$;

2″. *for every* μ-*measurable set* $A \subset T$ *with* σ-*finite measure, there exists a* μ-*negligible set* $N \subset A$ *and a countable set* $H \subset E$ *such that* $f(A - N) \subset \bar{H}$.

The implication $2' \Rightarrow 2''$ follows from the fact that every μ-integrable set is contained in the union of a sequence of sets of $\mathscr{C}$ and a μ-negligible set. The other implications are evident.

If the space E is of countable type, then the condition 2 is superfluous. In particular, this remark is valid for $E = \bar{R}$.

It follows that a real (finite or infinite) function is μ-measurable if and only if it is measurable with respect to the tribe $\mathcal{T}(\mu)$, in the sense of the definition 3. All the preceding results stated for real functions, measurable with respect to a tribe, remain valid for real functions, measurable with respect to a measure.

Examples.

1. A set $A \subset T$ is μ-measurable if and only if its characteristic function φ_A is μ-measurable.

2. A function $f: T \to E$ taking on a finite set of different values $a_1, a_2, \ldots, a_n$ is μ-measurable if and only if the set $\overset{-1}{f}(a_i)$ is μ-measurable for $1 \leqq i \leqq n$.

The functions $f: T \to E$ taking on a finite set of values will be called, in this case too, step functions.

3. A function $f: T \to E$ which takes on a countable set of different values $a_1, a_2, \ldots$ is μ-measurable if and only if the sets $\overset{-1}{f}(a_n)$ are μ-measurable.

In fact if f is μ-measurable, then $\overset{-1}{f}(a_n)$ is μ-measurable, since the set $\{a_n\}$ is closed.

Conversely, if the sets $\overset{-1}{f}(a_n)$ are μ-measurable, then for every set $B \subset E$ (not necessarily Borel set) we have

$$\overset{-1}{f}(B) = \bigcup_{a_n \in B} \overset{-1}{f}(a_n),$$

hence $\overset{-1}{f}(B)$ is μ-measurable, therefore the condition 1 of the definition 4 is verified. The condition 2 is also verified, whence f is μ-measurable.

4. Let E be a separated topological vector space. Every step function $f = \sum_{i=1}^{n} \varphi_{A_i} x_i$ with A_i μ-measurable subsets of T and $x_i \in E$, is μ-measurable. In fact, we can write $f = \sum_{j=1}^{m} \varphi_{B_j} y_j$ with B_j disjoint μ-measurable sets and y_j different from each other and from 0. Then $B_j = \overset{-1}{f}(y_j)$ and $T - \bigcup_{j=1}^{m} B_j = \overset{-1}{f}(0)$ and we are in the case of the example 2.

5. If E is a separated topological vector space, every μ-negligible function $f\colon T \to E$ (i. e. equal to 0 μ-almost everywhere) is μ-measurable.

Proposition 9. *Let $f, g\colon T \to E$ be two functions. If f is μ-measurable and if $f(t) = g(t)$, μ-almost everywhere, then g is μ-measurable.*

The proof follows immediately from definition 4.

Proposition 10. *If a function $f\colon T \to E$ is μ-measurable and if the function $g\colon T \to E$ is equal to f on a μ-measurable set $A \subset T$ and constant on $T - A$, then g is μ-measurable.*

The condition 2 of the definition 4 is verified easily for the function g.

Let now $G \subset E$ be an open set. If $g(T - A) \notin G$, then $\overset{-1}{g}(G) = \overset{-1}{f}(G) \in \mathcal{T}(\mu)$. If $g(T - A) \in G$, then $\overset{-1}{g}(G) = \overset{-1}{f}(G) \cup (T - A) \in \mathcal{T}(\mu)$. Thus the condition 1 of the definition 4 is also verified, whence g is μ-measurable.

The most important case is that of a *metrizable* space E. We shall show that in this case, in the condition 1 of the definition 4 we can take only open spheres or only closed spheres instead of open sets.

Lemma 2. *Let E be a metrizable space and $f\colon T \to E$ a function such that for every closed sphere $S \subset E$, the set $\overset{-1}{f}(S)$ is μ-measurable. Then for every countable set $H \subset E$, the set $\overset{-1}{f}(\overline{H})$ is μ-measurable.*

For every $\varepsilon > 0$ and every countable set $H \subset E$ put

$$U_\varepsilon = \bigcup_{x \in H} S_\varepsilon(x)$$

where $S_\varepsilon(x)$ is the closed sphere with centre in x and radius ε.

We have

$$\overset{-1}{f}(U_\varepsilon) = \bigcup_{x \in H} \overset{-1}{f}(S_\varepsilon(x)),$$

whence the set $\overset{-1}{f}(U_\varepsilon)$ is μ-measurable. We have also $\bar{H} \subset U_\varepsilon$. Moreover, taking $\varepsilon = \frac{1}{n}$ and noting $U_n = U_\varepsilon$ we have

$$\bar{H} = \bigcap_{n=1}^{\infty} U_n;$$

hence

$$\overset{-1}{f}(\bar{H}) = \bigcap_{n=1}^{\infty} \overset{-1}{f}(U_n),$$

therefore $\overset{-1}{f}(\bar{H})$ is μ-measurable.

Proposition 11. *Let E be a metrizable space. A function $f\colon T \to E$ is μ-measurable if and only if the following two conditions are fulfilled:*

1. *for every closed (respectively open) sphere $S \subset E$, the set $\overset{-1}{f}(S)$ is μ-measurable;*

2. *for every μ-integrable set $A \subset T$, there exists a μ-negligible set $N \subset A$ and a countable set $H \subset E$ such that $f(A - N) \subset \bar{H}$.*

Let d be a distance on E compatible with the topology of E. If f is μ-measurable, then the two conditions are verified.

Conversely, suppose that the two conditions are fulfilled, for example, for closed spheres in the condition 1.

In order to prove that f is μ-measurable, it is sufficient to show that for every closed set $F \subset E$, the set $\overset{-1}{f}(F)$ is μ-measurable; and in order to prove that $\overset{-1}{f}(F)$ is μ-measurable, it is sufficient to show that $\overset{-1}{f}(F) \cap A$ is μ-measurable for every μ-integrable set $A \subset T$. Let then $F \subset E$ be a closed set and let $A \subset T$ be a μ-integrable set. From the condition 2 we deduce that there exists a μ-negligible set $N \subset A$ and a countable set $H \subset E$ such that $f(A - N) \subset \bar{H}$. Then, putting $A' = A - N$, we have

$$\overset{-1}{f}(F) \cap A' = \overset{-1}{f}(F \cap \bar{H}) \cap A'.$$

The closed set $F \cap \bar{H}$ contains a dense countable subset. From the preceding lemma we deduce that $\overset{-1}{f}(F \cap \bar{H})$ is μ-measurable; hence $\overset{-1}{f}(F \cap \bar{H}) \cap A'$ is μ-measurable, therefore $\overset{-1}{f}(F) \cap A = (\overset{-1}{f}(F) \cap A') \cup (\overset{-1}{f}(F) \cap N)$ is μ-measurable, consequently $\overset{-1}{f}(F)$ is μ-measurable.

If the condition 1 is verified for open spheres, it is also verified for closed spheres, since

$$\{x;\, d(x, x_0) \leqq a\} = \bigcap_{n=1}^{\infty} \left\{x;\, d(x, x_0) < a + \frac{1}{n}\right\}.$$

The proposition is completely proved.

Remark. In the condition 2 we can take only sets $A \in \mathscr{C}$, or only sets A with σ-finite measure.

For functions with values in a *normed* space we have the following characterization.

Proposition 12. *Let E be a normed space. A function $f\colon T \to E$ is μ-measurable if and only if the following two conditions are verified:*

1. *for every continuous linear functional $x' \in E'$, the scalar function $t \to \langle f(t), x'\rangle$ is μ-measurable;*

2. *for every μ-integrable set $A \subset T$, there exists a μ-negligible set $N \subset A$ and a countable set $H \subset E$ such that $f(A - N) \subset \bar{H}$.*

Suppose first that f is μ-measurable and let $x' \in E'$. If $G \subset R$ is open, then the set $G_1 = \overset{-1}{x'}(G)$ is open in E; hence $\overset{-1}{f}(G_1)$ is μ-measurable, therefore the function $x' \circ f = \langle f, x'\rangle$ is μ-measurable.

Conversely, suppose that the two conditions are verified. We shall show that for every closed sphere $S \subset E$, the set $\overset{-1}{f}(S)$ is μ-measurable and whence, by proposition 11, that f is μ-measurable.

Let $S_r(a)$ be a closed sphere with center $a \in E$ and radius r, and let $A \subset T$ be a μ-integrable set. From the condition 2 we deduce that there exists a μ-negligible set $N \subset A$ and a countable set $H \subset E$ such that $f(A - N) \subset \bar{H}$. Denote by V the closed vector space generated by $H \cup \{a\}$. Since V contains a dense countable subset, there exists a sequence (z_n') in the dual space V' of V such that

$$|x| = \sup_n \frac{|\langle x, z_n\rangle|}{|z_n|}, \quad \text{for every} \quad x \in V.$$

Then

$$(A - N) \cap \overset{-1}{f}(S_r(a)) = (A - N) \cap \bigcap_{n=1}^{\infty} \{t;\, |\langle f(t), z_n\rangle - \langle a, z_n\rangle| \leqq r\, |z_n|\}.$$

The functions $t \to |\langle f(t), z_n\rangle - \langle a, z_n\rangle|$ are μ-measurable, therefore the sets from the right side are μ-measurable, consequently the set of the left side is μ-measurable too. It follows that $\overset{-1}{f}(S_r(a))$ is μ-measurable whence the condition 2 of the proposition 11 is verified. From this proposition we deduce that f is μ-measurable.

Remark. In the condition 2 we can take only sets $A \in \mathscr{C}$ or only sets A with σ-finite measure.

6. SEQUENCES OF μ-MEASURABLE FUNCTIONS

Theorem 1 (Egorov). *Let E be a metrizable space and (f_n) a sequence of μ-measurable functions defined on T with values in E. If the sequence (f_n) converges μ-almost everywhere to a function $f: T \to E$, then:*

1. *the function f is μ-measurable;*

2. *for every μ-integrable set $A \subset T$ and every $\varepsilon > 0$, there exists a set $B \in \mathscr{S}(\mathscr{C})$ with $B \subset A$ and $\mu(A - B) < \varepsilon$, such that sequence (f_n) converges uniformly to f on B.*

Let d be a distance on E compatible with the topology of E. We shall prove first the second part. Let $A \subset T$ be a μ-integrable set and $\varepsilon > 0$. There exists a μ-negligible set $N \subset A$ such that $f_n(t) \to f(t)$ for every $t \in A' = A - N$ and a countable set $H \subset E$ such that $f_n(A') \subset \bar{H}$ for every n. We remark that the set

$$\{t;\, t \in A',\, d(f_p(t), f_q(t)) < \alpha\}$$

is μ-measurable for each pair (p, q) of indices and for every $\alpha > 0$, since it is the countable union of the sets of the form

$$\left\{t;\, t \in A',\, d(f_p(t), x) < \alpha - \frac{\alpha}{n}\right\} \cap \left\{t;\, t \in A',\, d(f_q(t), x) < \frac{\alpha}{n}\right\}$$

with $x \in H$ and $n \geqq 2$.

For every pair (n, r) of natural numbers, put

$$A_{n,r} = \bigcap_{p,q>n} \left\{t \in A';\, d(f_p(t), f_q(t)) < \frac{1}{r}\right\}.$$

The sets $A_{n,r}$ are μ-measurable and for each fixed r the sequence $(A_{n,r})$ is increasing and $A' = \bigcup_{n=1}^{\infty} A_{n,r}$, since the sequence (f_n) converges to f on A'. It follows that $\lim_{n\to\infty} \mu(A' - A_{n,r}) = 0$, consequently we can find a natural number n_r such that

$$\mu(A' - A_{n_r,r}) < \frac{\varepsilon}{2^{r+1}}.$$

The set $A_0 = \bigcap_{r=1}^{\infty} A_{n_r,r}$ is μ-measurable and we have $A_0 \subset A' \subset A$ and

$$\mu(A - A_0) = \mu(A' - A_0) = \mu\left(\bigcup_{r=1}^{\infty} (A' - A_{n_r,r})\right)$$

$$\leqq \sum_{r=1}^{\infty} \mu(A' - A_{n_r,r}) < \frac{\varepsilon}{2}.$$

For each r and each $t \in A_0$ we have $t \in A_{n_r,r}$ whence $d(f_p(t), f_q(t)) < \dfrac{1}{r}$ for $p > n_r$ and $q > n_r$. It follows that the sequence (f_n) converges uniformly on A_0 to f.

We can find a set $B \in \mathscr{S}$ with $B \subset A_0$ and $\mu(A_0 - B) < \frac{\varepsilon}{2}$. Then $B \subset A$, $\mu(A - B) < \varepsilon$ and (f_n) converges uniformly on B to f.

In addition, we have $f(B) \subset f(A') \subset \bar{H}$, since $f_n(A') \subset \bar{H}$ for each n and $f_n(t) \to f(t)$ for each $t \in A'$. Thus, the second part is proved. At the same time, we proved that f verifies the condition 2 of the definition of the measurable functions.

Since the sequence (f_n) converges uniformly on B to f, for every natural number r, there exists a number n_r such that for $p \geqq n_r$ and $t \in B$ we have $d(f_p(t), f(t)) \leqq \frac{1}{r}$.

For every $\alpha > 0$ and every $x \in E$ we have then

$$\{t \in B; d(f(t), x) \leqq \alpha\} = \bigcap_{r=1}^{\infty} \bigcap_{p \geqq n_r} \left\{t \in B; d(f_p(t), x) \leqq \alpha + \frac{1}{r}\right\},$$

i.e.

$$\overset{-1}{f}(S_\alpha(x)) \cap B = \bigcap_{r=1}^{\infty} \bigcap_{p \geqq n_r} \overset{-1}{f_p}(S_{\alpha+1/r}(x)) \cap B.$$

It follows that the set of the left hand side of the last equality is μ-measurable.

Using the second part of the theorem, for every μ-integrable set $A \subset T$ we find a sequence (B_n) of disjoint sets of $\mathscr{S}$, such that $A - \bigcup B_n$ is μ-negligible and (f_n) converges uniformly to f on each B_n. Namely, we take $B_1 \in \mathscr{S}$ with $B_1 \subset A$ and $\mu(A - B_1) < 1$ such that (f_n) converges uniformly on B_1. For $n \geqq 2$, we take $B_n \in \mathscr{S}$ with $B_n \subset A - \bigcup_{i<n} B_i$ and $\mu\left(A - \bigcup_{i \leqq n} B_i\right) < \frac{1}{n}$ such that (f_n) converges uniformly on B_n. Then the sets B_n are disjoint and

$$\mu\left(A - \bigcup_{n=1}^{\infty} B_n\right) \leqq \mu(A - B_n) < \frac{1}{n},$$

whence the set $N = A - \bigcup_{n=1}^{\infty} B_n$ is μ-negligible.

For every closed sphere $S \subset E$ and every n the set $\overset{-1}{f}(S) \cap B_n$ is μ-measurable. From the equality

$$\overset{-1}{f}(S) \cap A = \left[\bigcup_{n=1}^{\infty} \overset{-1}{f}(S) \cap B_n\right] \cup (\overset{-1}{f}(S) \cap N)$$

it follows that $\overset{-1}{f}(S) \cap A$ is μ-measurable, whence $\overset{-1}{f}(S)$ is μ-measurable. From the proposition 11 we deduce then that f is μ-measurable, and the theorem is completely proved.

Corollary 1. *Let E be a metrizable space and (f_n) a sequence of μ-measurable functions defined on T with values in E, and converging μ-almost everywhere to a function $f: T \to E$.*

Every μ-measurable set $A \subset T$ with σ-finite measure is the union of a μ-negligible set N and a sequence (A_n) of disjoint μ-integrable sets, such that f_n converges uniformly to f on each A_n.

Suppose first that A is μ-integrable. There exists a μ-integrable set $A_1 \in \mathscr{S}$ with $A_1 \subset A$ such that $\mu(A - A_1) \leqq 1$ and (f_n) converges uniformly to f on A_1. Then, by induction, for every $n \geqq 2$ we find a set $A_n \in \mathscr{S}$ with $A_n \subset A - \bigcup_{i<n} A_i$, such that $\mu\left(A - \bigcup_{i \leqq n} A_i\right) < \frac{1}{n}$ and (f_n) converges uniformly to f on A_n. The sets A_n are disjoint and the set $N = A - \bigcup_{n=1}^{\infty} A_n$ is μ-negligible since

$$\mu(N) \leqq \mu\left(A - \bigcup_{i \leqq n} A_n\right) \leqq \frac{1}{n}, \quad \text{for every } n.$$

If A is the union of a sequence (B_k) of μ-integrable sets, we can take the sets B_k disjoint. Each B_k is the union of a μ-negligible set N_k and a sequence (B_{kn}) of sets of $\mathscr{S}$, such that on each B_{kn} the sequence (f_n) converges uniformly to f. The set $N = \bigcup_{k=1}^{\infty} N_k$ is μ-negligible and $A - N = \bigcup_{k,n=1}^{\infty} B_{kn}$. We arrange then the double sequence (B_{kn}) into a sequence (A_n).

Corollary 2. *Let E be a metrizable space, (f_n) a sequence of μ-measurable functions defined on T with values in E and A a μ-measurable set such that the sequence (f_n) converges μ-almost everywhere on A.*

If $f: T \to E$ is a function equal μ-almost everywhere to the limit of (f_n) on A and constant on $T - A$, then f is μ-measurable.

Let $f(t) = \alpha \in E$ for $t \in T - A$. The functions g_n equal to f_n on A and equal to α on $T - A$ are μ-measurable and the sequence (g_n) converges μ-almost everywhere to f.

Corollary 3. *Let E be a metrizable space and $f: T \to E$ a function. If for every set $A \in \mathscr{C}$, there exists a sequence (g_n) of μ-measurable functions converging to f μ-almost everywhere on A, then f is μ-measurable.*

Let $A \in \mathscr{C}$. From the corollary 2 we deduce that the function f_A equal to f on A and to $\alpha \in E$ on $T - A$ is μ-measurable. There exists then a μ-negligible set $N \subset A$ and a countable set $H \subset E$ such that $f_A(A - N) \subset \bar{H}$; it follows that $f(A - N) \subset \bar{H}$, whence the condition 2 of the definition 4 is verified.

Let now $G \subset E$ be an open set. If $G = E$, then $\overset{-1}{f}(G) = T \in \mathfrak{T}(\mu)$. If $G \neq E$, then for every set $A \in \mathscr{C}$ we choose f_A such that $f_A(t) = \alpha \notin G$ for $t \in T - A$. Since f_A is μ-measurable, the set $\overset{-1}{f_A}(G) = \overset{-1}{f}(G) \cap A$ is μ-measurable. It follows that $\overset{-1}{f}(G)$ is μ-measurable, whence the condition 1 of the definition 4 is also verified.

In some cases the measurable functions can be approximated by measurable step functions.

Proposition 13. *If $f: T \to E$ is a μ-measurable function taking a countable set of values, then there exists a sequence (f_n) of μ-measurable step functions converging to f on T.*

Let $a_1, a_2, \ldots$ be the values of f. For each n the set $A_n = \overset{-1}{f}(a_n)$ is μ-measurable. The step function

$$f_n(t) = \begin{cases} a_i, & \text{for} \quad t \in A_i, \quad 1 \leqq i \leqq n, \\ a \in E, & \text{for} \quad t \in T - \bigcup_{i=1}^{n} A_i \end{cases}$$

is μ-measurable and the sequence (f_n) converges to f on T.

We shall show now that the measurable functions can be approximated uniformly by functions having countably many values.

Proposition 14. *Let E be a metrizable space and $f: T \to E$ a μ-measurable function. For every μ-measurable set $A \subset T$ with σ-finite measure there exists a μ-negligible set $N \subset A$ and a sequence (f_n) of μ-measurable functions—each of them taking a countable set of values—converging uniformly to f on $A - N$.*

If E is a normed space, we can choose the functions f_n such that $|f_n(t)| \leqq |f(t)|$ for every n and every $t \in T$.

Let d be a distance on E compatible with the topology of E. Let $A \subset T$ be a μ-measurable set with σ-finite measure. There exists a μ-negligible set $N \subset A$ and a countable set $H \subset E$ such that $f(A') \subset \overline{H}$ where $A' = A - N$. Put the elements of H in a sequence (a_n). For each n and p consider the closed sphere $S_{\frac{1}{n}}(a_p)$ with center a_p and radius $\frac{1}{n}$.

Then the set

$$A_{n,p} = A' \cap \overset{-1}{f}(S_{\frac{1}{n}}(a_p))$$

is μ-measurable. For fixed n we define by recurrence the disjoint μ-measurable sets $B_{n,p}$, taking $B_{n,1} = A_{n,1}$ and $B_{n,p} = A_{n,p} - \bigcup_{i<p} A_{n,i}$. We have $A' = \bigcup_{p=1}^{\infty} B_{n,p}$. The function

$$f_n(t) = \begin{cases} a_p, & \text{for} \quad t \in B_{n,p} \quad \text{and} \quad p = 1, 2, \ldots, \\ b \in E, & \text{for} \quad t \in T - A' \end{cases}$$

is μ-measurable, takes a countable set of values and

$$d(f(t), f_n(t)) < \frac{1}{n}, \quad \text{for} \quad t \in A',$$

whence the sequence (f_n) converges uniformly on A' to f.

Suppose now that E is a normed space. For each n and p put

$$\alpha_{n,p} = \inf |f(t)|, \quad \text{for} \quad t \in B_{n,p}.$$

We define now the function

$$f_n(t) = \begin{cases} a_p \dfrac{\alpha_{n,p}}{|a_p|}, & \text{for} \quad t \in B_{n,p} \quad \text{and} \quad p = 1, 2, \ldots, \\ 0, & \text{for} \quad t \in T - A' \end{cases}$$

$\left(\text{here we consider } a_p \dfrac{\alpha_{n,p}}{|a_p|} = 0 \text{ if } a_p = 0\right)$. We have then $|f_n(t)| \leqq |f(t)|$ for every $t \in T$. For $t \in B_{n,p}$ we have

$$|f_n(t) - f(t)| = \left| a_p \frac{\alpha_{n,p}}{|a_p|} - f(t) \right| \leqq |a_p - f(t)| + \left| a_p - a_p \frac{\alpha_{n,p}}{|a_p|} \right|$$

$$= |a_p - f(t)| + \big| |a_p| - \alpha_{n,p} \big| \leqq \frac{2}{n},$$

whence the sequence (f_n) converges uniformly on A' to f. Thus the proposition is completely proved.

Proposition 15. *Let E be a metrizable space and $f: T \to E$ a μ-measurable function. If the set $f(T)$ is relatively compact, then there exists a sequence (f_n) of μ-measurable step functions converging uniformly to f on T.*

If E is a normed space we can take the functions f_n such that $|f_n(t)| \leqq |f(t)|$ for every n and every $t \in T$.

Since $f(T)$ is compact, it can be covered by a finite number of spheres $S_1, \ldots, S_k$ of radius $\frac{1}{n}$. The sets $A_i = \overset{-1}{f}(S_i)$ are μ-measurable and their union is equal to T. Put $B_1 = A_1$ and $B_j = A_j - \bigcup_{i<j} A_i$ for $2 \leqq j \leqq k$.

The sets B_i are μ-measurable and disjoint, $B_i \subset A_i$ for every i and $\bigcup_{i=1}^{k} B_i = T$. Consider now the step function $f_n(t) = a_i \in S_i$ for $t \in B_i$, $1 \leqq i \leqq k$.

For every $t \in T$ we have

$$|f_n(t) - f(t)| \leqq \frac{2}{n},$$

whence the sequence (f_n) converges uniformly to f on T.

If E is a normed space, we prove as in proposition 14 that we can take $|f_n(t)| \leqq |f(t)|$ for every n and every $t \in T$.

Remark. This proposition is valid, in particular, for bounded scalar functions.

Theorem 2. *Let E be a metrizable space and $f: T \to E$ a μ-measurable function. For every μ-measurable set $A \subset T$ with σ-finite measure there exists a μ-negligible set $N \subset A$ and a sequence (g_n) of $\mathscr{S}(\mathscr{C})$-step functions converging to f on $A - N$.*

If E is a normed space, we can choose the functions g_n such that $|g_n(t)| \leqq |f(t)|$ for every n and every $t \in T$.

a) Let $A \subset T$ be a μ-measurable set of σ-finite measure. Let (f_n) be a sequence of μ-measurable functions having a countable set of values and converging uniformly to f on a set $A' = A - N$, where N is μ-negligible. From the proof of the proposition 14 we deduce that we can choose the functions f_n such that

$$d(f_n(t), f(t)) < \frac{1}{n}, \quad \text{for every} \quad n \quad \text{and} \quad t \in A'.$$

From the proposition 13 it follows that for each n there exists a sequence $(f_{n,p})_{1 \leqq p < \infty}$ of μ-measurable step functions converging to f_n on T.

b) Let A'' be a μ-integrable set with $A'' \subset A'$. We shall show that for every $\varepsilon > 0$ we can find a μ-integrable set $B \subset A''$ with $\mu(A'' - B) < \varepsilon$ such that for each n, the sequence $(f_{n,p})_{1 \leqq p < \infty}$ converges uniformly to f_n on B. In fact, using the theorem of Egorov, we can find a μ-integrable set $A_n \subset A''$ with $A_n \in \mathscr{S}$ and $\mu(A'' - A_n) < \frac{\varepsilon}{2^n}$ such that the sequence $(f_{n,p})$ converges uniformly to f_n on A_n. The set $B = \bigcap_{n=1}^{\infty} A_n$ is μ-integrable, belongs to $\mathscr{S}$ and

$$\mu(A'' - B) \leqq \sum_{n=1}^{\infty} \mu(A'' - A_n) < \varepsilon$$

and for each n, the sequence $(f_{n,p})_{1 \leqq p < \infty}$ converges uniformly to f_n on B.

c) Let (A_i) be a sequence of disjoint μ-integrable sets with union equal to A'. For each A_i we can find a sequence $(B_{i,j})$ of μ-integrable sets of $\mathscr{S}$ such that the set $N_i = A_i - \bigcup_{j=1}^{\infty} B_{i,j}$ is μ-negligible and on each B_{ij}, the sequence $(f_{n,p})_{1 \leqq p < \infty}$ converges uniformly to f_n. In fact from b) we deduce that for every i and j we can find a μ-integrable set $B_{i,j} \subset A_i$ with $B_{i,j} \in \mathscr{S}$ and

$$\mu(A_i - B_{i,j}) < \frac{1}{j}$$

such that on $B_{i,j}$, each sequence $(f_{n,p})_{1 \leqq p < \infty}$ converges uniformly to f_n. For every i put $N_i = A_i - \bigcup_{j=1}^{\infty} B_{i,j}$. We have then

$$\mu(N_i) = \mu(A_i - \bigcup_j B_{i,j}) \leqq \mu(A_i - B_{i,j}) \leqq \frac{1}{j},$$

for every j, whence $\mu(N_i) = 0$, i.e. N_i is μ-negligible.

d) For each k the set

$$B_k = \bigcup_{i,j \leqq k} B_{i,j}$$

is μ-integrable, the sequence (B_k) is increasing, and on each B_k, each sequence $(f_{n,p})_{1 \leqq p < \infty}$ converges uniformly to f_n. The set

$$N' = A - \bigcup_{k=1}^{\infty} B_k = N \cup \left(\bigcup_{k=1}^{\infty} N_k \right)$$

is μ-negligible.

For each n we find an index p_n such that

$$d(f_{n,p_n}(t), f_n(t)) < \frac{1}{n}, \quad \text{for} \quad t \in B_n.$$

Then

$$d(f_{n,p_n}(t), f(t)) \leqq \frac{2}{n}, \quad \text{for} \quad t \in B_n.$$

It follows that

$$\lim_{n \to \infty} f_{n,p_n}(t) = f(t), \quad \text{for} \quad t \in \bigcup_{n=1}^{\infty} B_n.$$

For each n we take a $\mathscr{S}$-step function g_n equal to f_{n,p_n} μ-almost everywhere. The sequence (g_n) converges to f μ-almost everywhere on A.

If E is a normed space, we can take $|f_n(t)| \leqq |f(t)|$ for every n and $t \in T$. We can take also the sequences $(f_{n,p})$ such that $|f_{n,p}(t)| \leqq |f_n(t)|$ for every p, n and $t \in T$. It follows that $|f_{n,p_n}(t)| \leqq |f(t)|$ for every n and $t \in T$. We can take then $|g_n(t)| \leqq |f(t)|$ for every n and $t \in T$. The theorem is completely proved.

Corollary. *Let E be a normed space. A function $f: T \to E$ is μ-measurable if and only if $f\varphi_A$ is μ-measurable for every set $A \in \mathscr{C}$.*

We use the proposition 10, corollary 3 of the theorem 1 and theorem 2.

Theorem 3. *Let (E_n) be a sequence of metrizable spaces, $E = \prod_n E_n$ their cartesian product and F a metrizable space. For each n let $f_n: T \to E_n$ be a μ-measurable function and let $f = (f_n): T \to E$ be the function defined by the equality*

$$f(t) = (f_n(t)) \in E, \quad \textit{for} \quad t \in T.$$

For every continuous mapping $u: E \to F$, the function $u \circ f: T \to F$ is μ-measurable.

Let $A \subset T$ be a μ-integrable set. For each n there exists a μ-negligible set $N_n \subset A$ and a sequence $(f_{n,p})_{1 \leqq p < \infty}$ of μ-measurable step functions converging to f_n on $A - N_n$. The set $N = \bigcup_{n=1}^{\infty} N_n$ is μ-negligible, and for every $t \in A - N$ and every n we have

$$\lim_{p \to \infty} f_{n,p}(t) = f_n(t).$$

For each p, the function $\boldsymbol{f}_p = (f_{n,p})$: $T \to E$ has a countable set of values and is μ-measurable. The preceding equality becomes

$$\lim_{p\to\infty} f_p(t) = f(t), \quad \text{for} \quad t \in A - N.$$

It follows that

$$\lim_{p\to\infty} u(f_p(t)) = u(f(t)), \quad \text{for} \quad t \in A - N.$$

The functions $u \circ \boldsymbol{f}_p$ are μ-measurable and have a countable set of values. From the corollary 2 of the theorem of Egorov, it follows that $u \circ f$ is μ-measurable.

Corollary 1. *Let E be a normed space, $\boldsymbol{f}, \boldsymbol{g}$: $T \to E$ two measurable functions and α a scalar. Then the functions $\boldsymbol{f} + \boldsymbol{g}$ and $\alpha\boldsymbol{f}$ are μ-measurable. If E is an algebra, then the function $\boldsymbol{fg}$ is μ-measurable.*

The set of the μ-measurable functions $\boldsymbol{f}$: $T \to E$ is a vector space (and an algebra, in case E is an algebra).

Corollary 2. *Let E be a normed space. If $\boldsymbol{f}$: $T \to E$ is a μ-measurable function, then the function $|\boldsymbol{f}|$ is μ-measurable.*

Corollary 3. *Let E, F be two normed spaces. If U: $T \to \mathscr{L}(E, F)$ and $\boldsymbol{f}$: $T \to E$ are μ-measurable then the function $t \to U(t)\boldsymbol{f}(t)$ (with values in F) is μ-measurable.*

In particular:

Corollary 4. *If $\boldsymbol{f}$: $T \to E$ and $\boldsymbol{g}$: $T \to E'$ are μ-measurable, then the scalar function $t \to \langle \boldsymbol{f}(t), \boldsymbol{g}(t) \rangle$ is μ-measurable.*

Corollary 5. *If $\boldsymbol{f}$: $T \to E$ and φ: $T \to R$ are μ-measurable, then the function $\boldsymbol{f}\varphi$ is μ-measurable.*

7. SIMPLY MEASURABLE OPERATOR FUNCTIONS

Let E, F be two Banach spaces and $\mathscr{L}^*(E, F)$ the vector space of the linear mappings of E into F. For every $G \in \mathscr{L}^*(E, F)$ we put

$$|G| = \sup_{\substack{|x| \leqq 1 \\ x \in E}} |Gx| \leqq \infty.$$

Definition 5. We *say that a function U: $T \to \mathscr{L}^*(E, F)$ is simply μ-measurable if for every $x \in E$, the function $t \to U(t)\,x$ (with values in F) is μ-measurable.*

If $\boldsymbol{m}$ is a measure with finite variation we say that U is simply $\boldsymbol{m}$-measurable if U is simply $|\boldsymbol{m}|$-measurable.

If E is the space of the scalars, then $\mathscr{L}^*(E, F) = F$; in this case U is simply μ-measurable if and only if U is μ-measurable.

Every μ-measurable function $U: T \to \mathscr{L}(E, F)$ is also simply μ-measurable (corollary 3 of the theorem 3) but the converse is not generally true.

It is easy to verify that if $U, V: T \to \mathscr{L}^*(E, F)$ are two simply μ-measurable functions, then $U + V$ and αU are simply μ-measurable.

Proposition 16. *If $U: T \to \mathscr{L}^*(E, F)$ is simply μ-measurable and if $f: T \to E$ is μ-measurable, then the function $t \to U(t) f(t)$ is μ-measurable.*

Let $A \in \mathscr{C}$. Since f is μ-measurable, there exists a sequence (f_n) of μ-measurable step functions converging to f on A (theorem 2). Then the sequence (Uf_n) converges to Uf on A and for every n the function Uf_n is μ-measurable, therefore Uf is μ-measurable (corollary 3 of the theorem 1).

If $U: T \to \mathscr{L}(E, F)$ is μ-measurable, then $|U|$ is μ-measurable (corollary 2 of the theorem 3). Sometimes $|U|$ is μ-measurable even if U is simply μ-measurable.

Proposition 17. *If $U: T \to \mathscr{L}^*(E, F)$ is simply μ-measurable and if E is of countable type, then $|U|$ is μ-measurable.*

In fact, if (x_n) is a sequence dense in E, then for every n the function $t \to U(t)\, x_n$ is μ-measurable, therefore the function $t \to |U(t)\, x_n|$ is μ-measurable. Then the function $t \to \dfrac{|U(t)\, x_n|}{|x_n|}$ is also μ-measurable and we have

$$|U(t)| = \sup_n \frac{|U(t)\, x_n|}{|x_n|}, \quad \text{for every} \quad t \in T,$$

therefore $|U|$ is μ-measurable (proposition 6).

Remark. More generally: if U is simply μ-measurable and if for every $A \in \mathscr{C}$ there exists a countable set $H \subset E$ such that

$$|U(t)| = \sup_{x \in H} \frac{|U(t)\, x|}{|x|}$$

μ-almost everywhere on A, then $|U|$ is μ-measurable.

In certain cases the simply measurable functions are measurable.

Proposition 18. *A function $U: T \to \mathscr{L}(E, F)$ is μ-measurable if and only if:*

1. *U is simply μ-measurable;*

2. *for every $A \in \mathscr{C}$ there exists a μ-negligible set $N \subset A$ and a countable set $H \subset \mathscr{L}(E, F)$ such that $U(A - N) \subset \overline{H}$.*

In fact if U is μ-measurable, then U is simply μ-measurable and from the proposition 11 we deduce that the condition 2 is also fulfilled.

Conversely assume conditions 1 and 2. To prove that U is μ-measurable, it is sufficient to show that for every closed sphere $S \subset \mathscr{L}(E, F)$ the set $\overset{-1}{U}(S)$ is μ-measurable (proposition 11).

Let S be a closed sphere of $\mathscr{L}(E, F)$, with centre $a \in \mathscr{L}(E, F)$ and radius $r > 0$ and let $A \in \mathscr{C}$. Let $N \subset A$ be a μ-negligible set and $H \subset \mathscr{L}(E, F)$ a countable set such that $U(A - N) \subset \bar{H}$. Let $g: T \to \mathscr{L}(E, F)$ be a function equal to U on $T - N$ such that $g(A) \subset \bar{H}$ (for example we take $b \in H$ and put $g(t) = b$ for $t \in N$). The set $H \cup \{a\}$ is countable and can be arranged in a sequence $a_1, a_2, \ldots, a_n, \ldots$ For each a_n and for each m there exists $x_{n,m} \in E$ with $|x_{n,m}| = 1$ and $|a_n x_{n,m}| > |a_n| - \frac{1}{m}$. Then $|a_n| = \sup_m |a_n x_{n,m}|$.

Let V be the closed vector subspace of $\mathscr{L}(E, F)$ generated by $H \cup \{a\}$. For each $v \in V$ we have

$$|v| = \sup_{n,m} |v x_{n,m}|.$$

For each n and m the function $t \to g(t)\, x_{n,m} - a x_{n,m}$ is μ-measurable (condition 1). Then the function $t \to |g(t)\, x_{n,m} - a x_{n,m}|$ is μ-measurable, therefore the set

$$A_{n,m} = \{t;\, |g(t)\, x_{n,m} - a x_{n,m}| \leqq r\, |x_{n,m}|\}$$

is μ-measurable. Since

$$|g(t) - a| = \sup_{n,m} |(g(t) - a)\, x_{n,m}|, \quad \text{for} \quad t \in A,$$

we deduce that

$$A \cap \overset{-1}{g}(S) = \bigcap_{n,m=1}^{\infty} (A_{n,m} \cap A),$$

therefore $A \cap \overset{-1}{g}(S)$ is μ-measurable. Then $A \cap \overset{-1}{U}(S)$ is also μ-measurable, therefore $\overset{-1}{U}(S)$ is μ-measurable, and the proposition is proved.

Remark. Instead of $A \in \mathscr{C}$ we can take in the condition 2 μ-integrable sets A, or μ-measurable sets A with σ-finite measure.

Corollary. *If $U: T \to \mathscr{L}(E, F)$ is simply μ-measurable and if there exists a countable set $H \subset \mathscr{L}(E, F)$ such that $U(t) \in \bar{H}$ μ-almost everywhere (in particular, if $\mathscr{L}(E, F)$ is of countable type), then U is μ-measurable.*

8. WEAKLY MEASURABLE OPERATOR FUNCTIONS

Let E, F be two Banach spaces and $Z \subset F'$ a *norming* subspace, i.e. such that

$$|y| = \sup_{z \in Z} \frac{|\langle y, z \rangle|}{|z|}, \quad \text{for every} \quad y \in F.$$

Then we can plunge F in Z' isometrically. We can take, for example, $Z = F'$; or if F is the conjugate space of a space S, we can take $Z = S \subset S'' = F'$.

Definition 6. *We say that a function $U: T \to \mathscr{L}^*(E, F)$ is Z-weakly μ-measurable, if for every $x \in E$ and every $z \in Z$, the function $t \to \langle U(t)x, z \rangle$ is μ-measurable.*

To say that U is Z-weakly μ-measurable means that for every $z \in Z$, the function $U \circ z: T \to \mathscr{L}(E, C)$ is simply μ-measurable.

We say that a function $\boldsymbol{f}: T \to F$ is Z-weakly μ-measurable if, considered with values in $\mathscr{L}(R, F)$, it is Z-weakly μ-measurable, i.e. if for every $z \in Z$, the function $\langle \boldsymbol{f}, z \rangle$ is μ-measurable.

Then, to say that $U: T \to \mathscr{L}^*(E, F)$ is Z-weakly μ-measurable means that for every $x \in E$ the function $t \to U(t)x$ is Z-weakly μ-measurable.

If F is the space of the scalars, to say that a function $U: T \to \mathscr{L}(E, C) = E'$ is E-weakly μ-measurable means that U is simply μ-measurable, i.e. that for every $x \in E$ the function Ux is μ-measurable.

If $U, V: T \to \mathscr{L}^*(E, F)$ are Z-weakly μ-measurable then $U + V$ and αU are Z-weakly μ-measurable.

Proposition 19. *If $U: T \to \mathscr{L}^*(E, F)$ is Z-weakly μ-measurable and if the functions $\boldsymbol{f}: T \to E$ and $\boldsymbol{h}: T \to Z$ are μ-measurable then the function $\langle U\boldsymbol{f}, \boldsymbol{h} \rangle$ is μ-measurable.*

Let $A \in \mathscr{C}$. Since $\boldsymbol{f}$ and $\boldsymbol{h}$ are μ-measurable, there exist two sequences of μ-measurable step functions $(\boldsymbol{f}_n)$ of $\mathscr{E}_E(\mu)$ and $(\boldsymbol{h}_n)$ of $\mathscr{E}_Z(\mu)$ converging respectively to $\boldsymbol{f}$ and $\boldsymbol{h}$ on A. The functions $\langle U\boldsymbol{f}_n, \boldsymbol{h}_n \rangle$ are μ-measurable and converge to $\langle U\boldsymbol{f}, \boldsymbol{h} \rangle$ on A, therefore $\langle U\boldsymbol{f}, \boldsymbol{h} \rangle$ is μ-measurable (corollary 3 of the theorem 1).

If U is weakly measurable and $\boldsymbol{f}$ is measurable it does not follow that the functions $U\boldsymbol{f}$ and $|U\boldsymbol{f}|$ are measurable. In certain cases these functions are also measurable. We consider first a particular case.

Proposition 20. *If $\boldsymbol{h}: T \to F$ is Z-weakly μ-measurable and if there exists a countable norming set $S \subset Z$, then the function $|\boldsymbol{h}|$ is μ-measurable.*

In fact, for every $z \in S$, the function $\langle \boldsymbol{h}, z \rangle$ is μ-measurable, therefore $|\langle \boldsymbol{h}, z \rangle|$ is μ-measurable, consequently $\dfrac{|\langle \boldsymbol{h}, z \rangle|}{|z|}$ is μ-measurable. Since

$$|\boldsymbol{h}(t)| = \sup_{z \in S} \frac{|\langle \boldsymbol{h}(t), z \rangle|}{|z|}, \quad \text{for every} \quad t \in T$$

and since S is countable, we deduce that $|\boldsymbol{h}|$ is μ-measurable.

Remark. More generally: if $\boldsymbol{h}$: $T \to F$ is Z-weakly μ-measurable and if for every $A \in \mathscr{C}$ there exists a countable set $S \subset Z$ such that

$$|\boldsymbol{h}(t)| = \sup_{z \in S} \frac{|\langle \boldsymbol{h}(t), z \rangle|}{|z|}$$

μ-almost everywhere on A, then $|\boldsymbol{h}|$ is μ-measurable.

Proposition 21. *If U: $T \to \mathscr{L}^*(E, F)$ is Z-weakly μ-measurable and $\boldsymbol{f}$: $T \to E$ is μ-measurable and if there exists a countable norming subset $S \subset Z$, then the function $t \to |U(t)\boldsymbol{f}(t)|$ is μ-measurable.*

We apply the proposition 20 to the function $\boldsymbol{h} = U\boldsymbol{f}$.

Remark. There exists a countable norming subset $S \subset Z$ in each of the following cases:

1. F is the conjugate space of a Banach space G of countable type and $Z = G$; in this case we can take $S = Z$.

2. F' is of countable type and $Z = F'$; in this case we take $S = Z$ (we remark that in this case F is also of countable type).

3. F is of countable type and $Z = F'$; in this case, if (x_n) is a sequence dense in F, and if for each n we take $z_n \in F'$ with $|z_n| = 1$ and $\langle x_n, z_n \rangle = |x_n|$, then (z_n) is a norming sequence in Z.

In this last case we have more:

Proposition 22. *If U: $T \to \mathscr{L}^*(E, F)$ is Z-weakly μ-measurable and if for every $x \in E$ there exists a countable set $H \subset F$ such that $U(t)x \in \bar{H}$ μ-almost everywhere (in particular if F is of countable type), then U is simply μ-measurable.*

In fact, for every $x \in E$, the function $\boldsymbol{f} = Ux$: $T \to F$ is Z-weakly μ-measurable.

If we consider $F \subset Z' = \mathscr{L}(Z, C)$, then the function $\boldsymbol{f}$: $T \to \mathscr{L}(Z, C)$ is simply μ-measurable. If $H \subset F$ is a countable set such that $\boldsymbol{f}(t) \in \bar{H}$ μ-almost everywhere, then $H \subset \mathscr{L}(Z, C)$; according to the corollary of the proposition 18, the function $\boldsymbol{f}$ is μ-measurable, therefore U is simply μ-measurable.

Corollary. *If F is of countable type, then every Z-weakly μ-measurable function $\boldsymbol{f}$: $T \to F$ is μ-measurable.*

In some cases the function $|U|$ is μ-measurable.

Proposition 23. *If U: $T \to \mathscr{L}^*(E, F)$ is Z-weakly μ-measurable, if E is of countable type and if there exists a countable norming subset $S \subset Z$, then the function $|U|$ is μ-measurable.*

If (x_n) is a sequence dense in E, then

$$|U(t)| = \sup_n \frac{|U(t)\, x_n|}{|x_n|}, \quad \text{for} \quad t \in T.$$

Since every function $t \to \frac{|U(t)x_n|}{|x_n|}$ is μ-measurable (proposition 21), it follows that $|U|$ is μ-measurable.

Remark. Other sufficient conditions for $|U|$ to be μ-measurable are given in proposition 5, § 11.

Proposition 24. *If $U: T \to \mathscr{L}(E, F)$ is Z-weakly μ-measurable and if there exists a countable set $H \subset \mathscr{L}(E, F)$ such that $U(t) \in \bar{H}$ μ-almost everywhere (in particular if $\mathscr{L}(E, F)$ is of countable type), then U is μ-measurable.*

Let $x \in E$. The function $f = Ux$ is Z-weakly μ-measurable, Hx is a countable subset of F and $f(t) \in \overline{Hx}$ μ-almost everywhere, therefore f is μ-measurable, consequently U is simply μ-measurable. From the corollary of the proposition 18 we deduce that U is μ-measurable.

§ 7. INTEGRATION OF STEP FUNCTIONS

1. DEFINITION AND PROPERTIES

Let $\mathscr{C}$ be a *clan* of subsets of T, X a *vector space* and $\boldsymbol{m}: \mathscr{C} \to X$ an *additive* set function.

In the next sections we shall suppose that X is a Banach space and that $\boldsymbol{m}$ is countably additive and with finite variation, but in this section, devoted to the integration of the step functions, these conditions are not needed.

Let E and F be two vector spaces and let $(u, v) \to uv$ be a *bilinear* mapping of $X \times E$ into F. Then we can integrate with respect to $\boldsymbol{m}$ step functions $f: T \to E$, and the integral $\int f\, d\boldsymbol{m}$ belongs to F.

Examples.

1. Denote by $\mathscr{L}^*(E, F)$ the space of the linear mappings $U: E \to F$. We can take $X \subset \mathscr{L}^*(E, F)$ and the natural bilinear mapping $(u, v) \to uv$ with $u \in X$ and $v \in E$. The general situation of a bilinear mapping uv of $X \times E$ into F can be always reduced to this case, identifying an element $u \in X$ with the linear mapping $v \to uv$ of E into F and then $X \subset \mathscr{L}^*(E, F)$.

It follows that we can integrate with respect to an additive operator valued set function $\boldsymbol{m}: \mathscr{C} \to \mathscr{L}^*(E, F)$ step functions $f: T \to E$, and the integral $\int f\, d\boldsymbol{m}$ belongs to F.

2. We can take $E \subset \mathscr{L}^*(X, F)$ and the natural mapping $(v, u) \to vu$ with $v \in E$ and $u \in X$. The general situation can be always reduced to this case, identifying an element $v \in E$ with the linear mapping $u \to uv$ of X into F and then $E \subset \mathscr{L}^*(X, F)$.

It follows that we can integrate with respect to an additive set function $\boldsymbol{m}: \mathscr{C} \to X$ operator valued step functions $f: T \to \mathscr{L}^*(X, F)$ and the integral belongs to F.

3. If we identify an element $x \in X$ with the linear mapping $\alpha \to \alpha x$ of R into X, i.e. if we consider $X = \mathscr{L}^*(R, X)$ then we can integrate with respect to $\boldsymbol{m}: \mathscr{C} \to X$, *scalar* step functions $\varphi: T \to R$ and the integral belongs to X.

If X is a complex vector space, we can take C instead of R.

4. If we identify an element $x \in X$ with the linear functional $x^* \to \langle x, x^* \rangle$ defined on the algebraic conjugate X^* of X, i.e. if we consider $X \subset X^{**} = \mathscr{L}^*(X^*, C)$ then we can integrate with respect to $\boldsymbol{m}: \mathscr{C} \to X$ step functions $f: T \to X^*$ and the integral is a *scalar*.

5. If $X = C$, then for every complex vector space E we can consider $C \subset \mathscr{L}^*(E, E)$ identifying a scalar α with the linear mapping $x \to \alpha\, x$ of E into E. It follows that we can integrate with respect to a *scalar* additive set function $\boldsymbol{m}$ step functions f with values in an arbitrary complex vector space E and the integral $\int f\, d\boldsymbol{m}$ belongs to E. In this example, we can consider R instead of C.

In the sequel we shall assume that the vector spaces X, E and F and the bilinear mapping $(u, v) \to uv$ of $X \times E$ into F are chosen. For $u \in X$ and $v \in E$ we shall write also vu instead of uv.

The $\mathscr{C}$-step functions will be called, simply, step functions and the space $\mathscr{E}_E(\mathscr{C})$ of the $\mathscr{C}$-step functions $f: T \to E$ will be denoted by $\mathscr{E}_E$.

Proposition 1. *If* $\sum_{i=1}^{n} \varphi_{A_i} x_i = 0$, *where* $A_i \in \mathscr{C}$ *and* $x_i \in E$, *then*

$$\sum_{i=1}^{n} \boldsymbol{m}(A_i)\, x_i = 0.$$

If $A_i = \emptyset$, then $\boldsymbol{m}(A_i) = 0$. Without loss of generality we shall suppose that the sets A_i are nonvoid, putting aside, if necessary, the void sets.

According to lemma 1, § 6, there exists a finite family $(B_j)_{j \in J}$ of disjoint sets of $\mathscr{C}$ such that each A_i is the union of a certain number of sets B_j. We can suppose that the sets B_j are nonvoid, putting aside, if necessary, those of them which are void.

For each i we denote by J_i the set of the indices $j \in J$ for which we have $B_j \subset A_i$. We have then $A_i = \bigcup_{j \in J_i} B_j$, therefore

$$\varphi_{A_i} = \sum_{j \in J_i} \varphi_{B_j} = \sum_{j \in J} \alpha_{ij} \varphi_{B_j}$$

where $\alpha_{ij} = 1$ if $j \in J_i$ and $\alpha_{ij} = 0$ if $j \notin J_i$. It follows that

$$0 = \sum_i \varphi_{A_i} x_i = \sum_i \Big(\sum_j \alpha_{ij} \varphi_{B_j} \Big) x_i = \sum_j \Big(\sum_i x_i \alpha_{ij} \Big) \varphi_{B_j},$$

therefore $\sum_i x_i \alpha_{ij} = 0$ for each j. We deduce then that

$$\sum_i \boldsymbol{m}(A_i)\, x_i = \sum_i \Big(\sum_j \alpha_{ij} \boldsymbol{m}(B_j) \Big) x_i = \sum_j \Big(\sum_i x_i \alpha_{ij} \Big) \boldsymbol{m}(B_j) = 0.$$

Corollary. *If* $\sum_{i=1}^{n} \varphi_{A_i} x_i = \sum_{j=1}^{m} \varphi_{B_j} y_j$, *where* A_i *and* B_j *are sets of* $\mathscr{C}$ *and* x_i, y_j *are elements of* E, *then*

$$\sum_{i=1}^{n} \boldsymbol{m}(A_i)\, x_i = \sum_{j=1}^{m} \boldsymbol{m}(B_j)\, y_j .$$

Definition 1. *For every step function* $\boldsymbol{f} = \sum_{i=1}^{n} \varphi_{A_i} x_i$, *where* $A_i \in \mathscr{C}$ *and* $x_i \in E$, *we shall call integral of* $\boldsymbol{f}$ *with respect to* $\boldsymbol{m}$ *the element of* F, *denoted by* $\int \boldsymbol{f}\, d\boldsymbol{m}$, *and defined by the equality*

$$\int \boldsymbol{f}\, d\boldsymbol{m} = \sum_{i=1}^{n} \boldsymbol{m}(A_i)\, x_i .$$

From the preceding corollary we deduce that the integral $\int \boldsymbol{f}\, d\boldsymbol{m}$ depends only on $\boldsymbol{f}$, and is independent on the particularly way in which $\boldsymbol{f}$ is written as a step function.

According to this definition, we have

$$\int \varphi_A \, d\boldsymbol{m} = \boldsymbol{m}(A) \quad \text{for every} \quad A \in \mathscr{C}.$$

The integral $\int \boldsymbol{f}\, d\boldsymbol{m}$ will also be denoted by $\int \boldsymbol{f}(t)\, d\boldsymbol{m}$, or $\int \boldsymbol{f}(t)\, d\boldsymbol{m}(t)$.

If $\boldsymbol{f} = \sum \varphi_{A_i} x_i$ is a step function with $A_i \in \mathscr{C}$ and $x_i \in E$, and if $A \in \mathfrak{T}(\mathscr{C})$ (i.e. $A \cap B \in \mathscr{C}$ for every $B \in \mathscr{C}$), then $\boldsymbol{f}\varphi_A$ is again a step function of $\mathscr{E}_E(\mathscr{C})$:

$$\boldsymbol{f}\varphi_A = \sum \varphi_{A_i \cap A} x_i .$$

We shall write, in this case,

$$\int_A \boldsymbol{f}\, d\boldsymbol{m} = \int \varphi_A \boldsymbol{f}\, d\boldsymbol{m}.$$

The following properties are easily derived from the above definition:

1. *The mapping* $\boldsymbol{f} \to \int \boldsymbol{f}\, d\boldsymbol{m}$ *of* $\mathscr{E}_E(\mathscr{C})$ *into* F *is linear:*

$$\int (\alpha \boldsymbol{f} + \beta \boldsymbol{g})\, d\boldsymbol{m} = \alpha \int \boldsymbol{f}\, d\boldsymbol{m} + \beta \int \boldsymbol{g}\, d\boldsymbol{m}.$$

In particular:

2. *If* $\boldsymbol{f} \in \mathscr{E}_E(\mathscr{C})$ *and if* A, B *are disjoint sets of* $\mathfrak{T}(\mathscr{C})$, *then*

$$\int_{A \cup B} \boldsymbol{f}\, d\boldsymbol{m} = \int_A \boldsymbol{f}\, d\boldsymbol{m} + \int_B \boldsymbol{f}\, d\boldsymbol{m}.$$

3. *For every step function* $\boldsymbol{f} \in \mathscr{E}_E(\mathscr{C})$ *the mapping* $\boldsymbol{m} \to \int \boldsymbol{f}\, d\boldsymbol{m}$ *is linear: if* $\boldsymbol{m}$ *and* $\boldsymbol{n}$ *are additive set functions on* $\mathscr{C}$ *with values in* X *and if* α, β *are scalars, then*

$$\int \boldsymbol{f}\, d(\alpha \boldsymbol{m} + \beta \boldsymbol{n}) = \alpha \int \boldsymbol{f}\, d\boldsymbol{m} + \beta \int \boldsymbol{f}\, d\boldsymbol{n}.$$

4. *If φ is a scalar step function of $\mathscr{E}_C(\mathscr{C})$ and $x \in E$, then $\varphi x \in \mathscr{E}_E(\mathscr{C})$ and*

$$\int \varphi x \, d\boldsymbol{m} = x \int \varphi \, d\boldsymbol{m}.$$

The integral of the *scalar* step functions, with respect to an additive *scalar* set function μ has additional properties.

5. *If $U: E \to F$ is a linear mapping and if $\boldsymbol{f} \in \mathscr{E}_E(\mathscr{C})$ then $U \circ \boldsymbol{f} \in \mathscr{E}_F(\mathscr{C})$ and*

$$U \int \boldsymbol{f} \, d\mu = \int U \circ \boldsymbol{f} \, d\mu.$$

6. *If $\mu \geqq 0$, then the mapping $\varphi \to \int \varphi \, d\mu$ of $\mathscr{E}(\mathscr{C})$ in R is positive, i.e. if $\varphi \geqq 0$ then $\int \varphi \, d\mu \geqq 0$.*

7. *If $\mu \geqq 0$, then the mapping $\varphi \to \int \varphi \, d\mu$ of $\mathscr{E}(\mathscr{C})$ in R is increasing, i.e. if $\varphi_1 \leqq \varphi_2$ then*

$$\int \varphi_1 \, d\mu \leqq \int \varphi_2 \, d\mu.$$

8. *If $\mu \geqq 0$ and $\varphi \geqq 0$, and if $A \subset B$ are sets of $\mathfrak{T}(\mathscr{C})$, then*

$$\int_A \varphi \, d\mu \leqq \int_B \varphi \, d\mu.$$

9. *If μ and ν are real additive set functions defined on $\mathscr{C}$ and if $\mu \leqq \nu$, then for every function $\varphi \geqq 0$ of $\mathscr{E}(\mathscr{C})$ we have*

$$\int \varphi \, d\mu \leqq \int \varphi \, d\nu.$$

If X, E and F are normed spaces, we can consider the *semi-variation* $\tilde{\boldsymbol{m}}$ of $\boldsymbol{m}$.

10. *Suppose that X, E and F are normed spaces and that $X \subset \mathscr{L}(E, F)$. Then for every set $A \subset T$ we have*

$$\tilde{\boldsymbol{m}}(A) = \sup \left| \int \boldsymbol{f} \, d\boldsymbol{m} \right| \leqq \infty$$

where the supremum is taken for all step functions $\boldsymbol{f} = \sum \varphi_{A_i} x_i$ of $\mathscr{E}_E(\mathscr{C}, A)$ with $\|\boldsymbol{f}\| \leqq 1$.

In fact every step function $\boldsymbol{f} = \sum \varphi_{A_i} x_i$ of $\mathscr{E}_E(\mathscr{C})$ with $\|\boldsymbol{f}\| \leqq 1$ can be written in the form $\sum \varphi_{B_j} y_j$ with B_j disjoint sets of $\mathscr{C}$ contained in A and $|y_j| \leqq 1$.

11. *If X, E and F are normed spaces such that $X \subset \mathscr{L}(E, F)$, then for every set $A \subset T$ and for every step function $\boldsymbol{f} \in \mathscr{E}_E(\mathscr{C}, A)$ we have*

$$\left| \int \boldsymbol{f} \, d\boldsymbol{m} \right| \leqq \|\boldsymbol{f}\| \, \tilde{\boldsymbol{m}}(A).$$

2. CONVERGENCE IN MEAN ON THE SPACE $\mathscr{E}_E(\mathscr{C})$

Let $\mathscr{C}$ be a *clan*, X a *Banach* space and $\boldsymbol{m}: \mathscr{C} \to X$ an *additive* set function with *finite variation* $|\boldsymbol{m}|$. Let E, F be two normed spaces and $(u, v) \to uv$ a bilinear mapping of $X \times E$ into F such that $|uv| \leqq |u|\,|v|$.

We can have for example $X \subset \mathscr{L}(E, F)$, $E \subset \mathscr{L}(X, F)$, $X \subset \mathscr{L}(R, X)$ or $X \subset \mathscr{L}(X', R)$. If $X = C$, then for every complex Banach space E we can consider $C \subset \mathscr{L}(E)$ and if $X = R$, then for every real Banach space E we can consider $R \subset \mathscr{L}(E)$.

Proposition 2. *If* $f \in \mathscr{E}_E(\mathscr{C})$ *then* $|f| \in \mathscr{E}(\mathscr{C})$ *and*

$$\left|\int f\,d\boldsymbol{m}\right| \leqq \int |f|\,d|\boldsymbol{m}|.$$

Write $f = \sum \varphi_{A_i} x_i$ with A_i disjoint sets of $\mathscr{C}$ and $x_i \in E$. Then $|f| = \sum \varphi_{A_i} |x_i|$; hence $|f| \in \mathscr{E}(\mathscr{C})$ and

$$\int |f|\,d|\boldsymbol{m}| = \sum |\boldsymbol{m}|\,(A_i)\,|x_i|.$$

Then

$$\left|\int f\,d\boldsymbol{m}\right| = \left|\sum \boldsymbol{m}(A_i)\,x_i\right| \leqq \sum |\boldsymbol{m}(A_i)|\,|x_i| \leqq \sum |\boldsymbol{m}|\,(A_i)\,|x_i| = \int |f|\,d|\boldsymbol{m}|.$$

In the sequel we shall write $\mu = |\boldsymbol{m}|$. The inequality of the preceding proposition is then

$$\left|\int f\,d\boldsymbol{m}\right| \leqq \int |f|\,d\mu.$$

For every step function $f \in \mathscr{E}_E(\mathscr{C})$ put

$$N_1(f, \boldsymbol{m}) = N_1(f, \mu) = \int |f|\,d\mu.$$

If no confusion is possible, we shall write $N_1(f)$. The mapping $f \to N_1(f)$ of $\mathscr{E}_E(\mathscr{C})$ into R is a semi-norm:

1. $N_1(f) \geqq 0$, $N_1(0) = 0$;
2. $N_1(f + g) \leqq N_1(f) + N(g)$;
3. $N_1(\alpha f) = |\alpha|\,N_1(f)$.

We have also

4. $N_1(f) = N_1(|f|)$;
5. $N_1(f) \leqq N_1(g)$ if $|f| \leqq |g|$.

The semi-norm N_1 defines on the space $\mathscr{E}_E(\mathscr{C})$ a topology called the *topology of the convergence in mean.*

The inequality

$$\left|\int f\,dm\right| \leqq \int |f|\,d\mu$$

is now written

$$\left|\int f\,dm\right| \leqq N_1(f),$$

whence the mapping $f \to \int f\,dm$ of $\mathscr{E}_E(\mathscr{C})$ into F is *continuous* for the topology of the convergence in mean (or for the semi-norm N_1).

A sequence (f_n) of $\mathscr{E}_E$ is a Cauchy sequence for N_1 if $\lim_{n,m\to\infty} N_1(f_n - f_m) = 0$, i.e.

$$\lim_{n,m\to\infty} \int |f_n - f_m|\,d\mu = 0.$$

Proposition 3. *If (f_n) is a Cauchy sequence of $\mathscr{E}_E(\mathscr{C})$, then:*

1. *$(|f_n|)$ is a Cauchy sequence of positive step functions.*
2. *$(\varphi_A f_n)$ is a Cauchy sequence of $\mathscr{E}_E(\mathscr{C})$, for each $A \in \mathfrak{T}(\mathscr{C})$.*
3. *the sequence of the integrals $(\int f_n\,dm)$ is a Cauchy sequence in F.*

We have

$$\big||f_n| - |f_m|\big| \leqq |f_n - f_m|$$

and

$$|\varphi_A f_n - \varphi_A f_m| = \varphi_A\,|f_n - f_m| \leqq |f_n - f_m|,$$

whence

$$N_1(|f_n| - |f_m|) \leqq N_1(f_n - f_m),$$
$$N_1(\varphi_A f_n - \varphi_A f_m) \leqq N_1(f_n - f_m).$$

From these inequalities we deduce the first two sentences. The third sentence follows from

$$\left|\int f_n\,dm - \int f_m\,dm\right| = \left|\int (f_n - f_m)\,dm\right| \leqq N_1(f_n - f_m).$$

We see now how we can define the integral of other functions than step functions:

If F is a *Banach space* and if (f_n) is a Cauchy sequence of step functions of $\mathscr{E}_E(\mathscr{C})$ which converges simply (i.e. in every point $t \in T$) to a function $f\colon T \to E$, we are led to define the integral of f with respect to m by the equality

$$\int f\,dm = \lim_{n\to\infty} \int f_n\,dm.$$

Before doing so, we have to make sure that the limit is independent on the Cauchy sequence (f_n) of step functions which converges simply to f, but depends only on f. We shall see that this is possible if $\boldsymbol{m}$ is a *measure* with finite variation. For this purpose in the next section we shall study the properties of the Cauchy sequences of step functions.

3. CAUCHY SEQUENCES OF STEP FUNCTIONS

Let $\mathscr{C}$ be a *clan*, X a Banach space and $\boldsymbol{m}: \mathscr{C} \to X$ *a measure* with *finite variation* μ. Consider the tribe $\mathcal{T}(\mu)$ of the μ-measurable subsets of T and the outer measure μ^* induced by μ. Consider then the semi-tribe $\Sigma(\mu)$ of the μ-integrable sets. For every set $A \in \Sigma(\mu)$ we shall write $\mu(A)$ instead of $\mu^*(A)$. Consider also the measure $\boldsymbol{m}$ extended to $\Sigma(\mu)$.

In this way, we can consider from the beginning that $\boldsymbol{m}$ is a complete measure defined on the semi-tribe $\Sigma(\mu)$, with finite variation μ.

Let E be a *normed* space and F be a *Banach* space and let $(u, v) \to uv$ be a bilinear mapping of $X \times E$ into F such that $|uv| \leqq |u|\,|v|$.

The space of the step functions of the form

$$f = \sum \varphi_{A_i} x_i \quad \text{with} \quad A \in \Sigma(\mu) \quad \text{and} \quad x_i \in E$$

will be denoted, simply, by $\mathscr{E}_E(\mu)$. If $f \in \mathscr{E}_E(\mu)$ and $A \in \mathcal{T}(\mu)$ we have $f\varphi_A \in \mathscr{E}_E(\mu)$. We shall write also $\mathscr{E}_E(\boldsymbol{m})$ instead of $\mathscr{E}_E(\mu)$.

We shall see, first, that the property 2 of the integral can be strengthened:

Proposition 4. *For every step function $f \in \mathscr{E}_E(\mu)$ and for every sequence (A_i) of disjoint sets of $\mathcal{T}(\mu)$ we have*

$$\int_{\bigcup_{i=1}^{\infty} A_i} f\,d\mu = \sum_{i=1}^{\infty} \int_{A_i} f\,d\mu .$$

If we write

$$f = \sum_{j=1}^{n} \varphi_{B_j} x_j, \quad \text{with} \quad B_j \in \Sigma(\mu) \quad \text{and} \quad x_i \in E,$$

and $A = \bigcup_{i=1}^{\infty} A_i$, then $A \cap B_j \in \Sigma(\mu)$ for every j, therefore

$$f\varphi_A = \sum_{j=1}^{n} \varphi_{A \cap B_j} x_j \in \mathscr{E}_E(\mu).$$

For each i we have

$$f\varphi_{A_i} = \sum_{j=1}^{n} \varphi_{A_i \cap B_j} x_j ,$$

therefore

$$\int_A f\,dm = \int \varphi_A f\,dm = \sum_{j=1}^{n} m(A \cap B_j)\,x_j$$
$$= \sum_{j=1}^{n} m\left[\left(\bigcup_{i=1}^{\infty} A_i\right) \cap B_j\right] x_j = \sum_{j=1}^{n} m\left[\bigcup_{i=1}^{\infty} (A_i \cap B_j)\right] x_j$$
$$= \sum_{j=1}^{n} \sum_{i=1}^{\infty} m(A_i \cap B_j)\,x_j = \sum_{i=1}^{\infty} \sum_{j=1}^{n} m(A_i \cap B_j)\,x_j$$
$$= \sum_{i=1}^{\infty} \int \varphi_{A_i} f\,dm = \sum_{i=1}^{\infty} \int_{A_i} dm.$$

Proposition 5. *Suppose that E is a Banach space. If* (f_n) *is a Cauchy sequence of step functions of* $\mathscr{E}_E(\mu)$, *then the set function* $\boldsymbol{n}: \mathcal{C}(\mu) \to E$ *defined by the equality*

$$\boldsymbol{n}(A) = \lim_{n \to \infty} \int_A f_n\,d\mu, \quad \text{for} \quad A \in \mathcal{C}(\mu),$$

is a measure on $\mathcal{C}(\mu)$.

We remark first that for every set $A \in \mathcal{C}(\mu)$, $(\varphi_A f_n)$ is a Cauchy sequence of step functions of $\mathscr{E}_E(\mu)$, therefore $\left(\int_A f_n\,d\mu\right)$ is a Cauchy sequence in the Banach space F, whence the limit $\lim_{n\to\infty} \int_A f_n\,d\mu$ exists.

Let $\varepsilon > 0$. We can find a number $N(\varepsilon)$ such that for $n \geqq N(\varepsilon)$ and $m \geqq N(\varepsilon)$ we have

$$\int |f_n - f_m|\,d\mu < \frac{\varepsilon}{3}.$$

Then, for $n, m \geqq N(\varepsilon)$ and $A \in \mathcal{C}(\mu)$ we have

$$\left|\int_A f_n\,d\mu - \int_A f_m\,d\mu\right| \leqq \int_A |f_n - f_m|\,d\mu \leqq \int |f_n - f_m|\,d\mu < \frac{\varepsilon}{3},$$

whence, for $m \to \infty$ we obtain

$$\left|\int_A f_n\,d\mu - \boldsymbol{n}(A)\right| < \frac{\varepsilon}{3}, \quad \text{for} \quad n \geqq N(\varepsilon) \quad \text{and} \quad A \in \mathcal{C}(\mu).$$

Let A and B be two *disjoint* sets of $\mathcal{C}(\mu)$. Then

$$\int_{A\cup B} f_n\,d\mu = \int_A f_n\,d\mu + \int_B f_n\,d\mu,$$

whence, for $n \to \infty$ we obtain

$$\boldsymbol{n}(A \cup B) = \boldsymbol{n}(A) + \boldsymbol{n}(B),$$

i.e. $\boldsymbol{n}$ is *additive* on $\mathcal{C}(\mu)$. Then $\boldsymbol{n}$ is *finitely additive* on $\mathcal{C}(\mu)$.

Let now (A_i) be a sequence of *disjoint* sets of $\mathcal{T}(\mu)$ and put $A = \bigcup_{i=1}^{\infty} A_i$. Taking a fixed number $n \geqq N(\varepsilon)$ we have

$$\left| \boldsymbol{n}(A) - \int_A f_n \, d\mu \right| < \frac{\varepsilon}{3} \quad \text{and} \quad \left| \boldsymbol{n}\left(\bigcup_{i=1}^{k} A_i \right) - \int_{\bigcup_{i=1}^{n} A_i} f_n \, d\mu \right| < \frac{\varepsilon}{3},$$

i.e.

$$\left| \sum_{i=1}^{k} \boldsymbol{n}(A_i) - \sum_{i=1}^{k} \int_{A_i} f_n \, d\mu \right| < \frac{\varepsilon}{3}, \quad \text{for every} \quad k \in N.$$

For the fixed number n we have (proposition 4)

$$\int_A f_n \, d\mu = \sum_{i=1}^{\infty} \int_{A_i} f_n \, d\mu,$$

therefore we can find $K(\varepsilon)$ such that for $k \geqq K(\varepsilon)$ we have

$$\left| \int_A f_n \, d\mu - \sum_{i=1}^{k} \int_{A_i} f_n \, d\mu \right| < \frac{\varepsilon}{3}.$$

Then, for $k \geqq K(\varepsilon)$ we have

$$\begin{aligned} \left| \boldsymbol{n}(A) - \sum_{i=1}^{k} \boldsymbol{n}(A_i) \right| &\leqq \left| \boldsymbol{n}(A) - \int_A f_n \, d\mu \right| + \left| \int_A f_n \, d\mu - \sum_{i=1}^{k} \int_{A_i} f_n \, d\mu \right| \\ &\quad + \left| \sum_{i=1}^{k} \int_{A_i} f_n \, d\mu - \sum_{i=1}^{k} \boldsymbol{n}(A_i) \right| \\ &< \frac{\varepsilon}{3} + \frac{\varepsilon}{3} + \frac{\varepsilon}{3} = \varepsilon, \end{aligned}$$

therefore

$$\boldsymbol{n}(A) = \lim_{k \to \infty} \sum_{i=1}^{k} \boldsymbol{n}(A_i) = \sum_{i=1}^{\infty} \boldsymbol{n}(A_i),$$

i.e. $\boldsymbol{n}$ is *countably additive*. Thus $\boldsymbol{n}$ is a measure on $\mathcal{T}(\mu)$.

Remark. We can prove in the same manner that for a Cauchy sequence (f_n) of step functions of $\mathscr{E}_E(\mu)$, the set function $\boldsymbol{n}\colon \mathcal{T}(\mu) \to F$ defined by the equality

$$\boldsymbol{n}(A) = \lim_{n \to \infty} \int_A f_n \, dm$$

is a measure on $\mathcal{T}(\mu)$.

In the sequel we shall use proposition 5 only in the case of a Cauchy sequence (φ_n) of *positive* step functions of $\mathscr{E}(\mu)$. In this case the equality

$$\nu(A) = \lim_{n \to \infty} \int_A \varphi_n \, d\mu, \quad \text{for} \quad A \in \mathcal{T}(\mu),$$

defines a *positive measure* on $\mathcal{T}(\mu)$.

Proposition 6. *If (f_n) is a Cauchy sequence of step functions of $\mathscr{E}_E(\mu)$, then for every $\varepsilon > 0$ there exists a number $\delta(\varepsilon) > 0$, such that*

$$\int_A |f_n|\, d\mu < \varepsilon$$

for every $n \in N$ and every set $A \in \Sigma(\mu)$ with $\mu(A) < \delta(\varepsilon)$.

Let $\varepsilon > 0$. Since (f_n) is a Cauchy sequence in $\mathscr{E}_E(\mu)$, we can find a natural number n_0 such that

$$\int |f_n - f_m|\, d\mu < \frac{\varepsilon}{2}, \quad \text{for} \quad n, m \geqq n_0.$$

Choose $\delta(\varepsilon) > 0$ such that

$$\delta(\varepsilon)\, \|f_n\| < \frac{\varepsilon}{2}, \quad \text{for} \quad n \leqq n_0,$$

where $\|f_n\| = \sup\limits_{t \in T} |f_n(t)|$. Namely, if $\|f_n\| = 0$ for every $n \leqq n_0$ we take $\delta(\varepsilon) = 1$, if $\|f_n\| \neq 0$ for some $n \leqq n_0$, we take

$$\delta(\varepsilon) = \inf \left\{ \frac{\varepsilon}{2\, \|f_n\|};\quad \|f_n\| \neq 0, \quad n \leqq n_0 \right\}.$$

Let $A \in \Sigma(\mu)$ with $\mu(A) < \delta(\varepsilon)$. Then, for $n \leqq n_0$ we have

$$\int_A |f_n|\, d\mu \leqq \|f_n\|\, \mu(A) \leqq \|f_n\|\, \delta(\varepsilon) < \frac{\varepsilon}{2} < \varepsilon$$

and for $n > n_0$ we have

$$\int_A |f_n|\, d\mu \leqq \int_A |f_n - f_{n_0}|\, d\mu + \int_A |f_{n_0}|\, d\mu$$
$$\leqq \int |f_n - f_{n_0}|\, d\mu + \int_A |f_{n_0}|\, d\mu < \frac{\varepsilon}{2} + \frac{\varepsilon}{2} = \varepsilon.$$

Thus, for every $n \in N$ and every set $A \in \Sigma(\mu)$ with $\mu(A) < \delta(\varepsilon)$ we have

$$\int_A |f_n| d\mu < \varepsilon.$$

Proposition 7. *Suppose that E is a Banach space. If (f_n) is a Cauchy sequence of step functions of $\mathscr{E}_E(\mu)$ then:*

1. *There exists a subsequence (f_{n_k}) convergent almost everywhere to a function f: $T \to E$;*

2. *for every number* $\delta > 0$ *there exists a set* $F_\delta \in \Sigma(\mu)$ *with* $\mu(F_\delta) < \delta$ *such that the sequence* (f_{n_k}) *converges uniformly on* $T - F_\delta$.

Let $0 < \varepsilon < 1$. For every pair (m, n) of natural numbers we put

$$E_{m,n}(\varepsilon) = \{t; |f_m(t) - f_n(t)| \geqq \varepsilon\}.$$

We have $E_{m,n}(\varepsilon) \in \Sigma(\mu)$ and

$$\int |f_n - f_m| \, d\mu \geqq \int_{E_{m,n}(\varepsilon)} |f_n - f_m| \, d\mu \geqq \varepsilon\mu(E_{m,n}(\varepsilon)).$$

Since (f_n) is a Cauchy sequence in $\mathscr{E}_E(\mu)$, we can find a number $N(\varepsilon)$ such that for $n, m \geqq N(\varepsilon)$ we have

$$\int |f_n - f_m| \, d\mu < \varepsilon^2 < \varepsilon.$$

It follows that for $n, m \geqq N(\varepsilon)$ we have

$$\mu(E_{m,n}(\varepsilon)) < \varepsilon.$$

If for every natural number k we take $\varepsilon = \frac{1}{2^k}$, we obtain the sequence of numbers

$$N_1 = N\left(\frac{1}{2}\right), \quad N_2 = N\left(\frac{1}{2^2}\right), \quad \ldots, N_k = N\left(\frac{1}{2^k}\right), \ldots$$

having the property that for every k and for every $n, m \geqq N_k$ we have

$$\int |f_n - f_m| \, d\mu < \frac{1}{2^k} \quad \text{and} \quad \mu\left(E_{m,n}\left(\frac{1}{2^k}\right)\right) < \frac{1}{2^k}.$$

Choose now the sequence

$$n_1 = N_1, \quad n_2 = \sup\{n_1 + 1, N_2\}, \ldots, \quad n_k = \sup\{n_{k-1} + 1, N_k\}, \ldots$$

We shall prove that the sequence $f_{n_1}, f_{n_2}, \ldots, f_{n_k}, \ldots$ fulfils the conditions of the proposition. For every k put

$$E_k = E_{n_k, n_{k+1}}\left(\frac{1}{2^k}\right) \in \Sigma(\mu) \quad \text{and} \quad F_k = \bigcup_{i=k}^{\infty} E_i \in \mathcal{T}(\mu).$$

If $t \notin F_k$, then $t \notin E_i$ for $i \geqq k$, therefore

$$|f_{n_i}(t) - f_{n_{i+1}}(t)| < \frac{1}{2^i}, \quad \text{for} \quad i \geqq k.$$

Then, for every $t \notin F_k$ and for every $j > i \geqq k$, we have

$$|f_{n_i}(t) - f_{n_j}(t)| \leqq |f_{n_i}(t) - f_{n_{i+1}}(t)| + \cdots + |f_{n_{j-1}}(t) - f_{n_j}(t)|$$
$$< \frac{1}{2^i} + \frac{1}{2^{i+1}} + \cdots + \frac{1}{2^{j-1}}$$
$$< \frac{1}{2^{i-1}} < \frac{1}{2^{k-1}}.$$

We deduce that for every $t \notin F_k$, the sequence $(f_{n_k}(t))$ is a Cauchy sequence in the Banach space E, therefore $(f_{n_k}(t))$ has a limit in E. If we define the function $f\colon T \to E$ by $f(t) = \lim_{k\to\infty} f_{n_k}(t)$ if the limit exists and $f(t) = 0$ in the contrary case, then from the preceding inequalities we deduce that the sequence (f_{n_k}) converges uniformly to f on the set $T - F_k$.

Let now $\delta > 0$. Choose k such that $\frac{1}{2^{k-1}} < \delta$ and take $F_\delta = F_k \in \mathcal{T}(\mu)$. Then

$$\mu^*(F_\delta) = \mu^*(F_k) = \mu^*\left(\bigcup_{i=k}^{\infty} E_i\right) \leqq \sum_{i=k}^{\infty} \mu(E_i) < \frac{1}{2^{k-1}} < \delta$$

and the sequence (f_{n_k}) is uniformly convergent on $T - F_\delta$ to f, thus the condition 2 of the proposition is fulfilled.

Denote by A the set of the points $t \in T$ for which the sequence $(f_{n_k}(t))$ does not converge. Since for every k, the sequence (f_{n_k}) is convergent on $T - F_k$, it follows that $A \subset F_k$ for every k, therefore $A \subset \bigcap_{k=1}^{\infty} F_k = F \in \Sigma(\mu)$. But

$$\mu(F) \leqq \mu(F_k) \leqq \frac{1}{2^{k-1}}$$

for every k, therefore $\mu(F) = 0$, whence $\mu(A) = 0$. Hence the sequence (f_{n_k}) converges almost everywhere to f and thus the condition 1 of the proposition is also fulfilled.

Corollary 1. *If (f_n) is a Cauchy sequence of scalar step functions of $\mathscr{E}_C(\mu)$ then:*

1. *There exists a subsequence (f_{n_k}) convergent almost everywhere to a scalar function f;*

2. *for every number $\delta > 0$ there exists a set $F_\delta \in \Sigma(\mu)$ with $\mu(F_\delta) < \delta$ such that (f_{n_k}) converges uniformly on $T - F_\delta$.*

Without supposing that E is a Banach space, we have the following

Corollary 2. *If (f_n) is a Cauchy sequence of step functions of $\mathscr{E}_E(\mu)$ and if (f_n) converges almost everywhere to a function $f\colon T \to E$, then we can find a subsequence (f_{n_k}) having the property that for every number $\delta > 0$, there exists a set $F_\delta \in \Sigma(\mu)$ with $\mu(F_\delta) < \delta$ such that (f_{n_k}) converges uniformly to f on $T - F_\delta$.*

Let $\tilde{E}$ be the completion of E. Then $\tilde{E}$ is a Banach space and we can consider the functions f_n to belong to $\mathscr{E}_{\tilde{E}}(\mu)$ and apply the preceding proposition.

Proposition 8. *If (f_n) is a Cauchy sequence of step functions of $\mathscr{E}_E(\mu)$, convergent almost everywhere to 0, then (f_n) converges to 0 in mean.*

We shall prove first that

$$\lim_{n\to\infty} \int_A |f_n|\, d\mu = 0, \quad \text{for every set} \quad A \in \mathcal{T}(\mu).$$

Let $A \in \Sigma(\mu)$ and $\varepsilon > 0$, and put $\varepsilon' = \dfrac{\varepsilon}{\mu(A) + 1}$. According to the proposition 6 we can find a number $\delta = \delta(\varepsilon')$ such that for every set $B \in \Sigma(\mu)$ with $\mu(B) < \delta$, we have

$$\int_B |f_n|\, d\mu < \varepsilon', \quad \text{for each} \quad n \in N.$$

According to the corollary 2 of proposition 7, we can find a subsequence (f_{n_k}) (convergent almost everywhere to 0) and a set $F_\delta \in \Sigma(\mu)$ with $\mu(F_\delta) < \delta$, such that the sequence (f_{n_k}) converges uniformly on $T - F_\delta$ to 0.

There exists then a number $N(\varepsilon) = N(\varepsilon')$ such that for every $k \geqq N(\varepsilon)$ and every $t \in T - F_\delta$ we have

$$|f_{n_k}(t)| < \varepsilon'.$$

For each number k put

$$E_k = \{t;\, t \in A,\, |f_{n_k}(t)| \geqq \varepsilon'\} \in \Sigma(\mu).$$

Thus, for $k \geqq N(\varepsilon)$ we have $E_k \subset F_\delta$; hence $\mu(E_k) < \delta$, consequently

$$\int_{E_k} |f_{n_k}|\, d\mu < \varepsilon'.$$

For $k \geqq N(\varepsilon)$ we have then

$$\int_A |f_{n_k}|\, d\mu = \int_{A-E_k} |f_{n_k}|\, d\mu + \int_{E_k} |f_{n_k}|\, d\mu$$
$$\leqq \varepsilon'\mu(A - E_k) + \varepsilon' \leqq \varepsilon'\mu(A) + \varepsilon' = \varepsilon,$$

therefore

$$\lim_{k\to\infty} \int_A |f_{n_k}|\, d\mu = 0,$$

i.e. the sequence $(f_{n_k}\varphi_A)$ converges in mean to 0. Since the Cauchy sequence $(f_n\varphi_A)$ of sets of $\mathscr{E}_E(\mu)$ contains a subsequence convergent in mean to 0, we deduce that the sequence $(f_n\varphi_A)$ converges itself in mean to 0:

$$\lim_{n\to\infty} \int_A |f_n|\, d\mu = 0.$$

Consider now the *positive measure* ν defined on the tribe $\mathcal{T}(\mu)$ by the equality (proposition 5)

$$\nu(A) = \lim_{n\to\infty} \int_A |f_n|\, d\mu, \quad \text{for} \quad A \in \mathcal{T}(\mu).$$

If for each number i we put $A_i = \{t; f_i(t) \neq 0\}$, we have $A_i \in \Sigma(\mu)$, thus

$$\nu(A_i) = \lim_{n\to\infty} \int_{A_i} |f_n|\, d\mu = 0,$$

whence, putting $A_0 = \bigcup_{i=1}^{\infty} A_i \in \mathcal{T}(\mu)$, we have $\nu(A_0) = 0$. On the other hand, for every n we have $f_n \varphi_{A_0} = f_n$, whence

$$\int_{A_0} |f_n|\, d\mu = \int |f_n|\, d\mu,$$

therefore

$$\lim_{n\to\infty} \int |f_n|\, d\mu = \lim_{n\to\infty} \int_{A_0} |f_n|\, d\mu = \nu(A_0) = 0,$$

i.e. the sequence (f_n) converges in mean to 0.

Proposition 9. *If (f_n) and (g_n) are two Cauchy sequences of $\mathscr{E}_E(\mu)$ converging μ-almost everywhere to the same function f, then*

$$\lim_{n\to\infty} \int f_n\, dm = \lim_{n\to\infty} \int g_n\, dm.$$

In fact, $(f_n - g_n)$ is a Cauchy sequence and converges to 0 μ-almost everywhere, whence it converges to 0 in mean. Then

$$\lim_{n\to\infty} \int (f_n - g_n)\, dm = 0,$$

whence

$$\lim_{n\to\infty} \int f_n\, dm = \lim_{n\to\infty} \int g_n\, dm.$$

§ 8. INTEGRABLE FUNCTIONS

In this paragraph we consider: a *clan* $\mathscr{C}$ of subsets of T, a Banach space X and a measure $\boldsymbol{m}: \mathscr{C} \to X$ with *finite variation* μ. We consider the measures $\boldsymbol{m}$ and μ extended to the semi-tribe $\Sigma(\mu)$ of the μ-integrable sets. We consider also two Banach spaces E and F and a bilinear mapping $(u, v) \to uv$ of $X \times E$ into F such that $|uv| \leqq |u|\,|v|$.

1. DEFINITION AND PROPERTIES

The results of the preceding paragraph lead to the following

Definition 1. *A function $f: T \to E$ is said to be $\boldsymbol{m}$-integrable (or integrable with respect to $\boldsymbol{m}$), if there exists a Cauchy sequence (f_n) of $\mathscr{E}_E(\mu)$, converging μ-almost everywhere to f.*

The integral of f with respect to $\boldsymbol{m}$ is the element $\int f\, d\boldsymbol{m} \in F$ defined by the equality

$$\int f\, d\boldsymbol{m} = \lim_{n\to\infty} \int f_n\, d\boldsymbol{m},$$

where (f_n) is a Cauchy sequence of $\mathscr{E}_E(\mu)$ converging μ-almost everywhere to f.

According to the proposition 9, § 7, the integral $\int f\, d\boldsymbol{m}$ does not depend on the sequence (f_n).

We shall write also $\int f(t)\, d\boldsymbol{m}$ or $\int f(t)\, d\boldsymbol{m}(t)$ instead of $\int f\, d\boldsymbol{m}$.

The set of the $\boldsymbol{m}$-integrable functions $f: T \to E$ will be denoted by $\mathscr{L}^1_E(T, \boldsymbol{m})$ or $\mathscr{L}^1_E(\boldsymbol{m})$ or $\mathscr{L}^1_E$.

If we consider $X = \mathscr{L}(C, X)$, then the preceding definition contains the integrability with respect to $\boldsymbol{m}$ of the *scalar* functions $\varphi: T \to C$. The space of the *real* $\boldsymbol{m}$-integrable functions will be denoted, simply, by $\mathscr{L}^1(T, \boldsymbol{m})$ or $\mathscr{L}^1(\boldsymbol{m})$ or $\mathscr{L}^1$.

If we take $\boldsymbol{m} = \mu$ and $F = E$, then the preceding definition contains the integrability with respect to μ of the functions $f: T \to E$.

The results which follow remain valid if we take $\boldsymbol{m} = \mu$ and $F = E$.

Every step function $f \in \mathscr{E}_E(\mu)$ is $\boldsymbol{m}$-integrable and its integrals according to the preceding definition and to the definition 1, § 7, are equal. In fact for every n we take $f_n = f$.

The properties of the integral of the step functions remain valid for integrable functions.

Proposition 1. *The set $\mathscr{L}^1_E(\boldsymbol{m})$ is a vector space and the mapping $f \to \int f\, d\boldsymbol{m}$ of $\mathscr{L}^1_E(\boldsymbol{m})$ into F is linear:*

$$\int (\alpha f + \beta g)\, d\boldsymbol{m} = \alpha \int f\, d\boldsymbol{m} + \beta \int g\, d\boldsymbol{m}.$$

In fact, if (f_n) and (g_n) are Cauchy sequences of $\mathscr{E}_E(\mu)$ converging almost everywhere respectively to f and g, then $(\alpha f_n + \beta g_n)$ is a Cauchy sequence and converges almost everywhere to $\alpha f + \beta g$.

Proposition 2. *If $f, g: T \to E$ are two functions equal $\boldsymbol{m}$-almost everywhere and if f is $\boldsymbol{m}$-integrable then g is $\boldsymbol{m}$-integrable and $\int f\, d\boldsymbol{m} = \int g\, d\boldsymbol{m}$.*

In fact, if (f_n) is a Cauchy sequence of $\mathscr{E}_E(\mu)$ converging almost everywhere to f, then (f_n) converges almost everywhere to g too.

We can extend now the definition 1 to *real extended* functions and to functions defined only almost everywhere.

A function f defined almost everywhere on T with values in E or in $\bar{R}$ is $\boldsymbol{m}$-integrable if there exists a Cauchy sequence of $\mathscr{E}_E(\mu)$, respectively of $\mathscr{E}(\mu)$, converging to f $\boldsymbol{m}$-almost everywhere, and we define $\int f\,d\boldsymbol{m} = \lim_{n\to\infty} \int f_n\,d\boldsymbol{m}$.

The set of the $\boldsymbol{m}$-integrable real extended functions is no more a vector space. The integrability and the integral of the real extended functions or of the functions defined almost everywhere reduces to that of the *finite* real functions respectively defined everywhere on T.

Proposition 3. *A real extended function $f: T \to \bar{R}$ or a function defined almost everywhere on T with values in E, is $\boldsymbol{m}$-integrable if and only if it is equal $\boldsymbol{m}$-almost everywhere to a finite $\boldsymbol{m}$-integrable function $g: T \to R$ respectively $g: T \to E$. In this case we have*

$$\int f\,d\boldsymbol{m} = \int g\,d\boldsymbol{m}.$$

In fact, let $f: T \to \bar{R}$ be $\boldsymbol{m}$-integrable, and let (f_n) be a Cauchy sequence of $\mathscr{E}(\mu)$ converging μ-almost everywhere to f. According to proposition 7, § 7, we can find a subsequence (f_{n_k}) converging μ-almost everywhere to a *finite* limit g. We put $g(t) = 0$ in the points of nonconvergence of (f_{n_k}). We deduce that g is μ-integrable, that f and g are equal μ-almost everywhere and that

$$\int f\,d\boldsymbol{m} = \lim_{k\to\infty} \int f_{n_k}\,d\boldsymbol{m} = \int g\,d\boldsymbol{m}.$$

Conversely if f is equal almost everywhere to a μ-integrable function $g: T \to R$, and if (f_n) is a Cauchy sequence of $\mathscr{E}(\mu)$ converging μ-almost everywhere to g, then (f_n) converges almost everywhere to f; hence f is $\boldsymbol{m}$-integrable, and

$$\int f\,d\boldsymbol{m} = \lim_{n\to\infty} \int f_n\,d\boldsymbol{m} = \int g\,d\boldsymbol{m}.$$

The statement concerning the functions defined almost everywhere is proved in the same way.

Corollary. *An integrable real extended function $f: T \to \bar{R}$ is finite μ-almost everywhere.*

The properties which follow will be stated only for *finite* functions and for functions defined everywhere but most of them remain valid for real extended functions, and for functions defined almost everywhere.

We remark that every $\boldsymbol{m}$-integrable function is $\boldsymbol{m}$-measurable as limit $\boldsymbol{m}$-almost everywhere of $\boldsymbol{m}$-measurable step functions (theorem 1, § 6).

Proposition 4. *If* $\boldsymbol{f} \in \mathscr{L}^1_{\mathrm{E}}(\boldsymbol{m})$, *then* $|\boldsymbol{f}| \in \mathscr{L}^1(\mu)$ *and*

$$\left|\int \boldsymbol{f}\, d\boldsymbol{m}\right| \leqq \int |\boldsymbol{f}|\, d\mu.$$

In fact, if $(\boldsymbol{f}_n)$ is a cauchy sequence of $\mathscr{E}_E(\mu)$ converging almost everywhere to $\boldsymbol{f}$, then $(|\boldsymbol{f}_n|)$ is a Cauchy sequence of $\mathscr{E}(\mu)$ converging almost everywhere to $(|\boldsymbol{f}|)$. The above inequality follows from

$$\left|\int \boldsymbol{f}_n\, d\boldsymbol{m}\right| \leqq \int |\boldsymbol{f}_n|\, d\mu.$$

Remark. The converse implication is not true. However we shall see (proposition 19) that if $|\boldsymbol{f}|$ is μ-integrable and if, in addition, $\boldsymbol{f}$ is $\boldsymbol{m}$-measurable, then $\boldsymbol{f}$ is also $\boldsymbol{m}$-integrable.

Corollary 1. *A real function f is μ-integrable if and only if f^+ and f^- are μ-integrable.*

We use the relations

$$f^+ = \frac{1}{2}(|f| + f), \quad f^- = \frac{1}{2}(|f| - f) \quad \text{and} \quad f = f^+ - f^-.$$

Corollary 2. *If f and g are real μ-integrable functions, then the functions* $\sup(f, g)$ *and* $\inf(f, g)$ *are μ-integrable.*

In fact

$$\sup(f, g) = \frac{1}{2}(f + g + |f - g|) \quad \text{and} \quad \inf(f, g) = -\sup(-f, -g).$$

This corollary will be stated below for a sequence of integrable functions.

Let us remark that if $\boldsymbol{f} \in \mathscr{L}^1_{\mathrm{E}}(\boldsymbol{m})$ and if A is μ-measurable, then $\boldsymbol{f}\varphi_A \in \mathscr{L}^1_{\mathrm{E}}(\boldsymbol{m})$. We shall write

$$\int_A \boldsymbol{f}\, d\boldsymbol{m} = \int \varphi_A \boldsymbol{f}\, d\boldsymbol{m}.$$

Proposition 5. *If* $\boldsymbol{f} \in \mathscr{L}^1_{\mathrm{E}}(\boldsymbol{m})$ *and if* (A_n) *is a sequence of disjoint* $\boldsymbol{m}$*-measurable sets, then*

$$\int_{\bigcup_{n=1}^{\infty} A_n} \boldsymbol{f}\, d\boldsymbol{m} = \sum_{n=1}^{\infty} \int_A \boldsymbol{f}\, d\boldsymbol{m}.$$

Let $(\boldsymbol{f}_n)$ be a Cauchy sequence of $\mathscr{E}_E(\mu)$ converging μ-almost everywhere to $\boldsymbol{f}$. For every set $A \in \mathcal{T}(\mu)$ put

$$\boldsymbol{n}(A) = \int_A \boldsymbol{f}\, d\boldsymbol{m} = \lim_{n \to \infty} \int \boldsymbol{f}_n\, d\boldsymbol{m}.$$

According to the propostion 5, § 7, the set function $\boldsymbol{n}$ is countably additive on $\mathcal{T}(\mu)$.

Proposition 6. *If* $\varphi \in \mathcal{L}^1(\boldsymbol{m})$ *and* $x \in E$, *then* $\varphi x \in \mathcal{L}^1_E(\boldsymbol{m})$ *and*

$$\int \varphi x \, d\boldsymbol{m} = x \int \varphi \, d\boldsymbol{m}.$$

In fact, if (φ_n) is a Cauchy sequence of $\mathscr{E}(\mu)$ converging almost everywhere to φ, then $(\varphi_n x)$ is a Cauchy sequence of $\mathscr{E}_E(\mu)$ converging almost everywhere to φx and for every n we have

$$\int \varphi_n x \, d\boldsymbol{m} = x \int \varphi_n \, d\boldsymbol{m}.$$

We pass then to the limit in this equality.

For a scalar measure we have the following property:

Proposition 7. *Let* m *be a scalar measure and* $U: E \to F$ *a continuous linear operation. If* $f \in \mathcal{L}^1_E(m)$, *then* $U \circ f \in \mathcal{L}^1_F(m)$ *and*

$$\int U \circ f \, dm = U \int f \, dm.$$

In fact, if (f_n) is a Cauchy sequence of $\mathscr{E}_E(m)$ converging almost everywhere to f, then $(U \circ f_n)$ is a Cauchy sequence of $\mathscr{E}_F(m)$ converging almost everywhere to $U \circ f$.

Corollary. *Let* m *be a scalar measure. If* $f \in \mathcal{L}^1_E(m)$ *and if* $x' \in E'$, *then* $\langle f, x' \rangle \in \mathcal{L}^1_C(m)$ *and*

$$\int \langle f, x' \rangle \, dm = \left\langle \int f \, dm, x' \right\rangle.$$

The integral of the real functions with respect to the *positive* measure μ has additional properties.

Proposition 8. *If* $\varphi \geqq 0$ *is* μ*-integrable, then* $\int \varphi \, d\mu \geqq 0$.

In fact, if (φ_n) is a Cauchy sequence of $\mathscr{E}(\mu)$ converging almost everywhere to φ, then $(|\varphi_n|)$ is a Cauchy sequence of $\mathscr{E}(\mu)$ converging almost everywhere to $|\varphi| = \varphi$ and for every n we have $\int |\varphi_n| \, d\mu \geqq 0$.

Corollary 1. *Let* $\varphi_1, \varphi_2 \in \mathcal{L}^1(\mu)$. *If* $\varphi_1 \leqq \varphi_2$, *then*

$$\int \varphi_1 \, d\mu \leqq \int \varphi_2 \, d\mu$$

Corollary 2. *Let* $\varphi \geqq 0$ *be* μ*-integrable. If* $A \subset B$ *are two* μ*-measurable sets, then*

$$\int_A \varphi \, d\mu \leqq \int_B \varphi \, d\mu.$$

Corollary 3. *If* $f \in \mathscr{L}^1_E(\mu)$ *and if* $A \in \mathfrak{T}(\mu)$, *then*

$$\int_A |f|\, d\mu \leqq \|f\|_A\, \mu^*(A),$$

where $\|f\|_A = \sup_{t \in A} |f(t)|$.

If $\|f\|_A = 0$, then $\int_A |f|\, d\mu = 0$. Suppose then that $\|f\|_A > 0$. If $\mu^*(A) = \infty$ the inequality is verified. If $\mu^*(A) < \infty$, then A is μ-integrable and we have $|f|\, \varphi_A \leqq \|f\|_A\, \varphi_A$, hence

$$\int_A |f|\, d\mu \leqq \|f\|_A \int \varphi_A\, d\mu = \|f\|_A\, \mu(A).$$

Proposition 9. *If* $f \in \mathscr{L}^1_E(\mu)$, *then the set* $E = \{t; f(t) \neq 0\}$ *is equal to the union of a* μ*-negligible set and of a sequence of* μ*-integrable sets of the tribe* $\mathscr{T}$ *generated by* $\mathscr{C}$.

In fact, let (f_n) be a sequence of step functions of $\mathscr{E}_E(\mu)$ converging to f μ-almost everywhere and let E_0 be a μ-negligible set such that $f_n(t) \to f(t)$ for every $t \in T - E_0$. For every n, the set $E_n = \{t; f_n(t) \neq 0\}$ belongs to $\Sigma(\mu)$ and we have $E \subset \bigcup_{n=0}^{\infty} E_n$. Since f is μ-measurable, the set E is μ-measurable, hence $F_n = E \cap E_n \in \Sigma(\mu)$ for $n = 0, 1, 2, \ldots$ and we have $E = \bigcup_{n=0}^{\infty} F_n$, where F_0 is μ-negligible. Since $F_n \in \Sigma(\mu)$, it is of the form (proposition 12, § 5) $F_n = A_n \cup N_n$ with $A_n \in \mathscr{T}$ and N_n μ-negligible. The set $A_0 = \bigcup_{n=0}^{\infty} N_n$ is μ-negligible and we have $E = \bigcup_{n=0}^{\infty} A_n$.

Corollary 1. *If* $f \in \mathscr{L}^1_E(\mu)$ *then the set* $E = \{t; f(t) \neq 0\}$ *is contained in the union of a* μ*-negligible set and of a sequence of sets of* $\mathscr{C}$.

In fact, if we write $E = \bigcup_{n=0}^{\infty} A_n$ with A_0 μ-negligible and $A_n \in \mathscr{T}$ for $n = 1, 2, \ldots$, then every A_n with $n \geqq 1$ is contained in a sequence of sets of $\mathscr{C}$.

Corollary 2. *If* $f \in \mathscr{L}^1_E(\mu)$ *then for every* $\alpha > 0$, *the set* $E_\alpha = \{t; |f(t)| \geqq \alpha\}$ *is* μ*-integrable.*

We remark first that $|f|$ is μ-measurable, hence the set E_α is μ-measurable. The set $E = \{t; f(t) \neq 0\}$ is equal to the union of a sequence $(E_n)_{0 \leqq n < \infty}$ of μ-integrable sets (proposition 9). If we put $A_n = E_\alpha \cap E_n$ then A_n is μ-integrable and $E_\alpha = \bigcup_{n=0}^{\infty} A_n$. We can consider the sequence (A_n) increasing, hence

$$\mu^*(E_\alpha) = \lim_{n \to \infty} \mu(A_n).$$

For every n we have $\varphi_{A_n} \leqq \frac{1}{\alpha}|f|$, hence

$$\mu(A_n) \leqq \frac{1}{\alpha}\int |f|\, d\mu < \infty,$$

therefore, passing to the limit,

$$\mu^*(E_\alpha) \leqq \frac{1}{\alpha}\int |f|\, d\mu < \infty,$$

consequently E_α is μ-integrable.

Proposition 10. *Let $f \in \mathscr{L}^1_E(\boldsymbol{m})$. We have $\int |f|\, d\mu = 0$ if and only if $f(t) = 0$ μ-almost everywhere. In this case we have $\int f\, d\boldsymbol{m} = 0$.*

If $f(t) = 0$ μ-almost everywhere, for every n we take the step function $f_n = 0$. Then

$$\int f\, d\boldsymbol{m} = \lim_{n\to\infty} \int f_n\, d\boldsymbol{m} = 0.$$

In particular, since $|f(t)| = 0$ μ-almost everywhere, we have

$$\int |f|\, d\mu = 0.$$

Conversely, suppose that $\int |f|\, d\mu = 0$. For every n the set $A_n = \left\{t;\ |f(t)| \geqq \frac{1}{n}\right\}$ is μ-integrable and we have

$$0 = \int |f|\, d\mu \geqq \int_A |f|\, d\mu \geqq \frac{1}{n}\mu(A_n) \geqq 0.$$

It follows that A_n is μ-negligible. Since

$$E = \{t; f(t) \neq 0\} = \bigcup_{n=1}^{\infty} A_n,$$

it follows that E is μ-negligible, i.e. $f(t) = 0$ μ-almost everywhere.

Corollary 1. *Let $f \in \mathscr{L}^1_E(\boldsymbol{m})$ and $A \in \mathcal{T}(\mu)$ such that $f(t) \neq 0$ for every $t \in A$. We have $\int_A |f|\, d\mu = 0$ if and only if A is μ-negligible. In this case we have $\int_A f\, d\boldsymbol{m} = 0$.*

In fact, we apply the preceding proposition to the function $f\varphi_A$.

Corollary 2. *Let $f, g \in \mathscr{L}^1_E(\boldsymbol{m})$. We have $\int |f - g|\, d\mu = 0$ if and only if $f(t) = g(t)$ μ-almost everywhere. In this case we have*

$$\int f\, d\boldsymbol{m} = \int g\, d\boldsymbol{m}.$$

Corollary 3. *Let* $f \in \mathscr{L}^1_E(m)$, *A and B two measurable sets. If* $\mu(A \,\Delta\, B) = 0$, *then*

$$\int_A f\,dm = \int_B f\,dm.$$

In fact, in this case the functions $f\varphi_A$ and $f\varphi_B$ belong to $\mathscr{L}^1_E(m)$ and are equal μ-almost everywhere.

Proposition 11. *Let* $f \in \mathscr{L}^1(\mu)$. *If*

$$\int_A f\,d\mu \geqq 0, \quad \textit{for every} \quad A \in \mathscr{C},$$

then $f(t) \geqq 0$ μ*-almost everywhere.*

Let us show first that we have

$$\int_A f\,d\mu \geqq 0, \quad \text{for every} \quad A \in \Sigma(\mu).$$

In fact, the set function ν defined on $\mathcal{T}(\mu)$ by the equality

$$\nu(A) = \int_A f\,d\mu, \quad \text{for} \quad A \in \mathcal{T}(\mu),$$

is countably additive (proposition 5) and by hypothesis it is positive on $\mathscr{C}$. The restriction λ of ν to $\mathscr{C}$ is a positive measure. The outer measure λ^* is positive and countably additive on the tribe $\mathscr{T}$ generated by $\mathscr{C}$ and is equal to ν on $\mathscr{C}$. It follows (§ 2, proposition 6) that λ^* and ν are equal on $\mathscr{T}$ hence ν is positive on $\mathscr{T}$. Finally, every set $A \in \Sigma(\mu)$ is of the form $A = A' \cup N$ with $A' \in \mathscr{T}$ and N μ-negligible. Then $\nu(A) = \nu(A') \geqq 0$.

Since f is μ-measurable, the sets $A_n = \left\{t; f(t) < -\frac{1}{n}\right\}$, are μ-measurable and contained in the μ-integrable set $\left\{t; |f(t)| > \frac{1}{n}\right\}$, hence A_n is μ-integrable.

The set $A = \{t; f(t) < 0\}$ is μ-measurable and we have $A = \bigcup_{n=1}^{\infty} A_n$. Since the sequence (A_n) is increasing we have $\nu(A) = \lim_{n\to\infty} \nu(A_n) \geqq 0$ and $f\varphi_A \leqq -\frac{1}{n}\varphi_{A_n}$ for every n, therefore

$$0 \leqq \int_A f\,d\mu \leqq -\frac{1}{n}\int f\varphi_{A_n}\,d\mu = -\frac{1}{n}\mu(A_n) \leqq 0.$$

It follows that $\mu(A_n) = 0$ for every n, hence A is μ-negligible, consequently $f(t) \geqq 0$ μ-almost everywhere.

Corollary 1. *If* $f \in \mathscr{L}^1(\mu)$ *and if*

$$\int_A f\,d\mu \leqq 0, \quad \textit{for every} \quad A \in \mathscr{C},$$

then $f(t) \leqq 0$ μ*-almost everywhere.*

Corollary 2. *If* $f \in \mathscr{L}^1(\mu)$ *and if*

$$\int_A f\,d\mu = 0, \quad \textit{for every} \quad A \in \mathscr{C},$$

then $f(t) = 0$ μ*-almost everywhere.*

Remark. We shall see (corollary 1 of the theorem 6, § 10) that the last corollary remains valid for vector functions $\boldsymbol{f} \in \mathscr{L}^1_E(\mu)$.

2. CONVERGENCE IN MEAN ON THE SPACE $\mathscr{L}^1_E$

Like for the step functions, for every $\boldsymbol{m}$-integrable function $\boldsymbol{f} \in \mathscr{L}^1_E(\boldsymbol{m})$ we put

$$N_1(\boldsymbol{f}) = N_1(\boldsymbol{f}, \boldsymbol{m}) = N_1(\boldsymbol{f}, \mu) = \int |\boldsymbol{f}|\,d\mu.$$

N_1 is a semi-norm on the space $\mathscr{L}^1_E(\boldsymbol{m})$. The topology defined on $\mathscr{L}^1_E(\boldsymbol{m})$ by the semi-norm N_1 will be called the topology of the convergence in mean. The inequality

$$\left|\int \boldsymbol{f}\,d\boldsymbol{m}\right| \leqq \int |\boldsymbol{f}|\,d\mu, \quad \text{for} \quad \boldsymbol{f} \in \mathscr{L}^1_E(\boldsymbol{m}),$$

is written now

$$\left|\int \boldsymbol{f}\,d\boldsymbol{m}\right| \leqq N_1(\boldsymbol{f}),$$

hence the mapping $\boldsymbol{f} \to \int \boldsymbol{f}\,d\boldsymbol{m}$ of $\mathscr{L}^1_E(\boldsymbol{m})$ into F is continuous for the topology of the convergence in mean. From the inequality

$$|N_1(\boldsymbol{f}) - N_1(\boldsymbol{g})| \leqq N_1(\boldsymbol{f} - \boldsymbol{g})$$

we deduce that the semi-norm N_1 is also continuous on $\mathscr{L}^1_E(\boldsymbol{m})$. To say that a sequence $(\boldsymbol{f}_n)$ of $\mathscr{L}^1_E(\boldsymbol{m})$ converges in mean to a function $\boldsymbol{f} \in \mathscr{L}^1_E(\boldsymbol{m})$ means that

$$\lim_{n\to\infty} N_1(\boldsymbol{f}_n - \boldsymbol{f}) = 0, \quad \text{i.e.} \quad \lim_{n\to\infty} \int |\boldsymbol{f}_n - \boldsymbol{f}|\,d\mu = 0.$$

If $(\boldsymbol{f}_n)$ converges in mean to $\boldsymbol{f}$, then

$$\lim_{n\to\infty} N_1(\boldsymbol{f}_n) = N_1(\boldsymbol{f}), \quad \text{i.e.} \quad \lim_{n\to\infty} \int |\boldsymbol{f}_n|\,d\mu = \int |\boldsymbol{f}|\,d\mu$$

because N_1 is continuous, and

$$\lim_{n\to\infty} \int \boldsymbol{f}_n\,d\boldsymbol{m} = \int \boldsymbol{f}\,d\boldsymbol{m}$$

because the integral is continuous. The converse statement is not true: we can have $\lim_{n\to\infty}\int f_n\,dm = \int f\,dm$ for a sequence (f_n) which does not converge to f.

According to the proposition 10, the closure of 0 in $\mathscr{L}^1_E(\boldsymbol{m})$ is the subspace $\mathscr{N}^\infty_E(\boldsymbol{m})$ of the $\boldsymbol{m}$-negligible functions $f\colon T \to E$.

If $N_1(f - g) = 0$ then $f(t) = g(t)$ μ-almost everywhere.

The quotient space $\mathscr{L}^1_E/\mathscr{N}^\infty_E$ is denoted by L^1_E. The equivalence class of a function $f \in \mathscr{L}^1_E$ is denoted by $\tilde{f}$. For every element $\tilde{f} \in L^1_E$ we put

$$\|\tilde{f}\|_1 = N_1(f).$$

The definition of $\|\tilde{f}\|_1$ is independent on the function $f \in \tilde{f}$. The mapping $\tilde{f} \to \|\tilde{f}\|_1$ is a norm on L^1_E.

Proposition 12. *If (f_n) is a Cauchy sequence of step functions of $\mathscr{E}_E(\mu)$ converging μ-almost everywhere to a function $f \in \mathscr{L}^1_E(\mu)$, then (f_n) converges in mean to f.*

Let $\varepsilon > 0$. Since (f_n) is a Cauchy sequence, there exists $N(\varepsilon)$ such that for $n, m \geqq N(\varepsilon)$ we have

$$\int |f_n - f_m|\,d\mu < \varepsilon.$$

For fixed $n \geqq N(\varepsilon)$, the sequence $(f_n - f_m)_{1 \leqq m < \infty}$ is a Cauchy sequence of step functions of $\mathscr{E}_E(\mu)$ converging μ-almost everywhere to $f_n - f$; hence $(|f_n - f_m|)_{1 \leqq m < \infty}$ is a Cauchy sequence of positive step functions of $\mathscr{E}(\mu)$ converging μ-almost everywhere to $|f_n - f|$, consequently,

$$\int |f_n - f|\,d\mu = \lim_{m\to\infty}\int |f_n - f_m|\,d\mu \leqq \varepsilon,$$

i.e. $N_1(f_n - f) \leqq \varepsilon$ for $n \geqq N(\varepsilon)$, hence (f_n) converges in mean to f.

Corollary. *The space $\mathscr{E}_E(\mu)$ is dense in $\mathscr{L}^1_E(\boldsymbol{m})$.*

This corollary is strengthened by the following

Proposition 13. *The subspace $\mathscr{E}_E(\mathscr{C})$ of the $\mathscr{C}$-step functions of $\mathscr{L}^1_E(\boldsymbol{m})$ is dense in $\mathscr{L}^1_E(\boldsymbol{m})$.*

Let $f \in \mathscr{L}^1_E(\boldsymbol{m})$ and $\varepsilon > 0$. There exists a function $g \in \mathscr{E}_E(\mu)$ such that

$$\int |f - g|\,d\mu < \frac{\varepsilon}{2}.$$

Write

$$g = \sum_{i=1}^{n} \varphi_{A_i} x_i$$

with $A_i \in \Sigma(\mu)$ and $x_i \neq 0$. For each set A_i there exists (§ 5, proposition 13) a set $B_i \in \mathscr{C}$ with

$$\mu(A_i \, \Delta \, B_i) < \frac{\varepsilon}{2n\,|x_i|}.$$

The function

$$h = \sum_{i=1}^{n} \varphi_{B_i} x_i$$

belongs to $\mathscr{E}_E(\mathscr{C})$ and we have

$$|g - h| = \left| \sum_{i=1}^{n} (\varphi_{A_i} - \varphi_{B_i})\, x_i \right| \leqq \sum_{i=1}^{n} |\varphi_{A_i} - \varphi_{B_i}|\, |x_i| = \sum_{i=1}^{n} \varphi_{A_i \Delta B_i} |x_i|.$$

Then

$$\int |g - h| \, d\mu \leqq \sum \mu(A_i \, \Delta \, B_i)\, |x_i| < \frac{\varepsilon}{2},$$

hence

$$N_1(f - h) \leqq N_1(f - g) + N_1(g - h) < \varepsilon.$$

Consequently $\mathscr{E}_E(\mathscr{C})$ is dense in $\mathscr{L}^1_E(\boldsymbol{m})$.

Corollary. *For every function $f \in \mathscr{L}^1_E(\boldsymbol{m})$ there exists a Cauchy sequence of step functions of $\mathscr{E}_E(\mathscr{C})$ converging μ-almost everywhere to f.*

Since $\mathscr{E}_E(\mathscr{C})$ is dense in $\mathscr{L}^1_E(\boldsymbol{m})$, there exists a sequence (f_n) of functions of $\mathscr{E}_E(\mathscr{C})$ converging in mean to f. It follows that (f_n) is a Cauchy sequence. From the proposition 7, § 7, it follows that there exists a sequence (f_{n_k}) converging almost everywhere to a function $g: T \to E$. We deduce first that g is $\boldsymbol{m}$-integrable and that (f_{n_k}) converges in mean to g. Using the inequality $N_1(f - g) \leqq N_1(f - f_{n_k}) + N_1(g - f_{n_k})$, for every $k \in N$, and letting $k \to \infty$, we deduce that $N_1(f - g) = 0$, hence $f(t) = g(t)$ μ-almost everywhere. We see then that (f_{n_k}) is the desired sequence.

Theorem 1. *The space $\mathscr{L}^1_E(\boldsymbol{m})$ is complete.*

Let (f_n) be a Cauchy sequence of $\mathscr{L}^1_E(\boldsymbol{m})$:

$$\lim_{\substack{n \to \infty \\ m \to \infty}} \int |f_n - f_m| \, d\mu = 0.$$

For each n there exists a step function $g_n \in \mathscr{E}_E(\mu)$ such that

$$\int |f_n - g_n| \, d\mu < \frac{1}{n}.$$

Since

$$\int |g_n - g_m| \, d\mu \leqq \int |g_n - f_n| \, d\mu + \int |f_n - f_m| \, d\mu + \int |f_m - g_m| \, d\mu$$

we deduce that

$$\lim_{\substack{n\to\infty \\ m\to\infty}} \int |g_n - g_m| \, d\mu = 0,$$

hence (g_n) is a Cauchy sequence. It contains a subsequence (g_{n_k}) converging μ-almost everywhere to a function $f\colon T \to E$. It follows that f is μ-integrable and that (g_{n_k}) converges in mean to f. Since the Cauchy sequence (g_n) contains a subsequence converging to f in mean, the sequence (g_n) converges to f in mean:

$$\lim_{n\to\infty} \int |g_n - f| \, d\mu = 0.$$

Then

$$\int |f_n - f| \, d\mu \leqq \int |f_n - g_n| \, d\mu + \int |g_n - f| \, d\mu,$$

hence

$$\lim_{n\to\infty} \int |f_n - f| \, d\mu = 0,$$

i.e. (f_n) converges in mean to f.

Corollary. *The space $L^1_E(m)$ is a Banach space.*

The proposition 7, § 7, concerning the step functions can now be extended for integrable functions:

Proposition 14. *If (f_n) is a sequence of functions of $\mathscr{L}_E(\mu)$ converging in mean to a function $f \in \mathscr{L}^1_E(\mu)$, then there exists a subsequence (f_{n_k}) converging μ-almost everywhere to f.*

For every natural number k we can find a number n_k such that

$$\int |f_{n_k} - f| \, d\mu < \frac{1}{2^{2k}}.$$

We shall show that (f_{n_k}) is the desired sequence. According to the corollary 2 of the proposition 9, the set

$$E_k = \left\{t;\, |f_{n_k}(t) - f(t)| \geqq \frac{1}{2^k}\right\}$$

is μ-integrable and we have

$$\int |f_{n_k} - f| \, d\mu \geqq \int_{E_k} |f_{n_k} - f| \, d\mu \geqq \frac{1}{2^k} \mu(E_k),$$

hence

$$\mu(E_k) < \frac{1}{2^k}.$$

The set

$$F_k = \bigcup_{i=k}^{\infty} E_i$$

is μ-integrable and for $t \in T - F_k$ we have $t \notin E_i$ for $i \geqq k$, hence

$$|f_{n_i}(t) - f(t)| < \frac{1}{2^i} \quad \text{for} \quad i \geqq k.$$

It follows that on $T - F_k$ the sequence (f_{n_i}) converges uniformly to f. The set

$$F = \bigcap_{k=1}^{\infty} F_k$$

is μ-integrable and

$$\mu(F) \leqq \mu(F_k) \leqq \sum_{i=k}^{\infty} \mu(E_i) \leqq \frac{1}{2^k}, \quad \text{for every} \quad k,$$

hence $\mu(F) = 0$. Since

$$T - F = \bigcup_{k=1}^{\infty} (T - F_k),$$

we deduce that on $T - F$ the sequence (f_{n_k}) converges to f. The set A on which (f_{n_k}) does not converge to f is contained in F, hence A is μ-negligible, consequently (f_{n_k}) converges μ-almost everywhere to f.

Proposition 15. *If (f_n) is a Cauchy sequence of functions of $\mathscr{L}^1_E(\mu)$, then for every $\varepsilon > 0$ there exists a number $\delta(\varepsilon) > 0$ such that*

$$\int_A |f_n| \, d\mu < \varepsilon$$

for every $n \in N$ and every $A \in \Sigma(\mu)$ with $\mu(A) < \delta(\varepsilon)$.

Let $\varepsilon > 0$. For every n there exists a step function $g_n \in \mathscr{E}_E(\mu)$ such that

$$\int |f_n - g_n| \, d\mu < \frac{\varepsilon}{2n}.$$

It follows that for every μ-measurable set A we have

$$\int_A |f_n - g_n| \, d\mu < \frac{\varepsilon}{2n},$$

therefore

$$\int_A |f_n|\, d\mu < \int_A |g_n|\, d\mu + \frac{\varepsilon}{2n}.$$

From the inequalities

$$\int |g_n - g_m|\, d\mu \leqq \int |g_n - f_n|\, d\mu + \int |f_n - f_m|\, d\mu + \int |f_m - g_m|\, d\mu$$

we deduce that (g_n) is a Cauchy sequence of step functions. We apply then the proposition 6, § 7, and find a number $\delta(\varepsilon) > 0$ such that

$$\int_A |g_n|\, d\mu < \frac{\varepsilon}{2}$$

for every n and every $A \in \Sigma(\mu)$ with $\mu(A) < \delta(\varepsilon)$.

Then

$$\int_A |f_n|\, d\mu \leqq \int_A |g_n|\, d\mu + \frac{\varepsilon}{2n} < \frac{\varepsilon}{2} + \frac{\varepsilon}{2} = \varepsilon$$

for every n and every $A \in \Sigma(\mu)$ with $\mu(A) < \delta(\varepsilon)$.

Corollary. *If $f \in \mathscr{L}^1_E(\mu)$, then for every $\varepsilon > 0$ there exists $\delta(\varepsilon) > 0$ such that*

$$\int_A |f|\, d\mu < \varepsilon$$

for every $A \in \Sigma(\mu)$ with $\mu(A) < \delta(\varepsilon)$.

Proposition 16. *Let μ and ν be two positive measures defined on the clan $\mathscr{C}$. If $\mu \leqq \nu$ then $\mathscr{L}^1_E(\mu) \supset \mathscr{L}^1_E(\nu)$ and*

$$\int |f|\, d\mu \leqq \int |f|\, d\nu, \quad \text{for} \quad f \in \mathscr{L}^1_E(\nu).$$

In fact $\Sigma(\mu) \supset \Sigma(\nu)$, hence $\mathscr{E}_E(\mu) \supset \mathscr{E}_E(\nu)$. From the proposition 11, § 5, it follows that

$$\mu(A) \leqq \nu(A), \quad \text{for} \quad A \in \Sigma(\nu),$$

hence

$$\int |f|\, d\mu \leqq \int |f|\, d\nu, \quad \text{for} \quad f \in \mathscr{E}_E(\nu).$$

Let now $f \in \mathscr{L}^1_E(\nu)$. There exists a Cauchy sequence (f_n) of $\mathscr{E}_E(\nu)$ converging ν-almost everywhere to f.

Then (f_n) is also a Cauchy sequence in $\mathscr{E}_E(\mu)$ and converges to f μ-almost everywhere. It follows that $f \in \mathscr{L}^1_E(\mu)$ and

$$\int |f|\, d\mu = \lim_{n\to\infty} \int |f_n|\, d\mu, \quad \int |f|\, d\nu = \lim_{n\to\infty} \int |f_n|\, d\nu.$$

Since for every n we have

$$\int |f_n| \, d\mu \leqq \int |f_n| \, d\nu$$

it follows that

$$\int |f| \, d\mu \leqq \int |f| \, d\nu.$$

3. CRITERIA OF INTEGRABILITY

The following proposition shows that if we start from Cauchy sequences of integrable functions (instead of step functions) converging almost everywhere, we do not obtain new functions.

Proposition 17. *If (f_n) is a Cauchy sequence of $\mathscr{L}^1_E(\mu)$ converging μ-almost everywhere to a function $f\colon T \to F$, then f is μ-integrable and (f_n) converges in mean to f. In this case we have*

$$\int f \, dm = \lim_{n\to\infty} \int f_n \, dm.$$

Since $\mathscr{L}^1(\mu)$ is complete, there exists a function $g \in \mathscr{L}^1_E(\mu)$ such that (f_n) converges in mean to f. From the proposition 14 we deduce that there exists a subsequence (f_{n_k}) converging to g μ-almost everywhere. But (f_{n_k}) converges also to f μ-almost everywhere. It follows that $f(t) = g(t)$ μ-almost everywhere, hence f is μ-integrable and (f_n) converges to f in mean.

Theorem 2 (Beppo-Levi). *If (f_n) is an increasing sequence of real μ-integrable functions and if*

$$\sup_n \int f_n \, d\mu < \infty,$$

then the function $\sup_n f_n$ *(with finite or $+\infty$ values) is μ-integrable and we have*

$$\int \sup_n f_n \, d\mu = \sup_n \int f_n \, d\mu = \lim_{n\to\infty} \int f_n \, d\mu.$$

We show that (f_n) is a Cauchy sequence. Put

$$a = \sup_n \int f_n \, d\mu < \infty$$

and let $\varepsilon > 0$. There exists a number $N(\varepsilon)$ such that

$$\left| \int f_n \, d\mu - a \right| < \frac{\varepsilon}{2}, \quad \text{for} \quad n \geqq N(\varepsilon).$$

For $n, m \geqq N(\varepsilon)$ we have either $f_n \leqq f_m$ or $f_m \leqq f_n$ and

$$\int |f_n - f_m|\, d\mu = \left|\int f_n\, d\mu - \int f_m\, d\mu\right| \leqq \left|\int f_n\, d\mu - a\right| + \left|\int f_m\, d\mu - a\right| < \varepsilon,$$

hence (f_n) is a Cauchy sequence, therefore it converges in mean to a function $g \in \mathscr{L}^1$. There exists then (proposition 14) a subsequence (f_{n_k}) converging to g μ-almost everywhere. But (f_{n_k}) converges everywhere to the function $f = \sup_n f_n$. It follows that $g(t) = f(t)$ μ-almost everywhere, hence f is μ-integrable, and (f_n) converges in mean to f. We deduce then

$$\int f\, d\mu = \lim_{n\to\infty} \int f_n\, d\mu = \sup_n \int f_n\, d\mu$$

because the sequence of the integrals is increasing.

Corollary 1. *If (f_n) is an increasing sequence of real μ-integrable functions and if*

$$\sup_n \int |f_n|\, d\mu < \infty,$$

then the function $\sup_n f_n$ *is μ-integrable and we have*

$$\int \sup_n f_n\, d\mu = \sup_n \int f_n\, d\mu.$$

Corollary 2. *If (f_n) is a decreasing sequence of real μ-integrable functions and if*

$$\inf_n \int f_n\, d\mu > -\infty, \quad \text{or} \quad \sup_n \int |f_n|\, d\mu < \infty,$$

then the function $\inf_n f_n$ *is μ-integrable and we have*

$$\int \inf_n f_n\, d\mu = \inf_n \int f_n\, d\mu.$$

We apply the preceding theorem and corollary to the increasing sequence $(-f_n)$.
The theorem 2 and its corollaries can be stated as follows:

If (f_n) is a monotone sequence of real μ-integrable functions and if the sequence $\left(\int f_n\, d\mu\right)$ has a finite limit, then the function $\lim_{n\to\infty} f_n$ *is μ-integrable and we have*

$$\int \lim_{n\to\infty} f_n\, d\mu = \lim_{n\to\infty} \int f_n\, d\mu.$$

Corollary 3. *If (f_n) is a sequence of positive μ-integrable functions and if*

$$\sum_{n=1}^{\infty} \int f_n\, d\mu < \infty$$

then the function $\sum_{n=1}^{\infty} f_n$ *(with finite or* $+\infty$ *values) is* μ*-integrable and we have*

$$\int \sum_{n=1}^{\infty} f_n \, d\mu = \sum_{n=1}^{\infty} \int f_n \, d\mu .$$

We apply the theorem 2 to the increasing sequence of μ-integrable functions

$$g_n = \sum_{i=1}^{n} f_i .$$

Corollary 4. *Let* (f_n) *be a sequence of real* μ*-integrable functions and* g *a positive* μ*-integrable function. If* $|f_n| \leqq g$, μ*-almost everywhere for each* n*, then the function* $\sup_n f_n$ *is* μ*-integrable and we have*

$$\sup_n \int f_n \, d\mu \leqq \int \sup_n f_n \, d\mu .$$

If for every n we put $g = \sup(f_1, f_2, \ldots, f_n)$, then (g_n) is an increasing sequence of μ-integrable functions and we have $\sup_n g_n = \sup_n f_n$. On the other hand $g_n \leqq g$ for every n, and $\sup_n \int g_n \, d\mu \leqq \int g \, d\mu < \infty$, therefore $\sup_n f_n = \sup_n g_n$ is μ-integrable. We have then $\int f_n \, d\mu \leqq \int \sup_n f_n \, d\mu$ for every n, therefore $\sup_n \int f_n \, d\mu \leqq \int \sup_n f_n \, d\mu$.

Proposition 18. *Let* A *be a countable directed set of indices,* $(f_\alpha)_{\alpha \in A}$ *a family of real* μ*-integrable functions and* g *a positive* μ*-integrable function. If* $|f_\alpha| \leqq g$ *for every* n*, then the function* $\limsup_{\alpha \in A} f_\alpha$ *is* μ*-integrable and we have*

$$\limsup_{\alpha \in A} \int f_\alpha \, d\mu \leqq \int \limsup_{\alpha \in A} f_\alpha \, d\mu .$$

Since A is countable and directed we can find a sequence (α_n) of A with the property that for every α there exists n such that $\alpha_n \leqq \alpha$. From the corollary 4 of the proposition 17 we deduce that for every n, the function $g_n = \sup_{p \geqq 0} f_{\alpha_{n+p}}$ is μ-integrable and

$$\sup_{p \geqq 0} \int f_{\alpha_{n+p}} \, d\mu \leqq \int g_n \, d\mu .$$

The sequence (g_n) is decreasing and $|g_n| \leqq g$; hence $g_n \geqq -g$, therefore

$$\inf_n \int g_n \, d\mu \geqq -\int g \, d\mu > -\infty .$$

From the corollary 2 of the theorem 2 we deduce that the function $\limsup_{\alpha \in A} f_\alpha = \inf_n g_n$ is μ-integrable and

$$\int \inf_n g_n \, d\mu = \inf_n \int g_n \, d\mu \geqq \inf_n \sup_{p \geqq 0} \int f_{\alpha_{n+p}} \, d\mu,$$

i.e.

$$\int \limsup_{\alpha \in A} f_\alpha \, d\mu \geqq \limsup_{\alpha \in A} \int f_\alpha \, d\mu.$$

Theorem 3 (Lebesgue dominated theorem). *Let (f_n) be a sequence of $\mathscr{L}^1_E(\boldsymbol{m})$ convergent $\boldsymbol{m}$-almost everywhere to a function $f\colon T \to E$. If there exists a positive μ-integrable function g such that $|f_n| \leqq g$ μ-almost everywhere, for each n, then the limit f is μ-integrable and (f_n) converges in mean to f. In this case we have*

$$\int f \, d\boldsymbol{m} = \lim_{n \to \infty} \int f_n \, d\boldsymbol{m}.$$

The sequence $(|f_n - f_m|)$ converges to 0 μ-almost everywhere as $n \to \infty$ and $m \to \infty$ independently. Then

$$\limsup_{n,m \to \infty} |f_n - f_m| = 0, \quad \boldsymbol{m}\text{-almost everywhere},$$

hence considering the countable set $A = N \times N$ directed by the order $(n, m) \leqq (n', m')$ if $n \leqq n'$ and $m \leqq m'$, we have (proposition 18)

$$\limsup_{n,m \to \infty} \int |f_n - f_m| \, d\mu \leqq \int \limsup_{n,m \to \infty} |f_n - f_m| \, d\mu = 0.$$

If follows that (f_n) is a Cauchy sequence of $\mathscr{L}^1_E(\boldsymbol{m})$. Then (proposition 17) the limit f is $\boldsymbol{m}$-integrable and (f_n) converges in mean to f.

Proposition 19. *If the function $f\colon T \to E$ is μ-measurable and if there exists a positive μ-integrable function g such that*

$$|f| \leqq g \quad \mu\text{-almost everywhere},$$

then f is μ-integrable.

Since g is μ-integrable, g vanishes outside the union of a sequence (A_n) of μ-integrable sets (proposition 9). We can consider the sequence (A_n) increasing.

There exists (§ 6, theorem 2) a sequence (f_n) of measurable step functions of $\mathscr{E}_E(\mu)$ convergent to f μ-almost everywhere, such that $|f_n| \leqq |f|$ for each n.

Then $|f_n| \leqq g$ μ-almost everywhere, for each n and (f_n) are μ-integrable, therefore, by the theorem of Lebesgue, f is μ-integrable.

Proposition 20. *A function $f\colon T \to E$ belongs to $\mathscr{L}^1_E(\mu)$ if and only if f is μ-measurable and $|f| \in \mathscr{L}^1(\mu)$.*

If $f \in \mathscr{L}^1_E(\mu)$, then $|f| \in \mathscr{L}^1(\mu)$ (proposition 4) and f is μ-measurable, as limit μ-almost everywhere of a sequence of step functions of $\mathscr{E}_E(\mu)$.

Conversely, if f is μ-measurable and $|f| \in \mathscr{L}^1(\mu)$, then, from proposition 19 (with $g = |f|$), we deduce that f is μ-integrable.

The following proposition is known as Fatou's lemma:

Proposition 21. *If (f_n) is a sequence of positive μ-integrable functions and if*

$$\liminf_{n\to\infty} \int f_n \, d\mu < \infty,$$

then the function $\liminf_{n\to\infty} f_n$ *is μ-integrable and we have*

$$\int \liminf_{n\to\infty} f_n \, d\mu \leqq \liminf_{n\to\infty} \int f_n \, d\mu.$$

For each n, the function $g_n = \inf(f_n, f_{n+1}, \ldots)$ is positive, μ-measurable and $g_n \leqq f_{n+p}$, hence g_n is μ-integrable and we have

$$\int g_n \, d\mu \leqq \int f_{n+p} \, d\mu,$$

consequently

$$\int g_n \, d\mu \leqq \inf_{p \geqq 0} \int f_{n+p} \, d\mu.$$

The sequence (g_n) is increasing and

$$\sup_n \int g_n \, d\mu \leqq \liminf_{n\to\infty} \int f_{n+p} \, d\mu < \infty.$$

From the theorem 2 we deduce that $\sup_n g_n = \liminf_{n\to\infty} f_n$ is μ-integrable and

$$\int \sup_n g_n \, d\mu = \sup_n \int g_n \, d\mu,$$

hence

$$\int \liminf_{n\to\infty} f_n \, d\mu \leqq \liminf_{n\to\infty} \int f_n \, d\mu.$$

Corollary. *If (f_n) is a sequence of $\mathscr{L}^1_E(\mu)$ converging μ-almost everywhere to a function $f\colon T \to E$ and if*

$$\liminf_{n\to\infty} \int |f_n| \, d\mu < \infty,$$

then f is μ-integrable.

In fact, $|f|$ is the limit μ-almost everywhere if the sequence $(|f_n|)$, hence $|f|$ is μ-integrable and

$$\int |f| \, d\mu \leqq \lim_{n\to\infty} \int |f_n| \, d\mu < \infty .$$

Since f is μ-measurable it follows that it is μ-integrable.

Proposition 22. *If (f_n) is a sequence of functions of $\mathscr{L}^1_E(\mu)$ converging uniformly to a function $f\colon T \to E$, and vanishing outside a μ-integrable set A, then $f \in \mathscr{L}^1_E(\mu)$ and (f_n) converges in mean to f.*

Since $f_n(t) = 0$ for $t \notin A$ and every n, we have

$$\int |f_n - f_m| \, d\mu = \int_A |f_n - f_m| \, d\mu \leqq \|f_n - f_m\| \, \mu(A),$$

whence (f_n) is a Cauchy sequence in $\mathscr{L}^1_E(\mu)$. It follows that f is μ-integrable and that (f_n) converges in mean to f.

Corollary. *Every function which is totally measurable with respect to $\Sigma(\mu)$ is **m**-integrable.*

4. THE SPACE L^1

Let μ be a positive measure on T. We have denoted by $\mathscr{N}^\infty(\mu)$ the set of the real μ-negligible functions and by $L^1(\mu)$ the quotient space $\mathscr{L}^1(\mu)/\mathscr{N}^\infty(\mu)$. The equivalence class of a function $f \in \mathscr{L}^1(\mu)$ was denoted by $\tilde{f}$ and we put $\|\tilde{f}\|_1 = N_1(f)$. The mapping $\tilde{f} \to \|\tilde{f}\|_1$ is a norm on $L^1(\mu)$ and $L^1(\mu)$ is a Banach space for this norm (corollary of the theorem 1).

If $f, g \in \mathscr{L}^1(\mu)$ and $f(t) \leqq g(t)$ μ-almost everywhere, then for every function $f' \in \tilde{f}$ and $g' \in \tilde{g}$ we have also $f'(t) \leqq g'(t)$ μ-almost everywhere. We can then define the relation $\tilde{f} \leqq \tilde{g}$ which means $f(t) \leqq g(t)$ μ-almost everywhere. The relation $\tilde{f} \leqq \tilde{g}$ does not depend on the functions f and g but only on the classes $\tilde{f}$ and $\tilde{g}$. This is an order relation on $L^1(\mu)$.

If $f_1, f_2 \in \mathscr{L}^1(\mu)$ and if $g = \sup(f_1, f_2)$ and $h = \inf(f_1, f_2)$, then

$$\tilde{g} = \sup(\tilde{f}_1, \tilde{f}_2) \quad \text{and} \quad \tilde{h} = \inf(\tilde{f}_1, \tilde{f}_2).$$

We remark that for an arbitrary family H of functions of $\mathscr{L}^1(\mu)$ with $f_\infty(t) = \sup_{f \in H} f(t)$ in $\mathscr{L}^1(\mu)$, we have in general

$$\tilde{f}_\infty \neq \sup_{f \in H} \tilde{f}.$$

The theorem 2, stated for *sequences* of functions of $\mathscr{L}^1(\mu)$ can now be extended for arbitrary directed families of $L^1(\mu)$.

Theorem 4. *Let $H \subset L^1$ be a filtering (for $\leqq$) set of equivalence classes of positive functions. The set H has a least upper bound in $L^1(\mu)$ if and only if* $\sup_{\tilde{f} \in H} \|\tilde{f}\|_1 < \infty$. *In this case* $\sup H$ *is the limit in $L^1(\mu)$ of the filter of the sections of H:*

$$\sup_{\tilde{f} \in H} \tilde{f} = \lim_{\tilde{f} \in H} \tilde{f}.$$

If there exists $\tilde{g} = \sup H$ in $L^1(\mu)$, then $\tilde{f} \leqq \tilde{g}$; hence $\|\tilde{f}\|_1 \leqq \|\tilde{g}\|_1$ for every $\tilde{f} \in H$, therefore

$$\sup_{\tilde{f} \in H} \|\tilde{f}\|_1 \leqq \|\tilde{g}\|_1 < \infty.$$

Conversely, suppose that $\sup_{\tilde{f} \in H} \|\tilde{f}\|_1 < \infty$. Since the mapping $\tilde{f} \to \|\tilde{f}\|_1$ is increasing, this mapping has a limit following the filter of the sections of H and

$$\lim_{\tilde{f} \in H} \|\tilde{f}\|_1 = \sup_{\tilde{f} \in H} \|\tilde{f}\|_1 < \infty.$$

From the equality

$$\|\tilde{f} - \tilde{h}\|_1 = \|\tilde{f}\|_1 - \|\tilde{h}\|_1$$

for $\tilde{h} \leqq \tilde{f}$, we deduce that the filter of the sections of H is a Cauchy filter in the Banach space $L^1(\mu)$, hence it has a limit $\tilde{g} \in L^1(\mu)$. It follows that $\tilde{g}$ is the least upper bound in $L^1(\mu)$ of the directed set H. Thus, the theorem is proved.

§ 9. THE SPACES $\mathcal{M}_E^\infty$ AND $\mathcal{L}_E^\infty$

1. INTEGRATION OF TOTALLY MEASURABLE FUNCTIONS

Let $\mathscr{C}$ be a clan, E and F two *Banach* spaces and $\boldsymbol{m}: \mathscr{C} \to X = \mathscr{L}(E, F)$ an *additive* set function with *finite semi-variation* $\tilde{\boldsymbol{m}}$.

In this case we shall extend the integral with respect to $\boldsymbol{m}$ from the step functions of $\mathscr{E}_E(\mathscr{C})$ to the totally measurable functions of $\mathscr{M}_E(\mathscr{C})$.

We shall prove first the following

Proposition 1. *If (f_n) is a uniform convergent sequence of step functions of $\mathscr{E}_E(\mathscr{C})$ vanishing outside a certain set $A \in \mathscr{C}$, then the sequence of the integrals $(\int f_n\, d\boldsymbol{m})$ is convergent in F.*

In fact

$$\left|\int f_n\, d\boldsymbol{m} - \int f_m\, d\boldsymbol{m}\right| = \left|\int (f_n - f_m)\, d\boldsymbol{m}\right| \leqq \|f_n - f_m\|\, \tilde{\boldsymbol{m}}(A).$$

Since (f_n) is uniformly convergent, $\|f_n - f_m\| \to 0$ as $n \to \infty$ and $m \to \infty$, therefore $(\int f_n\, d\boldsymbol{m})$ is a Cauchy sequence in the Banach space F.

Proposition 2. *Let* (f_n) *and* (g_n) *be two sequences of step functions of* $\mathscr{E}_E(\mathscr{C})$ *vanishing outside a certain set* $A \in \mathscr{C}$. *If the sequences* (f_n) *and* (g_n) *are uniformly convergent to the same limit, then*

$$\lim_{n\to\infty} \int f_n \, dm = \lim_{n\to\infty} \int g_n \, dm.$$

In fact, the sequence $(f_n - g_n)$ converges uniformly to 0 and

$$\left| \int (f_n - g_n) \, dm \right| \leq \|f_n - g_n\| \, \dot{\tilde{m}}(A),$$

whence

$$\lim_{n\to\infty} \int (f_n - g_n) \, dm = 0.$$

Since the sequences $(\int f_n \, dm)$ and $(\int g_n \, dm)$ are convergent, we deduce that they have the same limit.

Definition 1. *For every totally measurable function* $f \in \mathscr{M}_E(\mathscr{C})$ *we define the integral* $\int f \, dm$ *by the equality*

$$\int f \, dm = \lim_{n\to\infty} \int f_n \, dm$$

where (f_n) *is an arbitrary sequence of step functions of* $\mathscr{E}_E(\mathscr{C})$ *vanishing outside a certain set of* $\mathscr{C}$ *and converging uniformly to* f.

From the proposition 2 it follows that the integral $\int f \, dm$ does not depend on the sequence (f_n) but depends only on f.

If $f \in \mathscr{M}_E(\mathscr{C})$ and if $A \in \mathcal{T}(\mathscr{C})$, then $f\varphi_A \in \mathscr{M}_E(\mathscr{C})$. We write

$$\int_A f \, dm = \int f\varphi_A \, dm.$$

Remarks.

1°. The integral of a step function $f \in \mathscr{E}_E(\mathscr{C})$ according to the preceding definition is equal to that of definition 1 of § 7. In fact we take the sequence $f_n = f$.

2°. If m is *countably additive* and with *finite variation* μ, then every totally measurable function $f \in \mathscr{M}_E(\mathscr{C})$ is μ-integrable (corollary of the proposition 22, § 8) and its integral according to the preceding definition is equal to that of the definition 1 of § 8 (see § 8, proposition 22).

All the properties of the integral of the step functions remain valid, by passing to the limit, for totally measurable functions:

1. *If $f, g \in \mathcal{M}_E(\mathscr{C})$ and α, β are scalars, then*

$$\int (\alpha f + \beta g)\, dm = \alpha \int f\, dm + \beta \int g\, dm.$$

2. *If $f \in \mathcal{M}_E(\mathscr{C})$ and if A, B are disjoint sets of $\mathfrak{T}(\mathscr{C})$, then*

$$\int_{A \cup B} f\, dm = \int_A f\, dm + \int_B g\, dm.$$

3. *If $f \in \mathcal{M}_E(\mathscr{C})$, if α, β are scalars and if m, $n: \mathscr{C} \to \mathscr{L}(E, F)$ are additive set functions with finite semi-variation, then*

$$\int f\, d(\alpha m + \beta n) = \alpha \int f\, dm + \beta \int f\, dn.$$

4. *If $\varphi \in \mathcal{M}(\mathscr{C})$ and $x \in E$, then $\varphi x \in \mathcal{M}_E(\mathscr{C})$ and*

$$\int \varphi x\, dm = x \int \varphi\, dm.$$

If μ is a *scalar* additive set function on $\mathscr{C}$ with finite semi-variation, we have additional properties:

5. *If $U: E \to F$ is a continuous linear mapping and $f \in \mathcal{M}_E(\mathscr{C})$, then $U \circ f \in \mathcal{M}_F(\mathscr{C})$ and*

$$\int U \circ f\, d\mu = U \int f\, d\mu.$$

6. *If $\mu \geqq 0$ and $\varphi \geqq 0$, then $\int \varphi\, d\mu \geqq 0$.*

7. *If $\mu \geqq 0$ and $\varphi_1 \leqq \varphi_2$, then $\int \varphi_1\, d\mu \leqq \int \varphi_2\, d\mu$.*

8. *If $\mu \geqq 0$, $\varphi \geqq 0$ and if $A \subset B$ are sets of $\mathfrak{T}(\mathscr{C})$, then*

$$\int_A \varphi\, d\mu \leqq \int_B \varphi\, d\mu.$$

9. *If μ and ν are real additive set functions on $\mathscr{C}$ with finite semi-variation such that $\mu \leqq \nu$ and if $\varphi \geqq 0$, then*

$$\int \varphi\, d\mu \leqq \int \varphi\, d\nu.$$

10. *For every set $A \in \mathfrak{T}(\mathscr{C})$ and for every function $f \in \mathcal{M}_E(\mathscr{C}, A)$ we have*

$$\left| \int f\, dm \right| \leq \|f\|\, \tilde{m}(A).$$

In fact, we take a sequence (f_n) of $\mathscr{E}_E(\mathscr{C}, A)$ converging uniformly to f.

11. *For every set $A \in \mathcal{T}(\mathscr{C})$ we have*

$$\tilde{\boldsymbol{m}}(A) = \sup \left| \int f\, d\boldsymbol{m} \right| \leqq \infty, \quad \textit{for} \quad f \in \mathscr{M}_E(\mathscr{C}, A) \quad \textit{with} \quad \|f\| \leqq 1.$$

In fact, from the property 10 of the integral of the step functions, § 7, we deduce that

$$\tilde{\boldsymbol{m}}(A) \leqq \sup \left| \int f\, d\boldsymbol{m} \right|, \quad \text{for} \quad f \in \mathscr{M}_E(\mathscr{C}, A) \quad \text{with} \quad \|f\| \leqq 1.$$

From the above property 10 we deduce

$$\sup \left| \int f\, d\boldsymbol{m} \right| \leqq \tilde{\boldsymbol{m}}(A), \quad \text{for} \quad f \in \mathscr{M}_E(\mathscr{C}, A) \quad \text{with} \quad \|f\| \leqq 1.$$

12. *If $\boldsymbol{m}$ has finite variation $|\boldsymbol{m}|$, then for every function $f \in \mathscr{M}_E(\mathscr{C})$ we have*

$$\left| \int f\, d\boldsymbol{m} \right| \leqq \int |f|\, d|\boldsymbol{m}|.$$

2. LINEAR OPERATIONS ON THE SPACE $\mathscr{M}_E(\mathscr{C})$

Let $U: \mathscr{M}_E(\mathscr{C}) \to F$ be a linear operation. For every set $A \subset T$ we design by U_A the restriction of U to the subspace $\mathscr{M}_E(\mathscr{C}, A)$ and we put

$$\|U_A\| = \sup |Uf|, \quad \text{for} \quad f \in \mathscr{M}_E(\mathscr{C}, A) \quad \text{with} \quad \|f\| \leqq 1,$$

and

$$|||U_A||| = \sup \sum |U(\varphi_{A_i} x_i)|,$$

where the supremum is taken for all the functions $f = \sum \varphi_{A_i} x_i \in \mathscr{M}_E(\mathscr{C}, A)$ with A_i disjoint and $\|f\| \leqq 1$.

Since for $A \in \mathcal{T}(\mathscr{C})$ the space $\mathscr{E}_E(\mathscr{C}, A)$ is dense in $\mathscr{M}_E(\mathscr{C}, A)$, we have

$$\|U_A\| \leqq |||U_A|||, \quad \text{for} \quad A \in \mathcal{T}(\mathscr{C}).$$

The condition $\|U_A\| < \infty$ means that U_A is continuous on $\mathscr{M}_E(\mathscr{C}, A)$.

Proposition 3. *If $U: \mathscr{M}_E(\mathscr{C}) \to C$ is a linear functional, then we have*

$$\|U_A\| = |||U_A||| \leqq \infty, \quad \textit{for} \quad A \in \mathcal{T}(\mathscr{C}).$$

In fact, let $f = \sum_{i=1}^{n} \varphi_{A_i} x_i \in \mathscr{E}_E(\mathscr{C}, A)$ with A_i disjoint and $\|f\| \leqq 1$. For every i let α_i be a complex number with $|\alpha_i| = 1$ such that

$$|U(\varphi_{A_i} x_i)| = \alpha_i U(\varphi_{A_i} x_i) = U(\varphi_{A_i} \alpha_i x_i).$$

Then $g = \sum \varphi_{A_i}\alpha_i x_i \in \mathscr{E}_E(\mathscr{C}, A)$ and $\|g\| = \|f\| \leqq 1$ and we have

$$\sum |U(\varphi_{A_i}x_i)| = U(\sum \varphi_{A_i}\alpha_i x_i) = |U(g)| \leqq \|U_A\|;$$

hence $|||U_A||| \leqq \|U_A\|$, therefore $\|U_A\| = |||U_A|||$.

Proposition 4. *For every set $A \in \mathcal{T}(\mathscr{C})$ and for every finite family (f_i) of $\mathcal{M}_E(\mathscr{C}, A)$ with $|f_i|\,|f_j| = 0$ for $i \neq j$, we have*

$$\sum |U(f_i)| \leqq |||U_A|||\,\|\sum f_i\|.$$

If $U_A = 0$, then $U(f_i) = 0$ for each i and the inequality is verified. If $|||U_A||| = \infty$ the inequality is verified, even if $\|\sum f_i\| = 0$, since in this case $f_i = 0$ and $U(f_i) = 0$ for each i.

Assume therefore that $0 < |||U_A||| < \infty$. Then $\|U_A\| < \infty$, i.e. U_A is continuous on $\mathcal{M}_E(\mathscr{C}, A)$.

Let $(f_i)_{1 \leqq i \leqq n}$ be a finite family of $\mathcal{M}_E(\mathscr{C}, A)$ with $|f_i|\,|f_j| = 0$ for $i \neq j$ and let $\varepsilon > 0$. For each i there exists a step function $g_i \in \mathscr{E}_E(\mathscr{C}, A)$ such that $\|f_i - g_i\| < \eta = \min\left(\frac{\varepsilon}{2}, \frac{\varepsilon}{2n\|U_A\|}\right)$. Then $|f_i(t)| \leqq |g_i(t)| + \eta$ for every $t \in T$. The set $A_i = \{t; |g_i(t)| \geqq \eta\}$ belongs to $\mathscr{C}$ and we have $|f_i(t)| \neq 0$ for $t \in A_i$ and $|f_i(t)| < 2\eta$ for $t \notin A_i$. It follows that the sets A_i are disjoint and contained in A. We have then $\|f_i - \varphi_{A_i}g_i\| < 2\eta$, therefore

$$\|\varphi_{A_i}g_i\| \leqq \|f_i\| + 2\eta \leqq \|\sum f_i\| + \varepsilon,$$

and

$$|U(f_i) - U(\varphi_{A_i}g_i)| \leqq \|U_A\|\,2\eta < \frac{\varepsilon}{n},$$

consequently

$$|U(f_i)| < |U(\varphi_{A_i}g_i)| + \frac{\varepsilon}{n}.$$

If we write

$$\varphi_{A_i}g_i = \sum_j \varphi_{A_{ij}}x_{ij}$$

with A_{ij} disjoint sets of $\mathscr{C}$ contained in A_i, then

$$|x_{ij}| \leqq \|\sum f_i\| + \varepsilon$$

and

$$\begin{aligned}\sum_{i=1}^n |U(f_i)| &\leqq \sum_{i=1}^n \left|U\Big(\sum_j \varphi_{A_{ij}}x_{ij}\Big)\right| + \varepsilon \leqq \sum_{i,j} |U(\varphi_{A_{ij}}x_{ij})| + \varepsilon \\ &\leqq |||U_A|||\,(\|\sum f_i\| + \varepsilon) + \varepsilon,\end{aligned}$$

consequently, ε being arbitrary,

$$\sum |U(f_i)| \leqq |||U_A|||\,\|\sum f_i\|.$$

Proposition 5. *For every set $A \in \mathcal{T}(\mathscr{C})$ we have:*

1. $\|\|U_A\|\| = \sup \sum |U(\varphi_{A_i} f)|$ *(finite sums) for $f \in \mathscr{M}_E(\mathscr{C}, A)$ with $\|f\| \leqq 1$ and A_i disjoint sets of $\mathcal{T}(\mathscr{C})$.*

2. $\|\|U_A\|\| = \sup \sum |U(\varphi_i x_i)|$ *(finite sums) for $\varphi_i \in \mathscr{M}(\mathscr{C}, A)$ with $|\varphi_i| \leqq 1$ and $\varphi_i \varphi_j = 0$ if $i \neq j$, and for $x_i \in E$ with $|x_i| \leqq 1$.*

3. $\|\|U_A\|\| = \sup \sum |U(\varphi_i f)|$ *(finite sums) for $f \in \mathscr{M}_E(\mathscr{C}, A)$ with $\|f\| \leqq 1$ and for $\varphi_i \in \mathscr{M}(\mathscr{C})$ with $|\varphi_i| \leqq 1$ and $\varphi_i \varphi_j = 0$ if $i \neq j$.*

4. $\|\|U_A\|\| = \sup \sum |U(f_i)|$ *(finite sums) for $f_i \in \mathscr{M}_E(\mathscr{C}, A)$ with $\|f_i\| \leqq 1$ and $|f_i|\,|f_j| = 0$ if $i \neq j$.*

Let us denote by $\mathscr{A}_A$ the set of the functions $\sum f_i$ for which the supremum is taken in each of the four cases. We have $\|\sum f_i\| \leqq 1$ and from the proposition 4 we deduce that

$$\sup \sum |U(f_i)| \leqq \|\|U_A\|\|, \quad \text{for} \quad \sum f_i \in \mathscr{A}_A.$$

On the other hand, $\mathscr{A}_A$ contains all the step functions of the form $\sum \varphi_{A_i} x_i$ with A_i disjoint sets of $\mathscr{C}$ contained in A and $|x_i| \leqq 1$, therefore, from the definition of $\|\|U_A\|\|$ we deduce that

$$\|\|U_A\|\| \leqq \sup \sum |U(f_i)|, \quad \text{for} \quad \sum f_i \in \mathscr{A}_A.$$

Remarks.

1°. We have also for every set $A \in \mathcal{T}(\mathscr{C})$

$$\|U_A\| = \sup |\sum U(f_i)|, \quad \text{for} \quad \sum f_i \in \mathscr{A}_A,$$

in each of the cases of the preceding proposition.

2°. In each of the preceding cases we have

$$\|\|U_A\|\| = \sup \sum |U(f_i)|, \quad \text{for} \quad \sum |f_i| \leqq \varphi_A.$$

We say that a linear real functional $L: \mathscr{M}(\mathscr{C}) \to R$ is *positive*, if

$$L(\varphi) \geqq 0, \quad \text{for} \quad \varphi \geqq 0.$$

Proposition 6. *If $L: \mathscr{M}(\mathscr{C}) \to R$ is a positive linear functional, then*

$$\|L_A\| = L(\varphi_A) < \infty, \quad \textit{for every} \quad A \in \mathscr{C}.$$

In fact, if $A \in \mathscr{C}$ and $\varphi \in \mathscr{M}(\mathscr{C}, A)$, we have

$$-\varphi_A \|\varphi\| \leqq \varphi \leqq \|\varphi\| \varphi_A,$$

hence, L being positive, therefore increasing,

$$-\|\varphi\| L(\varphi_A) \leqq L(\varphi) \leqq \|\varphi\| L(\varphi_A),$$

therefore

$$|L(\varphi)| \leqq L(\varphi_A)\,\|\varphi\|,$$

consequently

$$\|L_A\| \leqq L(\varphi_A) < \infty.$$

On the other hand, $L(\varphi_A) \leqq \|L_A\|$, whence

$$\|L_A\| = L(\varphi_A).$$

Theorem 1. *There is an isomorphism $U \leftrightarrow \boldsymbol{m}$ between the space of the linear mappings $U: \mathcal{M}_E(\mathscr{C}) \to F$ with $\|U_A\| < \infty$ for every $A \in \mathscr{C}$, and the space of the additive set functions $\boldsymbol{m}: \mathscr{C} \to \mathscr{L}(E, F)$ with finite semi-variation $\tilde{\boldsymbol{m}}$, given by the equality*

$$U(f) = \int f\, d\boldsymbol{m}, \quad \textit{for} \quad f \in \mathcal{M}_E(\mathscr{C}).$$

Moreover, if U and $\boldsymbol{m}$ are in correspondence, then for every set $A \in \mathfrak{T}(\mathscr{C})$ we have

$$\|U_A\| = \tilde{\boldsymbol{m}}(A) \leqq \infty$$

and

$$|||U_A||| = \bar{\boldsymbol{m}}(A) \leqq \infty$$

where $\bar{\boldsymbol{m}}$ is the variation of $\boldsymbol{m}$.

If $\boldsymbol{m}: \mathscr{C} \to \mathscr{L}(E, F)$ is an additive set function with finite semi-variation $\tilde{\boldsymbol{m}}$, then the linear mapping $U: \mathcal{M}_E(\mathscr{C}) \to F$ defined by the equality

$$U(f) = \int f\, d\boldsymbol{m}, \quad \text{for} \quad f \in \mathcal{M}_E(\mathscr{C}),$$

is linear.

From the property 11 of the integral of the totally measurable functions, we deduce that

$$\|U_A\| = \tilde{\boldsymbol{m}}(A), \quad \text{for} \quad A \in \mathfrak{T}(\mathscr{C}).$$

In particular,

$$\|U_A\| = \tilde{\boldsymbol{m}}(A) < \infty, \quad \text{for} \quad A \in \mathscr{C}.$$

The correspondence $\boldsymbol{m} \to U$ is evidently linear and one-to-one, since $U = 0$ implies $\boldsymbol{m} = 0$.

Conversely, let $U: \mathcal{M}_E(\mathscr{C}) \to F$ be a linear mapping with $\|U_A\| < \infty$ for $A \in \mathscr{C}$. For every $A \in \mathscr{C}$ and $x \in E$ put

$$\boldsymbol{m}(A)\, x = U(\varphi_A x).$$

It is easy to see that for fixed $A \in \mathscr{C}$, the mapping $\boldsymbol{m}(A): x \to U(\varphi_A x)$ is linear and continuous:

$$|\boldsymbol{m}(A)\, x| = |U(\varphi_A x)| \leqq \|U_A\|\, |x|,$$

whence $\boldsymbol{m}(A) \in \mathscr{L}(E, F)$ and

$$|\boldsymbol{m}(A)| \leqq \|U_A\|.$$

The mapping $\boldsymbol{m}: A \to \boldsymbol{m}(A)$ of $\mathscr{C}$ into $\mathscr{L}(E, F)$ is additive. For every step function $\boldsymbol{f} = \sum \varphi_{A_i} x_i$ of $\mathscr{E}_E(\mathscr{C})$ we have

$$\int \boldsymbol{f}\, d\boldsymbol{m} = \sum \boldsymbol{m}(A_i)\, x_i = \sum U(\varphi_{A_i} x_i) = U(\boldsymbol{f}).$$

For every set $A \in \mathfrak{C}(\mathscr{C})$ we have then

$$\tilde{\boldsymbol{m}}(A) = \sup \left| \int \boldsymbol{f}\, d\boldsymbol{m} \right| = \sup |U(\boldsymbol{f})| = \|U_A\|,$$

the supremum being taken for all $\boldsymbol{f} \in \mathscr{E}_E(\mathscr{C}, A)$ with $\|\boldsymbol{f}\| \leqq 1$. If $A \in \mathscr{C}$, then $\tilde{\boldsymbol{m}}(A) = \|U_A\| < \infty$, whence $\boldsymbol{m}$ has finite semi-variation.

Let now $\boldsymbol{f} \in \mathscr{M}_E(\mathscr{C})$ and let $A \in \mathscr{C}$ be such that $\boldsymbol{f} \in \mathscr{M}_E(\mathscr{C}, A)$. There exists a sequence $(\boldsymbol{f}_n)$ of $\mathscr{E}_E(\mathscr{C}, A)$ converging uniformly to $\boldsymbol{f}$. Then

$$U(\boldsymbol{f}) = \lim_{n\to\infty} U(\boldsymbol{f}_n) = \lim_{n\to\infty} \int \boldsymbol{f}_n\, d\boldsymbol{m} = \int \boldsymbol{f}\, d\boldsymbol{m}.$$

Finally, let $A \in \mathfrak{C}(\mathscr{C})$ and let $\boldsymbol{f} = \sum \varphi_{A_i} x_i$ be a function of $\mathscr{E}_E(\mathscr{C}, A)$ with disjoint A_i and $\|\boldsymbol{f}\| \leqq 1$. Then $|x_i| \leqq 1$ for every i and we have

$$\sum |U(\varphi_{A_i} x_i)| = \sum |\boldsymbol{m}(A_i)\, x_i| \leqq \sum |\boldsymbol{m}(A_i)| \leqq \bar{\boldsymbol{m}}(A),$$

whence

$$|||U_A||| \leqq \bar{\boldsymbol{m}}(A).$$

Conversely, let $A \in \mathfrak{C}(\mathscr{C})$, let $(A_i)_{1 \leqq i \leqq n}$ be a family of disjoint sets of $\mathscr{C}$ contained in A and let $\varepsilon > 0$. For each i there exists an element $x_i \in E$ with $|x_i| \leqq 1$, such that

$$|\boldsymbol{m}(A_i)| \leqq |\boldsymbol{m}(A_i)\, x_i| + \frac{\varepsilon}{n}.$$

Then $\boldsymbol{f} = \sum \varphi_{A_i} x_i \in \mathscr{E}_E(\mathscr{C}, A)$ and we have $\|\boldsymbol{f}\| \leqq 1$ and

$$\sum |\boldsymbol{m}(A_i)| - \varepsilon \leqq \sum |\boldsymbol{m}(A_i)\, x_i| = \sum |U(\varphi_{A_i} x_i)| \leqq |||U_A|||,$$

whence

$$\bar{\boldsymbol{m}}(A) - \varepsilon \leqq |||U_A|||.$$

ε being arbitrary, we deduce

$$\bar{\boldsymbol{m}}(A) \leqq |||U_A|||,$$

therefore

$$\bar{\boldsymbol{m}}(A) = |||U_A|||.$$

The theorem is completely proved.

Corollary 1. *There exists an isomorphism* $U \leftrightarrow \boldsymbol{m}$ *between the space of the linear functionals* $U: \mathscr{M}_E(\mathscr{C}) \to C$ *with* $\|U_A\| < \infty$ *for* $A \in \mathscr{C}$ *and the space of the additive set function* $\boldsymbol{m}: \mathscr{C} \to E'$ *with finite variation* $\bar{\boldsymbol{m}}$, *given by the equality*

$$U(f) = \int f\, d\boldsymbol{m}, \quad \text{for} \quad f \in \mathscr{M}_E(\mathscr{C}).$$

If U *and* $\boldsymbol{m}$ *are in correspondence, then*

$$\|U_A\| = \bar{\boldsymbol{m}}(A) \leqq \infty, \quad \text{for} \quad A \in \mathfrak{C}(\mathscr{C}).$$

Corollary 2. *There is an isomorphism* $U \leftrightarrow \boldsymbol{m}$ *between the space of the continuous linear mappings* $U: \mathscr{M}_E(\mathscr{C}) \to F$ *and the space of the additive set functions* $\boldsymbol{m}: \mathscr{C} \to \mathscr{L}(E, F)$ *with bounded semi-variation* $\tilde{\boldsymbol{m}}$, *given by the equality*

$$U(f) = \int f\, d\boldsymbol{m}, \quad \text{for} \quad f \in \mathscr{M}_E(\mathscr{C}).$$

If U *and* $\boldsymbol{m}$ *are in correspondence, then*

$$\|U\| = \tilde{\boldsymbol{m}}(T).$$

Corollary 3. *There is an isomorphism* $L \leftrightarrow \mu$ *between the set of the positive linear functionals* $L: \mathscr{M}(\mathscr{C}) \to R$ *and the set of the positive additive set functions* $\mu: \mathscr{C} \to R$ *given by the equality*

$$L(\varphi) = \int \varphi\, d\mu, \quad \text{for} \quad \varphi \in \mathscr{M}(\mathscr{C}).$$

If L *and* μ *are in correspondence, then*

$$\|L_A\| = \bar{\mu}(A) \leqq \infty, \quad \text{for} \quad A \in \mathfrak{C}(\mathscr{C}),$$

and

$$\|L_A\| = \mu(A) < \infty, \quad \text{for} \quad A \in \mathscr{C}.$$

Theorem 2. *For every linear mapping* $U: \mathscr{M}_E(\mathscr{C}) \to F$ *with* $\|U_A\| < \infty$ *for* $A \in \mathscr{C}$, *there exists a linear mapping* $U': \mathscr{M}(\mathscr{C}) \to \mathscr{L}(E, F)$ *with* $\|U'_A\| < \infty$ *for* $A \in \mathscr{C}$, *and only one such that*

$$U(\varphi x) = U'(\varphi)x, \quad \text{for} \quad \varphi \in \mathscr{M}(\mathscr{C}) \quad \text{and} \quad x \in E.$$

Moreover, for every set $A \in \mathfrak{C}(\mathscr{C})$ *we have*

$$\|U'_A\| \leqq \|U_A\| \leqq +\infty$$

and

$$\|\!|U'_A|\!\| = \|\!|U_A|\!\| \leqq +\infty$$

and there exists an additive set function $\boldsymbol{m}: \mathscr{C} \to \mathscr{L}(E, F)$ *with finite semi-variation* $\tilde{\boldsymbol{m}}$ *such that*

$$U(f) = \int f\, d\boldsymbol{m}, \quad \textit{for} \quad f \in \mathscr{M}_E(\mathscr{C}),$$

and

$$U'(\varphi) = \int \varphi\, d\boldsymbol{m}, \quad \textit{for} \quad \varphi \in \mathscr{M}(\mathscr{C}).$$

Let $U: \mathscr{M}_E(\mathscr{C}) \to F$ be a linear mapping with $\|U_A\| < \infty$ for $A \in \mathscr{C}$, and let $\boldsymbol{m}: \mathscr{C} \to \mathscr{L}(E, F)$ be the additive measure with finite semi-variation $\tilde{\boldsymbol{m}}$ (with respect to the spaces E and F) corresponding to U by the theorem 1, such that

$$U(f) = \int f\, d\boldsymbol{m}, \quad \text{for} \quad f \in \mathscr{M}_E(\mathscr{C}),$$

and

$$\|U_A\| = \tilde{\boldsymbol{m}}(A), \quad |||U_A||| = \bar{\boldsymbol{m}}(A), \quad \text{for} \quad A \in \mathcal{C}(\mathscr{C}).$$

From the inequality $\tilde{\boldsymbol{m}}_{R,X}(A) \leqq \tilde{\boldsymbol{m}}(A) < \infty$ for $A \in \mathscr{C}$, where $X = \mathscr{L}(E, F)$, we deduce from the theorem 1 that there exists a linear mapping $U': \mathscr{M}(\mathscr{C}) \to \mathscr{L}(E, F)$ such that

$$U'(\varphi) = \int \varphi\, d\boldsymbol{m}, \quad \text{for} \quad \varphi \in \mathscr{M}(\mathscr{C}),$$

and

$$\|U'_A\| = \tilde{\boldsymbol{m}}_{R,X}(A), \quad |||U'_A||| = \bar{\boldsymbol{m}}(A), \quad \text{for} \quad A \in \mathcal{C}(\mathscr{C}).$$

From the equality

$$\int \varphi x\, d\boldsymbol{m} = x \int \varphi\, d\boldsymbol{m}, \quad \text{for} \quad \varphi \in \mathscr{M}(\mathscr{C}) \quad \text{and} \quad x \in E,$$

we deduce

$$U(\varphi x) = U'(\varphi)x$$

and from the inequality $\tilde{\boldsymbol{m}}_{R,X} \leqq \tilde{\boldsymbol{m}}$ we deduce that

$$\|U'_A\| \leqq \|U_A\|, \quad \text{for} \quad A \in \mathcal{C}(\mathscr{C}).$$

We deduce also that

$$|||U'_A||| = |||U_A|||, \quad \text{for} \quad A \in \mathcal{C}(\mathscr{C}).$$

To prove the uniqueness of U', let $U'': \mathscr{M}(\mathscr{C}) \to X$ be a linear mapping verifying the equality

$$U(\varphi x) = U''(\varphi)x, \quad \text{for} \quad \varphi \in \mathscr{M}(\mathscr{C}) \quad \text{and} \quad x \in E.$$

Then

$$U''(\varphi)x = U'(\varphi)x, \quad \text{for} \quad \varphi \in \mathscr{M}(\mathscr{C}) \quad \text{and} \quad x \in E;$$

hence

$$U''(\varphi) = U'(\varphi), \quad \text{for} \quad \varphi \in \mathcal{M}(\mathscr{C}),$$

therefore $U'' = U'$.

The theorem is completely proved.

Remarks.

1°. The correspondence $U \to U'$ is linear and one-to-one, for if $U' = 0$, then $\boldsymbol{m} = 0$, whence $U = 0$.

2°. There are linear mappings $U': \mathcal{M}(\mathscr{C}) \to \mathscr{L}(E, F)$ with $\|U'_A\| < \infty$ for $A \in \mathscr{C}$, which do not correspond to any linear mapping $U: \mathcal{M}_E(\mathscr{C}) \to F$.

3. DOMINATED OPERATIONS

Definition 2. *We say that a linear mapping $U: \mathcal{M}_E(\mathscr{C}) \to F$ is dominated if there exists a positive linear functional L on $\mathcal{M}(\mathscr{C})$ such that*

$$|U(f)| \leqq L(|f|), \quad \textit{for} \quad f \in \mathcal{M}_E(\mathscr{C}).$$

If U and L verify this inequality we say that U is dominated by L.

Proposition 7. *Every positive linear functional $L: \mathcal{M}(\mathscr{C}) \to R$ is dominated (by itself).*

In fact, for every $\varphi \in \mathcal{M}(\mathscr{C})$ we have

$$-|\varphi| \leqq \varphi \leqq |\varphi|,$$

hence, L being increasing,

$$-L(|\varphi|) \leqq L(\varphi) \leqq L(|\varphi|),$$

therefore

$$|L(\varphi)| \leqq L(|\varphi|).$$

From the corollary 3 of the theorem 1 we deduce the following:

Proposition 8. *A linear mapping $U: \mathcal{M}_E(\mathscr{C}) \to F$ is dominated if and only if there exists a positive additive set function μ on $\mathscr{C}$ such that*

$$|U(f)| \leqq \int |f| \, d\mu, \quad \textit{for} \quad f \in \mathcal{M}_E(\mathscr{C}).$$

If U and μ verify this inequality we say that U is dominated by μ.

Proposition 9. *If the linear mapping $U: \mathcal{M}_E(\mathscr{C}) \to F$ is dominated, then $\|U_A\| < \infty$ for every $A \in \mathscr{C}$.*

In fact, if μ is a positive additive set function on $\mathscr{C}$ dominating U, then for every set $A \in \mathscr{C}$ and for every function $f \in \mathscr{M}_E(\mathscr{C}, A)$ we have

$$|U(f)| \leqq \int |f| \, d\mu \leqq \|f\| \, \mu(A),$$

whence

$$\|U_A\| \leqq \mu(A) < \infty.$$

Remark. There are linear mappings $U: \mathscr{M}_E(\mathscr{C}) \to F$ with $\|U_A\| < \infty$ for $A \in \mathscr{C}$ which are not dominated. However, if $F = C$, we shall see (corollary 2 of the theorem 3) that every linear *functional* $U: \mathscr{M}_E(\mathscr{C}) \to C$ with $\|U_A\| < \infty$ for $A \in \mathscr{C}$ is dominated.

Theorem 3. *There is an isomorphism $U \leftrightarrow \boldsymbol{m}$ between the space of the dominated mappings $U: \mathscr{M}_E(\mathscr{C}) \to F$ and the space of the additive set functions $\boldsymbol{m}: \mathscr{C} \to \mathscr{L}(E, F)$ with finite variations $|\boldsymbol{m}|$ given by the equality*

$$U(f) = \int f \, d\boldsymbol{m}, \quad \textit{for} \quad f \in \mathscr{M}_E(\mathscr{C}).$$

Moreover, if U and $\boldsymbol{m}$ are in correspondence, we have

$$|||U_A||| = |\boldsymbol{m}| (A), \quad \textit{for} \quad A \in \mathscr{C},$$

and $|\boldsymbol{m}|$ is the least positive additive set function dominating U.

Consider the isomorphism $U \leftrightarrow \boldsymbol{m}$ stated in theorem 1. We have to prove that U is dominated if and only if the corresponding set function $\boldsymbol{m}$ has finite variation.

If $\boldsymbol{m}$ has finite variation $|\boldsymbol{m}|$, then

$$|U(f)| = \left| \int f \, d\boldsymbol{m} \right| \leqq \int |f| \, d|\boldsymbol{m}|, \quad \text{for} \quad f \in \mathscr{M}_E(\mathscr{C}),$$

therefore U is dominated by $|\boldsymbol{m}|$.

Conversely, suppose that U is dominated by some positive additive set function μ. Then for every $A \in \mathscr{C}$ and $x \in E$ we have

$$|\boldsymbol{m}(A)\, x| = \left| \int \varphi_A x \, d\boldsymbol{m} \right| = |U(\varphi_A x)| \leqq \int \varphi_A |x| \, d\mu \leqq \mu(A)\, |x|,$$

whence

$$|\boldsymbol{m}(A)| \leqq \mu(A) < \infty.$$

It follows that $\boldsymbol{m}$ has finite variation $|\boldsymbol{m}|$ and we have $|\boldsymbol{m}| \leqq \mu$. Since μ is arbitrary, we deduce that $|\boldsymbol{m}|$ is the least positive additive set function dominating U.

Remark. We shall denote by μ_U the least positive additive set function dominating U. Then, if U and $\boldsymbol{m}$ are in correspondence, we have $\mu_U = |\boldsymbol{m}|$.

The positive linear functional L defined on $\mathcal{M}(\mathscr{C})$ by the equality

$$L(\varphi) = \int \varphi \, d\mu_U, \quad \text{for} \quad \varphi \in \mathcal{M}(\mathscr{C})$$

is the least positive linear functional dominating U.

Corollary 1. *Let X be a Banach space. There exists an isomorphism $U \leftrightarrow \boldsymbol{m}$ between the space of the dominated linear operators $U: \mathcal{M}(\mathscr{C}) \to X$ and the space of the additive set functions $\boldsymbol{m}: \mathscr{C} \to X$ with finite variation $|\boldsymbol{m}|$, given by the equality*

$$U(\varphi) = \int \varphi \, d\boldsymbol{m}, \quad \textit{for} \quad \varphi \in \mathcal{M}(\mathscr{C}).$$

If U and $\boldsymbol{m}$ are in correspondence, we have

$$|||U_A||| = |\boldsymbol{m}|(A), \quad \textit{for} \quad A \in \mathscr{C},$$

and

$$\mu_U = |\boldsymbol{m}|.$$

Corollary 2. *If $U: \mathcal{M}_E(\mathscr{C}) \to C$ is a linear functional with $\|U_A\| < \infty$ for $A \in \mathscr{C}$, then U is dominated.*

In fact, for the additive set function $\boldsymbol{m}: \mathscr{C} \to \mathscr{L}(E, F)$ with finite semi-variation, corresponding to U by theorem 1, the variation and the semi-variation are equal, whence $\boldsymbol{m}$ has finite variation. Then, by theorem 3, U is dominated.

Corollary 3. *A linear mapping $U: \mathcal{M}_E(\mathscr{C}) \to F$ is dominated if and only if $|||U_A||| < \infty$ for every $A \in \mathscr{C}$. If U is dominated, then*

$$\mu_U(A) = |||U_A|||, \quad \textit{for} \quad A \in \mathscr{C}.$$

Theorem 4. *There is an isomorphism $U \leftrightarrow U'$ between the space of the dominated linear mappings $U: \mathcal{M}_E(\mathscr{C}) \to F$ and the space of the dominated linear mappings $U': \mathcal{M}(\mathscr{C}) \to \mathscr{L}(E, F)$ given by the equality*

$$U(\varphi x) = U'(\varphi)\, x, \quad \textit{for} \quad \varphi \in \mathcal{M}(\mathscr{C}) \quad \textit{and} \quad x \in E.$$

If U and U' are in correspondence, then

$$\mu_U = \mu_{U'}$$

and there exists a common additive set function $\boldsymbol{m}: \mathscr{C} \to \mathscr{L}(E, F)$ with finite variation such that

$$U(f) = \int f \, d\boldsymbol{m}, \quad \textit{for} \quad f \in \mathcal{M}_E(\mathscr{C}),$$

and

$$U'(\varphi) = \int \varphi \, d\boldsymbol{m}, \quad \textit{for} \quad \varphi \in \mathcal{M}(\mathscr{C}).$$

Consider the isomorphic correspondence $U \to U'$ stated in theorem 2. If U is dominated, then by theorem 3, the corresponding additive set function $\boldsymbol{m}: \mathscr{C} \to \mathscr{L}(E, F)$ has finite variation and $\mu_U = |m|$. By theorem 2 we have also

$$U'(\varphi) = \int \varphi \, d\boldsymbol{m}, \quad \text{for} \quad \varphi \in \mathscr{M}(\mathscr{C}),$$

hence, by theorem 3, U' is dominated and $\mu_{U'} = |\boldsymbol{m}|$, therefore $\mu_U = \mu_{U'}$.

Let now U': $\mathscr{M}(\mathscr{C}) \to \mathscr{L}(E, F)$ be a dominated linear mapping. By theorem 3, there exists an additive set function $\boldsymbol{m}$: $\mathscr{C} \to \mathscr{L}(E, F)$ with finite variation such that

$$U'(\varphi) = \int \varphi \, d\boldsymbol{m}, \quad \text{for} \quad \varphi \in \mathscr{M}(\mathscr{C}).$$

The linear mapping U: $\mathscr{M}_E(\mathscr{C}) \to F$ defined by

$$U(f) = \int f \, d\boldsymbol{m}, \quad \text{for} \quad f \in \mathscr{M}_E(\mathscr{C}),$$

is dominated and for $\varphi \in \mathscr{M}(\mathscr{C})$ and $x \in E$ we have

$$U(\varphi x) = \int \varphi x \, d\boldsymbol{m} = x \int \varphi \, d\boldsymbol{m} = U'(\varphi)\, x.$$

This completes the proof.

Remark. We shall identify the corresponding mappings U and U' and we shall write U instead of U'. With this convention, for every dominated linear mapping U: $\mathscr{M}(\mathscr{C}) \to \mathscr{L}(E, F)$ we have

$$U(\varphi x) = U(\varphi)\, x, \quad \text{for} \quad \varphi \in \mathscr{M}(\mathscr{C}) \quad \text{and} \quad x \in E.$$

Theorem 5. *Let* U: $\mathscr{M}_E(\mathscr{C}) \to F$ *be a dominated linear operation and let* $\boldsymbol{m}: \mathscr{C} \to \mathscr{L}(E, F)$ *be the corresponding additive set function with finite variation such that*

$$U(f) = \int f \, d\boldsymbol{m}, \quad \textit{for} \quad f \in \mathscr{M}_E(\mathscr{C}).$$

Then $\boldsymbol{m}$ *is countably additive if and only if, for every decreasing sequence* (φ_n) *of functions of* $\mathscr{M}(\mathscr{C})$ *such that* $\varphi_n(t) \to 0$ *for every* $t \in T$, *we have* $U(\varphi_n) \to 0$.

Suppose that $\boldsymbol{m}$ is countably additive. Then its variation $|\boldsymbol{m}|$ is countably additive and the functions of $\mathscr{M}(\mathscr{C})$ are $|\boldsymbol{m}|$-integrable. If (φ_n) is a decreasing sequence of $\mathscr{M}(\mathscr{C})$ converging to zero, we have $\int \varphi_n \, d|\boldsymbol{m}| \to 0$. From the relations

$$|U(\varphi_n)| = \left| \int \varphi_n \, d\boldsymbol{m} \right| \leq \int \varphi_n \, d|\boldsymbol{m}|$$

we deduce that $U(\varphi_n) \to 0$.

Conversely, suppose that $U(\varphi_n) \to 0$ for every decreasing sequence (φ_n) of $\mathcal{M}(\mathscr{C})$ converging to zero. Let (A_n) be a decreasing sequence of sets of $\mathscr{C}$ with void intersection. Then the sequence (φ_{A_n}) is decreasing and converges to zero, therefore

$$\boldsymbol{m}(A_n) = U(\varphi_{A_n}) \to 0$$

and this condition is sufficient for $\boldsymbol{m}$ to be countably additive.

4. THE SEMI-NORM N_∞

Let $\mathcal{N}$ be a *hereditary clan* of subsets of T, i.e. a clan such that $A \in \mathcal{N}$ and $B \subset A$ imply $B \in \mathcal{N}$. The sets of $\mathcal{N}$ are called *$\mathcal{N}$-negligible*. A property $P(t)$ defined for every $t \in T$ is said to be true *$\mathcal{N}$-almost everywhere* if the set on which P is not true is $\mathcal{N}$-negligible. If E is a vector space, a function f: $T \to E$ is $\mathcal{N}$-negligible, if $f(t) = 0$ $\mathcal{N}$-almost everywhere.

Examples.

1. If μ is a positive (finite or infinite) subadditive set function defined on a clan $\mathscr{C}$, we can take $\mathcal{N}$ the hereditary clan generated by the sets $A \in \mathcal{T}(\mathscr{C})$ having the property that $\mu(B) = 0$ for every $B \in \mathscr{C}$ with $B \subset$ A.

In particular, μ can be the semi-variation of an additive set function on $\mathscr{C}$.

We remark that if $\mathscr{C}$ is a *tribe* and if μ is *countably additive*, then $\mathcal{N}$ is a *tribe*.

2. If μ is a positive measure on a clan $\mathscr{C}$, we can take $\mathcal{N}$ the class of the μ-negligible sets. In this case $\mathcal{N}$ is a tribe.

Let E be a Banach space. For every function f: $T \to E$ or f: $T \to \bar{R}$ we denote by $N_\infty(f, \mathcal{N})$ or by $\|f\|_\infty$ the greatest lower bound of the numbers $\alpha \leqq +\infty$ such that $|f(t)| \leqq \alpha$, $\mathcal{N}$-almost everywhere. We deduce easily the following properties:

1. $0 \leqq \|f\|_\infty \leqq \infty$;
2. $\|\alpha f\|_\infty = |\alpha| \, \|f\|_\infty$;
3. $\|f + g\|_\infty \leqq \|f\|_\infty + \|g\|_\infty$;
4. $\|f\|_\infty \leqq \|f\|$.
5. For every $\varepsilon > 0$ we have

$$|f(t)| \leqq \|f\|_\infty + \varepsilon \quad \mathcal{N}\text{-almost everywhere.}$$

5′. If $\mathcal{N}$ is a tribe, then

$$|f(t)| \leqq \|f\|_\infty \quad \mathcal{N}\text{-almost everywhere.}$$

6. If $|f(t)| = |g(t)|$ $\mathcal{N}$-almost everywhere, then

$$\|f\|_\infty = \|g\|_\infty.$$

7. If f is $\mathcal{N}$-negligible, then $\|f\|_\infty = 0$.

7′. If $\mathcal{N}$ is a tribe, then $\|f\|_\infty = 0$ if and only if f is $\mathcal{N}$-negligible.

8. If $f: T \to E$ and $\varphi: T \to R$, then

$$\|f\varphi\|_\infty \leqq \|f\|_\infty \|\varphi\|_\infty .$$

8′. If E is a Banach algebra, then

$$\|fg\|_\infty \leqq \|f\|_\infty \|g\|_\infty .$$

5. ALMOST TOTALLY MEASURABLE FUNCTIONS

Let $\mathscr{C}$ be a *clan* of subsets of T and $\mathcal{N}$ a *hereditary clan* contained in $\mathscr{C}$. Let E be a Banach space.

We shall design by $\mathcal{M}_E^\infty(\mathscr{C},\mathcal{N})$ or $\mathcal{M}_E^\infty(\mathscr{C})$ the set of the functions $f: T \to E$ which are equal $\mathcal{N}$-almost everywhere to functions of $\mathcal{M}_E(\mathscr{C})$.

For every set $A \subset T$ we design by $\mathcal{M}_E^\infty(\mathscr{C},\mathcal{N}, A)$ or $\mathcal{M}_E^\infty(\mathscr{C}, A)$ the subset of the functions of $\mathcal{M}_E^\infty(\mathscr{C},\mathcal{N})$ vanishing outside A.

The functions of $\mathcal{M}_E^\infty(\mathscr{C})$ are called $\mathcal{N}$*-almost totally measurable,* or almost totally measurable, if the clan $\mathcal{N}$ is understood.

We see that $\mathcal{M}_E^\infty(\mathscr{C})$ is a vector space.

We shall consider on it the topology defined by the semi-norm $\|f\|_\infty = N_\infty(f,\mathcal{N})$.

For every set $A \in \mathcal{C}(\mathscr{C})$, the spaces $\mathscr{E}_E(\mathscr{C}, A)$ and $\mathcal{M}_E(\mathscr{C}, A)$ are dense in $\mathcal{M}_E^\infty(\mathscr{C}, A)$. If $\mathcal{N}$ is a tribe, then $\mathcal{M}_E^\infty(\mathscr{C}, A)$ is complete.

Let now E and F be two Banach spaces, and $\boldsymbol{m}: \mathscr{C} \to \mathscr{L}(E, F)$ an additive set function with *finite semi-variation* $\tilde{\boldsymbol{m}}$, absolutely continuous with respect to $\mathcal{N}$, i.e. such that $\boldsymbol{m}(A) = 0$ for every $A \in \mathcal{N}$. Then $\tilde{\boldsymbol{m}}(A) = 0$ for every $A \in \mathcal{N}$.

We can then extend the integral with respect to $\boldsymbol{m}$ from the space $\mathcal{M}_E(\mathscr{C})$ of the totally measurable functions to the space $\mathcal{M}_E^\infty(\mathscr{C})$.

We prove first the following

Proposition 10. *If two functions $f,g \in \mathcal{M}_E(\mathscr{C})$ are equal $\mathcal{N}$-almost everywhere, then*

$$\int f\,d\boldsymbol{m} = \int g\,d\boldsymbol{m}.$$

In fact, the function $\boldsymbol{h} = f - g$ is $\mathcal{N}$-negligible. The set $N = \{t; \boldsymbol{h}(t) \neq 0\}$ is $\mathcal{N}$-negligible; hence $\tilde{\boldsymbol{m}}(N) = 0$, therefore

$$\left|\int \boldsymbol{h}\,d\boldsymbol{m}\right| \leqq \|\boldsymbol{h}\|\ \tilde{\boldsymbol{m}}(N) = 0,$$

consequently $\int f\,d\boldsymbol{m} = \int g\,d\boldsymbol{m}$.

Definition 3. *For every function* $f \in \mathscr{M}_E^\infty(\mathscr{C})$ *we define the integral* $\int f\,dm$ *by the equality*

$$\int f\,dm = \int g\,dm$$

where g *is an arbitrary function of* $\mathscr{M}_E(\mathscr{C})$ *equal to* f $\mathscr{N}$*-almost everywhere.*

From the preceding proposition we deduce that the integral $\int f\,dm$ depends only on f.

If $f \in \mathscr{M}_E^\infty(\mathscr{C})$ and $A \in \mathcal{T}(\mathscr{C})$ then $f\varphi_A \in \mathscr{M}_E^\infty(\mathscr{C})$. We write as usually

$$\int_A f\,dm = \int f\varphi_A\,dm.$$

The properties of the integral of the totally measurable functions remain valid for functions of $\mathscr{M}_E^\infty(\mathscr{C})$. We state separately the properties 10 and 11 in the following form:

Proposition 11. *For every set* $A \in \mathcal{T}(\mathscr{C})$ *we have*

$$\tilde{m}(A) = \sup\left|\int f\,dm\right|$$

where the supremum is taken for all the functions f *of* $\mathscr{M}_E(\mathscr{C}, A)$ *(or of* $\mathscr{M}_E^\infty(\mathscr{C}, A)$*) such that* $\|f\|_\infty \leqq 1$.

Denote by $\mathscr{D}$ the set of the functions $f \in \mathscr{M}_E(\mathscr{C}, A)$ with $\|f\|_\infty \leqq 1$. Let $f \in \mathscr{D}$ and let $\varepsilon > 0$. We have $|f(t)| \leqq 1 + \varepsilon$ $\mathscr{N}$-almost everywhere; hence the set

$$N = \{t; |f(t)| > 1 + \varepsilon\} \quad \text{is } \mathscr{N}\text{-negligible.}$$

The set $g = f\varphi_{A-N}$ belongs to $\mathscr{M}_E(\mathscr{C}, A)$ and $\|g\| \leqq 1 + \varepsilon$. On the other hand, $f(t) = g(t)$ $\mathscr{N}$-almost everywhere, whence

$$\left|\int f\,dm\right| = \left|\int g\,dm\right| \leqq (1 + \varepsilon)\,\tilde{m}(A).$$

It follows that

$$\sup\left|\int f\,dm\right| \leqq (1 + \varepsilon)\,\tilde{m}(A), \quad \text{for} \quad f \in \mathscr{D},$$

whence, ε being arbitrary,

$$\sup\left|\int f\,dm\right| \leqq \tilde{m}(A), \quad \text{for} \quad f \in \mathscr{D}.$$

The converse inequality follows from the inequality $\|f\|_\infty \leqq \|f\|$.

The part concerning $\mathscr{M}_E^\infty(\mathscr{C}, A)$ is then easily derived.

Corollary. *For every set* $A \in \mathfrak{T}(\mathscr{C})$ *and for every function* $f \in \mathscr{M}_E^\infty(\mathscr{C}, A)$ *we have*

$$\left|\int f\,dm\right| \leqq \|f\|_\infty\, \tilde{m}(A) \leqq \|f\|\, \tilde{m}(A) \leqq \infty.$$

6. OPERATIONS ON $\mathscr{M}_E^\infty(\mathscr{C})$

Let $\mathscr{C}$ be a *clan*, $\mathscr{N}$ a *hereditary clan* contained in $\mathscr{C}$, E and F two Banach spaces. Consider the space $\mathscr{M}_E^\infty(\mathscr{C})$ with the semi-norm $\|f\|_\infty = N_\infty(f, \mathscr{N})$.

Let $U: \mathscr{M}_E^\infty(\mathscr{C}) \to F$ be a linear mapping. For every set $A \subset T$ we design by U_A the restriction of U to the space $\mathscr{M}_E^\infty(\mathscr{C}, A)$. We put

$$\|U_A\|_\infty = \sup |U(f)|, \quad \text{for} \quad f \in \mathscr{M}_E^\infty(\mathscr{C}, A) \quad \text{with} \quad \|f\|_\infty \leqq 1,$$

and

$$|||U_A|||_\infty = \sup \sum |U(\varphi_{A_i} x_i)|$$

where the supremum is taken for all the step functions $f = \sum \varphi_{A_i} x_i \in \mathscr{E}_E(\mathscr{C}, A)$ with disjoint A_i and $\|f\|_\infty \leqq 1$.

We have

$$\|U_A\|_\infty \leqq |||U_A|||_\infty, \quad \text{for every} \quad A \in \mathfrak{T}(\mathscr{C}).$$

If $F = C$, we prove as in proposition 3 that

$$\|U_A\|_\infty = |||U_A|||_\infty, \quad \text{for} \quad A \in \mathfrak{T}(\mathscr{C}).$$

The inequality $\|U_A\|_\infty < \infty$ means that U_A is continuous on $\mathscr{M}_E^\infty(\mathscr{C}, A)$ for the semi-norm $\|f\|_\infty$.

If $A \in \mathfrak{T}(\mathscr{C})$, then $\mathscr{E}_E(\mathscr{C}, A)$ is dense in $\mathscr{M}_E^\infty(\mathscr{C}, A)$, therefore

$$\|U_A\|_\infty = \sup \left|\sum U(\varphi_{A_i} x_i)\right|,$$

the supremum being taken for $f = \sum \varphi_{A_i} x_i \in \mathscr{E}_E(\mathscr{C}, A)$ with $\|f\|_\infty \leqq 1$.

We are interested in linear operations $U: \mathscr{M}_E^\infty(\mathscr{C}) \to F$ vanishing on the $\mathscr{N}$-negligible functions. Such an operation can be identified with its restriction to the space $\mathscr{M}_E(\mathscr{C})$, therefore we shall denote both of them by the same letter U.

We remark that if $\|U_A\|_\infty < \infty$ for every $A \in \mathscr{C}$, then $U(f) = 0$ for every $\mathscr{N}$-negligible function f.

Proposition 12. *If* $U: \mathscr{M}_E^\infty(\mathscr{C}) \to F$ *is a linear mapping vanishing for* $\mathscr{N}$*-negligible sets, then for every set* $A \in \mathfrak{T}(\mathscr{C})$ *we have*

$$\|U_A\|_\infty = \|U_A\| \quad \textit{and} \quad |||U_A|||_\infty = |||U_A|||.$$

Let $A \in \mathfrak{T}(\mathscr{C})$ and $f = \sum \varphi_{A_i} x_i \in \mathscr{E}_E(\mathscr{C}, A)$ with disjoint A_i and $\|f\|_\infty \leqq 1$. Let $\varepsilon > 0$. There exists a $\mathscr{N}$-negligible set $N \in \mathscr{C}$ such that $|f(t)| \leqq 1 + \varepsilon$ outside N.

Then $g = f\varphi_{A-N} \in \mathcal{E}_E(\mathcal{C}, A)$ and $\|g\| \leqq 1 + \varepsilon$. On the other hand $f(t) = g(t)$ $\mathcal{N}$-almost everywhere; hence $U(f) = U(g)$, consequently

$$|U(f)| = |U(g)| \leqq (1 + \varepsilon) \|U_A\|,$$

therefore

$$\|U_A\|_\infty \leqq (1 + \varepsilon) \|U_A\|.$$

We have also

$$\sum |U(\varphi_{A_i} x_i)| = \sum |U(\varphi_{A_i - N} x_i)| \leqq (1 + \varepsilon) \|\|U_A\|\|,$$

whence

$$\|\|U_A\|\|_\infty \leqq (1 + \varepsilon) \|\|U_A\|\|.$$

ε being arbitrary, we deduce

$$\|U_A\|_\infty \leqq \|U_A\| \quad \text{and} \quad \|\|U_A\|\|_\infty \leqq \|\|U_A\|\|.$$

The converse inequalities follow from the inequality $\|f\|_\infty \leqq \|f\|$.

A real linear functional $L: \mathcal{M}^\infty(\mathcal{C}, \mathcal{N}) \to R$ is *positive* if $L(\varphi) \geqq 0$ for every function $\varphi \in \mathcal{M}^\infty(\mathcal{C})$ such that $\varphi \geqq 0$ $\mathcal{N}$-almost everywhere.

If L is positive, then $L(\varphi) = 0$ for every $\mathcal{N}$-negligible function φ. In particular, $L(\varphi_A) = 0$ for every set $A \in \mathcal{N}$.

From the preceding proposition and from the proposition 6 we deduce the following

Corollary. *If L is a positive linear functional on $\mathcal{M}^\infty(\mathcal{C})$ then*

$$\|L_A\|_\infty = L(\varphi_A), \quad \textit{for every} \quad A \in \mathcal{C}.$$

Theorem 6. *There is an isomorphism $U \leftrightarrow \boldsymbol{m}$ between the space of the linear mappings $U: \mathcal{M}_E^\infty(\mathcal{C}) \to F$ with $\|U_A\|_\infty < \infty$ for $A \in \mathcal{C}$, and the set of the additive set functions $\boldsymbol{m}: \mathcal{C} \to \mathcal{L}(E, F)$ with finite semi-variation $\tilde{\boldsymbol{m}}$ and absolutely continuous with respect to $\mathcal{N}$, given by the equality*

$$U(f) = \int f\, d\boldsymbol{m}, \quad \textit{for} \quad f \in \mathcal{M}_E^\infty(\mathcal{C}).$$

If U and $\boldsymbol{m}$ are in correspondence, then for every set $A \in \mathcal{C}(\mathcal{C})$ we have

$$\|U_A\|_\infty = \tilde{\boldsymbol{m}}(A) \quad \textit{and} \quad \|\|U_A\|\|_\infty = \bar{\boldsymbol{m}}(A).$$

Let $\boldsymbol{m}: \mathcal{C} \to \mathcal{L}(E, F)$ be an additive set function with finite semi-variation $\tilde{\boldsymbol{m}}$ and absolutely continuous with respect to $\mathcal{N}$. Then $\int f\, d\boldsymbol{m} = 0$ for every $\mathcal{N}$-negligible function $f: T \to E$. We define the linear mapping $U: \mathcal{M}_E^\infty(\mathcal{C}) \to F$ by the equality

$$U(f) = \int f\, d\boldsymbol{m}, \quad \text{for} \quad f \in \mathcal{M}_E^\infty(\mathcal{C}).$$

We have then $U(f) = 0$ for every $\mathscr{N}$-negligible function f; hence, using the theorem 1 and the proposition 12, we deduce

$$\|U_A\|_\infty = \|U_A\| = \tilde{m}(A) \quad \text{and} \quad |||U_A|||_\infty = |||U_A||| = \bar{m}(A)$$

for every $A \in \mathfrak{T}(\mathscr{C})$.

The correspondence $\boldsymbol{m} \to U$ is linear and one-to-one.

Conversely, let $U: \mathscr{M}_E^\infty(\mathscr{C}) \to F$ be a linear mapping with $\|U_A\|_\infty < \infty$ for $A \in \mathscr{C}$. It follows that $U(f) = 0$ for every $\mathscr{N}$-negligible function f; hence, by proposition 12, we have

$$\|U_A\| = \|U_A\|_\infty < \infty, \quad \text{for} \quad A \in \mathscr{C}.$$

Using the theorem 1 we find an additive set function $\boldsymbol{m}: \mathscr{C} \to \mathscr{L}(E, F)$ with finite semi-variation such that

$$U(f) = \int f\,d\boldsymbol{m}, \quad \text{for} \quad f \in \mathscr{M}_E(\mathscr{C}),$$

and this equality remains valid for $f \in \mathscr{M}_E^\infty(\mathscr{C})$. For every set $A \in \mathscr{N}$ we have $\boldsymbol{m}(A) = U(\varphi_A) = 0$; hence $\boldsymbol{m}$ is absolutely continuous with respect to $\mathscr{N}$ and thus the theorem is completely proved.

We say that a linear mapping $U: \mathscr{M}_E^\infty(\mathscr{C}) \to F$ is *dominated* if its restriction to the space $\mathscr{M}_E(\mathscr{C})$ is dominated.

If U vanishes for $\mathscr{N}$-negligible functions, then U is dominated if and only if $|||U_A|||_\infty < \infty$ for every $A \in \mathscr{C}$.

From the preceding theorem we deduce the following:

Corollary. *The equality*

$$U(f) = \int f\,d\boldsymbol{m}, \quad \textit{for} \quad f \in \mathscr{M}_E^\infty(\mathscr{C}),$$

realizes an isomorphism $U \leftrightarrow \boldsymbol{m}$ between the space of the dominated linear operations $U: \mathscr{M}_E^\infty(\mathscr{C}, \mathscr{N}) \to F$ vanishing for $\mathscr{N}$-negligible functions and the space of the additive set functions $\boldsymbol{m}: \mathscr{C} \to \mathscr{L}(E, F)$ with finite variation $\bar{\boldsymbol{m}}$ and absolutely continuous with respect to $\mathscr{N}$, and we have

$$|||U_A|||_\infty = \bar{m}(A), \quad \textit{for} \quad A \in \mathfrak{T}(\mathscr{C}).$$

$\boldsymbol{m}$ is countably additive if and only if $U(\varphi_n) \to 0$ for every decreasing sequence (φ_n) of functions of $\mathscr{M}^\infty(\mathscr{C})$ such that $\varphi_n(t) \to 0$ $\mathscr{N}$-almost everywhere.

Theorem 7. *If $T \in \mathscr{C}$, then every extremal point of the unit ball S^* of the dual of $\mathscr{M}^\infty(\mathscr{C})$ is of the form $x^* = \alpha y^*$ where $|\alpha| = 1$ and y^* is multiplicative.*

Let x^* be an extremal point of S^*. We prove first that $|x^*| = 1$. It is evident that $x^* \neq 0$, whence $z^* = \dfrac{x^*}{|x^*|} \in S^*$ and $x^* = |x^*| z^* + (1 - |x^*|) 0$. Since x^* is an extremal point, we can not have $0 < |x^*| < 1$, whence $|x^*| = 1$.

Since x^* is a continuous linear functional on $\mathcal{M}^\infty(\mathcal{C})$, there exists an additive real set function λ defined on $\mathcal{C}$, absolutely continuous with respect to μ, such that $|\lambda|(T) = |x^*| = 1$ and

$$x^*(f) = \int f \, d\lambda, \quad \text{for} \quad f \in \mathcal{M}^\infty(\mathcal{C}).$$

We prove now that for every pair A, B of disjoint sets of $\mathcal{C}$ we have either $\lambda(A) = 0$ or $\lambda(B) = 0$.

Suppose, on the contrary, that there exist two disjoint sets $E_1, E_2 \in \mathcal{C}$ with $\lambda(E_1) \neq 0$ and $\lambda(E_2) \neq 0$. The set functions λ_1 and λ_2 defined on $\mathcal{C}$ by the equalities

$$\lambda_1(A) = \lambda(A \cap E_1), \quad \lambda_2(A) = \lambda(A - E_1), \quad \text{for} \quad A \in \mathcal{C},$$

are additive and with finite variation and we verify easily that

$$|\lambda_1|(A) = |\lambda|(A \cap E_1), \quad |\lambda_2|(A) = |\lambda|(A - E_1), \quad \text{for} \quad A \in \mathcal{C}.$$

If we put $\alpha = |\lambda|(T)$, $\alpha_1 = |\lambda_1|(T)$, and $\alpha_2 = |\lambda_2|(T)$, we have $1 = \alpha = \alpha_1 + \alpha_2$. Since $\alpha_1 \neq 0$ and $\alpha_2 \neq 0$ we put

$$v_1 = \frac{\lambda_1}{\alpha_1} \quad \text{and} \quad v_2 = \frac{\lambda_2}{\alpha_2}.$$

For the corresponding functionals x_1^* and x_2^* defined on $\mathcal{M}^\infty(\mathcal{C})$ by

$$x_1^*(f) = \int f \, dv_1 \quad \text{and} \quad x_2^*(f) = \int f \, dv_2$$

we have $|x_1^*| = |x_2^*| = 1$, whence $x_1^*, x_2^* \in S^*$.

Since $\lambda = \alpha_1 v_1 + (1 - \alpha_2) v_2$, we deduce $x^* = \alpha_1 x_1^* + (1 - \alpha_2) x_2^*$; hence $x_1^* = x_2^* = x^*$, therefore $v_1 = v_2 = \lambda$, consequently $0 \neq \lambda(E_1) = v_2(E_1) = 0$ and we get a contradiction.

For every set $E \in \mathcal{C}$, the sets E and $T - E$ are disjoint and we have either $\lambda(E) = 0$ or $\lambda(T - E) = 0$; hence

$$\lambda(E) [\lambda(T) - \lambda(E)] = 0,$$

therefore λ takes only two values, namely 0 and $\lambda(T)$. Then the set function $m = \dfrac{\lambda}{\lambda(T)}$ takes only the values 0 and 1. Then

$$m(A \cap B) = m(A) \, m(B), \quad \text{for} \quad A, B \in \mathcal{C}.$$

In fact, if $m(A) = 0$ or if $m(B) = 0$, then $m(A \cap B) = 0$; if $m(A) = m(B) = 1$, then $m(A - A \cap B) = 1 - m(A \cap B)$ and $m(B - A \cap B) = 1 - m(A \cap B)$; since the sets $A - A \cap B$ and $B - A \cap B$ are disjoint, we have either $m(A - A \cap B) = 0$ or $m(B - A \cap B) = 0$, therefore $m(A \cap B) = 1$.

Consider now the positive linear functional y^* defined on $\mathscr{M}^\infty(\mathscr{C})$ by the equality

$$y^*(f) = \int f\,dm, \quad \text{for} \quad f \in \mathscr{M}^\infty(\mathscr{C}).$$

We have $|y^*| = m(T) = 1$.

From the equality $\lambda = \alpha m$, with $\alpha = \lambda(T)$, we deduce that $x^* = \alpha y^*$ and $|\alpha| = |\lambda(T)| = |\lambda|(T) = 1$.

We have to show that y^* is multiplicative. We remark that for $A, B \in \mathscr{C}$ we have

$$y^*(\varphi_A \varphi_B) = y^*(\varphi_A)\, y^*(\varphi_B).$$

If $g \in \mathscr{M}^\infty(\mathscr{C})$, then the set

$$\mathscr{M}_g = \{f \in \mathscr{M}^\infty(\mathscr{C});\quad y^*(fg) = y^*(f)\, y^*(g)\}$$

is a closed linear subspace of $\mathscr{M}^\infty(\mathscr{C})$. If $g = \varphi_A$, then from the preceding remark we deduce that $\mathscr{M}_g = \mathscr{M}^\infty(\mathscr{C})$. It follows that if $f \in \mathscr{M}^\infty(\mathscr{C})$, then $\mathscr{M}_f$ contains all the characteristic functions; hence $\mathscr{M}_f = \mathscr{M}^\infty(\mathscr{C})$, therefore

$$y^*(fg) = y^*(f)\, y^*(g) \quad \text{for} \quad f, g \in \mathscr{M}^\infty(\mathscr{C}).$$

Conversely, let y^* be a continuous linear and multiplicative functional on $\mathscr{M}^\infty(\mathscr{C})$. We prove that y^* is an extremal point of S^*. Suppose that there exists a number α with $0 < \alpha < 1$, and two functionals $y_1^*, y_2^* \in S^*$ with $|y_1^*| = |y_2^*| = 1$ such that

$$y^* = \alpha y_1^* + (1 - \alpha)\, y_2^*.$$

Let m, μ_1 and μ_2 be the additive set functions defined on $\mathscr{C}$ corresponding respectively to y^*, y_1^* and y_2^*. We have then $|\mu_1|(T) = |y_1^*| = 1$, $|\mu_2|(T) = |y_2^*| = 1$ and

$$m = \alpha\mu_1 + (1 - \alpha)\, \mu_2.$$

Since y^* is multiplicative, m is also multiplicative:

$$m(A \cap B) = m(A)\, m(B), \quad \text{for} \quad A, B \in \mathscr{C},$$

whence m takes only the values 0 and 1.

If $m(A) = 1$, then

$$\begin{aligned} 1 = m(A) &= |\alpha\mu_1(A) + (1 - \alpha)\, \mu_2(A)| \\ &\leqq \alpha|\mu_1|(A) + (1 - \alpha)\, |\mu_2|(A) \\ &\leqq \alpha|\mu_1|(T) + (1 - \alpha)\, |\mu_2|(T) = 1, \end{aligned}$$

whence $|\mu_1|(A) = |\mu_2|(A) = 1$. We have then

$$\alpha[|\mu_1|(A) - \mu_1(A)] + (1 - \alpha)[|\mu_2|(A) - \mu_2(A)] = 0,$$

whence $\mu_1(A) = |\mu_1|(A) = 1$ and $\mu_2(A) = |\mu_2|(A) = 1$. In particular, $\mu_1(T) = \mu_2(T) = m(T) = 1$.

If $m(A) = 0$, then $m(T - A) = 1$, whence $\mu_1(T - A) = \mu_2(T - A) = 1$, therefore $\mu_1(A) = \mu_2(A) = 0$.

It follows that $\mu_1 = \mu_2 = m$; hence $y_1^* = y_2^* = y^*$, consequently y^* is an extremal point of S^*.

Finally, if y^* is a continuous linear and multiplicative functional in S^* and if $|\alpha| = 1$, then $x^* = \alpha y^*$ is an extremal point in S^*. In fact, if $0 < \beta < 1$ and $x^* = \beta x_1^* + (1 - \beta) x_2^*$, where $x_1^*, x_2^* \in S^*$, and $|x_1^*| = |x_2^*| = 1$, then $y^* = \beta \frac{x_1^*}{\alpha} + (1 - \beta)\frac{x_2^*}{\alpha}$; hence $\frac{x_1^*}{\alpha} = \frac{x_2^*}{\alpha} = y^*$, therefore $x_1^* = x_2^* = x^*$, consequently x^* is extremal.

The proposition is completely proved.

7. THE SPACE $\mathcal{L}_E^\infty(\mu)$

Let μ be a *positive measure* defined on a *clan* $\mathscr{C}$ and E a Banach space. Consider the *tribe* $\mathscr{N}$ of the μ-negligible sets. For every function $f: T \to E$ or $f: T \to \bar{R}$ we shall write $N_\infty(f, \mu) = N_\infty(f, \mathscr{N}) = \|f\|_\infty$. From the section 4 we deduce the following properties:

1. $N_\infty(f, \mu) = 0$ if and only if $f(t) = 0$ μ-almost everywhere;

2. $N_\infty(\alpha f) = |\alpha| N_\infty(f)$;

3. $N_\infty(f + g) \leqq N_\infty(f) + N_\infty(g)$.

We shall denote by $\mathcal{L}_E^\infty(\mu)$ or $\mathcal{L}_E^\infty$ the set of the *μ-measurable* functions $f: T \to E$ with $N_\infty(f, \mu) < \infty$. We shall write $\mathcal{L}^\infty(\mu)$ instead of $\mathcal{L}_R^\infty(\mu)$. From the properties of N_∞ we deduce that $\mathcal{L}_E^\infty(\mu)$ is a vector space and that N_∞ is a semi-norm on it. The space $\mathcal{L}^\infty(\mu)$ is an algebra.

A sequence (f_n) of $\mathcal{L}_E^\infty$ converges in $\mathcal{L}_E^\infty$ if and only if there exists a μ-negligible set $N \subset T$ such that on $T - N$ the sequence (f_n) is uniformly convergent.

Proposition 13. *The space $\mathcal{L}_E^\infty(\mu)$ is complete.*

Let (f_n) be a Cauchy sequence in $\mathcal{L}_E^\infty(\mu)$: for every n there exists an integer k_n such that for $r \geqq k_n$ and $s \geqq k_n$ we have $N_\infty(f_r - f_s) \leqq \frac{1}{n}$; there exists then a μ-negligible set A_{rs} such that $|f_r(t) - f_s(t)| \leqq \frac{1}{n}$ for $t \notin A_{rs}$. If A_n is the union of the sets

A_{rs} with $r \geqq k_n$ and $s \geqq k_n$, then A_n is μ-negligible and for $t \notin A_n$ we have $|f_r(t) - f_s(t)| \leqq \frac{1}{n}$ for $r \geqq k_n$ and $s \geqq k_n$. The set $A = \bigcup_{n=1}^{\infty} A_n$ is negligible and (f_n) converges uniformly on $T - A$ to a function f that we take null on A. On the other hand, the sequence $N_\infty(f_n)$ converges to a number a and

$$|f_n(t)| \leqq N_\infty(f_n) \quad \text{almost everywhere;}$$

hence

$$|f(t)| \leqq a \qquad \text{almost everywhere,}$$

therefore $f \in \mathscr{L}_E^\infty(\mu)$. Since (f_n) converges uniformly on $T - A$ to f, it follows that $N_\infty(f_n - f) \to 0$, i.e. f_n converges to f in $\mathscr{L}^\infty(\mu)$. Thus, the proposition is proved.

The closure of the origin in $\mathscr{L}_E^\infty(\mu)$ is the set $\mathscr{N}_E^\infty$ of the μ-negligible sets. The quotient space $L_E^\infty = \mathscr{L}_E^\infty / \mathscr{N}_E^\infty$ is a Banach space with the norm $N_\infty(\tilde{f}) = N_\infty(f)$, where $\tilde{f}$ is the equivalence class modulo $\mathscr{N}_E^\infty$ of the function f. If E is a Banach algebra, then L_E^∞ is also a Banach algebra.

Proposition 14. *The space $\mathscr{E}(\mu)$ of the real μ-measurable step functions is dense in $\mathscr{L}^\infty(\mu)$.*

Let $f \in \mathscr{L}^\infty(\mu)$. The function

$$g(t) = \begin{cases} f(t), & \text{if } |f(t)| \leqq N_\infty(f), \\ N_\infty(f), & \text{if } |f(t)| > N_\infty(f), \end{cases}$$

is bounded and equal to f μ-almost everywhere, whence g is μ-measurable. There exists then a sequence (g_n) of μ-measurable step functions converging uniformly to g, whence $N_\infty(g_n - g) \to 0$. Since $g - g_n = f - g_n$ μ-almost everywhere, we have $N_\infty(g - g_n) = N_\infty(f - g_n)$, whence $N_\infty(f - g_n) \to 0$

Corollary 1. *The space $\mathscr{L}^\infty(\mu)$ is equal to the space of almost totally measurable functions $\mathscr{M}^\infty(\mathfrak{T}(\mu), \mathscr{N})$, where $\mathfrak{T}(\mu)$ is the tribe of the μ-measurable sets and $\mathscr{N}$ is the tribe of the μ-negligible sets.*

The theorem 6 and its corollary can now be stated in the following form:

Corollary 2. *There exists an isomorphism $U \leftrightarrow \boldsymbol{m}$ between the space of the continuous linear mappings $U: \mathscr{L}^\infty(\mu) \to F$ and the space of the additive set functions $\boldsymbol{m}: \mathfrak{T}(\mu) \to F$ with bounded semi-variation $\tilde{\boldsymbol{m}}_{R,F}$ and absolutely continuous with respect to μ (i.e. vanishing on μ-negligible sets), given by the equality*

$$U(f) = \int f\, d\boldsymbol{m}, \quad \text{for} \quad f \in \mathscr{L}^\infty(\mu).$$

If U and $\boldsymbol{m}$ are in correspondence, we have

$$\|U\|_\infty = \tilde{\boldsymbol{m}}_{R,F}(T)$$

and

$$|||U|||_\infty = \bar{\boldsymbol{m}}(T).$$

In case $|||U|||_\infty < \infty$, the corresponding set function $\boldsymbol{m}$ is countably additive if and only if $U(\varphi_n) \to 0$ for every decreasing sequence (φ_n) of functions of $\mathscr{L}^\infty(\mu)$ such that $\varphi_n(t) \to 0$ μ-almost everywhere.

The theorem 7 can be stated as follows:

Corollary 3. *Every extremal point of the unit ball S^* of the dual of $\mathscr{L}^\infty(\mu)$ is of the form $x^* = \alpha y^*$, where $|\alpha| = 1$ and y^* is multiplicative.*

Proposition 15. *Let E, F, G be three Banach spaces and $(u, v) \to uv$ a bilinear mapping of $E \times F$ into G such that $|uv| \leqq |u|\,|v|$. If $\boldsymbol{f} \in \mathscr{L}^1_E(\mu)$ and $\boldsymbol{g} \in \mathscr{L}^\infty_F(\mu)$, then $\boldsymbol{fg} \in \mathscr{L}^1_G(\mu)$ and we have*

$$\left|\int \boldsymbol{fg}\, d\mu\right| \leqq \int |\boldsymbol{f}|\,|\boldsymbol{g}|\, d\mu \leqq N_1(\boldsymbol{f})\, N_\infty(\boldsymbol{g}).$$

In fact, $\boldsymbol{fg}$ is μ-measurable, $|\boldsymbol{f}|\, N_\infty(\boldsymbol{g})$ is μ-integrable and $|\boldsymbol{fg}| \leqq |\boldsymbol{f}|\, N_\infty(\boldsymbol{g})$ μ-almost everywhere. From the proposition 20, § 8, we deduce that $\boldsymbol{fg}$ is μ-integrable. We have then

$$\left|\int \boldsymbol{fg}\, d\mu\right| \leqq \int |\boldsymbol{f}|\,|\boldsymbol{g}|\, d\mu \leqq N_\infty(\boldsymbol{g}) \int |\boldsymbol{f}|\, d\mu = N_\infty(\boldsymbol{g})\, N_1(\boldsymbol{f}).$$

Remark. The inequality

$$\int |\boldsymbol{f}|\,|\boldsymbol{g}|\, d\mu \leqq N_1(\boldsymbol{f})\, N_\infty(\boldsymbol{g})$$

is a particular case of Hölder's inequality (see § 12, proposition 9).

§ 10. MEASURES DEFINED BY DENSITIES

1. LOCALLY INTEGRABLE FUNCTIONS

Let $\mathscr{C}$ be a *clan* of subsets of T, E a Banach space and μ a *positive* measure on $\mathscr{C}$.

Definition 1. *A function $\boldsymbol{f}$ defined on T with values in E or in $\bar{R}$ is said to be locally integrable with respect to μ, or locally μ-integrable, if for every set $A \in \mathscr{C}$ the function $\boldsymbol{f}\varphi_A$ is μ-integrable.*

If $\boldsymbol{m}$ is a *vector measure* with *finite variation* μ defined on $\mathscr{C}$, we say that a function is locally $\boldsymbol{m}$-integrable if it is locally μ-integrable.

Every μ-integrable function is locally μ-integrable. If a function f is μ-measurable and bounded on every set $A \in \mathscr{C}$, then f is locally μ-integrable.

Every locally μ-integrable function is μ-measurable.

Proposition 1. *Let $\mathscr{S}$ be the semi-tribe generated by the clan $\mathscr{C}$. A function f defined on T with values in E or in $\bar{R}$ is locally μ-integrable if and only if $f\varphi_A$ is μ-integrable for every set $A \in \mathscr{S}$.*

In fact, every set $A \in \mathscr{C}$ belongs to $\mathscr{S}$. On the other hand if $A \in \mathscr{S}$ there exists a set $B \in \mathscr{C}$ with $A \subset B$ (corollary of the proposition 10, § 1); if $f\varphi_B$ is μ-integrable, then $f\varphi_A = f\varphi_B\varphi_A$ is also μ-integrable.

Remarks.

1°. If f is locally μ-integrable and if A is a μ-measurable set, it may happen that $f\varphi_A$ should not be μ-integrable even if $A \in \mathscr{T}(\mathscr{C})$ and $\mu^*(A) < \infty$.

2°. If $T \in \mathscr{C}$, to say that a function f is locally μ-integrable means that f is μ-integrable.

Proposition 2. *Let f and g be two locally μ-integrable functions defined on T with values in E and let α be a scalar. Then the functions $f + g$, αf and $|f|$ are locally μ-integrable.*

The proof is immediate.

Remark. A locally μ-integrable function $g: T \to \bar{R}$ is equal μ-almost everywhere to a locally μ-integrable function g' which is *finite* everywhere.

The following results stated for *finite* locally integrable functions remain valid also for functions with values in $\bar{R}$.

2. MEASURES DEFINED BY DENSITIES

Let X, E, F be three Banach spaces. Suppose that there exists a mapping $(u, v) \to uv$ of $X \times E$ into F such that $|uv| \leqq |u|\,|v|$. We can have, for example, $X \subset \mathscr{L}(E, F)$ or $E \subset \mathscr{L}(X, F)$.

Let $\mathscr{C}$ be a *clan*, $\boldsymbol{m}: \mathscr{C} \to X$ a *measure with finite variation* and $\boldsymbol{g}: T \to E$ a *locally $\boldsymbol{m}$-integrable* function.

For every set $A \in \mathscr{C}$, the function $\varphi_A \boldsymbol{g}$ is $\boldsymbol{m}$-integrable. Put

$$\boldsymbol{n}(A) = \int_A \boldsymbol{g}\, d\boldsymbol{m}, \quad \text{for} \quad A \in \mathscr{C}.$$

The set function $\boldsymbol{n}: \mathscr{C} \to F$ is countably additive.

The positive function $|\boldsymbol{g}|$ is also locally $|\boldsymbol{m}|$-integrable. The set function

$$\nu(A) = \int_A |\boldsymbol{g}|\, d|\boldsymbol{m}|, \quad \text{for} \quad A \in \mathscr{C},$$

is a positive measure on $\mathscr{C}$ and we have

$$|\boldsymbol{n}(A)| \leqq \int_A |\boldsymbol{g}|\, d|\boldsymbol{m}| = \nu(A), \quad \text{for} \quad A \in \mathscr{C}.$$

It follows that $\boldsymbol{n}$ is a measure with finite variation and $|\boldsymbol{n}| \leqq \nu$.

Definition 2. *We say that the measure* $\boldsymbol{n}$ *is the product of the measure* $\boldsymbol{m}$ *by the function* $\boldsymbol{g}$, *or that* $\boldsymbol{n}$ *is the measure with density* $\boldsymbol{g}$ *and base* $\boldsymbol{m}$.

The measure $\boldsymbol{n}$ is denoted by $\boldsymbol{gm}$; the measure ν is denoted then by $|\boldsymbol{g}|\,|\boldsymbol{m}|$. The inequality $|\boldsymbol{n}| \leqq \nu$ is now written

$$|\boldsymbol{gm}| \leqq |\boldsymbol{g}|\,|\boldsymbol{m}|.$$

The definition 2 contains in particular the definition of the product of a vector measure by a *scalar* function, and the product of a *scalar* measure by a vector function.

We shall see that in these two cases we have the equality $|\boldsymbol{gm}| = |\boldsymbol{g}|\,|\boldsymbol{m}|$.

3. INTEGRATION WITH RESPECT TO A POSITIVE MEASURE DEFINED BY DENSITY

Let μ be a *positive* measure defined on a clan $\mathscr{C}$, g a *positive* locally μ-integrable function and $\nu = g\mu$. We have therefore

$$\nu(A) = \int_A g\, d\mu, \quad \text{for} \quad A \in \mathscr{C}.$$

Every set A of the semi-tribe $\mathscr{S}$ generated by $\mathscr{C}$ is μ-integrable, and the preceding equality remains valid for $A \in \mathscr{S}$. In fact, the two members of this equality are countable additive on $\mathscr{S}$ and are equal on $\mathscr{C}$ (§ 2, proposition 6). We shall see (corollary 1 of the theorem 1) that this equality remains valid for every ν-integrable set $A \subset T$.

Consider the set $G = \{t;\, g(t) \neq 0\}$. The set G is, evidently, μ-measurable.

Proposition 3. *A set* $A \subset T$ *is* ν*-negligible if and only if the set* $A \cap G$ *is* μ*-negligible.*

Let A be ν-negligible and prove that $A \cap G$ is μ-negligible. If $A \in \mathscr{S}$, then

$$\int_A g\, d\mu = \nu(A) = 0,$$

hence the positive function $\varphi_A g$ is μ-negligible, consequently the set $A \cap G$ is μ-negligible. The statement is then proved successively for $A \in \mathscr{T} = \mathscr{T}(\mathscr{C})$, for $A \in \mathscr{T}(\nu)$ — since A is contained in some set $B \in \mathscr{T}$ with $\nu^*(B) = 0$ — and for $A \in \mathfrak{T}(\nu)$ — since $A \cap B \in \mathscr{T}(\nu)$ for $B \in \mathscr{T}$.

To prove the converse implication, we remark first that:

if $A \subset T$ is μ-negligible, then A is ν-negligible,

considering successively $A \in \mathscr{S}$, $A \in \mathscr{T}$, $A \in \mathscr{T}(\mu)$ and $A \in \mathfrak{T}(\mu)$. We remark then that:

if $A \subset T$ is μ-measurable, then A is ν-measurable,

considering first $A \in \mathscr{T}(\mu)$ — since $A = A' \cup N$ with $A \in \mathscr{T}$ and N μ-negligible — and then $A \in \mathfrak{T}(\mu)$. In particular, it follows that:

G is ν-measurable and $T - G$ is ν-negligible.

In fact, $\nu(B) = 0$ for every $B \in \mathscr{S}$ with $B \subset T - G$.

Suppose now that $A \cap G$ is μ-negligible. Then $A \cap G$ is ν-negligible and $A - G$ is ν-negligible, therefore $A = (A - G) \cup (A \cap G)$ is ν-negligible.

Corollary. *If A is μ-negligible, then A is ν-negligible. A set $A \subset G$ is ν-negligible if and only if it is μ-negligible.*

Proposition 4. *A function **f** defined on T with values in a Banach space E or in $\bar{R}$ is ν-negligible if and only if **f**g is μ-negligible.*

In fact, if we put $A = \{t; \boldsymbol{f}(t) \neq 0\}$ then we have $A \cap G = \{t; \boldsymbol{f}(t)\, g(t) \neq 0\}$.

Proposition 5. *A set $A \subset T$ is ν-measurable if and only if $A \cap G$ is μ-measurable.*

Suppose first that A is contained in a set of the tribe $\mathscr{T}$ generated by $\mathscr{C}$. If A is ν-measurable, then $A = A' \cup N$ with $A' \in \mathscr{T}$ and N ν-negligible. It follows that $N \cap G$ is μ-negligible and $A \cap G = (A' \cap G) \cup (N \cap G)$. Since G is μ-measurable, we deduce that $A' \cap G$ is μ-measurable, hence $A \cap G$ is μ-measurable.

Conversely, if $A \cap G$ is μ-measurable, then the set $A \cap G$ also is ν-measurable. But we have $A = (A - G) \cup (A \cap G)$ and $A - G$ is ν-negligible, consequently A is ν-measurable.

If A is an arbitrary set, then A is ν-measurable, if and only if $A \cap B$ is ν-measurable for every $B \in \mathscr{C}$ (corollary 2 of theorem 2, § 5), hence if and only if $A \cap B \cap G$ is μ-measurable for every $B \in \mathscr{C}$, consequently if and only if $A \cap G$ is μ-measurable.

Corollary 1. *If A is μ-measurable, then A is ν-measurable. A set $A \subset G$ is ν-measurable if and only if it is μ-measurable.*

Corollary 2. *A set $A \subset T$ is ν-measurable if and only if the function $\varphi_A g$ is μ-measurable.*

If A is ν-measurable, then $A \cap G$ is μ-measurable. Since g is μ-measurable, it follows that $\varphi_A g = \varphi_{A \cap G} g$ is μ-measurable.

Conversely, suppose that $\varphi_A g$ is μ-measurable. Then the set $A \cap G = \{t; (\varphi_A g)(t) \neq 0\}$ is μ-measurable, consequently A is ν-measurable.

Proposition 6. *A function f defined on T with values in a Banach space E or in $\bar{R}$ is ν-measurable if and only if fg is μ-measurable.*

Suppose that f is ν-measurable and let $A \in \mathscr{C}$. There exists a ν-negligible set $N \subset A$ and a sequence (f_n) of ν-measurable step functions converging to f on $A - N$. From the corollary 2 of the proposition 5 we deduce that the functions $f_n g$ are μ-measurable and converge to the function fg on $A - N$. Since the functions $f_n g$ and fg vanish on $T - G$, we deduce that $f_n g$ converges to fg on $A - (N \cap G)$ and the set $N' = N \cap G$ is μ-negligible. Since the set $A \in \mathscr{C}$ is arbitrary, we deduce that fg is μ-measurable.

Conversely, suppose that fg is μ-measurable. The function

$$h(t) = \begin{cases} \dfrac{1}{g(t)}, & \text{if} \quad g(t) \neq 0, \\ 1, & \text{if} \quad g(t) = 0, \end{cases}$$

is μ-measurable, hence $f\varphi_G = fgh$ is μ-measurable. Let $A \in \mathscr{C}$. There exists a μ-negligible (hence ν-negligible) set $N \subset A$ and a sequence (f_n) of μ-measurable step functions converging to $f\varphi_G$ on $A - N$. The functions $f_n\varphi_G$ are also μ-measurable step functions and converge to $f\varphi_G$ on $A - N$. The set $N' = (A - G) \cup N$ is ν-negligible and on $A - N'$ the sequence (f_n) converges to f. From the corollary 1 of the proposition 5 we deduce that the functions f_n are ν-measurable, hence f is ν-measurable.

Theorem 1. *A function f defined on T with values in a Banach space E or in $\bar{R}$ is ν-integrable if and only if fg is μ-integrable. In this case we have*

$$\int f\, d\nu = \int fg\, d\mu .$$

Suppose first that f is a step function of the form $f = \sum \varphi_{A_i} x_i$ with $A_i \in \mathscr{C}$ and $x_i \in E$ (or $x_i \in R$). Then

$$\int f\, d\nu = \sum \nu(A_i)\, x_i = \sum \int_{A_i} g x_i\, d\mu = \int g \sum \varphi_{A_i} x_i\, d\mu = \int fg\, d\mu .$$

Suppose now that f is ν-integrable. Let (f_n) be a sequence of $\mathscr{C}$-step functions converging to f ν-almost everywhere (except for a ν-negligible set N) and in mean in the space $\mathscr{L}^1_E(\nu)$. It follows that (f_n) is a Cauchy sequence in $\mathscr{L}^1_E(\nu)$, i.e.

$$\lim_{n,m\to\infty} \int |f_n - f_m|\, d\nu = 0.$$

Then the sequence $(f_n g)$ converges to fg μ-almost everywhere (except for the μ-negligible set $N \cap G$) and we have

$$\int |f_n g - f_m g|\, d\mu = \int |f_n - f_m|\, g\, d\mu = \int |f_n - f_m|\, d\nu ,$$

hence $(f_n g)$ is a Cauchy sequence in the space $\mathscr{L}^1_E(\mu)$. It follows that fg is μ-integrable and that $(f_n g)$ converges to fg in mean in the space $\mathscr{L}^1_E(\mu)$. For each n we have

$$\int f_n \, d\nu = \int f_n g \, d\mu ,$$

hence, passing to the limit,

$$\int f \, d\nu = \int fg \, d\mu .$$

Suppose now that fg is μ-integrable. There exists a sequence (f_n) of $\mathscr{C}$-step functions converging to fg μ-almost everywhere (except for a μ-negligible set N) and in mean in the space $\mathscr{L}^1_E(\mu)$. Then f is ν-measurable. In order to prove that f is ν-integrable, it is sufficient to show that $|f|$ is ν-integrable.

There exists an increasing sequence (φ_n) of ν-measurable step functions converging to $|f|$ (§ 6, proposition 7). We have $\varphi_n(t) \leqq |f(t)|$ for every n and every $t \in T$. The functions $\varphi_n g$ are positive and μ-measurable and $\varphi_n(t)\, g(t) \leqq |f(t)|\, g(t)$ for every n and every $t \in T$. Since $|f|\, g$ is μ-integrable, we deduce that the functions $\varphi_n g$ are μ-integrable and we have

$$\sup_n \int \varphi_n g \, d\mu \leqq \int |f| \, g \, d\mu < \infty .$$

Since for every n we have

$$\int \varphi_n \, d\nu = \int \varphi_n g \, d\mu$$

we deduce that

$$\sup_n \int \varphi_n \, d\nu < \infty ,$$

consequently (§ 8, theorem 2), the function $|f|$ is ν-integrable. The theorem is thus completely proved.

Corollary 1. *A set $A \subset T$ is ν-integrable if and only if the function $\varphi_A g$ is μ-integrable. In this case we have*

$$\nu(A) = \int_A g \, d\mu .$$

Corollary 2. *Let $\mu \geqq 0$ be a positive measure defined on $\mathscr{C}$, $g_1 \geqq 0$ a locally μ-integrable function, and E a Banach space. A function g_2: $T \to E$ is locally $g_1\mu$-integrable if and only if $g_2 g_1$ is locally μ-integrable. In this case we have*

$$g_2(g_1\mu) = (g_2 g_1)\, \mu .$$

The function g_2 is locally $g_1\mu$-integrable if and only if for every $A \in \mathscr{C}$ the function $\varphi_A g_2$ is $g_1\mu$-integrable, hence if and only if for every $A \in \mathscr{C}$, the function $\varphi_A g_2 g_1$ is μ-integrable, therefore if and only if $g_2 g_1$ is locally μ-integrable. For every $A \in \mathscr{C}$ we have then

$$\int \varphi_A g_2 \, d(g_1\mu) = \int \varphi_A g_2 g_1 \, d\mu,$$

i.e.

$$\int_A g_2 \, d(g_1\mu) = \int_A g_2 g_1 \, d\mu,$$

hence

$$g_2(g_1\mu) = (g_2 g_1)\,\mu.$$

4. INTEGRATION WITH RESPECT TO A VECTOR MEASURE DEFINED BY DENSITY

Let X, E, F be three Banach spaces and $(u, v) \to uv$ a bilinear mapping of $X \times E$ into F such that $|uv| \leqq |u|\,|v|$.

We shall consider three cases: 1. m is a scalar measure; 2. g is a *scalar* locally m-integrable function; 3. f is a scalar function.

Consider first the case where the measure is scalar valued.

Theorem 2. *Let μ be a scalar measure with finite variation on a clan $\mathscr{C}$, $g: T \to X$ a locally μ-integrable function, and f a function defined on T with values in E or in $\bar{R}$.*

a) *If f is $|g|\,|\mu|$-negligible, then f is $g\mu$-negligible and fg is μ-negligible.*

b) *If f is $|g|\,|\mu|$-measurable, then f is $g\mu$-measurable and fg is μ-measurable.*

c) *If f is $|g|\,|\mu|$-integrable, then f is $g\mu$-integrable and fg is μ-integrable, and we have*

$$\int f\, d(g\mu) = \int fg \, d\mu.$$

The first part, concerning the measure $g\mu$, follows from $|g\mu| \leqq |g|\,|\mu|$. We have to prove the part concerning μ.

Suppose that f is $|g|\,|\mu|$-negligible. We deduce that $|f|$ is $|g|\,|\mu|$-negligible, hence $|f|\,|g|$ is $|\mu|$-negligible, consequently fg is μ-negligible. Thus the property a) is proved.

Suppose now that f is $|g|\,|\mu|$-measurable. Then $f|g|$ is $|\mu|$-measurable. Since $|g|$ is $|\mu|$-measurable, the function

$$h(t) = \begin{cases} f(t) = \dfrac{f(t)\,|g(t)|}{|g(t)|}, & \text{if} \quad g(t) \neq 0, \\ 0, & \text{if} \quad g(t) = 0, \end{cases}$$

is $|\mu|$-measurable, hence $gh = fg$ is $|\mu|$-measurable. The property b) is also proved.

If f is $|g|\,|\mu|$-integrable, then $f|g|$ is $|\mu|$-integrable, hence $|f|\,|g|$ is $|\mu|$-integrable. Since fg is μ-measurable, from the inequality $|fg| \leqq |f|\,|g|$ we deduce that fg is μ-integrable.

Let (f_n) be a sequence of step functions converging in mean to f in the space $\mathscr{L}^1_E(|g|\,|\mu|)$:

$$\lim_{n\to\infty} \int |f_n - f|\, d(|g|\,|\mu|) = 0.$$

Since f and f_n are $|g|\,|\mu|$-integrable, the functions fg and $f_n g$ are μ-integrable, and from the inequalities

$$\left|\int fg\, d\mu - \int f_n g\, d\mu\right| \leqq \int |fg - f_n g|\, d|\mu|$$

$$\leqq \int |f - f_n|\,|g|\, d|\mu| = \int |f - f_n|\, d(|g|\,|\mu|)$$

we deduce that

$$\lim_{n\to\infty} \int f_n g\, d\mu = \int fg\, d\mu.$$

On the other hand, f and f_n are $g\mu$-integrable and from the inequalities

$$\left|\int f\, d(g\mu) - \int f\, d(g\mu)\right| \leqq \int |f - f_n|\, d|g\mu| \leqq \int |f - f_n|\, d(|g|\,|\mu|)$$

we deduce that

$$\lim_{n\to\infty} \int f_n\, d(g\mu) = \int f\, d(g\mu).$$

It is easy to verify that for the step functions f_n we have

$$\int f_n\, d(g\mu) = \int f_n g\, d\mu,$$

hence, passing to the limit, we obtain

$$\int f\, d(g\mu) = \int fg\, d\mu,$$

and the theorem is completely proved.

Corollary 1. *Let μ be a scalar measure on $\mathscr{C}$, $g\colon T \to X$ a locally μ-integrable function such that*

$$|g\mu| = |g|\,|\mu|$$

and f a function defined on T with values in E or in $\bar{R}$.

If f is $g\mu$-negligible (respectively measurable, integrable), then fg is μ-negligible (respectively measurable, integrable).

In the next sections we shall see (theorem 6) that we have always $|g\mu| = |g|\,|\mu|$.

Corollary 2. *Let μ be a scalar measure on $\mathscr{C}$, $g_1\colon T \to X$ a locally μ-integrable function, and g_2 a function defined on T with values in E or in $\bar{R}$.*

If g_2 is locally $|g_1|\,|\mu|$-integrable, then g_2 is locally $g_1\mu$-integrable, $g_2 g_1$ is locally μ-integrable and we have

$$g_2(g_1\mu) = (g_2 g_1)\,\mu.$$

Consider now the case where the function g is scalar valued.

Theorem 3. *Let $\boldsymbol{m}\colon \mathscr{C} \to X$ be a measure with finite variation, $g\colon T \to C$ a scalar locally $\boldsymbol{m}$-integrable function and f a function defined on T with values in E or in $\bar{R}$.*

a) *The function f is $|g|\,|\boldsymbol{m}|$-negligible if and only if fg is $\boldsymbol{m}$-negligible.*
If f is $|g|\,|\boldsymbol{m}|$-negligible, then f is $g\boldsymbol{m}$-negligible.

b) *The function f is $|g|\,|\boldsymbol{m}|$-measurable if and only if fg is $\boldsymbol{m}$-measurable.*
If f is $|g|\,|\boldsymbol{m}|$-measurable, then f is $g\boldsymbol{m}$-measurable.

c) *The function f is $|g|\,|\boldsymbol{m}|$-integrable if and only if fg is $\boldsymbol{m}$-integrable.*
If f is $|g|\,|\boldsymbol{m}|$-integrable, then f is $g\boldsymbol{m}$-integrable and we have

$$\int f\,d(g\boldsymbol{m}) = \int fg\,d\boldsymbol{m}.$$

We prove as in the theorem 2 that if f is $|g|\,|\boldsymbol{m}|$-negligible (measurable, integrable), then f is $g\boldsymbol{m}$-negligible (measurable, integrable), and that fg is $\boldsymbol{m}$-negligible (measurable, integrable), as well as the equality

$$\int f\,d(g\boldsymbol{m}) = \int fg\,d\boldsymbol{m}.$$

If fg is $\boldsymbol{m}$-negligible, then $|fg| = |f|\,|g|$ is $|\boldsymbol{m}|$-negligible, hence $|f|$ is $|g|\,|\boldsymbol{m}|$-negligible, therefore f is $|g|\,|\boldsymbol{m}|$-negligible.

Suppose now that fg is $\boldsymbol{m}$-measurable. Since g is $|\boldsymbol{m}|$-measurable, the function

$$h'(t) = \begin{cases} \dfrac{|g(t)|}{g(t)}, & \text{if } \; g(t) \neq 0, \\ 0, & \text{if } \; g(t) = 0, \end{cases}$$

is $|\boldsymbol{m}|$-measurable, hence the function $f|g| = fgh'$ is $|\boldsymbol{m}|$-measurable. It follows that f is $|g|\,|\boldsymbol{m}|$-measurable.

If fg is $\boldsymbol{m}$-integrable, then fg is $\boldsymbol{m}$-measurable and the function $|f|\,|g| = |fg|$ is $|\boldsymbol{m}|$-integrable. It follows that f is $|g|\,|\boldsymbol{m}|$-measurable and $|f|$ is $|g|\,|\boldsymbol{m}|$-integrable, hence f is $|g|\,|\boldsymbol{m}|$-integrable.

Corollary 1. *Let* $\boldsymbol{m}: \mathscr{C} \to X$ *be a measure with finite variation and* $g: T \to C$ *a scalar locally* $\boldsymbol{m}$*-integrable function such that*

$$|g\boldsymbol{m}| = |g|\,|\boldsymbol{m}|.$$

A function $f: T \to E$ (*or* $f: T \to \bar{R}$) *is* $g\boldsymbol{m}$*-negligible (measurable, integrable) if and only if* fg *is* $\boldsymbol{m}$*-negligible (measurable, integrable).*

We shall see (§ 13, theorem 7) that we have always $|g\boldsymbol{m}| = |g|\,|\boldsymbol{m}|$ if $\boldsymbol{m}$ has the direct sum property (see definition 5).

Corollary 2. *Let* $\boldsymbol{m}: \mathscr{C} \to X$ *be a measure with finite variation,* $g_1: T \to C$ *a scalar locally* $\boldsymbol{m}$*-integrable function, and* $\boldsymbol{g}_2$ *a function defined on* T *with values in* E *or in* $\bar{R}$. *Then* $\boldsymbol{g}_2$ *is locally* $|g_1|\,|\boldsymbol{m}|$*-integrable if and only if* $\boldsymbol{g}_2 g_1$ *is locally* $\boldsymbol{m}$*-integrable.*

If $\boldsymbol{g}_2$ *is locally* $|g_1|\,|\boldsymbol{m}|$*-integrable, then* $\boldsymbol{g}_2$ *is locally* $g_1\boldsymbol{m}$*-integrable and we have*

$$\boldsymbol{g}_2(g_1\boldsymbol{m}) = (\boldsymbol{g}_2 g_1)\,\boldsymbol{m}.$$

Consider, finally, the case where f is *scalar valued.*

Theorem 4. *Let* $\boldsymbol{m}: \mathscr{C} \to X$ *be a measure with finite variation,* $\boldsymbol{g}: T \to E$ *a locally* $\boldsymbol{m}$*-integrable function, and* f *a scalar function.*

a) *If* f *is* $|\boldsymbol{g}|\,|\boldsymbol{m}|$*-negligible, then* f *is* $\boldsymbol{g}\boldsymbol{m}$*-negligible.*

a′) *The function* f *is* $|\boldsymbol{g}|\,|\boldsymbol{m}|$*-negligible if and only if* $f\boldsymbol{g}$ *is* $\boldsymbol{m}$*-negligible.*

b) *If* f *is* $|\boldsymbol{g}|\,|\boldsymbol{m}|$*-measurable, then* f *is* $\boldsymbol{g}\boldsymbol{m}$*-measurable and* $f\boldsymbol{g}$ *is* $\boldsymbol{m}$*-measurable.*

b′) *If* f *is real valued, then* f *is* $|\boldsymbol{g}|\,|\boldsymbol{m}|$*-measurable if and only if* $f\boldsymbol{g}$ *is* $\boldsymbol{m}$*-measurable.*

c) *If* f *is* $|\boldsymbol{g}|\,|\boldsymbol{m}|$*-integrable, then* f *is* $\boldsymbol{g}\boldsymbol{m}$*-integrable and* $f\boldsymbol{g}$ *is* $\boldsymbol{m}$*-integrable, and we have*

$$\int f\,d(\boldsymbol{g}\boldsymbol{m}) = \int f\boldsymbol{g}\,d\boldsymbol{m}.$$

c′) *If* f *is real valued, then* f *is* $|\boldsymbol{g}|\,|\boldsymbol{m}|$*-integrable if and only if* $f\boldsymbol{g}$ *is* $\boldsymbol{m}$*-integrable.*

The properties a), b), c) are proved like in the theorem 2. The property a′) is proved as in theorem 3.

Suppose now that f is real valued and that $f\boldsymbol{g}$ is $\boldsymbol{m}$-measurable. Then the function $|f\boldsymbol{g}| = |f|\,|\boldsymbol{g}|$ is $|\boldsymbol{m}|$-measurable, therefore $|f|$ is $|\boldsymbol{g}|\,|\boldsymbol{m}|$-measurable. From the theorem 2 we deduce that $|f|\,\boldsymbol{g}$ is $|\boldsymbol{m}|$-measurable.

Since $|f|\,\boldsymbol{g}$ and $f\boldsymbol{g}$ are $\boldsymbol{m}$-measurable, the functions

$$f^+\boldsymbol{g} = \frac{1}{2}(|f| + f)\,\boldsymbol{g} \quad \text{and} \quad f^-\boldsymbol{g} = \frac{1}{2}(|f| - f)\,\boldsymbol{g}$$

are also $\boldsymbol{m}$-measurable. As before, we deduce that the functions $f^+|\boldsymbol{g}|$ and $f^-|\boldsymbol{g}|$ are $|\boldsymbol{m}|$-measurable, therefore the functions f^+ and f^- are $|\boldsymbol{g}|\,|\boldsymbol{m}|$-measurable, hence the function $f = f^+ - f^-$ is $|\boldsymbol{g}|\,|\boldsymbol{m}|$-measurable too.

The property c′) is proved then as in the theorem 3.

Corollary 1. *Let* $\boldsymbol{m}\colon \mathscr{C} \to X$ *be a measure with finite variation,* $\boldsymbol{g}\colon T \to E$ *a locally* $\boldsymbol{m}$*-integrable function such that*

$$|\boldsymbol{g}\boldsymbol{m}| = |\boldsymbol{g}|\,|\boldsymbol{m}|.$$

A real function $f\colon T \to R$ *is* $\boldsymbol{g}\boldsymbol{m}$*-negligible (measurable, integrable) if and only if* $f\boldsymbol{g}$ *is* $\boldsymbol{m}$*-negligible (measurable, integrable).*

Corollary 2. *Let* $\boldsymbol{m}\colon \mathscr{C} \to X$ *be a measure with finite variation,* $\boldsymbol{g}_1\colon T \to E$ *a locally* $\boldsymbol{m}$*-integrable function, and* g_2 *a scalar function.*

If g_2 *is locally* $|\boldsymbol{g}_1|\,|\boldsymbol{m}|$*-integrable, then* g_2 *is locally* $\boldsymbol{g}_1\boldsymbol{m}$*-integrable,* $g_2\boldsymbol{g}_1$ *is locally* $\boldsymbol{m}$*-integrable and we have*

$$g_2(\boldsymbol{g}_1\boldsymbol{m}) = (g_2\boldsymbol{g}_1)\,\boldsymbol{m}.$$

If g_2 *is real valued, then* g_2 *is locally* $|\boldsymbol{g}_1|\,|\boldsymbol{m}|$*-integrable if and only if* $g_2\boldsymbol{g}_1$ *is locally* $\boldsymbol{m}$*-integrable.*

5. PROPERTIES OF MEASURES DEFINED BY DENSITIES

In this section we give some properties of measures with bases *scalar* measures.

Proposition 7. *Let* μ *be a scalar measure,* E *a Banach space,* $\boldsymbol{f}, \boldsymbol{g}\colon T \to E$ *two locally* μ*-integrable functions, and* α *a scalar. Then*

$$(\boldsymbol{f} + \boldsymbol{g})\,\mu = \boldsymbol{f}\mu + \boldsymbol{g}\mu \quad \text{and} \quad (\alpha\boldsymbol{f})\,\mu = \alpha(\boldsymbol{f}\mu).$$

The proof is immediate.

Proposition 8. *Let* μ *and* ν *be two scalar measures,* E *a Banach space,* $\boldsymbol{g}\colon T \to E$ *a function, and* α, β *scalars.*

If $\boldsymbol{g}$ *is locally integrable with respect to* μ *and* ν*, then* $\boldsymbol{g}$ *is locally* $(\alpha\mu + \beta\nu)$*-integrable and we have*

$$\boldsymbol{g}(\alpha\mu + \beta\nu) = \alpha(\boldsymbol{g}\mu) + \beta(\boldsymbol{g}\nu).$$

The proof is immediate.

Proposition 9. *Let* $\mu \geqq 0$ *be a measure and* $g\colon T \to R$ *a locally* μ*-integrable function. We have* $g\mu \geqq 0$ *if and only if* $g(t) \geqq 0$ μ*-almost everywhere.*

We use the proposition 11, § 8 for $g\varphi_B$, for every $B \in \mathscr{C}$.

Corollary. *Let* $\mu \geqq 0$ *be a measure and* $g_1, g_2\colon T \to R$ *two locally* μ*-integrable functions. We have* $g_1\mu \leqq g_2\mu$ *if and only if* $g_1(t) \leqq g_2(t)$ μ*-almost everywhere.*

Proposition 10. *Let $\mu \geqq 0$ be a positive measure on $\mathscr{C}$, E a Banach space, and $\boldsymbol{g}: T \to E$ a locally μ-integrable function. Then*

$$|\boldsymbol{g}\mu| = |\boldsymbol{g}|\,\mu.$$

Consider the function $\boldsymbol{f}$ defined on T by the equalities

$$\boldsymbol{f}(t) = \begin{cases} \dfrac{\boldsymbol{g}(t)}{|\boldsymbol{g}(t)|}, & \text{if} \quad \boldsymbol{g}(t) \neq 0, \\ \boldsymbol{x}_0 \in E, \quad \text{with} \quad |\boldsymbol{x}_0| = 1, & \text{if} \quad \boldsymbol{g}(t) = 0. \end{cases}$$

Then $\boldsymbol{f}$ is μ-measurable and $|\boldsymbol{g}|$ is μ-measurable. It follows that $\boldsymbol{f}|\boldsymbol{g}|$ is μ-measurable, whence $\boldsymbol{f}$ is measurable with respect to the positive measure $\lambda = |\boldsymbol{g}|\,\mu$. We have then $\boldsymbol{f}|\boldsymbol{g}| = \boldsymbol{g}$ and $|\boldsymbol{f}(t)| \equiv 1$, consequently $\boldsymbol{f}$ is locally λ-integrable.

Let $A \in \mathscr{C}$ and $\varepsilon > 0$. The function $\boldsymbol{f}\varphi_A$ is λ-integrable. There exists then a $\mathscr{C}$-step function $\boldsymbol{h} \in \mathscr{L}_E^1(\lambda)$ with

$$\int_A |\boldsymbol{f} - \boldsymbol{h}|\, d\lambda < \frac{\varepsilon}{2}.$$

It follows that

$$\lambda(A) = \int_A |\boldsymbol{f}|\, d\lambda < \int_A |\boldsymbol{h}|\, d\lambda + \frac{\varepsilon}{2}.$$

Write

$$\boldsymbol{h} = \sum_{i=1}^{n} \varphi_{A_i} \boldsymbol{x}_i$$

with A_i disjoint sets of $\mathscr{C}$ and $\boldsymbol{x}_i \in E$. We can take the sets A_i contained in A. For every i there exists $\boldsymbol{x}_i' \in E'$ with $|\boldsymbol{x}_i'| = 1$ and $\langle \boldsymbol{x}_i, \boldsymbol{x}_i' \rangle = |\boldsymbol{x}_i|$. The function

$$\boldsymbol{h}' = \sum_{i=1}^{n} \varphi_{A_i} \boldsymbol{x}_i'$$

is a $\mathscr{C}$-step function and we have

$$|\boldsymbol{h}'(t)| = 1 \quad \text{and} \quad \langle \boldsymbol{h}(t), \boldsymbol{h}'(t) \rangle = |\boldsymbol{h}(t)|, \quad \text{for} \quad t \in \bigcup_{i=1}^{n} A_i.$$

The function $\boldsymbol{h}'$ is integrable with respect to every measure on $\mathscr{C}$, in particular, with respect to the measure $|\boldsymbol{f}|\,\lambda$. Then the function $\langle \boldsymbol{f}, \boldsymbol{h}' \rangle$ is integrable with respect to λ and we have

$$\int \langle \boldsymbol{f}, \boldsymbol{h}' \rangle\, d\lambda = \int \boldsymbol{h}'\, d(\boldsymbol{f}\lambda).$$

It follows that

$$\lambda(A) - \frac{\varepsilon}{2} < \int_A |h|\, d\lambda = \int_A \langle h, h' \rangle\, d\lambda$$

$$= \left| \int_A \langle h, h' \rangle\, d\lambda \right| \leqq \left| \int_A \langle f, h' \rangle\, d\lambda \right| + \left| \int_A \langle f - h, h' \rangle\, d\lambda \right|$$

$$\leqq \left| \int_A h'\, d(f\lambda) \right| + \int_A |f - h|\, |h'|\, d\lambda$$

$$\leqq \int_A |h|\, d|f\lambda| + \int_A |f - h|\, d\lambda \leqq |f\lambda|\,(A) + \frac{\varepsilon}{2}.$$

ε being arbitrary, we deduce

$$\lambda(A) \leqq |f\lambda|\,(A),$$

hence $\lambda \leqq |f\lambda| \leqq |f|\,\lambda = \lambda$, consequently $|f\lambda| = \lambda$. Then

$$|g\mu| = |(f|g|)\,\mu| = |f(|g|\mu)| = |f\lambda| = \lambda = |g|\,\mu$$

and thus the proposition is proved.

Remark. We shall prove (theorem 6) that we have

$$|g\mu| = |g|\,|\mu|$$

for every *scalar* measure μ and every locally μ-integrable function $g: T \to E$.

Corollary 1. *Let μ be a positive measure, E a Banach space, and $g: T \to E$ a locally μ-integrable function.*

We have $g\mu = 0$ if and only if $g(t) = 0$ μ-almost everywhere.

If g is μ-negligible, then, evidently, $g\mu = 0$.

Conversely, suppose that $g\mu = 0$. Then $|g\mu| = 0$ and from the equality $|g\mu| = |g|\,\mu$ we deduce that $|g|\,\mu = 0$, i.e.

$$\int_A |g|\, d\mu = 0, \quad \text{for every } A \in \mathscr{C}.$$

From the corollary 2 of the proposition 11, § 8, we deduce that $|g|\varphi_B$ is μ-negligible for every $B \in \mathscr{C}$, hence $g(t) = 0$ μ-almost everywhere.

Corollary 2. *Let μ be a positive measure, E a Banach space, and $g_1, g_2: T \to E$ two locally μ-integrable functions. We have $g_1\mu = g_2\mu$ if and only if $g_1(t) = g_2(t)$ μ-almost everywhere.*

Remark. These corollaries will be extended for arbitrary scalar measures (corollaries 1 and 2 of the theorem 6).

Proposition 11. *Let μ be a positive measure and g a real function. Then g is locally μ-integrable if and only if g^+ and g^- are locally μ-integrable. In this case we have*

$$(g\mu)^+ = g^+\mu \quad \textit{and} \quad (g\mu)^- = g^-\mu.$$

If g is locally μ-integrable, then $|g|$ is locally μ-integrable, and from the equalities

$$g^+ = \frac{1}{2}(|g| + g), \quad g^- = \frac{1}{2}(|g| - g)$$

we deduce that g^+ and g^- are locally μ-integrable. The converse implication follows from the equality $g = g^+ - g^-$.

If g is locally μ-integrable then we have

$$(g\mu)^+ = \frac{1}{2}(|g\mu| + g\mu) = \frac{1}{2}(|g|\,\mu + g\mu) = \frac{1}{2}(|g| + g)\,\mu = g^+\mu$$

and

$$(g\mu)^- = \frac{1}{2}(|g\mu| - g\mu) = \frac{1}{2}(|g| - g)\,\mu = g^-\mu.$$

Remark. We shall see (corollary 3 of the theorem 6) that if μ is a real measure and $g \geqq 0$ is a locally μ-integrable positive function, then

$$(g\mu)^+ = g\mu^+ \quad \text{and} \quad (g\mu)^- = g\mu^-.$$

6. ABSOLUTELY CONTINUOUS MEASURES

Let $\mathscr{C}$ be a clan, μ and ν two *positive measures* defined on $\mathscr{C}$.

Definition 3. *We say that the measure ν is absolutely continuous with respect to μ if every μ-negligible set is ν-negligible.*

A vector measure $\boldsymbol{n}$ with *finite variation* $|\boldsymbol{n}|$ defined on $\mathscr{C}$ is said to be absolutely continuous with respect to a vector measure $\boldsymbol{m}$ with finite variation $|\boldsymbol{m}|$ defined on $\mathscr{C}$, if $|\boldsymbol{n}|$ is absolutely continuous with respect to $|\boldsymbol{m}|$.

Proposition 12. *If ν is absolutely continuous with respect to μ, then every μ-measurable set is ν-measurable: $\mathfrak{T}(\mu) \subset \mathfrak{T}(\nu)$.*

Let $\mathscr{T}$ be the tribe generated by $\mathscr{C}$. If $E \in \mathfrak{T}(\mu)$, then for every $A \in \mathscr{C}$ the set $E \cap A$ is μ-measurable and contained in $A \in \mathscr{T}$, therefore it is of the form $E \cap A = B \cup N$ with $B \in \mathscr{T}$ and N μ-negligible. Since N is also ν-negligible, we deduce that $E \cap A$ is ν-measurable, therefore $E \in \mathfrak{T}(\nu)$.

Proposition 13. *Let $\mathscr{S}$ be the semi-tribe generated by $\mathscr{C}$. Then ν is absolutely continuous with respect to μ if and only if $A \in \mathscr{S}$ and $\mu(A) = 0$ imply $\nu(A) = 0$.*

Suppose first that ν is absolutely continuous with respect to μ. It follows then, in particular that $A \in \mathcal{S}$ and $\mu(A) = 0$ imply $\nu(A) = 0$.

Conversely, suppose that $A \in \mathcal{S}$ and $\mu(A) = 0$ imply $\nu(A) = 0$ and let $E \in \mathcal{C}(\mu)$ with $\mu^*(E) = 0$. We shall show that $E \in \mathcal{C}(\nu)$ and $\nu^*(E) = 0$.

a) Suppose first that E belongs to the tribe $\mathcal{T}$ generated by $\mathscr{C}$. Then $E = \bigcup_{n=1}^{\infty} A_n$ with $A_n \in \mathcal{S}$. It follows that $\mu(A_n) = 0$ for every n; hence $\nu(A_n) = 0$, consequently $\nu^*(E) = 0$.

b) Suppose then that $E \in \mathcal{T}(\mu)$. Then (§ 5, proposition 4) there exists a set $A \in \mathcal{T}$ with $A \supset E$, and $\mu^*(A) = \mu^*(E) = 0$. From a) we deduce that $\nu^*(A) = 0$, whence $\nu^*(E) = 0$. It follows in particular that $E \in \mathcal{T}(\nu)$.

c) Suppose finally that $E \in \mathcal{C}(\mu)$. For every set $A \in \mathcal{T}$ we have then $A \cap E \in \mathcal{T}(\mu)$ and $\mu^*(A \cap E) = 0$. From b) it follows that $A \cap E \in \mathcal{T}(\nu)$ and $\nu^*(A \cap E) = 0$. We deduce then (corollary 2 of the theorem 2, § 5) that $E \in \mathcal{C}(\nu)$ and from the proposition 7, § 5, it follows that

$$\nu^*(E) = \sup_{A \in \mathcal{T}} \nu(A \cap E) = 0,$$

therefore ν is absolutely continuous with respect to μ.

Remark. If $\mu(A) = 0$ implies $\nu(A) = 0$ only for the sets $A \in \mathscr{C}$ it does not follow that ν is absolutely continuous with respect to μ.

Proposition 14. *If ν is absolutely continuous with respect to μ, then for every $\varepsilon > 0$ there exists a number $\delta(\varepsilon) > 0$ such that for every μ-integrable set $A \subset T$ with $\mu(A) < \delta$ we have $\nu(A) < \varepsilon$.*

Conversely, if for every $\varepsilon > 0$ there exists $\delta(\varepsilon) > 0$ such that $A \in \mathscr{C}$ and $\mu(A) < \delta(\varepsilon)$ imply $\nu(A) < \varepsilon$, then ν is absolutely continuous with respect to μ.

Suppose first that ν is absolutely continuous with respect to μ and let $\varepsilon > 0$. Suppose that the condition of the proposition is not verified, i.e. for every $\delta > 0$ there exists a μ-measurable set A_δ with $\mu(A_\delta) < \delta$ but $\nu^*(A_\delta) \geqq \varepsilon$. Taking $\delta = \frac{1}{2^n}$ and $A_n = A_\delta$, we have $\mu(A_n) < \frac{1}{2^n}$ and $\nu^*(A_n) \leqq \varepsilon$ for every n. If we put

$$A = \bigcap_{n=1}^{\infty} \bigcup_{p=1}^{\infty} A_{n+p}$$

the set A is μ-measurable and we have

$$\mu^*(A) \leqq \mu^*\left(\bigcup_{p=1}^{\infty} A_{n+p}\right) \leqq \sum_{p=1}^{\infty} \mu(A_{n+p}) < \frac{1}{2^{p-1}}$$

for every p, hence $\mu^*(A) = 0$. Since ν is absolutely continuous with respect to μ, it follows that $\nu^*(A) = 0$. On the other hand,

$$\nu^*\left(\bigcup_{p=1}^{\infty} A_{n+p}\right) \geqq \nu^*(A_{n+p}) \geqq \varepsilon$$

for every n. Since the sequence

$$\left(\bigcup_{p=1}^{\infty} A_{n+p}\right)_{1 \leqq n < \infty}$$

is decreasing and its intersection is A, we deduce

$$\nu^*(A) = \lim_{n\to\infty} \nu^*\left(\bigcup_{p=1}^{\infty} A_{n+p}\right) \geqq \varepsilon$$

and we get a contradiction, and the first part of the proposition is proved.

Conversely, suppose verified the condition of the second part of the proposition and let E be a set of the semi-tribe $\mathscr{S}$ generated by $\mathscr{C}$, with $\mu(E) = 0$. We shall prove that $\nu(E) = 0$, hence, by proposition 13, it will follow that ν is absolutely continuous with respect to μ.

Let $\varepsilon > 0$. Since $\mu(E) = 0$, there exists a sequence (B_n) of sets of $\mathscr{C}$ such that $E \subset \bigcup_{n=1}^{\infty} B_n$ and $\sum_{n=1}^{\infty} \mu(B_n) < \delta(\varepsilon)$. If we put $F = \bigcup_{n=1}^{\infty} B_n$ and $A_n = \bigcup_{i=1}^{n} B_i$, then $A_i \in \mathscr{C}$, the sequence (A_n) is increasing and we have $E \subset F = \bigcup_{n=1}^{\infty} A_n$. Since $\mu(A_n) \leqq \mu(B_n) < \delta(\varepsilon)$, we deduce that $\nu(A_n) < \varepsilon$ for every n, therefore

$$\nu(E) \leqq \nu(F) = \lim_{n\to\infty} \nu(A_n) \leqq \varepsilon.$$

Since ε is arbitrary, we deduce that $\nu(E) = 0$, and the second part of the proposition is also proved.

As propositions 13 and 14 are, in general, not true if we take $\mathscr{C}$ instead of $\mathscr{S}$, we give the following

Definition 4. *Let X be a Banach space. A set function $\boldsymbol{m}$: $\mathscr{C} \to X$ is said to be absolutely continuous on $\mathscr{C}$ with respect to μ, if $A \in \mathscr{C}$ and $\mu(A) = 0$ imply $\boldsymbol{m}(A) = 0$.*

The absolute continuity of set functions with finite variation reduces to the absolute continuity of the variation:

Proposition 15. *Let $\boldsymbol{m}$: $\mathscr{C} \to X$ be a set function with finite variation $|\boldsymbol{m}|$. Then $\boldsymbol{m}$ is absolutely continuous with respect to μ on $\mathscr{C}$ if and only if $|\boldsymbol{m}|$ is absolutely continuous with respect to μ on $\mathscr{C}$.*

Suppose that $\boldsymbol{m}$ is absolutely continuous with respect to μ and let $A \in \mathscr{C}$ with $\mu(A) = 0$. Then for every $B \in \mathscr{C}$ with $B \subset A$ we have $\mu(B) = 0$, whence $\boldsymbol{m}(B) = 0$, consequently $|\boldsymbol{m}|(A) = 0$, therefore $|\boldsymbol{m}|$ is absolutely continuous with respect to μ. The other implication follows from the inequality $|\boldsymbol{m}(A)| \leqq |\boldsymbol{m}|(A)$.

According to the preceding definition, the proposition 13 can be stated as follows:

The measure ν is absolutely continuous with respect to μ, if and only if ν is absolutely continuous with respect to μ on the semi-tribe $\mathscr{S}$ generated by $\mathscr{C}$.

It follows also that if $\mathscr{C}$ is a *semi-tribe* then the absolute continuity on $\mathscr{C}$ is equivalent to the absolute continuity.

7. MEASURES WITH THE DIRECT SUM PROPERTY

Let $\mathscr{C}$ be a *clan* of subsets of T and μ a positive measure on $\mathscr{C}$.

Definition 5. *We shall denote by $C(\mu)$ the set of all the families $\mathscr{A} = (A_i)_{i \in I}$ of disjoint μ-integrable sets such that $T - \bigcup_{i \in I} A_i$ is μ-negligible and such that for every set $A \in \mathscr{C}$ there exists a μ-negligible set $N \subset A$ and an at most countable set $J \subset I$ with $A - N = \bigcup_{i \in J} (A \cap A_i)$.*

We say that the measure μ has the direct sum property if $C(\mu) \neq \emptyset$.

A measure with finite variation is said to have the direct sum property if its variation has the direct sum property.

Proposition 16. *Every σ-bounded measure μ has the direct sum property.*

In fact, suppose that T is the union of a sequence (E_n) of μ-integrable sets. Then we can take the sets E_n disjoint and $(E_n)_{1 \leqq n < \infty} \in C(\mu)$.

Corollary 1. *Every bounded measure has the direct sum property.*

Corollary 2. *If T belongs to the tribe $\mathscr{T}$ generated by $\mathscr{C}$, then every measure on $\mathscr{C}$ has the direct sum property.*

Remark. We shall see that every regular Borel measure on a locally compact space has the direct sum property.

We shall see also that the measures with the direct sum property have many properties of the bounded measures.

Proposition 17. *Let $\mathscr{A} = (A_i)_{i \in I} \in C(\mu)$. Then:*

1. *A set $N \subset T$ is μ-negligible if and only if $N \cap A_i$ is μ-negligible for every $i \in I$.*

1'. *Let $J \subset I$ and for every $i \in J$ let $N_i \subset A_i$ be a μ-negligible set. Then $N = \bigcup_{i \in J} N_i$ is μ-negligible.*

2. *A set $E \subset T$ is μ-measurable if and only if $E \cap A_i$ is μ-measurable for every $i \in I$.*

2'. *Let $J \subset I$ and for every $i \in J$ let $E_i \subset A_i$ be a μ-measurable set. Then $E = \bigcup_{i \in J} E_i$ is μ-measurable.*

3. *If E has σ-finite measure, then there exists a μ-negligible set $N \subset E$ and a finite or countable subset $J \subset I$ such that $E - N = \bigcup_{i \in J} (E \cap A_i)$.*

Suppose that $N \cap A_i$ is μ-negligible for every $i \in I$ and let $A \in \mathscr{C}$. Let $N_0 \subset A$ be a μ-negligible set and let $(A_i)_{i \in J}$ be a countable sub-family of sets of $\mathscr{A}$ with $A - N_0 = \bigcup_{i \in J} (A \cap A_i)$. The set $A \cap N$ is the union of the μ-negligible sets $A \cap A_i \cap N$ with $i \in J$ and $A \cap N_0 \cap N$, therefore $A \cap N$ is μ-negligible, consequently N is negligible (§ 5, proposition 9). Conversely, if N is μ-negligible, then $N \cap A_i$ is μ-negligible for every $i \in I$ and the statement 1 is proved. The statement 1' follows from 1, since $N \cap A_i = N_i$ for $i \in J$ and $N \cap A_i = \emptyset$ for $i \notin J$.

The statements 2 and 2' are proved in the same way, using the corollary 2 of the theorem 2, § 5.

The statement 3 is true first for sets of $\mathscr{T}$, which can be covered by a sequence of sets of $\mathscr{C}$. Then it remains true for μ-integrable sets, since every μ-integrable set E is of the form $A \cup N$ with $A \in \mathscr{T}$ and N μ-negligible. Finally, it follows that the statement 3 remains true for a countable union E of μ-integrable sets.

Proposition 18. *If μ has the direct sum property, then there exists a family $\mathscr{A} \in C(\mu)$ consisting of sets of the semi-tribe $\mathscr{S}$ generated by $\mathscr{C}$.*

Let $\mathscr{A}' = (A'_i)_{i \in I'} \in C(\mu)$. Every set A'_i is μ-integrable, therefore A'_i is the union of a μ-negligible set N'_i and a sequence $(A_{i,n})_{1 \leqq n < \infty}$ of disjoint sets of $\mathscr{S}$. The set $N' = \bigcup_{i \in I'} N'_i$ is μ-negligible. If we put $I = I' \times \{1, 2, \ldots\}$, then the family $\mathscr{A} = (A_{i,n})_{(i,n) \in I}$ consists of disjoint sets of $\mathscr{S}$ and

$$T - \bigcup_{(i,n) \in I} A_{i,n} = N \cup \left(T - \bigcup_{i \in I'} A_i\right),$$

whence $T - \bigcup A_{i,n}$ is μ-negligible. Every set $A \in \mathscr{C}$ verifies an equality of the form

$$A - N = \bigcup_{i \in J'} (A \cap A_i),$$

where $N \subset A$ is μ-negligible and $J' \subset I'$ is countable.

The set $N_0 = N \cup (A \cap N')$ is μ-negligible and we have

$$A - N_0 = \bigcup_{\substack{i \in J' \\ n \in N}} (A \cap A_{i,n}),$$

therefore $\mathscr{A} \in C(\mu)$.

Corollary. *Let ν be a measure on $\mathscr{C}$, absolutely continuous with respect to μ. If μ has the direct sum property, then ν has the direct sum property.*

In fact, since every μ-negligible set is also ν-negligible we deduce that if $\mathscr{A}$ is a family of $C(\mu)$ consisting of sets of $\mathscr{S}$, then $\mathscr{A} \in C(\nu)$.

Proposition 19. *Let $\mathscr{A} = (A_i)_{i \in I} \in C(\mu)$. Then:*

1. *A function f defined on T with values in a Banach space E or in $\bar{R}$ is μ-measurable if and only if $f\varphi_{A_i}$ is μ-measurable for every $i \in I$.*

2. *Let $\mathscr{K}$ be a class of μ-measurable sets with σ-finite measure such that $\mathscr{A} \subset \mathscr{K}$, let E be a set, and for every $K \in \mathscr{K}$ let $g_K\colon T \to E$ be a function such that for every pair (K, K') of sets of $\mathscr{K}$ the functions g_K and $g_{K'}$ are equal μ-almost everywhere on $K \cap K'$. There exists then a function $g\colon T \to E$ such that for every $K \in \mathscr{K}$ we have*

$$g(t) = g_K(t) \quad \mu\text{-almost everywhere on } K.$$

Moreover, if E is a Banach space and if the functions g_K are μ-measurable, then g is μ-measurable.

If f is μ-measurable, then every function $f\varphi_{A_i}$ is μ-measurable. Conversely, suppose that $f\varphi_{A_i}$ is μ-measurable for every $i \in I$ and let $A \in \mathscr{C}$. There exists a μ-negligible set $N \subset A$ and an at most countable set $J \subset I$ such that $A - N = \bigcup_{i \in J} (A \cap A_i)$. Then $f\varphi_A = \sum_{i \in J} f\varphi_A \varphi_{A_i}$ μ-almost everywhere, therefore $f\varphi_A$ is μ-measurable. It follows then that f is μ-measurable.

In order to prove the second statement let $N = T - \bigcup_{i \in I} A_i$ and define the function g by the equalities

$$g(t) = \begin{cases} g_A(t), & \text{for} \quad t \in A \quad \text{and} \quad A \in \mathscr{A}, \\ a \in E, & \text{for} \quad t \in N. \end{cases}$$

Let $K \in \mathscr{K}$ be an arbitrary set. Then

$$K = \left(\bigcup_{i \in J} (A_i \cap K) \right) \cup N_0,$$

where N_0 is μ-negligible and J is an at most countable subset of I. For each $i \in J$ there exists a μ-negligible set $N_i \subset A_i \cap K$ such that

$$g(t) = g_{A_i}(t) = g_K(t), \quad \text{for} \quad t \in A_i \cap K - N_i.$$

The set $N_K = N_0 \cup \left(\bigcup_{i \in J} N_i \right)$ is μ-negligible and for $t \in K - N_K$ we have

$$g(t) = g_K(t).$$

The statement concerning the measurability follows from the first statement.

8. THE THEOREM OF LEBESGUE-NIKODYM

Let $\mathscr{C}$ be a clan, μ a positive measure on $\mathscr{C}$ and g a scalar locally μ-integrable function. For every set $A \in \mathscr{C}$ put

$$\nu(A) = \int_A g \, d\mu .$$

Then ν is a measure on $\mathscr{C}$, absolutely continuous with respect to μ (§ 8, proposition 5).

Conversely, we shall prove that if μ has the direct sum property, then every scalar measure ν on $\mathscr{C}$, absolutely continuous with respect to μ is of the preceding form.

We prove first the following:

Proposition 20. *Let μ and ν be two positive non-null measures on $\mathscr{C}$. If ν is absolutely continuous with respect to μ, then there exists a number $k > 0$ and a set $A \in \mathscr{S}(\mathscr{C})$ with $\mu(A) > 0$ such that A is essentially positive with respect to the measure $\nu - k\mu$.*

Let $E \in \mathscr{S}$ be a set with $\nu(E) > 0$. For each n consider the measure $\sigma_n = \nu - \frac{1}{n}\mu$; the set E can be written $E = A_n \cup B_n$ with $A_n \cap B_n = 0$ such that A_n is essentially positive and B_n is essentially negative with respect to σ_n. Put

$$A_0 = \bigcup_{n=1}^{\infty} A_n \quad \text{and} \quad B_0 = \bigcap_{n=1}^{\infty} B_n = E - A_0 .$$

Since $B_0 \subset B_n$ and σ_n is negative on B_n we have $\sigma_n(B_0) \leqq 0$, i.e.

$$0 \leqq \nu(B_0) \leqq \frac{1}{n} \mu(B_0), \quad \text{for each } n,$$

hence $\nu(B_0) = 0$. It follows then that $\nu(A_0) = \nu(E) > 0$. Since ν is absolutely continuous with respect to μ, we deduce that $\mu(A_0) > 0$, whence

$$\sum_{n=1}^{\infty} \mu(A_n) \geqq \mu\left(\bigcup_{n=1}^{\infty} A_n\right) > 0 .$$

There exists a number n_0 such that $\mu(A_{n_0}) > 0$. Taking $k = \frac{1}{n_0}$ and $A = A_{n_0}$, the proposition is proved.

Theorem 5 (Lebesgue-Nikodym). *Let μ and ν be two scalar measures on $\mathscr{C}$. If μ has the direct sum property and if ν is absolutely continuous with respect to μ, then there exists a scalar locally μ-integrable function f_ν such that*

$$\nu(E) = \int_E f_\nu \, d\mu, \quad \textit{for every} \quad E \in \mathscr{C} .$$

Moreover, if $T \in \mathscr{C}$ we can take the function f_ν measurable with respect to the tribe $\mathscr{T}$ generated by $\mathscr{C}$.

1. Suppose first that $\mu \geqq 0$, $\nu \geqq 0$, and $T \in \mathscr{C}$. We design by $\mathscr{P}$ the set of the *positive* $\mathscr{T}$-measurable and μ-integrable functions f defined on T, such that

$$\int_E f\,d\mu \leqq \nu(E), \quad \text{for every} \quad E \in \mathscr{T},$$

and put

$$\alpha = \sup_{f \in \mathscr{P}} \int f\,d\mu.$$

We can find a sequence (f_n) of functions of $\mathscr{P}$ with $\lim\limits_{n\to\infty} \int f_n\,d\mu = \alpha$.

Let $E \in \mathscr{T}$ be an arbitrary set. For each natural number n consider the function $g_n = \sup(f_1, f_2, \ldots, f_n)$ and the sets

$$E_i = \{t \in E;\ g_n(t) = f_i(t),\ g_n(t) > f_j(t) \text{ for } 1 \leqq j \leqq i-1\},\quad i = 1, 2, \ldots, n.$$

The functions g_n are $\mathscr{T}$-measurable and μ-integrable and the sets E_i are disjoint, belong to $\mathscr{T}$ and their union is E, whence

$$\int_E g_n\,d\mu = \sum_{i=1}^{n} \int_{E_i} f_i\,d\mu \leqq \sum_{i=1}^{n} \nu(E_i) = \nu(E),$$

therefore $g_n \in \mathscr{P}$ for each n. Consider now the function $f_0 = \sup\limits_n f_n = \sup\limits_n g_n$. Since (g_n) is an increasing sequence, we deduce that f_0 is μ-integrable and

$$\int f_0\,d\mu = \lim_{n\to\infty} \int g_n\,d\mu = \sup_n \int g_n\,d\mu \leqq \alpha.$$

The function f_0 is also $\mathscr{T}$-measurable. From $f_n \leqq g_n$ it follows that $\int f_n\,d\mu \leqq \int g_n\,d\mu$; hence $f_0 \in \mathscr{P}$ and

$$\alpha = \lim_{n\to\infty} \int f_n\,d\mu \leqq \lim_{n\to\infty} \int g_n\,d\mu = \int f_0\,d\mu \leqq \alpha,$$

therefore

$$\int f_0\,d\mu = \alpha.$$

Since f_0 is μ-integrable, it is finite μ-almost everywhere. The function

$$f_\nu(t) = \begin{cases} f_0(t), & \text{if } f_0(t) < \infty, \\ 0, & \text{if } f_0(t) = \infty, \end{cases}$$

is positive, $\mathscr{T}$-measurable and μ-integrable and $\int f_\nu\,d\mu = \alpha$. For every set $E \in \mathscr{T}$ put

$$\nu_0(E) = \nu(E) - \int_E f_\nu\,d\mu.$$

Then ν_0 is a measure, absolutely continuous with respect to μ. We shall show that $\nu_0 = 0$. In fact, if $\nu_0 \neq 0$, according to the preceding proposition there exists a number $k > 0$ and a set $A \in \mathscr{T}$ with $\mu(A) > 0$, such that A is essentially positive with respect to the measure $\nu_0 - k\mu$. For every set $E \in \mathscr{T}$ we have then

$$k\mu(E \cap A) \leqq \nu_0(E \cap A) = \nu(E \cap A) - \int_{E \cap A} f_\nu \, d\mu.$$

The function $g = f_\nu + k\varphi_A$ is $\mathscr{T}$-measurable, and from the preceding inequality it follows that for every $E \in \mathscr{T}$ we have

$$\int_E g \, d\mu = \int_E f_\nu \, d\mu + k\mu(E \cap A) \leqq \int_{E-A} f_\nu \, d\mu + \nu(E \cap A)$$
$$\leqq \nu(E - A) + \nu(E \cap A) = \nu(E),$$

hence $g \in \mathscr{P}$. On the other hand

$$\int g \, d\mu = \int f_\nu \, d\mu + k\mu(A) > \alpha,$$

hence $g \notin \mathscr{P}$ and we get a contradiction. It follows therefore that $\nu_0 = 0$, i.e.

$$\nu(E) = \int_E f_\nu \, d\mu, \quad \text{for} \quad E \in \mathscr{T},$$

and the theorem is proved in this case.

2. Suppose now that $\mu \geqq 0$, $\nu \geqq 0$, the measure μ has the direct sum property, and let $\mathscr{A} = (A_i)_{i \in I} \in C(\mu)$ be a family consisting of sets of $\mathscr{S}$. For each A_i consider the tribe $\mathscr{T}_i$ of the sets of $\mathscr{S}$ contained in A_i, and denote by μ_i and ν_i the restrictions of the measures μ and ν to $\mathscr{T}_i$.

The measure ν_i is absolutely continuous with respect to μ_i, hence, according to the first part of the proof, for each i there exists a $\mathscr{T}_i$-measurable and μ_i-integrable function $f_i\colon A_i \to R$ such that

$$\nu_i(A) = \int_A f_i \, d\mu_i, \quad \text{for} \quad A \in \mathscr{T}_i.$$

The function f_i' defined on T by

$$f_i'(t) = \begin{cases} f_i(t), & \text{if} \quad t \in A_i, \\ 0, & \text{if} \quad t \notin A_i, \end{cases}$$

is then μ-integrable and we have

$$\nu(A) = \nu_i(A) = \int_A f_i \, d\mu_i = \int_A f_i' \, d\mu, \quad \text{for} \quad A \in \mathscr{T}_i.$$

We define now the function f_ν on T by the equality

$$f_\nu = \sum_{i \in I} f_i'.$$

From the proposition 19 we deduce that f_ν is μ-measurable. We prove that f_ν is locally μ-integrable. Let $E \in \mathscr{C}$. There exists a μ-negligible set $N \subset E$ and an at most countable set $J \subset I$ such that if we put $E_i = A_i \cap E$, we have

$$E - N = \bigcup_{i \in J} E_i.$$

Then

$$f_\nu \varphi_E = \sum_{i \in J} f_i' \varphi_{E_i} \quad \mu\text{-almost everywhere}$$

and

$$\sum_{i \in J} \int_{E_i} f_i' \, d\mu = \sum_{i \in J} \nu(E_i) = \nu\left(\bigcup_{i \in J} E_i\right) = \nu(E) < \infty.$$

It follows that $f_\nu \varphi_E$ is μ-integrable, hence f_ν is locally μ-integrable and we have

$$\int_E f \, d\mu = \sum_{i \in J} \int_{E_i} f_i' \, d\mu = \nu(E).$$

3. If $\mu \geqq 0$ and ν is a real measure, we have $\nu = \nu^+ - \nu^-$ where ν^+ and ν^- are positive measures, absolutely continuous with respect to μ. There exist then two locally μ-integrable positive functions f^+ and f^- such that

$$\nu^+(E) = \int_E f^+ \, d\mu \quad \text{and} \quad \nu^-(E) = \int_E f^- \, d\mu, \quad \text{for} \quad E \in \mathscr{C}.$$

The real function $f = f^+ - f^-$ is locally μ-integrable and we have

$$\nu(E) = \int_E f_\nu \, d\mu, \quad \text{for} \quad E \in \mathscr{C}.$$

4. If $\mu \geqq 0$ and if ν is a complex measure, we have $\nu = \nu_1 + i\nu_2$, where ν_1 and ν_2 are real measures, absolutely continuous with respect to μ. There exist then two locally μ-integrable real functions f_i such that

$$\nu_i(E) = \int_E f_i \, d\mu, \quad \text{for} \quad E \in \mathscr{C}, \quad i = 1, 2.$$

The function $f = f_1 + if_2$ is locally μ-integrable and we have

$$\nu(E) = \int_E f \, d\mu, \quad \text{for} \quad E \in \mathscr{C}.$$

5. Suppose now that μ is a scalar measure. Since μ is absolutely continuous with respect to $|\mu|$, there exists a locally μ-integrable scalar function ψ such that $\mu = \psi|\mu|$.

Then (proposition 10) $|\mu| = |\psi|\mu|| = |\psi|\,|\mu|$, and from the corollary 2 of the proposition 10 we deduce that $|\psi(t)| = 1$ μ-almost everywhere. The function

$$\varphi(t) = \begin{cases} \psi(t), & \text{if } |\psi(t)| = 1, \\ 1, & \text{if } |\psi(t)| \neq 1, \end{cases}$$

is also locally μ-integrable and we have $|\varphi(t)| \equiv 1$ and $\mu = \varphi|\mu|$. We have then

$$|\mu| = \left(\frac{1}{\varphi}\varphi\right)|\mu| = \frac{1}{\varphi}(\varphi|\mu|) = \frac{1}{\varphi}\mu.$$

On the other hand, ν is absolutely continuous with respect to $|\mu|$, therefore there exists a locally $|\mu|$-integrable function f such that $\nu = f|\mu|$. Then the function $_\nu = f\frac{1}{\varphi}$ is μ-measurable and locally μ-integrable and we have

$$\nu = f|\mu| = f\left(\frac{1}{\varphi}\mu\right) = \left(f\frac{1}{\varphi}\right)\mu = f_\nu\mu.$$

The theorem is completely proved.

Remark. In § 13 this theorem will be extended for vector measures.

From the preceding proof we deduce the

Corollary 1. *If μ is a scalar measure with the direct sum property on $\mathscr{C}$, there exists a locally μ-integrable scalar function φ with $|\varphi(t)| \equiv 1$ such that*

$$\mu = \varphi|\mu| \quad \textit{and} \quad |\mu| = \frac{1}{\varphi}\mu.$$

Corollary 2. *If μ is a real measure with the direct sum property, then there exist two disjoint sets $A, B \in \mathfrak{T}(\mu)$ such that $A \cup B = T$ and*

$$\mu^+ = \varphi_A|\mu|, \quad \mu^- = \varphi_B|\mu|.$$

In fact, let φ be a locally μ-integrable real function such that $|\varphi(t)| \equiv 1$ and $\mu = \varphi|\mu|$. The function φ takes only the values 1 and -1. Then $A = \{t;\ \varphi(t) = 1\}$ and $B = \{t;\ \varphi(t) = -1\}$ are the desired sets.

9. FURTHER PROPERTIES OF THE MEASURES DEFINED BY DENSITIES

Let $\mathscr{C}$ be a clan. The proposition 10 can now be extended.

Theorem 6. *Let E be a Banach space. If μ is a scalar measure on $\mathscr{C}$ and if $g: T \to E$ is a locally μ-integrable function, then*

$$|g\mu| = |g|\,|\mu|.$$

Suppose first that μ is bounded. According to the corollary 1 of the theorem 5, there exists a scalar μ-measurable function φ with $|\varphi(t)| \equiv 1$ and $\mu = \varphi|\mu|$. Then $\mathbf{g}\varphi$ is locally μ-integrable and we have $|\mathbf{g}\varphi| = |\mathbf{g}|$ and

$$\mathbf{g}\mu = \mathbf{g}(\varphi|\mu|) = (\mathbf{g}\varphi)\,|\mu|.$$

For the measure $(\mathbf{g}\varphi)\,|\mu|$ we have (proposition 10)

$$|(\mathbf{g}\varphi)\,|\mu|| = |\mathbf{g}\varphi|\,|\mu| = |\mathbf{g}|\,|\mu|.$$

It follows that

$$|\mathbf{g}\mu| = |(\mathbf{g}\varphi)\,|\mu|| = |\mathbf{g}|\,|\mu|.$$

Suppose now that μ is an arbitrary scalar measure. Let $A \in \mathscr{C}$. The measure $\varphi_A\mu$ is bounded and $\mathbf{g}\varphi_A$ is μ-integrable and we have

$$(\varphi_A \mathbf{g})\,\mu = \mathbf{g}(\varphi_A\mu).$$

From the first part of the proof we deduce that

$$|(\varphi_A \mathbf{g})\,\mu| = |\mathbf{g}(\varphi_A\mu)| = |\mathbf{g}|\,|\varphi_A\mu|.$$

We verify easily that for every $B \in \mathscr{C}$ with $B \subset A$ we have

$$[(\varphi_A \mathbf{g})\,\mu]\,(B) = (\mathbf{g}\mu)\,(B) \quad \text{and} \quad (\varphi_A\mu)\,(B) = \mu(B),$$

hence

$$|(\varphi_A \mathbf{g})\,\mu|\,(A) = |\mathbf{g}\mu|\,(A) \quad \text{and} \quad |\varphi_A\mu|\,(A) = |\mu|\,(A).$$

We have also

$$[|\mathbf{g}|\,|\varphi_A\mu|]\,(A) = (|\mathbf{g}|\,|\mu|)\,(A).$$

It follows then that

$$|\mathbf{g}\mu|\,(A) = (|\mathbf{g}|\,|\mu|)\,(A).$$

Since $A \in \mathscr{C}$ is arbitrary, we deduce that $|\mathbf{g}\mu| = |\mathbf{g}|\,|\mu|$.

The corollaries of the proposition 10 can now be extended for scalar measures.

Corollary 1. *Let μ be a scalar measure on $\mathscr{C}$, E a Banach space, and $\mathbf{g}: T \to E$ a locally μ-integrable function. We have $\mathbf{g}\mu = 0$ if and only if $\mathbf{g}(t) = 0$ μ-almost everywhere.*

The proof is the same as for the corollary 1 of the proposition 10.

This corollary can be stated in the following form:

We have

$$\int_A \mathbf{g}\,d\mu = 0, \quad \textit{for every} \quad A \in \mathscr{C},$$

if and only if $\mathbf{g}(t) = 0$ μ-almost everywhere.

Corollary 2. *Let μ be a scalar measure on $\mathscr{C}$, E a Banach space, and $\mathbf{g}_1, \mathbf{g}_2 : T \to E$ two locally μ-integrable functions. We have $\mathbf{g}_1\mu = \mathbf{g}_2\mu$ if and only if $\mathbf{g}_1(t) = \mathbf{g}_2(t)$ μ-almost everywhere.*

This corollary can be stated in the following form:

We have

$$\int_A \mathbf{g}_1 \, d\mu = \int_A \mathbf{g}_2 \, d\mu, \quad \textit{for every} \quad A \in \mathscr{C},$$

if and only if $\mathbf{g}_1(t) = \mathbf{g}_2(t)$ μ-almost everywhere.

Corollary 3. *Let μ be a real measure on $\mathscr{C}$ and $g \geqq 0$ a positive locally μ-integrable function. Then g is locally integrable with respect to μ^+ and μ^- and we have*

$$(g\mu)^+ = g\mu^+ \quad \textit{and} \quad (g\mu)^- = g\mu^-.$$

If g is locally μ-integrable, then g is locally $|\mu|$-integrable, and from the inequalities $\mu^+ \leqq |\mu|$ and $\mu^- \leqq |\mu|$ we deduce that g is locally integrable with respect to μ^+ and μ^-. Then

$$(g\mu)^+ = \frac{1}{2}(|g\mu| + g\mu) = \frac{1}{2}(g|\mu| + g\mu) = g\frac{1}{2}(|\mu| + \mu) = g\mu^+$$

and

$$(g\mu)^- = \frac{1}{2}(|g\mu| - g\mu) = g\frac{1}{2}(|\mu| - \mu) = g\mu^-.$$

10. SINGULAR MEASURES

Let $\mathscr{C}$ be a clan, μ and ν two positive measures defined on $\mathscr{C}$.

Definition 5. *We say that μ and ν are singular (to each other) if for every positive measure σ such that $\sigma \leqq \mu$ and $\sigma \leqq \nu$ we have $\sigma = 0$, i.e. if* $\inf(\mu, \nu) = 0$.

We say also that ν is *singular with respect* to μ, or that μ is *singular with respect* to ν. We say that two vector measures $\boldsymbol{m}$ and $\boldsymbol{n}$ with finite variation are singular if the variations $|\boldsymbol{m}|$ and $|\boldsymbol{n}|$ are singular.

A measure μ is said to be *concentrated* on a set $M \subset T$ if $T - M$ is μ-negligible, i.e. if M is μ-measurable and $\mu = \varphi_M \mu$.

Proposition 21. *If there exists two disjoint sets M and N such that μ is concentrated on M and ν is concentrated on N, then μ and ν are singular.*

In fact, let σ be a positive measure such that $\sigma \leqq \mu$ and $\sigma \leqq \nu$. Then M and N are σ-measurable. For every set $A \in \mathscr{C}$, the sets $A \cap M$ and $A - M$ are σ-integrable. Since $(A \cap M) \cap N = \emptyset$ we have $\sigma(A \cap M) \leqq \nu(A \cap M) = 0$; since $(A - M) \cap M = \emptyset$ we have $\sigma(A - M) \leqq \mu(A - M) = 0$; it follows that $\sigma(A) = \sigma(A \cap M) + \sigma(A - M) = 0$, therefore $\sigma = 0$, consequently μ and ν are singular.

Conversely:

Proposition 22. *If μ and ν are singular and if $\mu + \nu$ has the direct sum property, then there exist two disjoint sets M and N such that μ is concentrated on M and ν is concentrated on N.*

The measure $\lambda = \mu + \nu$ has the direct sum property and the measures μ and ν are absolutely continuous with respect to λ. There exist then two positive locally λ-integrable functions g and h such that $\mu = g\lambda$ and $\nu = h\lambda$.

The function $\inf(g, h)$ is positive and locally λ-integrable and we have $\inf(g, h)\lambda \leqq g\lambda = \mu$ and $\inf(g, h)\lambda \leqq h\lambda = \nu$. Since μ and ν are singular, we have $\inf(g, h)\lambda = 0$, therefore $\inf(g(t), h(t)) = 0$ λ-almost everywhere. There exist then two disjoint λ-measurable sets M and N such that $\varphi_M g = g$ and $\varphi_N h = h$ λ-almost everywhere. We have then $\mu = g\lambda = \varphi_M g\lambda = \varphi_M \mu$, therefore μ is concentrated on M, and $\nu = h\lambda = \varphi_N h\lambda = \varphi_N \nu$, therefore ν is concentrated on N.

Theorem 7 (Lebesgue's decomposition theorem). *Let μ be a positive measure on $\mathscr{C}$, X a Banach space, and $\boldsymbol{m}: \mathscr{C} \to X$ a measure with finite variation $|\boldsymbol{m}|$. If $|\boldsymbol{m}| + \mu$ has the direct sum property, then $\boldsymbol{m}$ can be written uniquely in the form*

$$\boldsymbol{m} = \boldsymbol{m}_0 + \boldsymbol{m}_1,$$

where $\boldsymbol{m}_0, \boldsymbol{m}_1: \mathscr{C} \to X$ are measures with finite variation such that $\boldsymbol{m}_0$ is absolutely continuous with respect to μ and $\boldsymbol{m}_1$ is singular with respect to μ.

The measure $\lambda = |\boldsymbol{m}| + \mu$ has the direct sum property and $|\boldsymbol{m}|$ is absolutely continuous with respect to λ, therefore there exists a locally λ-integrable function $g \geqq 0$ such that $|\boldsymbol{m}| = g\lambda$. Since $|\boldsymbol{m}| \leqq \lambda$ and $\mu \leqq \lambda$, the function g is locally integrable with respect to $|\boldsymbol{m}|$ and μ, we have $g\lambda = g|\boldsymbol{m}| + g\mu$. Since $g\mu \geqq 0$, we have $g|\boldsymbol{m}| \leqq g|\boldsymbol{m}| + g\mu = g\lambda = |\boldsymbol{m}|$, therefore $g(t) \leqq 1$ $\boldsymbol{m}$-almost everywhere. The disjoint sets

$$A = \{t; 0 \leqq g(t) < 1\} \quad \text{and} \quad B = \{t; g(t) = 1\}$$

are measurable with respect to λ, $|\boldsymbol{m}|$, and μ, and $\varphi_{A \cup B}(t) = 1$ $|\boldsymbol{m}|$-almost everywhere. For the measures $\boldsymbol{m}_0 = \varphi_A \boldsymbol{m}$ and $\boldsymbol{m}_1 = \varphi_B \boldsymbol{m}$ we have then

$$\boldsymbol{m} = \varphi_{A \cup B}\boldsymbol{m} = \varphi_A \boldsymbol{m} + \varphi_B \boldsymbol{m} = \boldsymbol{m}_0 + \boldsymbol{m}_1.$$

To prove that $\boldsymbol{m}_1$ is singular with respect to μ, we remark first that B is μ-negligible. In fact, for every set $C \in \mathscr{C}$, the set $C \cap B$ is integrable with respect to λ, $|\boldsymbol{m}|$, and μ, and we have

$$|\boldsymbol{m}|(C \cap B) = \int_{C \cap B} g \, d|\boldsymbol{m}| + \int_{C \cap B} g \, d\mu = |\boldsymbol{m}|(C \cap B) + \mu(C \cap B)$$

(since $g(t) = 1$ for $t \in C \cap B$), whence $\mu(C \cap B) = 0$, therefore B is μ-negligible. Thus $\boldsymbol{m}_1$ and μ are concentrated respectively on the disjoint sets B and $T - B$. From the proposition 21 we deduce that $\boldsymbol{m}_1$ and μ are singular.

To prove that $\boldsymbol{m}_0$ is absolutely continuous with respect to μ, let N be a μ-negligible set belonging to the semi-tribe $\mathscr{S}$ generated by $\mathscr{C}$. Then $\varphi_N g\mu = g(\varphi_N\mu) = 0$, therefore $\varphi_N|\boldsymbol{m}| = \varphi_N g|\boldsymbol{m}| + \varphi_N g\mu = \varphi_N g|\boldsymbol{m}|$. It follows that $\varphi_N(t) = g(t)\,\varphi_N(t)$ $|\boldsymbol{m}|$-almost everywhere, therefore $g(t) = 1$ $|\boldsymbol{m}|$-almost everywhere on N. We deduce then that $A \cap N$ is $|\boldsymbol{m}|$-negligible, therefore $\varphi_N|\boldsymbol{m}_0| = \varphi_N\varphi_A|\boldsymbol{m}| = \varphi_{A\cap N}|\boldsymbol{m}| = 0$, consequently N is $\boldsymbol{m}_0$-negligible. From the proposition 13 it follows that $\boldsymbol{m}_0$ is absolutely continuous with respect to μ.

To prove the uniqueness of the decomposition, suppose that we have also

$$\boldsymbol{m} = \boldsymbol{m}_0' + \boldsymbol{m}_1',$$

where $\boldsymbol{m}_0'$ is absolutely continuous with respect to μ and $\boldsymbol{m}_1'$ is singular with respect to μ. From the equality $\boldsymbol{m}_0' + \boldsymbol{m}_1' = \boldsymbol{m}_0 + \boldsymbol{m}_1$ we deduce that $\boldsymbol{m}_0 - \boldsymbol{m}_0' = \boldsymbol{m}_1' - \boldsymbol{m}_1 = \boldsymbol{n}$. The measure $\boldsymbol{n}$ is at the same time absolutely continuous and singular with respect to μ, whence $\boldsymbol{n} = 0$, therefore $\boldsymbol{m}_0' = \boldsymbol{m}_0$ and $\boldsymbol{m}_1' = \boldsymbol{m}_1$.

The theorem is completely proved.

11. CONDITIONAL EXPECTATIONS

As an application of the theorem of Lebesgue-Nikodym, we define in this section the conditional expectations which will be used to prove the existence of a lifting of $\mathscr{L}^\infty$.

Let $\mathscr{T}$ be a tribe of subsets of T and μ a *positive* measure on $\mathscr{T}$. We assume that $T \in \mathscr{T}$ and $\mu(T) = 1$. Let $\mathscr{F}$ be a subtribe of $\mathscr{T}$ such that $T \in \mathscr{F}$.

Every function $f\colon T \to R$ which is $\mathscr{F}$-measurable, is also $\mathscr{T}$-measurable, but it may happen that some $\mathscr{T}$-measurable functions should not be $\mathscr{F}$-measurable.

Proposition 23. *If $f\colon T \to R$ is a $\mathscr{T}$-measurable and μ-integrable function, then there exists a function $f_{\mathscr{F}}\colon T \to R$ which is $\mathscr{F}$-measurable and μ-integrable and verifies the equality*

$$\int_A f_{\mathscr{F}}\, d\mu = \int_A f\, d\mu, \quad \textit{for every} \quad A \in \mathscr{F}.$$

Denote by $\mu_{\mathscr{F}}$ the restriction of μ to $\mathscr{F}$. Then $\mu_{\mathscr{F}}$ is a positive measure on $\mathscr{F}$ and verifies the equality

$$\mu_{\mathscr{F}}(A) = \mu(A), \quad \text{for every} \quad A \in \mathscr{F}.$$

It follows that every function $g\colon T \to R$ which is $\mathscr{F}$-measurable and $\mu_{\mathscr{F}}$-integrable, is also $\mathscr{T}$-measurable and μ-integrable and we have

$$\int_A g\, d\mu_{\mathscr{F}} = \int_A g\, d\mu, \quad \text{for} \quad A \in \mathscr{F}.$$

Let now $f\colon T \to R$ be a $\mathcal{T}$-measurable and μ-integrable function. For every set $A \in \mathcal{F}$ we have $A \in \mathcal{T}$, hence $f\varphi_A$ is μ-integrable. Put

$$\nu(A) = \int_A f\,d\mu, \quad \text{for} \quad A \in \mathcal{F}.$$

Then ν is a real measure on $\mathcal{F}$. On the other hand, ν is absolutely continuous with respect to $\mu_{\mathcal{F}}$, since if $A \in \mathcal{F}$ and $\mu_{\mathcal{F}}(A) = 0$, then $\mu(A) = 0$, therefore $\nu(A) = 0$.

According to the theorem of Lebesgue-Nikodym, there exists a $\mathcal{F}$-measurable and $\mu_{\mathcal{F}}$-integrable function $f_{\mathcal{F}}\colon T \to R$ such that

$$\nu(A) = \int_A f_{\mathcal{F}}\,d\mu_{\mathcal{F}}, \quad \text{for} \quad A \in \mathcal{F}.$$

Since

$$\int_A f_{\mathcal{F}}\,d\mu_{\mathcal{F}} = \int_A f_{\mathcal{F}}\,d\mu, \quad \text{for} \quad A \in \mathcal{F},$$

we deduce

$$\int_A f_{\mathcal{F}}\,d\mu = \int_A f\,d\mu, \quad \text{for} \quad A \in \mathcal{F},$$

and the proposition is proved.

The function $f_{\mathcal{F}}$ is called the *conditional expectation* of f with respect to the tribe $\mathcal{F}$.

Remarks.

1°. If a $\mathcal{F}$-measurable function g differs from $f_{\mathcal{F}}$ only on a set $A \in \mathcal{F}$ with $\mu(A) = 0$, then g verifies also the conditions of the preceding proposition. It follows that the conditional expectation is not uniquely determined, but with the approximation of a μ-negligible set of $\mathcal{F}$.

2°. From the theorem of Lebesgue-Nikodym we deduce that if $f \geqq 0$ we can take $f_{\mathcal{F}} \geqq 0$.

3°. If $\mathcal{F}_1$ and $\mathcal{F}_2$ are two subtribes of $\mathcal{T}$ such that $T \in \mathcal{F}_1 \subset \mathcal{F}_2$, then

$$(f_{\mathcal{F}_2})_{\mathcal{F}_1} = f_{\mathcal{F}_1},$$

except for a μ-negligible set of $\mathcal{F}_1$.

Assume now that μ is a *complete measure*, i.e. if A is a μ-negligible set of $\mathcal{T}$, then every subset $B \subset A$ belongs to $\mathcal{T}$.

We assume also that $\mathcal{F}$ contains T and all the μ-negligible sets of $\mathcal{T}$.

Proposition 24. *Let $f\colon T \to R$ be a $\mathcal{T}$-measurable and μ-integrable function. If f is essentially bounded, then $f_{\mathcal{F}}$ is also essentially bounded and we have*

$$N_\infty(f_{\mathcal{F}}) \leqq N_\infty(f).$$

From the equality

$$\int_A f_{\mathscr{F}}\, d\mu = \int_A f\, d\mu, \quad \text{for} \quad A \in \mathscr{F},$$

we deduce that

$$\left|\int_A f_{\mathscr{F}}\, d\mu\right| \leqq \int_A |f|\, d\mu \leqq \int_A N_\infty(f)\, d\mu,$$

hence

$$\int_A - N_\infty(f)\, d\mu \leqq \int_A f_{\mathscr{F}} d\mu \leqq \int_A N_\infty(f)\, d\mu, \quad \text{for} \quad A \in \mathscr{F}.$$

It follows then that

$$-N_\infty(f) \leqq f_{\mathscr{F}} \leqq N_\infty(f) \quad \mu\text{-almost everywhere,}$$

hence

$$|f_{\mathscr{F}}| \leqq N_\infty(f) \quad \mu\text{-almost everywhere,}$$

therefore

$$N_\infty(f_{\mathscr{F}}) \leqq N_\infty(f).$$

12. MARTINGALES

The martingales will be used in the proof of the existence of a lifting of $\mathscr{L}^\infty$.

Let $\mathscr{T}$ be a tribe of subsets of T with $T \in \mathscr{T}$ and let μ be a positive measure on $\mathscr{T}$ with $\mu(T) = 1$.

Let $(\mathscr{F}_n)$ be an increasing sequence of tribes such that $T \in \mathscr{F}_n$ for every n. Let also (f_n) be a sequence of real functions defined on T, such that, for every n, f_n is $\mathscr{F}_n$-measurable.

Definition 6. *The sequence $(f_n, \mathscr{F}_n)$ is called a martingale, if for every n we have*

$$\int_A f_n\, d\mu = \int_A f_{n+1}\, d\mu, \quad \textit{for} \quad A \in \mathscr{F}_n.$$

The sequence $(f_n, \mathscr{F}_n)$ is called a semi-martingale, if for every n we have

$$\int_A f_n\, d\mu \leqq \int_A f_{n+1}\, d\mu, \quad \textit{for} \quad A \in \mathscr{F}_n.$$

Evidently, every martingale is a semi-martingale. To say that $(f_n, \mathscr{F}_n)$ is a martingale means that, for every n, the function f_n is the conditional expectation of f_{n+1} with respect to the tribe $\mathscr{F}_n$.

Examples.

1. If $f_n(t) \equiv \alpha$ for every $n \in N$, the sequence $(f_n, \mathscr{F}_n)$ is a martingale.

2. Let $f: T \to R$ be a $\mathscr{T}$-measurable and μ-integrable function. For each n denote by f_n the conditional expectation of f with respect to the tribe $\mathscr{F}_n$. Then the sequence $(f_n, \mathscr{F}_n)$ is a martingale. In fact, we have

$$\int_A f_n \, d\mu = \int_A f \, d\mu, \quad \text{for} \quad A \in \mathscr{F}_n,$$

and

$$\int_A f_{n+1} \, d\mu = \int_A f \, d\mu, \quad \text{for} \quad A \in \mathscr{F}_{n+1},$$

hence

$$\int_A f_n \, d\mu = \int_A f_{n+1} \, d\mu, \quad \text{for} \quad A \in \mathscr{F}_n.$$

We deduce immediately the following properties:

1. *If* $(f_n, \mathscr{F}_n)$ *and* $(g_n, \mathscr{F}_n)$ *are martingales (respectively semi-martingales), then* $(f_n + g_n, \mathscr{F}_n)$ *is a martingale (respectively semi-martingale).*

2. *If* $(f_n, \mathscr{F}_n)$ *is a martingale and* $\alpha \in R$, *then* $(\alpha f_n, \mathscr{F}_n)$ *is a martingale.*

2'. *If* $(f_n, \mathscr{F}_n)$ *is a semi-martingale and* $\alpha \geqq 0$, *then* $(\alpha f_n, \mathscr{F}_n)$ *is a semi-martingale.*

3. *If* $(f_n, \mathscr{F}_n)$ *is a semi-martingale, then* $(f_n^+, \mathscr{F}_n)$ *is a semi-martingale.*

In fact, let $A \in \mathscr{F}_n$. The set $A_n = \{t; f_n(t) \geqq 0\}$ belongs to $\mathscr{F}_n$ and we have $f_n^+ = f_n \varphi_{A_n}$, hence

$$\int_A f_n^+ \, d\mu = \int_{A \cap A_n} f_n \, d\mu \leqq \int_{A \cap A_n} f_{n+1} \, d\mu \leqq \int_{A \cap A_n} f_{n+1}^+ \, d\mu \leqq \int_A f_{n+1}^+ \, d\mu.$$

4. *If* $(f_n, \mathscr{F}_n)$ *is a martingale, then* $(|f_n|, \mathscr{F}_n)$ *is a semi-martingale.*

In fact, $f_n^- = -f_n - f_n^+$, hence $(f_n^-, \mathscr{F}_n)$ is a semi-martingale. From $|f_n| = f_n^+ + f_n^-$ it follows that $(|f_n|, \mathscr{F})$ is a semi-martingale.

13. CONVERGENCE THEOREMS FOR MARTINGALES

Let $\xi_1, \xi_2, \ldots, \xi_n$ be n real numbers and let $r_1 < r_2$. Denote by ν_1 the first of the indices i verifying $\xi_i \leqq r_1$ (if there exist such indices). We define then by recurrence ν_j as the first of the indices $i > \nu_{j-1}$ such that

$$\xi_i \geqq r_2, \quad \text{if } j \text{ is even},$$

$$\xi_i \leqq r_1, \quad \text{if } j \text{ is odd}$$

(if there exist such indices). We have therefore

$$\xi_{\nu_1} \leqq r_1, \xi_{\nu_2} \geqq r_2, \xi_{\nu_3} \leqq r_1, \ldots$$

The greatest even number j for which ν_j is defined is denoted by 2β. If ν_2 is not defined, we take $\beta = 0$.

Proposition 25. *Let $(f_n, \mathscr{F}_n)$ be a semi-martingale. For every $t \in T$ and every natural number n consider the function $\beta_n(t)$ corresponding to the numbers*

$$\xi_1 = f_1(t), \xi_2 = f_2(t), \ldots, \xi_n = f_n(t).$$

Then the function β_n is $\mathscr{F}_n$-measurable, μ-integrable, and we have

$$\int \beta_n \, d\mu = \frac{1}{r_2 - r_1} \int_{\{f_n \geqq r_1\}} (f_n - r_1) \, d\mu \leqq \frac{1}{r_2 - r_1} \left(\int |f_n| \, d\mu + |r_1| \right).$$

We shall suppose first $f_1 \geqq 0, f_2 \geqq 0, \ldots, f_n \geqq 0, \ldots$ and $r_1 = 0$. For every $t \in T$ we define, as before, the numbers $\nu_1(t), \nu_2(t), \ldots, \nu_n(t)$ and $\beta_n(t)$, starting from the numbers

$$\xi_1 = f_1(t), \xi_2 = f_2(t), \ldots, \xi_n = f_n(t),$$

where we put $\nu_j(t) = n + 1$ if the number $\nu_j(t)$ is not defined in the preceding way.

The functions $\nu_1, \nu_2, \ldots, \nu_n$ and β_n are *step functions*.

In fact, ν_1 can take only the values $1, 2, \ldots, n, n + 1$, and in general ν_j can take only the values $j, j + 1, \ldots, n, n + 1$.

The function β_n can take only the values $0, 1, 2, \ldots, k$, where k is such that $2k \leqq n \leqq 2k + 1$.

The functions $\nu_1, \nu_2, \ldots, \nu_n$ and β_n are *$\mathscr{F}_n$-measurable*. Moreover,

$$\{t; \nu_j(t) = k\} \in \mathscr{F}_k, \quad \text{for} \quad j = 1, 2, \ldots, n \quad \text{and } k \geqq j.$$

In fact, we have first

$$\{t; \nu_1(t) = 1\} = \{f_1(t) = 0\} \in \mathscr{F}_1,$$

$$\{t; \nu_1(t) = k\} = \bigcap_{i<k} \{t; f_i(t) > 0\} \cap \{t; f_k(t) = 0\} \in \mathscr{F}_k$$

for $k = 2, \ldots, n$, and

$$\{t; \nu_1(t) = n + 1\} = \bigcap_{i=1}^{n} \{t; f_i(t) > 0\} \in \mathscr{F}_n \subset \mathscr{F}_{n+1}$$

and then, by recurrence

$$\{t; \nu_{2m}(t) = k\} = \bigcap_{j=2m-1}^{k-1} (\{t; \nu_{2m-1}(t) = j\} \cap \{t; f_{j+1}(t) < r_2\} \cap \cdots$$

$$\cap \{f_{k-1}(t) < r_2\}) \cap \{t; f_k(t) \geqq r_2\} \in \bigcup_{j=2m-1}^{k} \mathscr{F}_j \subset \mathscr{F}_k$$

and

$$\{t;\, \nu_{2m-1}(t) = k\} = \bigcap_{j=2m}^{k-1} (\{t;\, \nu_{2m}(t) = j\} \cap \{t; f_{j+1}(t) > r_1\} \cap \cdots$$

$$\cap \{f_{k-1}(t) > r_1\}) \cap \{t; f_k(t) \leqq r_1\} \in \mathscr{F}_k.$$

$$\{t;\, \nu_j(t) = n+1\} = T - \bigcup_{k=1}^{n} \{t;\, \nu_j(t) = k\} \in \mathscr{F}_n \subset \mathscr{F}_{n+1}.$$

As for the functions β_n, we have

$$\{t;\, \beta_n(t) = 0\} = \{t;\, \nu_2(t) = n+1\} \in \mathscr{F}_n,$$

$$\{t;\, \beta_n(t) = 1\} = \{t;\, \nu_2(t) \leqq n\} \cap \{t;\, \nu_4(t) = n+1\} \in \mathscr{F}_n,$$

$$\{t;\, \beta_n(t) = j\} = \{t;\, \nu_{2j}(t) \leqq n\} \cap \{t;\, \nu_{2j+2}(t) = n+1\} \in \mathscr{F}_n.$$

We define now the functions $u_2, u_3, \ldots, u_n$ by the equalities

$$u_j(t) = \begin{cases} 1, & \text{if } j \leqq \nu_1(t), \\ 1, & \text{if } \nu_i(t) < j \leqq \nu_{i+1}(t) \text{ and } i \text{ is even}, \\ 0, & \text{if } \nu_i(t) < j \leqq \nu_{i+1}(t) \text{ and } i \text{ is odd}. \end{cases}$$

We have then

$$\{t;\, u_j(t) = 1\} = \bigcup_{i=\text{even}} [\{t;\, \nu_i(t) < j\} - \{t;\, \nu_{i+1}(t) < j\}] \in \mathscr{F}_{j-1},$$

hence u_j is $\mathscr{F}_{j-1}$-measurable. Put

$$f = f_1 + \sum_{j=2}^{n} u_j (f_j - f_{j+1}).$$

We have

$$f = f_1(1 - u_2) + f_2(u_2 - u_3) + \cdots + f_{n-1}(u_{n-1} - u_n) + u_n f_n.$$

For each $t \in T$ we deduce then

$$f(t) = f_{\nu_1(t)}(t) - f_{\nu_2(t)}(t) + f_{\nu_3(t)}(t) - f_{\nu_4(t)}(t) + \cdots + u_n(t) f_n(t).$$

But we have

$$f_{\nu_1(t)}(t) = f_{\nu_3(t)}(t) = \cdots = 0,$$

$$f_{\nu_2(t)}(t) \geqq r_2,\, f_{\nu_4(t)}(t) \geqq r_2,\, \ldots$$

and the number of the terms different from 0 is $\beta_n(t)$; on the other hand

$$u_n(t) f_n(t) \leqq f_n(t),.$$

hence

$$f(t) \leqq f_n(t) - \beta_n(t)\, r_2,$$

i.e.

$$f \leqq f_n - \beta_n r_2,$$

hence

$$\int f\,d\mu \leqq \int f_n\,d\mu - r_2 \int \beta_n\,d\mu.$$

Since $\{u_j(t) = 1\} \in \mathscr{F}_{j-1}$ and

$$\int u_j(f_j - f_{j-1})\,d\mu = \int_{\{u_j(t)=1\}} (f_j - f_{j-1})\,d\mu = 0$$

we deduce that

$$\int f\,d\mu = \int f_1\,d\mu + \sum_{j=2}^{n} \int u_j(f_j - f_{j-1})\,d\mu \geqq \int f_1\,d\mu \geqq 0,$$

hence

$$0 \leqq \int f_n\,d\mu - r_2 \int \beta_n\,d\mu,$$

consequently

$$\int \beta_n\,d\mu \leqq \frac{1}{r_2} \int f_n\,d\mu = \frac{1}{r_2 - r_1} \int (f_n - r_1)\,d\mu$$

and the proposition is proved in this case.

Consider now the general case and put

$$f_j' = \sup(f_j - r_1, 0) = (f_j - r_1)^+ = \frac{1}{2}(|f_j - r_1| + (f_j - r_1)).$$

We have, evidently, $f_j' \geqq 0$, and $(f_n', \mathscr{F}_n)$ is a semi-martingale. The function β_n computed for the functions $f_1, \ldots, f_n$ and the interval $[r_1, r_2]$ is equal to that computed for the positive functions $f_1', \ldots, f_n'$ and the interval $[0, r_2 - r_1]$. From the first part of the proof we deduce (since $\mu(T) = 1$)

$$\begin{aligned}\int \beta_n\,d\mu &\leqq \frac{1}{r_2 - r_1} \int f_n'\,d\mu = \frac{1}{r_2 - r_1} \int_{\{f_n(t) \geqq r_1\}} (f_n - r_1)\,d\mu \\ &= \frac{1}{r_2 - r_1} \int_{\{f_n(t) \geqq r_1\}} |f_n - r_1|\,d\mu \leqq \frac{1}{r_2 - r_1} \int (|f_n| + |r_1|)\,d\mu \\ &= \frac{1}{r_2 - r_1} \left(\int |f_n|\,d\mu + |r_1| \right).\end{aligned}$$

Proposition 26. *Let $(f_n, \mathscr{F}_n)$ be a martingale. If*

$$\sup_n \int |f_n|\,d\mu = K < \infty$$

then the sequence (f_n) converges μ-almost everywhere to a μ-integrable function.

For every $t \in T$ put

$$f_*(t) = \liminf_{n\to\infty} f_n(t) \quad \text{and} \quad f^*(t) = \limsup_{n\to\infty} f_n(t).$$

Let $r_1 < r_2$ and for every n consider the function β_n corresponding to the functions $f_1, f_2, \ldots, f_n$ and to the interval $[r_1, r_2]$. We have

$$\int \beta_n \, d\mu \leqq \frac{1}{r_2 - r_1}\left[\int |f_n| \, d\mu + |r_1|\right] \leqq a < \infty .$$

The sequence of functions (β_n) is increasing and $\lim_{n\to\infty} \beta_n(t) = \beta(t) \leqq \infty$. According to the theorem 2, § 8, the limit function β is μ-integrable, hence the set $\{t; \beta(t) = \infty\}$ is μ-negligible. But

$$\{t; \beta(t) = \infty\} = \{t; f_*(t) < r_1 < r_2 < f^*(t)\}.$$

It follows that the set

$$A = \{t; f_*(t) = f^*(t)\} = \bigcup_{r_1, r_2} \{t; f_*(t) < r_1 < r_2 < f^*(t)\}$$

for r_1 and r_2 rational, is μ-negligible, hence $f_*(t) = f^*(t)$ μ-almost everywhere. Put $g(t) = \lim_{n\to\infty} f_n(t)$ for $t \notin A$ and $g(t) = 0$ for $t \in A$. Then $|g(t)| = \lim_{n\to\infty} |f_n(t)|$ for $t \notin A$. According to Fatou's lemma (§ 8, proposition 21) the function $|g|$ is μ-integrable and

$$\int |g| \, d\mu \leqq \liminf_{n\to\infty} \int |f_n| \, d\mu \leqq K < \infty .$$

Since g is μ-measurable, it follows that g is μ-integrable (§ 8, proposition 20).

Proposition 27. *Let f be a $\mathscr{T}$-measurable and μ-integrable function and $(\mathscr{F}_n)$ an increasing sequence of tribes with $T \in \mathscr{F}_n \subset \mathscr{T}$. Denote by $\mathscr{F}_\infty$ the tribe generated by $\bigcup \mathscr{F}_n$ and for $1 \leqq n \leqq \infty$ denote by f_n the conditional expectation of f with respect to the tribe $\mathscr{F}_n$. Then we have*

$$\lim_{n\to\infty} f_n(t) = f_\infty(t) \quad \mu\text{-almost everywhere.}$$

The sequence $(f_n, \mathscr{F}_n)$ is a martingale. Moreover, since f_n is also the conditional expectation of f_∞ with respect to $\mathscr{F}_n$ (remark 3 after the proposition 23), we have

$$\int_A f_n \, d\mu = \int_A f_\infty \, d\mu, \quad \text{for} \quad A \in \mathscr{F}_n .$$

We prove (as for the properties 3 and 4 of the martingales) that for every n we have

$$\int_A |f_n| \, d\mu \leqq \int_A |f_\infty| \, d\mu, \quad \text{for every} \quad A \in \mathscr{F}_n,$$

therefore

$$\sup_n \int |f_n| \, d\mu \leqq \int |f_\infty| \, d\mu < \infty .$$

From the proposition 26 we deduce that the sequence (f_n) converges μ-almost everywhere to a function g.

We shall prove now that (f_n) is a Cauchy sequence in $\mathscr{L}^1(\mu)$. Let $\varepsilon > 0$. By the corollary of the proposition 15, § 8, there exists $\delta > 0$ such that

$$\int_B |f_\infty| \, d\mu < \frac{\varepsilon}{4}$$

for every $B \in \mathscr{T}$ with $\mu(B) < \delta$.

By the Egorov theorem, § 6, there exists a set $A \in \mathscr{T}$ with $\mu(T - A) < \delta$ such that the sequence (f_n) converges uniformly on A. There exists therefore $N(\varepsilon)$ such that for $n, m \geqq N(\varepsilon)$ we have $|f_n(t) - f_m(t)| < \frac{\varepsilon}{2}$ for every $t \in A$, therefore

$$\int_A |f_n - f_m| \, d\mu < \frac{\varepsilon}{2}.$$

Then

$$\begin{aligned} \int |f_n - f_m| \, d\mu &= \int_A |f_n - f_m| \, d\mu + \int_{T-A} |f_n - f_m| \, d\mu \\ &\leqq \frac{\varepsilon}{2} + \int_{T-A} |f_n| \, d\mu + \int_{T-A} |f_m| \, d\mu \\ &\leqq \frac{\varepsilon}{2} + 2\int_{T-A} |f_\infty| \, d\mu < \varepsilon \end{aligned}$$

for $n, m \geqq N(\varepsilon)$, i.e. (f_n) is a Cauchy sequence in $\mathscr{L}^1(\mu)$. Since (f_n) converges pointwise to g, we deduce that (f_n) converges in mean to g (§ 8, proposition 17), therefore, for every $A \in \mathscr{T}$, $(f_n \varphi_A)$ converges in mean to $g\varphi_A$. It follows that

$$\int_A g \, d\mu = \lim_{n \to \infty} \int_A f_n \, d\mu, \quad \text{for} \quad A \in \mathscr{T}.$$

Since for every $A \in \mathscr{F}_n$ we have

$$\int_A f_{n+p} \, d\mu = \int_A f_n \, d\mu,$$

we deduce that for every n we have

$$\int_A g \, d\mu = \int_A f_n \, d\mu, \quad \text{for} \quad A \in \mathscr{F}_n,$$

therefore, for every $A \in \bigcup \mathscr{F}_n$ we have

$$\int_A g\, d\mu = \int_A f_\infty\, d\mu.$$

Since f_∞ and g are $\mathscr{F}_\infty$-measurable and their integrals are countably additive on $\mathscr{F}_\infty$ and coincide on the clan $\bigcup \mathscr{F}_n$ which generates $\mathscr{F}_\infty$, we deduce that their integrals coincide on $\mathscr{F}_\infty$:

$$\int_A g\, d\mu = \int_A f_\infty\, d\mu, \quad \text{for} \quad A \in \mathscr{F}_\infty,$$

hence $f_\infty(t) = g(t)$, μ-almost everywhere, therefore

$$\lim_{n\to\infty} f_n(t) = f_\infty(t), \quad \mu\text{-almost everywhere.}$$

§ 11. THE LIFTING PROPERTY OF THE SPACE $\mathscr{L}^\infty$

1. DEFINITION AND PROPERTIES

Let μ be a *positive measure* defined on a clan $\mathscr{C}$. Let $\mathscr{N}$ be the *hereditary tribe* of the *μ-negligible* sets and $\mathscr{T}$ a *tribe of μ-measurable sets*, containing T and $\mathscr{N}$.

For two functions $f, g: T \to R$ we shall write $f \sim g$ if f and g are equal μ-almost everywhere. For two sets $A, B \subset T$ we shall write $A \sim B$ if $\varphi_A \sim \varphi_B$, i.e. if $A \Delta B \in \mathscr{N}$.

Consider the space $\mathscr{M}^\infty(\mathscr{T})$ of the $\mathscr{N}$-almost $\mathscr{T}$-totally measurable real functions, i.e. the space of the $\mathscr{T}$-measurable functions $f: T \to R$ with $\|f\|_\infty = N_\infty(f, \mu) < \infty$.

The space $\mathscr{M}(\mathscr{T})$ of the totally $\mathscr{T}$-measurable functions (i.e. the space of the bounded $\mathscr{T}$-measurable functions) and the space $\mathscr{E}(\mathscr{T})$ of the $\mathscr{T}$-step functions are dense in $\mathscr{M}^\infty(\mathscr{T})$ for the semi-norm $\|f\|_\infty$.

Definition 1. *A mapping $\varrho: \mathscr{M}^\infty(\mathscr{T}) \to \mathscr{M}^\infty(\mathscr{T})$ is said to be a lifting of $\mathscr{M}^\infty(\mathscr{T})$ if it verifies the following six conditions:*

I. $\varrho(f) \sim f$;

II. $f \sim g$ *implies* $\varrho(f) = \varrho(g)$;

III. $\varrho(\alpha f + \beta g) = \alpha\varrho(f) + \beta\varrho(g)$;

IV. $f \geqq 0$ *implies* $\varrho(f) \geqq 0$;

V. $f(t) \equiv \alpha$ *implies* $\varrho(f)(t) \equiv \alpha$;

VI. $\varrho(fg) = \varrho(f)\,\varrho(g)$.

If there exists a lifting of $\mathscr{M}^\infty(\mathscr{T})$ we say that $\mathscr{M}^\infty(\mathscr{T})$ has the lifting property. In this paragraph we shall prove that if μ has the direct sum property and is $\neq 0$ then $\mathscr{M}^\infty(\mathscr{T})$ has the lifting property.

From this definition we deduce that a lifting ϱ of $\mathscr{M}^\infty(\mathscr{T})$ has also the following properties:

7. *If* $f(t) \leqq g(t)$ *almost everywhere, then*

$$\varrho(f)(t) \leqq \varrho(g)(t), \quad \textit{for every} \quad t \in T.$$

In fact, we take a function $f' \sim f$ such that $f'(t) \leqq g(t)$ for every $t \in T$. Then $g - f' \geqq 0$, whence $\varrho(g - f') \geqq 0$. It follows that $\varrho(g) - \varrho(f') \geqq 0$, therefore $\varrho(f) = \varrho(f') \leqq \varrho(g)$.

8. $|\varrho(f)| = \varrho(|f|)$.

In fact,

$$\varrho(|f|)^2 = \varrho(|f|^2) = \varrho(f\bar{f}) = \varrho(f)^2 = |\varrho(f)|^2$$

and $\varrho(|f|) \geqq 0$, whence $\varrho(|f|) = |\varrho(f)|$.

9. $\|\varrho(f)\| = \|\varrho(f)\|_\infty = \|f\|_\infty$.

The equality $\|\varrho(f)\|_\infty = \|f\|_\infty$ follows from the properties I and II. On the other hand,

$$|f(t)| \leqq \|f\|_\infty \quad \text{almost everywhere;}$$

hence

$$|\varrho(f)(t)| = \varrho(|f|)(t) \leqq \|f\|_\infty = \|\varrho(f)\|_\infty \leqq \|\varrho(f)\|$$

for every $t \in T$, therefore $\|\varrho(f)\| = \|\varrho(f)\|_\infty$.

10. $\sup(\varrho(f), \varrho(g)) = \varrho(\sup(f, g))$,

$\inf(\varrho(f), \varrho(g)) = \varrho(\inf(f, g))$.

We use the equality

$$\sup(\alpha, \beta) = \frac{1}{2}(\alpha + \beta + |\alpha - \beta|).$$

Example. Consider the tribe $\mathscr{T}_0$ consisting of the negligible sets and their complements.

The space $\mathscr{M}^\infty(\mathscr{T}_0)$ consists of the functions which are constant almost everywhere.

If $f(t) = \alpha$ almost everywhere, we put $\varrho_0(f)(t) \equiv \alpha$. Then ϱ_0 is a lifting of $\mathscr{M}^\infty(\mathscr{T}_0)$.

A mapping $\varrho: \mathscr{M}(\mathscr{T}) \to \mathscr{M}(\mathscr{T})$ having the properties I–VI will be called a lifting of $\mathscr{M}(\mathscr{T})$.

From the property 9 we deduce that a lifting ϱ of $\mathscr{M}^\infty(\mathscr{T})$ is a mapping of $\mathscr{M}^\infty(\mathscr{T})$ into $\mathscr{M}(\mathscr{T})$. It follows that the restriction of ϱ to $\mathscr{M}(\mathscr{T})$ is a lifting of $\mathscr{M}(\mathscr{T})$.

Conversely, if ϱ is a lifting of $\mathscr{M}(\mathscr{T})$, we can extend it to a lifting of $\mathscr{M}^\infty(\mathscr{T})$, putting

$$\varrho(f) = \varrho(f'), \quad \text{for every} \quad f \in \mathscr{M}^\infty(\mathscr{T}),$$

where f' is an arbitrary function of $\mathscr{M}(\mathscr{T})$ such that $f \sim f'$.

It is therefore sufficient to prove the existence of a lifting of $\mathscr{M}(\mathscr{T})$.

2. LIFTING ON SETS

Let ϱ be a lifting of $\mathscr{M}^\infty(\mathscr{T})$. For every set $A \in \mathscr{T}$ the function $\varrho(\varphi_A)$ is positive and $\varrho(\varphi_A)\,\varrho(\varphi_A) = \varrho(\varphi_A)$, whence $\varrho(\varphi_A)$ is the characteristic function of a set of $\mathscr{T}$. We denote by $\varrho'(A)$ the set of $\mathscr{T}$ verifying the equality

$$\varphi_{\varrho'(A)} = \varrho(\varphi_A).$$

In this way we define a mapping $\varrho'\colon \mathscr{T} \to \mathscr{T}$ having the following properties:

I'. $\varrho'(A) \sim A$;

II'. $A \sim B$ implies $\varrho'(A) = \varrho'(B)$;

III'. $\varrho'(\emptyset) = \emptyset$ and $\varrho'(T) = T$;

IV'. $\varrho'(A \cap B) = \varrho'(A) \cap \varrho'(B)$;

V'. $\varrho'(A \cup B) = \varrho'(A) \cup \varrho'(B)$

and also the following properties:

6'. $A \subset B$ implies $\varrho'(A) \subset \varrho'(B)$;

7'. $A \cap B = \emptyset$ implies $\varrho'(A) \cap \varrho'(B) = \emptyset$;

8'. $\varrho'(A - B) = \varrho'(A) - \varrho'(B)$.

To prove V', we remark that $\varrho'(T - A) = T - \varrho'(A)$, then we prove the properties 7' and 8' and we write $A \cup B$ as union of the disjoint sets $A - B$, $A \cap B$ and $B - A$.

Conversely, we have

Proposition 1. *For every mapping $\varrho'\colon \mathscr{T} \to \mathscr{T}$ having the properties* I'–V', *there exists a lifting ϱ of $\mathscr{M}^\infty(\mathscr{T})$ and only one such that*

$$\varrho(\varphi_A) = \varphi_{\varrho'(A)}, \quad \textit{for} \quad A \in \mathscr{T}.$$

We remark that the set function $\boldsymbol{m}\colon \mathscr{T} \to \mathscr{E}(\mathscr{T})$ defined by

$$\boldsymbol{m}(A) = \varphi_{\varrho'(A)}, \quad \text{for} \quad A \in \mathscr{T},$$

is *additive*. If for every function $f \in \mathscr{E}(\mathscr{T})$ we put

$$\varrho(f) = \int f\, d\boldsymbol{m},$$

then $\varrho\colon \mathscr{E}(\mathscr{T}) \to \mathscr{E}(\mathscr{T})$ has all the properties I–VI, whence also the properties 7–10. In particular we have

$$\|\varrho(f)\|_\infty = \|f\|_\infty, \quad \text{for} \quad f \in \mathscr{E}(\mathscr{T}),$$

whence ϱ is continuous on $\mathscr{E}(\mathscr{T})$ for the topology defined by the semi-norm $\|f\|_\infty$. Since $\mathscr{E}(\mathscr{T})$ is dense in $\mathscr{M}^\infty(\mathscr{T})$ for this topology, we can extend uniquely ϱ to a continuous linear mapping of $\mathscr{M}^\infty(\mathscr{T})$ into $\mathscr{M}^\infty(\mathscr{T})$ denoted also by ϱ. We verify then easily that the extension ϱ has on $\mathscr{M}^\infty(\mathscr{T})$ all the properties I–VI.

The uniqueness of ϱ follows from the fact that $\mathscr{E}(\mathscr{T})$ is dense in $\mathscr{M}^\infty(\mathscr{T})$ and that ϱ is uniquely determined by its values on the characteristic functions φ_A of $\mathscr{E}(\mathscr{T})$.

Remark. As there exists a one-to-one correspondence between the set of the liftings of $\mathscr{M}^\infty(\mathscr{T})$ and the set of the mappings ϱ of $\mathscr{T}$ into $\mathscr{T}$ having the properties I′–V′, we shall denote by the same letter ϱ the lifting of $\mathscr{M}^\infty(\mathscr{T})$ and the corresponding mapping of $\mathscr{T}$ into $\mathscr{T}$. Then we have

$$\varphi_{\varrho(A)} = \varrho(\varphi_A), \quad \text{for} \quad A \in \mathscr{T}.$$

The following proposition is the only one where the values of the measure μ are used.

Proposition 2. *Let H be a μ-measurable set and $\mathscr{F}$ the tribe generated by $\mathscr{T}$ and H. If the measure μ is bounded, then every mapping $\lambda\colon \mathscr{T} \to \mathscr{T}$ having the properties* I′–V′ *can be extended to a mapping $\varrho\colon \mathscr{F} \to \mathscr{F}$ having the properties* I′–V′.

We shall divide the proof into several parts.

a) For every μ-measurable set X let $\mathscr{T}(X)$ be the tribe of the sets $A \in \mathscr{T}$ such that $A \cap X \sim \emptyset$ and let $X_\infty = \bigcup \lambda(A)$ for $A \in \mathscr{T}(X)$. If $A \in \mathscr{T}(X)$, then $\lambda(A) \in \mathscr{T}(X)$, since $\lambda(A) \sim A$, whence $\lambda(A) \cap X \sim A \cap X \sim \emptyset$.

We prove that we have also $X_\infty \in \mathscr{T}(X)$. We can choose an increasing sequence (A_n) of sets of $\mathscr{T}(X)$ such that, putting $B = \bigcup A_n$, we have

$$\sup_{A \in \mathscr{T}(X)} \mu(A) = \sup \mu(A_n) = \mu(B).$$

We have $B \in \mathscr{T}(X)$, whence, for every set $A \in \mathscr{T}(X)$, we have $A \cup B \in \mathscr{T}(X)$, consequently $\mu(B) \leqq \mu(A \cup B) \leqq \mu(B)$. It follows that for every set $A \in \mathscr{T}(X)$ we have $A \cup B \sim B$. (Here is the only place where the values of the measure μ are used.) We deduce

$$\lambda(A) \cup \lambda(B) = \lambda(A \cup B) = \lambda(B), \quad \text{whence} \quad \lambda(A) \subset \lambda(B).$$

It follows that $X_\infty = \lambda(B) \in \mathscr{T}(X)$. We deduce then that $\lambda(X_\infty) \in \mathscr{T}(X)$, whence $\lambda(X_\infty) = X_\infty$.

We remark that

$$X_\infty \cap (\complement X)_\infty = \emptyset.$$

In fact, $X_\infty \cap X \sim \emptyset$ and $(\complement X)_\infty \cap (\complement X) \sim \emptyset$; hence $X_\infty \cap (\complement X)_\infty \sim \emptyset$, therefore $\lambda(X_\infty) \cap \lambda((\complement X)_\infty) = \emptyset$, consequently $X_\infty \cap (\complement X)_\infty = \emptyset$.

b) For every μ-measurable set X put $O(X) = X \cap X_\infty$ and

$$\varrho(H) = (H \cup O(\complement H)) \cap \complement O(H) = (H \cap \complement O(H)) \cup O(\complement H),$$

$$\varrho(\complement H) = (\complement H \cup O(H)) \cap \complement O(\complement H) = (\complement H \cap \complement O(\complement H)) \cup O(H).$$

It follows that $\varrho(\complement H) = \complement \varrho(H)$.

c) For every set $C \in \mathscr{T}(H)$ we have $\lambda(C) \cap \varrho(H) = \emptyset$. In fact, since $\lambda(C) \subset H_\infty$, we have

$$\lambda(C) \cap H \cap \complement O(H) = \lambda(C) \cap H \cap (\complement H \cup \complement H_\infty) = \emptyset.$$

On the other hand, since $H_\infty \cap (\complement H)_\infty = \emptyset$, we have

$$\lambda(C) \cap O(\complement H) = \lambda(C) \cap \complement H \cap (\complement H)_\infty = \emptyset,$$

whence $\lambda(C) \cap \varrho(H) = \emptyset$.

d) For every set $C \in \mathscr{T}(\complement H)$ we have $\lambda(C) \cap \varrho(\complement H) = \emptyset$. In fact, we take in the preceding part $\complement H$ instead of H.

e) Let X be an arbitrary set of $\mathscr{F}$. There exist two sets $A,\ B \in \mathscr{T}$ such that

$$X = (A \cap H) \cup (B \cap \complement H).$$

In fact, the class of the sets having this property is a tribe containing $\mathscr{T}$ and H, whence $\mathscr{F}$ too. Put

$$\varrho(X) = (\lambda(A) \cap \varrho(H)) \cup (\lambda(B) \cap \varrho(\complement H)).$$

If A_1 and B_1 are other sets of $\mathscr{T}$ such that $X = (A_1 \cap H) \cup (B_1 \cap \complement H)$, then $A \,\Delta\, A_1 \in \mathscr{T}(H)$ and $B \,\Delta\, B_1 \in \mathscr{T}(\complement H)$; hence $\lambda(A \,\Delta\, A_1) \cap \varrho(H) = \emptyset$ and $\lambda(B \,\Delta\, B_1) \cap \varrho(\complement H) = \emptyset$, whence

$$\lambda(A) \cap \varrho(H) = \lambda(A_1) \cap \varrho(H)$$

and

$$\lambda(B) \cap \varrho(\complement H) = \lambda(B_1) \cap \varrho(\complement H),$$

therefore $\varrho(X)$ is independent on the choice of A and B. From the definition of ϱ it follows that for every set $A \in \mathscr{T}$ we have $\varrho(A) = \lambda(A)$ and that ϱ has on $\mathscr{F}$ all the properties I′–V′.

3. LINEAR LIFTINGS

Every mapping $\varrho\colon \mathscr{M}^\infty(\mathscr{T}) \to \mathscr{M}^\infty(\mathscr{T})$ having the properties I–V will be called a *linear lifting* of $\mathscr{M}^\infty(\mathscr{T})$. We denote by $C(\mathscr{T})$ the set of the linear liftings of $\mathscr{M}^\infty(\mathscr{T})$.

We shall show that for the existence of a lifting of $\mathscr{M}^\infty(\mathscr{T})$ it is sufficient to prove the existence of a linear lifting of $\mathscr{M}^\infty(\mathscr{T})$.

We shall prove first the following

Lemma 1. *Let* θ' *and* θ'' *be two mappings of* $\mathcal{T}$ *into* $\mathcal{T}$ *and let* D *be the set of the linear liftings* $\varrho \in C(\mathcal{T})$ *such that*

$$\varphi_{\theta'(A)} \leqq \varrho(\varphi_A) \leqq \varphi_{\theta''(A)}, \quad \textit{for} \quad A \in \mathcal{T}.$$

Then D *is convex and an element* $\varrho \in D$ *is extremal in* D *if and only if it is extremal in* $C(\mathcal{T})$.

Let $\varrho \in D$. Evidently, if ϱ is extremal in $C(\mathcal{T})$, then ϱ is extremal in D.

Conversely, assume that ϱ is not extremal in $C(\mathcal{T})$. There exist then two different points $\varrho_1, \varrho_2 \in C(\mathcal{T})$ and $0 < \alpha < 1$ such that $\varrho = \alpha\varrho_1 + (1-\alpha)\varrho_2$.

Let now $A \in \mathcal{T}$. We have

$$\varrho(\varphi_A)(t) = \alpha\varrho_1(\varphi_A)(t) + (1-\alpha)\varrho_2(\varphi_A)(t).$$

If $t \in \theta'(A)$, then $\varrho(\varphi_A)(t) = 1$, whence $\varrho_1(\varphi_A)(t) = 1$ and $\varrho_2(\varphi_A)(t) = 1$; if $t \in \theta''(A)$, then $\varphi_{\theta''(A)}(t) = 1$.

It follows that for every $t \in T$ we have

$$\varrho_1(\varphi_A)(t) \leqq \varphi_{\theta''(A)}(t) \quad \text{and} \quad \varrho_2(\varphi_A)(t) \leqq \varphi_{\theta''(A)}(t).$$

We deduce that $\varrho_1, \varrho_2 \in D$, whence ϱ is not extremal in D.

We conclude that if ϱ is extremal in D, then ϱ is extremal in $C(\mathcal{T})$ too.

The convexity of D is easily deduced from the definition of D.

Proposition 3. *For every linear lifting* $\varrho \in C(\mathcal{T})$ *of* $\mathcal{M}^\infty(\mathcal{T})$ *there exists a lifting* ϱ^* *of* $\mathcal{M}^\infty(\mathcal{T})$ *such that*

$$\varrho^*(\varphi_A) = \varrho(\varphi_A)$$

for every set $A \in \mathcal{T}$ *for which* $\varrho(\varphi_A)$ *is a characteristic function of a set.*

Let $\varrho \in C(\mathcal{T})$. We shall divide the proof into several parts.

a) We use the following notations: $I = \mathcal{M}(\mathcal{T}) \times T$, $R_{f,t} = R$ (the real line) for every $(f, t) \in I$ and $R^I = \prod_{(f,t)\in I} R_{f,t}$. We shall consider on R^I the usual product topology. Then R^I is a locally convex space.

Every linear lifting $\varrho \in C(\mathcal{T})$ can be identified with the element $(\varrho(f)(t))_{(f,t)\in I}$ of R^I. In this way $C(\mathcal{T})$ can be considered as a convex subset of R^I.

b) For every set $A \in \mathcal{T}$ put

$$\theta'(A) = \{t; \varrho(\varphi_A)(t) = 1\} \quad \text{and} \quad \theta''(A) = \{t; \varrho(\varphi_A)(t) \neq 0\}.$$

We have $\theta'(A) \sim \theta''(A) \sim A$ and $\varphi_{\theta'(A)} \leqq \varrho(\varphi_A) \leqq \varphi_{\theta''(A)}$.

c) Let D be the set of the linear liftings $\sigma \in C(\mathscr{T})$ such that $\varphi_{\theta'(A)} \leqq \sigma(\varphi_A) \leqq \varphi_{\theta''(A)}$ for $A \in \mathscr{T}$. Then D is a *convex* subset of R^I and $\varrho \in D$. For every $\sigma \in D$ and every $(f, t) \in I$ we have

$$|\sigma(f)(t)| \leqq \|f\|_\infty,$$

whence D is *bounded* in R^I.

d) We show now that D is *closed* in R^I. Consider the Banach algebra $\mathscr{B}$ of the bounded real functions $f: T \to R$ with norm $\|f\| = \sup_{t \in T} |f(t)|$.

Let $(\varrho_j)_{j \in J}$ be a directed family of elements of D, converging to an element of R^I. For every function $f \in \mathscr{M}^\infty(\mathscr{T})$ and every $t \in \mathscr{T}$ we have

$$\lim_{j \in J} \varrho_j(f)(t) = \varrho_\infty(f)(t).$$

Then ϱ_∞ is a mapping of $\mathscr{M}^\infty(\mathscr{T})$ into $\mathscr{B}$ and verifies the conditions II–V. In particular, $\|\varrho_\infty(f)\| \leqq \|f\|_\infty$ for every $f \in \mathscr{M}^\infty(\mathscr{T})$.

Since $\varphi_{\theta'(A)} \leqq \varrho_j(\varphi_A) \leqq \varphi_{\theta''(A)}$ for every $j \in J$ and $A \in \mathscr{T}$, we deduce that

$$\varphi_{\theta'(A)} \leqq \varrho_\infty(\varphi_A) \leqq \varphi_{\theta''(A)}, \quad \text{for} \quad A \in \mathscr{T}.$$

It follows then that $\varrho_\infty(\varphi_A) \in \mathscr{M}(\mathscr{T})$ and $\varrho_\infty(\varphi_A) \sim \varphi_A$ for every $A \in \mathscr{T}$. Then, for every function $f \in \mathscr{E}(\mathscr{T})$, we have $\varrho_\infty(f) \in \mathscr{M}(\mathscr{T})$ and $\varrho_\infty(f) \sim f$. Since $\mathscr{E}(\mathscr{T})$ is dense in $\mathscr{M}^\infty(\mathscr{T})$ for the semi-norm $\|f\|_\infty$ and ϱ_∞ is continuous on $\mathscr{M}^\infty(\mathscr{T})$ it follows that $\varrho_\infty(f) \sim f$ for every $f \in \mathscr{M}^\infty(\mathscr{T})$; hence $\varrho_\infty \in D$, therefore D is closed.

e) Since D is a *compact convex* part of R^I, by the theorem of Krein-Milman we deduce that there exists a point $\varrho^* \in D$ which is extremal in D. By the lemma 1, ϱ^* is also extremal in $C(\mathscr{T})$. We shall show that ϱ^* verifies also the condition VI.

f) Let $t_0 \in T$. We show that for every pair of functions $f, g \in \mathscr{M}^\infty(\mathscr{T})$ we have

$$\varrho^*(fg)(t_0) = \varrho^*(f)(t_0)\,\varrho^*(g)(t_0).$$

The set $A = \{t; \varrho^*(fg)(t) \neq \varrho^*(f)(t)\,\varrho^*(g)(t)\}$ is negligible, according to the property I of a linear lifting. If the set $\{t_0\}$ is not negligible we have $\{t_0\} \notin A$, whence the preceding equality is verified.

Assume now that $\{t_0\}$ is negligible. Consider the set P of the *positive* linear functionals x' on $\mathscr{M}^\infty(\mathscr{T})$ with $|x'| = x'(\varphi_T) = 1$.

The functional x'_0 defined on $\mathscr{M}^\infty(\mathscr{T})$ by the equality

$$x'_0(f) = \varrho^*(f)(t_0)$$

is positive and linear and $|x'_0| = x'_0(\varphi_T) = 1$, whence x'_0 belongs to P. We shall prove that x'_0 is extremal in P. In fact, if x'_0 is not extremal in P, then there exist two different points $x'_1, x'_2 \in P$ and $0 < \alpha < 1$ such that $x'_0 = \alpha x'_1 + (1 - \alpha)\, x'_2$.

For $j = 1, 2$ we define the mapping $\varrho_j: \mathscr{M}^\infty(\mathscr{T}) \to \mathscr{M}(\mathscr{T})$ by the equalities

$$\varrho_j(f)(t) = \varrho^*(f)(t), \quad \text{if} \quad t \neq t_0,$$

$$\varrho_j(f)(t_0) = x_j'(f).$$

We verify easily that ϱ_1 and ϱ_2 are different linear liftings in $C(\mathscr{T})$ and that $\varrho^* = \alpha\varrho_1 + (1-\alpha)\varrho_2$ and we get a contradiction, for ϱ^* is extremal in $C(\mathscr{T})$.

Since x_0' is extremal in P, it is multiplicative, i.e. $x_0'(fg) = x_0'(f)\,x_0'(g)$, whence

$$\varrho^*(fg)(t_0) = \varrho^*(f)(t_0)\,\varrho(g)(t_0).$$

Since t_0 is arbitrary in T, we deduce that ϱ^* is a lifting of $\mathscr{M}^\infty(\mathscr{T})$.

g) Suppose now that $A \in \mathscr{T}$ is such that $\varrho(\varphi_A)$ is a characteristic function, and prove that $\varrho^*(\varphi_A) = \varrho(\varphi_A)$. In fact, in this case we have $\varphi_{\theta'(A)} = \varphi_{\theta''(A)} = \varrho(\varphi_A)$. Since $\varrho^* \in D$ we have $\varphi_{\theta'(A)} \leqq \varrho^*(\varphi_A) \leqq \varphi_{\theta''(A)}$, whence $\varrho^*(\varphi_A) = \varrho(\varphi_A)$ and the proposition is completely proved.

Corollary. *If ϱ is a linear lifting of $\mathscr{M}^\infty(\mathscr{T})$ such that, for every set $A \in \mathscr{F}$, $\varrho(\varphi_A)$ is a characteristic function, then ϱ is a lifting of $\mathscr{M}^\infty(\mathscr{T})$.*

In fact, there exists a lifting ϱ of $\mathscr{M}^\infty(\mathscr{T})$ such that $\varrho^*(\varphi_A) = \varrho(\varphi_A)$ for every $A \in \mathscr{T}$. It follows that $\varrho^*(f) = \varrho(f)$, first for $f \in \mathscr{E}(\mathscr{T})$ and then for $f \in \mathscr{M}^\infty(\mathscr{T})$, for ϱ and ϱ^* are continuous on $\mathscr{M}^\infty(\mathscr{T})$ and $\mathscr{E}(\mathscr{T})$ is dense in $\mathscr{M}^\infty(\mathscr{T})$. It follows that $\varrho = \varrho^*$, i.e. ϱ is a lifting of $\mathscr{M}^\infty(\mathscr{T})$.

4. THE EXISTENCE OF THE LIFTING

We can now prove the existence of a lifting.

Theorem 1. *If μ has the direct sum property and if $\mu \neq 0$, then $\mathscr{L}^\infty(\mu)$ has the lifting property.*

Suppose first that μ is bounded. Denote by $\mathscr{E}$ the tribe of all the μ-measurable sets. Then $\mathscr{L}^\infty(\mu) = \mathscr{M}^\infty(\mathscr{E})$. Let H be the set of the pairs $(\mathscr{T}, \varrho_{\mathscr{T}})$ where $\mathscr{T}$ is a subtribe of $\mathscr{E}$, containing T and the μ-negligible sets, and $\varrho_{\mathscr{T}}$ is a lifting of $\mathscr{M}^\infty(\mathscr{T})$. The set H is nonvoid, because it contains the pair $(\mathscr{T}_0, \varrho_0)$. We consider on H the following order: $(\mathscr{F}, \varrho_{\mathscr{F}}) \leqq (\mathscr{G}, \varrho_{\mathscr{G}})$ if $\mathscr{F} \subset \mathscr{G}$ and $\varrho_{\mathscr{G}}$ is an extension of $\varrho_{\mathscr{F}}$. We shall prove that H is inductively ordered. For this purpose, let $\Phi = (\mathscr{T}_j, \varrho_j)_{j\in J}$ be a totally ordered family of elements of H, where, for simplicity, we put $\varrho_j = \varrho_{\mathscr{T}_j}$. Let $\mathscr{T}_\infty$ be the tribe generated by the union $\bigcup_{j\in J} \mathscr{T}_j$. We shall prove that there exists a lifting ϱ_∞ of $\mathscr{M}^\infty(\mathscr{T}_\infty)$ which extends every lifting ϱ_j, i.e. such that

$$(\mathscr{T}_\infty, \varrho_\infty) = \sup_{j\in J}(\mathscr{T}_j, \varrho_j).$$

If the family Φ contains a greatest element $(\mathscr{T}_{j_0}, \varrho_{j_0})$ we have $\mathscr{T}_\infty = \mathscr{T}_{j_0}$ and we take $\varrho_\infty = \varrho_{j_0}$.

If Φ does not contain a greatest element we have two possibilities:

a) For every countable family $(\mathscr{T}_j)_{j \in I}$ there exists $h \in J$ such that $\mathscr{T}_j \subset \mathscr{T}_h$ for every $j \in I$.

Let $f \in \mathscr{M}^\infty(\mathscr{T}_\infty)$. For each Borel set $A \subset R$ we have $\overset{-1}{f}(A) \in \mathscr{T}_\infty$, hence $\overset{-1}{f}(A)$ is contained in a tribe generated by a sequence of sets of $\bigcup_{j \in J} \mathscr{T}_j$. The tribe $\mathscr{T}(\mathscr{B})$ of the Borel sets of R is generated by a sequence of sets, for example, the intervals with rational ends. It follows that all the sets $\overset{-1}{f}(A)$ with $A \in \mathscr{T}(\mathscr{B})$ are contained in the same tribe, generated by a sequence $(A_i)_{i \in I}$ of sets of $\bigcup_{j \in J} \mathscr{T}_j$ such that for each $i \in I$, the set A_i belongs to a tribe $\mathscr{T}_i$ of Φ. If we denote by $\mathscr{T}_I$ the tribe generated by $\bigcup_{j \in I} \mathscr{T}_j$, then we have $\overset{-1}{f}(A) \in \mathscr{T}_I$ for each $A \in \mathscr{T}(\mathscr{B})$, whence f is $\mathscr{T}_I$-measurable, therefore $f \in \mathscr{M}^\infty(\mathscr{T}_I)$.

Let $h \in J$ be such that $\mathscr{T}_j \subset \mathscr{T}_h$ for each $j \in I$. Then $\mathscr{T}_I \subset \mathscr{T}_h$, whence $f \in \mathscr{M}^\infty(\mathscr{T}_h)$. If we put $\varrho_\infty(f) = \varrho_h(f)$, it is clear that $\varrho_\infty(f)$ depends only on f but does not depend on I and h.

It is easy to verify that ϱ_∞ is a lifting of $\mathscr{M}^\infty(\mathscr{T}_\infty)$ and that $\varrho_\infty(f) = \varrho_j(f)$ for each $j \in J$ and each $f \in \mathscr{M}^\infty(\mathscr{T}_j)$, whence $(\mathscr{T}_\infty, \varrho_\infty)$ is the least upper bound of Φ.

b) If the situation of the case a) is not verified, then there exists a sequence $(\mathscr{T}_{j(n)})_{n \in N}$ which is unbounded, i.e. such that, for each $h \in J$, there exists $n \in N$ with $\mathscr{T}_{j(n)} \supset \mathscr{T}_h$. We can suppose that the sequence $(\mathscr{T}_{j(n)})$ is increasing. In this case $\mathscr{T}_\infty$ is the tribe generated by $\bigcup_{n \in N} \mathscr{T}_{j(n)}$, since each tribe $\mathscr{T}_j$ is contained in a tribe $\mathscr{T}_{j(n)}$.

Let $f \in \mathscr{M}^\infty(\mathscr{T}_\infty)$. For each n, let f_n be the conditional expectation of f with respect to the tribe $\mathscr{T}_{j(n)}$. The function f_n is $\mathscr{T}_{j(n)}$-measurable and $\|f_n\|_\infty \leqq \|f\|_\infty$, whence $f_n \in \mathscr{M}^\infty(\mathscr{T}_{j(n)})$. Then $\|\varrho_{j(n)}(f_n)\| = \|f_n\|_\infty \leqq \|f\|_\infty$.

Let now $\mathscr{U}$ be an ultrafilter finer than the Frechet filter. For each $t \in T$ put

$$\varrho'(f)(t) = \lim_{\mathscr{U}} \varrho_{j(n)}(f_n)(t).$$

Then $|\varrho'(f)(t)| \leqq \|f\|_\infty$ for each $t \in T$.

The sequence $(f_n, \mathscr{T}_{j(n)})_{n \in N}$ is a martingale; hence, according to the theorem of convergence of the martingale (§ 10, proposition 27), we have

$$\lim_{n \to \infty} f_n(t) = f(t) \quad \text{almost everywhere.}$$

But for every n we have $\varrho_{j(n)}(f_n)(t) = f_n(t)$ almost everywhere; hence

$$\lim_{n\to\infty} \varrho_{j(n)}(f_n)(t) = f(t) \quad \text{almost everywhere,}$$

therefore $\varrho'(f)(t) = f(t)$ almost everywhere. We deduce that $\varrho'(f)$ is $\mathscr{T}_\infty$-measurable and that $\|\varrho'(f)\| \leqq \|f\|_\infty$, hence $\varrho'(f) \in \mathscr{M}^\infty(\mathscr{T}_\infty)$. It follows that ϱ' is a mapping of $\mathscr{M}^\infty(\mathscr{T}_\infty)$ into itself and we verify easily that ϱ' has the properties I–V. According to the proposition 3, there exists a lifting ϱ_∞ of $\mathscr{M}^\infty(\mathscr{T}_\infty)$ verifying the equality $\varrho_\infty(\varphi_A) = \varrho'(\varphi_A)$ for every set $A \in \mathscr{T}_\infty$ for which $\varrho'(\varphi_A)$ is a characteristic function.

Let $j \in J$ and $A \in \mathscr{T}_j$. There exists n_0 such that for $n \geqq n_0$ we have $\mathscr{T}_j \subset \mathscr{T}_{j(n)}$, hence $\varrho_j(\varphi_A) = \varrho_{j(n)}(\varphi_A)$. It follows that $\varrho'(\varphi_A) = \varrho_j(\varphi_A)$; hence $\varrho'(\varphi_A)$ is a characteristic function, therefore $\varrho_\infty(\varphi_A) = \varrho'(\varphi_A)$. Consequently $\varrho_\infty(\varphi_A) = \varrho_j(\varphi_A)$. We deduce then that $\varrho_\infty(f) = \varrho_j(f)$ for every $f \in \mathscr{M}^\infty(\mathscr{T}_j)$; hence $(\mathscr{T}_j, \varrho_j) \leqq (\mathscr{T}_\infty, \varrho_\infty)$, consequently $(\mathscr{T}_\infty, \varrho_\infty)$ is the least upper bound of the family Φ.

In this way we proved that H is inductively ordered. From the theorem of Zorn we deduce that there exists a maximal element $(\mathscr{L}, \varrho_{\mathscr{L}})$ in H. It remains to prove that $\mathscr{L} = \mathscr{E}$. In fact, suppose that there exists a set $A \in \mathscr{E}$ such that $A \notin \mathscr{L}$. Then $\varrho_{\mathscr{L}}$ can be extended to a lifting ϱ of $\mathscr{M}^\infty(\mathscr{T})$, where $\mathscr{T}$ is the tribe generated by $\mathscr{L}$ and A (proposition 2). Then $(\mathscr{L}, \varrho_{\mathscr{L}}) \leqq (\mathscr{T}, \varrho)$ and $\mathscr{L} \neq \mathscr{T}$; hence $(\mathscr{L}, \varrho_{\mathscr{L}})$ is not maximal and we get a contradiction. It follows that $\mathscr{L} = \mathscr{E}$, and that $\varrho_{\mathscr{L}}$ is a lifting of $\mathscr{M}^\infty(\mathscr{E})$, and the theorem is proved in case μ is bounded.

Suppose now that μ has the direct sum property and let $(T_k)_{k \in K}$ be a family of disjoint μ-integrable sets such that $T - \bigcup T_k$ is μ-negligible, $\mu(T_k) > 0$ for every $k \in K$, and every set $A \in \mathscr{C}$ is intersected by at most countably many sets T_k with $\mu(A \cap T_k) > 0$.

For each k consider the restriction μ_k of μ to the tribe $\mathscr{E}_k$ of the subsets of T_k, which are μ-measurable as subsets of T. From the preceding proof we deduce that for every k there exists a lifting ϱ_k of the space $\mathscr{M}^\infty(\mathscr{E}_k)$ of the functions $f\colon T_k \to R$ which are μ_k-measurable and $N_\infty(f, \mu_k) < \infty$. Let $A \subset T$ be a μ-integrable set with $\mu(A) > 0$ and let μ_A be the restriction of μ to the tribe $\mathscr{E}_A$ of the subsets of A which are μ-measurable as subsets of T. Let χ be a continuous linear and multiplicative functional on the algebra $\mathscr{M}^\infty(\mathscr{E}_A)$ (i.e. an extremal point of the unit ball of the dual of $\mathscr{M}^\infty(\mathscr{E}_A)$).

For every function $f \in \mathscr{L}^\infty(T, \mu)$ we define the function $\varrho(f)$ by the following equalities:

$$\varrho(f)(t) = \varrho_k(f_{T_k})(t), \quad \text{if} \quad t \in T_k, \quad k \in K,$$

$$\varrho(f)(t) = \chi(f_A), \qquad \text{if} \quad t \in T - \bigcup_{k \in K} T_k,$$

where by f_B we denote the restriction of f to B.

It follows that $\varrho(f)\,\varphi_{T_k}$ is μ-measurable for every $k \in K$, hence $\varrho(f)$ is μ-measurable. On the other hand, $\varrho(f)$ is bounded, whence $\varrho(f) \in \mathscr{L}^\infty(T, \mu)$.

It is easy to verify then that ϱ has all the properties of a lifting of $\mathscr{L}^\infty(\mu)$. The theorem is completely proved.

5. LIMITS OF MEASURABLE FUNCTIONS

Using the existence of a lifting, we can prove now that, in some cases, the limit of an uncountable set of measurable functions is also measurable.

Proposition 4. *Let μ be a positive measure. Assume that there exists a lifting ϱ of $\mathscr{L}^\infty(\mu)$. If $\mathscr{F}$ is a directed (for the relation $\leqq$) family of functions $\geqq 0$ of $\mathscr{L}^\infty(\mu)$ with $\varrho(f) = f$, then $f_\infty = \sup_{f \in \mathscr{F}} f$ is μ-measurable.*

Suppose first that f_∞ is bounded and let A be a μ-integrable set. Then $f_\infty \varphi_A \in \mathscr{L}^1(\mu)$ and

$$f_\infty \varphi_{\varrho(A)} = \sup_{f \in \mathscr{F}} f \varphi_{\varrho(A)}.$$

The functions $f \in \mathscr{F}$ are bounded because $\varrho(f) = f$. It follows that $f\varphi_A \in \mathscr{L}^1(\mu)$ for every $f \in \mathscr{F}$. The set

$$\mathscr{F}_A = \{\tilde{f}\tilde{\varphi}_{\varrho(A)};\quad f \in \mathscr{F}\}$$

of elements of $L^1(\mu)$ is directed and

$$\sup \|\tilde{f}\tilde{\varphi}_A\|_1 \leqq \int_A |f_\infty|\, d\mu < \infty.$$

According to the theorem 4, § 8, the set $\mathscr{F}_A$ has a least upper bound $\tilde{g} \in \mathscr{L}^1(\mu)$ and converges in $L^1(\mu)$ to $\tilde{g}$.

We can choose an increasing sequence (f_n) of functions of $\mathscr{F}$ such that $(f_n \varphi_{\varrho(A)})$ converges to g in $\mathscr{L}^1(\mu)$ and almost everywhere. Then

$$f_\infty(t)\, \varphi_{\varrho(A)}(t) \geqq \lim_{n \to \infty} f_n(t)\, \varphi_{\varrho(A)}(t) = g(t)$$

almost everywhere. It follows that $g \in \mathscr{L}^\infty(\mu)$ and

$$f_\infty(t)\, \varphi_{\varrho(A)}(t) \geqq \varrho(g)\,(t), \quad \text{for every} \quad t \in T.$$

From the inequality

$$g(t) \geqq f(t)\, \varphi_{\varrho(A)}(t) \quad \text{almost everywhere}$$

for every $f \in \mathscr{F}$, we deduce

$$\varrho(g)\,(t) \geqq \varrho(f)\, \varphi_{\varrho(A)}(t) = f(t)\, \varphi_{\varrho(A)}(t)$$

for every $t \in T$ and $f \in \mathscr{F}$, whence

$$\varrho(g)(t) \geqq f_\infty(t)\, \varphi_{\varrho(A)}(t), \quad \text{for} \quad t \in T.$$

We deduce that $f_\infty \varphi_{\varrho(A)} = \varrho(g)$, whence $f_\infty \varphi_{\varrho(A)}$ is μ-measurable. Since $f_\infty \varphi_{\varrho(A)} \sim f_\infty \varphi_A$ it follows that $f_\infty \varphi_A$ is μ-measurable. The integrable set A being arbitrary, the function f_∞ is μ-measurable.

Suppose now that f_∞ is not bounded. For each natural number p consider the set

$$\mathscr{F}_p = \{\inf(f, p); f \in \mathscr{F}\}.$$

Then $\mathscr{F}_p$ is directed and we have

$$\varrho(\inf(f, p)) = \inf(\varrho(f), \varrho(p)) = \inf(f, p)$$

and

$$\inf(f_\infty, p) = \sup_{f \in \mathscr{F}} \inf(f, p) = \sup_{g \in \mathscr{F}_p} g.$$

Since $\inf(f_\infty, p)$ is bounded, from the first part of the proof it follows that $\inf(f_\infty, p)$ is μ-measurable. From the equality

$$f_\infty = \sup_p (\inf(f_\infty, p))$$

we deduce that f_∞ is also μ-measurable.

Corollary. *If $\mathscr{A}$ is a class of μ-measurable sets with $\varrho(A) = A$ for $A \in \mathscr{A}$, then the union A_0 of the sets of $\mathscr{A}$ is μ-measurable.*

In fact, the class $\mathscr{A}'$ of the finite unions of the sets of $\mathscr{A}$ is directed and we have still $\varrho(A) = A$ for $A \in \mathscr{A}'$. On the other hand

$$\varphi_{A_0} = \sup \varphi_A, \quad \text{for} \quad A \in \mathscr{A}',$$

therefore, by the preceding proposition, A_0 is μ-measurable.

Theorem 2. *If $\mathscr{L}^\infty(\mu)$ has the lifting property, then μ has the direct sum property and is $\neq 0$.*

Let ϱ be a lifting of $\mathscr{L}^\infty(\mu)$. Since $\varrho(T) = T$, we deduce that T is not μ-negligible, therefore $\mu \neq 0$. Consider the set $\mathscr{F}$ of the classes $\mathscr{L}$ of disjoint μ-measurable sets $A \subset T$ with $\varrho(A) = A$ and $0 < \mu(A) < \infty$.

The set $\mathscr{F}$ is not empty. In fact, since $\mu \neq 0$, there exists an integrable set A with $0 < \mu(A) < \infty$ and we take $\mathscr{L}$ consisting only of $\varrho(A)$. The set $\mathscr{F}$ is ordered by inclusion. It is easy to verify that $\mathscr{F}$ is inductively ordered, therefore, by Zorn's lemma, $\mathscr{F}$ has at least one maximal element. Let $\mathscr{K}$ be a fixed maximal element of $\mathscr{F}$. We shall prove that $\mathscr{K} \in C(\mu)$.

By the corollary of the proposition 4 the set $T_0 = \bigcup_{A \in \mathscr{K}} A$ is μ-measurable. Then the set $N = T - T_0$ is μ-measurable too. The set N is also μ-negligible. In fact, if there exists a μ-integrable set $A' \subset N$ with $\mu(A') > 0$, then the class $\mathscr{K} \cup \{\varrho(A')\}$ would belong to $\mathscr{F}$ and would contain $\mathscr{K}$ strictly.

Let now B be a set of $\mathscr{C}$. The sets $B \cap A$ with $A \in \mathscr{K}$ are μ-measurable and disjoint and their union is $B \cap T_0$. Since μ is superadditive we have

$$\sum_{A \in \mathscr{K}} \mu(B \cap A) \leqq \mu(B \cap T_0) \leqq \mu(B) < \infty,$$

therefore the class of the sets $A \in \mathscr{K}$ such that $\mu(B \cap A) > 0$ is at most countable. It follows that μ has the direct sum property.

6. FUNCTIONS WITH THE LIFTING PROPERTY

Let μ be a *positive measure* on a clan $\mathscr{C}$. We suppose that $\mu \neq 0$ and that μ has the *direct sum property*. Let E and F be two Banach spaces and Z a norming subspace of F', i.e. such that

$$|y| = \sup_{z \in Z} \frac{|\langle y, z \rangle|}{|z|}, \quad \text{for every} \quad y \in F.$$

Then, we can plunge isometrically F in Z'.

We shall denote by $\mathscr{L}^*(E, F)$ the space of the linear mappings $U: E \to F$. For each $U \in \mathscr{L}^*(E, F)$ put

$$|U| = \sup_{\substack{|x| \leqq 1 \\ |z| \leqq 1}} |\langle Ux, z \rangle| = \sup_{|x| \leqq 1} |Ux| \leqq +\infty,$$

where $x \in E$ and $z \in Z$.

For every function $U: T \to \mathscr{L}^*(E, F)$, $\boldsymbol{x}: T \to E$, and $\boldsymbol{z}: T \to Z$ we shall denote with $\langle U\boldsymbol{x}, \boldsymbol{z} \rangle$ the function $t \to \langle U(t)\, \boldsymbol{x}(t), \boldsymbol{z}(t) \rangle$ and with $|U|$ the function $t \to |U(t)|$.

For two functions $U_1, U_2: T \to \mathscr{L}^*(E, F)$ we shall write $U_1 \equiv U_2$ if

$$\langle U_1 x, z \rangle \sim \langle U_2 x, z \rangle, \quad \text{for every} \quad x \in E \quad \text{and} \quad z \in Z.$$

Remarks.

1°. The relation $U_1 \equiv U_2$ depends not only on the spaces E and F but also on the space Z.

2°. If Z is of countable type, $U_1 \equiv U_2$ means that $U_1(t)\, x = U_2(t)\, x$ μ-almost everywhere, for each $x \in E$.

If E and Z are of countable type, $U_1 \equiv U_2$ means that $U_1(t) = U_2(t)$ μ-almost everywhere.

3°. If $F = C$, then $\mathscr{L}^*(E, C) = E^*$. In this case for two functions $f, g: T \to E^*$ the relation $f \equiv g$ means that, for every $x \in E$, we have

$$\langle x, f(t) \rangle = \langle x, g(t) \rangle \quad \mu\text{-almost everywhere.}$$

If $E = C$, then $\mathscr{L}^*(C, F) = F$. In this case, for two functions $f, g: T \to F$, the relation $f \equiv g$ means that for each $z \in Z$ we have

$$\langle f(t), z \rangle = \langle g(t), z \rangle \quad \mu\text{-almost everywhere.}$$

Let ϱ be a lifting of $\mathscr{L}^\infty(\mu)$.

Definition 2. *Let $U: T \to \mathscr{L}^*(E, F)$ be a function.*

a) *We shall write $\varrho(U) = U$ if for every $x \in E$ and $z \in Z$ we have $\langle Ux, z \rangle \in \mathscr{L}^\infty(\mu)$ and*

$$\varrho(\langle Ux, z \rangle) = \langle Ux, z \rangle.$$

b) *We shall write $\varrho[U] = U$ if there exists a family $\mathscr{A} \in C(\mu)$ such that for every $A \in \mathscr{A}$, $x \in E$, and $z \in Z$ we have $\langle Ux, z \rangle \varphi_A \in \mathscr{L}^\infty(\mu)$ and*

$$\varrho(\langle Ux, z \rangle \varphi_A) = \langle Ux, z \rangle \varphi_{\varrho(A)}.$$

We remark that the relations $\varrho(U) = U$ and $\varrho[U] = U$ are defined with respect to a certain space $Z \subset F'$, and that the relation $\varrho[U] = U$ is defined with respect to a certain family $\mathscr{A} \in C(\mu)$.

If we have $\varrho[U] = U$ with respect to a certain family $\mathscr{A} \in C(\mu)$ and if a μ-measurable set A is contained in some set $B \in \mathscr{A}$, then we have

$$\varrho(\langle Ux, z \rangle \varphi_A) = \langle Ux, z \rangle \varphi_{\varrho(A)} \quad \text{for} \quad x \in E \quad \text{and} \quad z \in Z.$$

It follows that if $U_1, U_2: T \to \mathscr{L}^*(E, F)$ are two functions with $\varrho[U_1] = U_1$ and $\varrho[U_2] = U_2$, then we can find a common family $\mathscr{A} \in C(\mu)$ to have at the same time $\varrho[U_1] = U_1$ and $\varrho[U_2] = U_2$ with respect to $\mathscr{A}$.

The functions U with $\varrho(U) = U$ or $\varrho[U] = U$ have the following properties:

1. $\varrho(U) = U$ implies $\varrho[U] = U$.

2. If $\varrho[U] = U$, then $\langle Ux, z \rangle$ is μ-measurable for every $x \in E$ and $z \in Z$.

3. If $U_1 \equiv U_2$, $\varrho(U_1) = U_1$, and $\varrho(U_2) = U_2$, then $U_1 = U_2$.

4. If $U_1 \equiv U_2$, $\varrho[U_1] = U_1$ and $\varrho[U_2] = U_2$, then

$$U_1(t) = U_2(t) \quad \mu\text{-almost everywhere.}$$

5. If $U_1(t) = U_2(t)$ μ-almost everywhere and $\varrho[U_1] = U_1$, then $\varrho[U_2] = U_2$.

In fact, let $\mathscr{A} = (A_j)_{j \in J}$ be a family of $C(\mu)$ such that

$$\varrho(\langle U_1 x, z\rangle \varphi_{A_j}) = \langle U_1 x, z\rangle \varphi_{\varrho(A_j)}$$

for every $j \in J$, $x \in E$, and $z \in Z$. Let N be the negligible set on which U_1 and U_2 differ. Each set $\varrho(A_j) \cap A_j - N$ is μ-integrable, therefore it is the union of a sequence (A_{jn}) of disjoint sets of $\mathscr{S}(\mathscr{C})$ and a μ-negligible set N_j. The sets A_{jn} form a family $\mathscr{A}'$ of $C(\mu)$ and it is easy to verify that we have $\varrho[U_2] = U_2$ with respect to $\mathscr{A}'$, since U_1 and U_2 coincide on each set A_{jn}.

6. If $\varrho(U) = U$, then $|U(t)| \leqq N_\infty(U) \leqq \infty$, for every $t \in T$.

In fact, for every $x \in E$ and $z \in Z$ we have $\langle Ux, z\rangle \in \mathscr{L}^\infty$ and $\varrho(\langle Ux, z\rangle) = \langle Ux, z\rangle$, whence, for every $t \in T$, we have

$$|\langle U(t)\,x, z\rangle| \leqq N_\infty(\langle Ux, z\rangle) \leqq |x|\,|z|\,N_\infty(U),$$

therefore $|U(t)| \leqq N_\infty(U)$ for every $t \in T$.

7. If $\varrho[U] = U$ with respect to a family $\mathscr{A} \in C(\mu)$, then, for each $A \in \mathscr{A}$ and for each $t \in A$, we have $|U(t)| \leqq N_\infty(U\varphi_A)$.

Proposition 5. *Let $U\colon T \to \mathscr{L}^*(E, F)$. If $\varrho[U] = U$, then the function $t \to |U(t)|$ is μ-measurable.*

Let $\mathscr{A} \in C(\mu)$ be a family such that

$$\varrho(\langle Ux, z\rangle \varphi_A) = \varphi_{\varrho(A)}\langle Ux, z\rangle$$

for $A \in \mathscr{A}$, $x \in E$, and $z \in Z$ and let $T_0 = \bigcup_{A \in \mathscr{A}} \varrho(A)$. The set $T - T_0$ is μ-negligible.

Consider the set $\mathscr{F}$ of the positive functions of the form $f = \sum_{i=1}^{n} \varphi_{A_i} |\langle Ux_i, z_i\rangle|$ where A_i are disjoint μ-measurable sets with $\varrho(A_i) = A_i$, and every A_i is contained in some set $\varrho(A)$ with $A \in \mathscr{A}$, and $x_i \in E$ with $|x_i| \leqq 1$, $z_i \in Z$ with $|z_i| \leqq 1$. In particular, $\mathscr{F}$ contains all the functions of the form $\varphi_{\varrho(A)}|\langle Ux, z\rangle|$ with $A \in \mathscr{A}$, $x \in E$, and $z \in Z$ with $|x| \leqq 1$ and $|z| \leqq 1$. We have

$$f(t) \leqq \sum_{i=1}^{n} \varphi_{A_i}(t)\,|U(t)| \leqq |U(t)|, \quad \text{for} \quad t \in T_0.$$

On the other hand, for each $t \in T_0$ and for each set $A \in \mathscr{A}$ with $t \in \varrho(A)$, we have

$$|U(t)| = \sup_{\substack{|x| \leqq 1 \\ |z| \leqq 1}} \varphi_{\varrho(A)}(t)\,|\langle U(t)\,x, z\rangle|.$$

It follows that

$$|U(t)| = \sup_{f \in \mathscr{F}} f(t), \quad \text{for} \quad t \in T_0.$$

For every function $f = \sum \varphi_{A_i} |\langle Ux_i, z_i \rangle|$ of $\mathscr{F}$ we have $\varrho(f) = f$. In fact, if for each i we have $A_i \subset \varrho(B_i)$ with $B_i \in \mathscr{A}$ then

$$f = \sum \varphi_{A_i} \varphi_{\varrho(B_i)} |\langle Ux_i, z_i \rangle|,$$

whence

$$\varrho(f) = \sum \varphi_{A_i} \varrho(\varphi_{\varrho(B_i)}) |\langle Ux_i, z_i \rangle| = \sum \varphi_{A_i} \varphi_{\varrho(B_i)} |\langle Ux_i, z_i \rangle| = f.$$

We show now that $\mathscr{F}$ is directed. Let $f_1, f_2 \in \mathscr{F}$. We remark that if A is μ-measurable and $\varrho(A) = A$, then $\varphi_A f_1 + \varphi_{T-A} f_2 \in \mathscr{F}$. Since there exists a μ-measurable set $B \subset T$ such that

$$\sup(f_1, f_2) = \varphi_B f_1 + \varphi_{T-B} f_2,$$

we deduce that for $A = \varrho(B)$ we have $\varrho(A) = A$ and

$$\sup(f_1, f_2) = \sup(\varrho(f_1), \varrho(f_2)) = \varrho(\sup(f_1, f_2))$$
$$= \varphi_{\varrho(B)} f_1 + \varphi_{\varrho(T-B)} f_2 = \varphi_A f_1 + \varphi_{T-A} f_2 \in \mathscr{F}.$$

According to the proposition 4 we deduce that the function f_∞ defined by the equality

$$f_\infty(t) = \sup_{f \in \mathscr{F}} f(t), \quad \text{for} \quad t \in T,$$

is μ-measurable. Since

$$|U(t)| = f_\infty(t), \quad \text{for} \quad t \in T_0,$$

and $T - T_0$ is μ-negligible, it follows that the function $|U|$ is μ-measurable.

Corollary. *If $\varrho[U] = U$, then, for each $x \in E$, the function $t \to |U(t)\,x|$ is μ-measurable.*

In fact, we have $\varrho[Ux] = Ux$, for each $x \in E$.

Proposition 6. *Let $U, U' : T \to \mathscr{L}^*(E, F)$ be two functions. If $U' \equiv U$, $\varrho[U'] = U'$ and if the function $t \to |U(t)|$ is μ-measurable, then*

$$|U'(t)| \leqq |U(t)| \quad \mu\text{-almost everywhere.}$$

Let $\mathscr{A} \in C(\mu)$ be a family such that

$$\varrho(\langle U'x, z \rangle \varphi_A) = \varphi_{\varrho(A)} \langle U'x, z \rangle,$$

for $A \in \mathscr{A}$, $x \in E$, and $z \in Z$. We remark that

$$\varphi_{\varrho(A)} |\langle U'x, z \rangle| = \varrho(\varphi_A |\langle U'x, z \rangle|)$$

and

$$\varphi_A |\langle U'x, z \rangle| \sim \varphi_A |\langle Ux, z \rangle|.$$

Then

$$\varphi_{\varrho(A)} |\langle U'x, z \rangle| = \varrho(\varphi_A |\langle Ux, z \rangle|) \leqq |x|\,|z|\,\varrho(\varphi_A |U|);$$

hence

$$\varphi_{\varrho(A)} |U'| \leqq \varrho(\varphi_A |U|) \sim \varphi_{\varrho(A)} |U|,$$

therefore $|U'(t)| \leqq |U(t)|$ almost everywhere on $\bigcup_{A \in \mathscr{A}} \varrho(A)$, i.e. almost everywhere.

In the case $F = Z'$, other properties are given in the following propositions.

Proposition 7. *Let $U: T \to \mathscr{L}^*(E, Z')$ be a function such that $\langle Ux, z \rangle$ is μ-measurable for every $x \in E$ and $z \in Z$.*

a) *If $N_\infty(Ux) < \infty$ for each $x \in E$, then there exists a function $U': T \to \mathscr{L}^*(E, Z')$ with $U' \equiv U$ and $\varrho(U') = U'$.*

b) *If there exists a family $\mathscr{A} \in C(\mu)$ with $N_\infty(Ux\varphi_A) < \infty$ for each $A \in \mathscr{A}$ and each $x \in E$, then there exists a function $U': T \to \mathscr{L}^*(E, Z')$ with $U' \equiv U$ and $\varrho[U'] = U'$.*

For each $x \in E$ and $z \in Z$ put $U_{x,z} = \varrho(\langle Ux, z \rangle)$. For each $t \in T$, the mapping $(x, z) \to U_{x,z}(t)$ is a bilinear functional on $E \times Z$; for fixed $x \in E$, the mapping $U_x(t): z \to U_{x,z}(t)$ is a linear functional on Z. This functional is continuous:

$$|U_x(t)\, z| = |U_{x,z}(t)| \leqq |z|\, N_\infty(Ux) < \infty,$$

whence $U_x(t) \in Z'$ and $|U_x(t)| \leqq N_\infty(Ux)$. The mapping $U'(t): x \to U_x(t)$ of E into Z' is linear; hence $U'(t) \in \mathscr{L}^*(E, Z')$. We have

$$\langle U'(t)\, x, z \rangle = \varrho(\langle Ux, z \rangle)\,(t),$$

for every $t \in T$, $x \in E$, and $z \in Z$, i.e.

$$\langle U'x, z \rangle = \varrho(\langle Ux, z \rangle) \in \mathscr{L}^\infty(\mu),$$

whence

$$\varrho(\langle U'x, z \rangle) = \langle U'x, z \rangle, \quad \text{i.e.} \quad \varrho(U') = U'.$$

On the other hand, $\langle U'x, z \rangle = \varrho(\langle Ux, z \rangle) \sim \langle Ux, z \rangle$ for every $x \in E$ and $z \in Z$, hence $U' \equiv U$. The statement a) is proved.

Suppose now that there exists a family $\mathscr{A} \in C(\mu)$ with $N_\infty(Ux\varphi_A) < \infty$ for $A \in \mathscr{A}$ and $x \in E$. For each $A \in \mathscr{A}$ we define as before a mapping $U_A: T \to \mathscr{L}^*(E, Z')$ such that $\langle U_A x, z \rangle = \varrho(\langle Ux, z \rangle\, \varphi_A)$. Take now a μ-integrable set A_0 with $\mu(A_0) > 0$, and $\sup_{t \in A_0} |U(t)\, x| < \infty$ for each $x \in E$, and consider on $E \times Z$ the functional

$$(x, z) \to \frac{1}{\mu(A_0)} \int_{A_0} \langle U(t)\, x, z \rangle\, d\mu(t).$$

There exists then a linear mapping $U_0: E \to Z'$ such that

$$\langle U_0 x, z \rangle = \frac{1}{\mu(A_0)} \int_A \langle U(t)\, x, z \rangle\, d\mu(t).$$

We define now the function $U': T \to \mathscr{L}^*(E, Z')$ by the equalities:

$$U'(t) = U_A(t), \quad \text{for} \quad t \in \varrho(A) \quad \text{and} \quad A \in \mathscr{A},$$

$$U'(t) = U_0, \quad \text{for} \quad t \in T - \bigcup_{A \in \mathscr{A}} \varrho(A).$$

We verify easily that $U' \equiv U$ and $\varrho[U'] = U'$. Thus the statement b) is also proved.

Lemma 2. *If $\varphi \geqq 0$ is μ-measurable and finite almost everywhere, there exists a family $\mathscr{A} \in C(\mu)$ such that φ is bounded on every set $A \in \mathscr{A}$.*

Since μ has the direct sum property, $C(\mu)$ is not void. Let $\mathscr{B} \in C(\mu)$ and let $B \in \mathscr{B}$. For every natural number n, the set

$$A_n(B) = \{t \in B;\ n - 1 \leqq \varphi(t) < n\}$$

is μ-measurable and contained in B; hence it is μ-integrable, therefore it is the union of a sequence $(A_{n,m})_{1 \leqq m < \infty}$ of disjoint sets of $\mathscr{S}$ and a μ-negligible set $N_n(B)$. Since φ is finite almost everywhere the set B is the union of the sequence $(A_n(B))_{1 \leqq n < \infty}$ and a μ-negligible $N_0(B)$ (on which $\varphi(t) = +\infty$). The set $N(B) = \bigcup_{n=0}^{\infty} N_n(B)$ is μ-negligible, hence the set $N = \bigcup_{B \in \mathscr{B}} N(B)$ is μ-negligible since the set $N \cap B = N(B)$ is μ-negligible for every $B \in \mathscr{B}$. Then the family $\mathscr{A} = (A_{n,m}(B))$ with $1 \leqq n < \infty$, $1 \leqq m < \infty$, and $B \in \mathscr{B}$, is a family of sets of $\mathscr{S}$, belongs to $C(\mu)$ and φ is bounded on each $A \in \mathscr{A}$.

Proposition 8. *Let $U: T \to \mathscr{L}^*(E, Z')$ be a function such that $\langle Ux, z\rangle$ is μ-measurable for every $x \in E$ and $z \in Z$.*

a) *If $|U| \in \mathscr{L}^\infty(\mu)$, then there exists a function $U': T \to \mathscr{L}^*(E, Z')$ with $U' \equiv U$, $\varrho(U') = U'$ and*

$$|U'(t)| \leqq |U(t)| \quad \textit{almost everywhere.}$$

b) *If $|U|$ is μ-measurable and finite μ-almost everywhere, then there exists a function $U': T \to \mathscr{L}^*(E, Z')$ with $U' \equiv U$, $\varrho[U'] = U'$ and*

$$|U'(t)| \leqq |U(t)|, \quad \textit{for every} \quad t \in T.$$

We prove the statement b). Since $|U|$ is μ-measurable and finite almost everywhere, we can find a family $\mathscr{A} \in C(\mu)$ such that the restriction of $|U|$ to each A of $\mathscr{A}$ is finite and bounded. Then $N_\infty(Ux\varphi_A) < \infty$ for each $A \in \mathscr{A}$ and each $x \in E$, therefore, by proposition 7, there exists a function $U': T \to \mathscr{L}^*(E, Z')$ with $U' \equiv U$ and $\varrho[U'] = U'$. From the proposition 6 we deduce then that $|U'(t)| \leqq |U(t)|$ μ-almost everywhere. If we modify U' on a μ-negligible set we have still $U' \equiv U$, and $\varrho[U'] = U'$ and we can realise to have $|U'(t)| \leqq |U(t)|$ for every $t \in T$.

The statement a) is proved in the same way.

§ 12. THE SPACES $\mathscr{L}_E^p$

1. DEFINITION AND PROPERTIES

Let μ be a *positive measure* defined on a clan $\mathscr{C}$ of subsets of T and E a Banach space. Let p be a real number such that $0 < p < \infty$.

Definition 1. *We denote by $\mathscr{L}_E^p(T, \mu)$ the set of the μ-measurable functions $f: T \to E$ such that $|f|^p$ is μ-integrable.*

For every function $f \in \mathscr{L}_E^p(T, \mu)$ we put

$$N_p(f, \mu) = \left(\int |f|^p \, d\mu\right)^{\frac{1}{p}}.$$

If a function f belongs to $\mathscr{L}_E^p(T, \mu)$ we say that f has the p-th power μ-integrable

We shall write also $\mathscr{L}_E^p(\mu)$ or $\mathscr{L}_E^p$ instead of $\mathscr{L}_E^p(T, \mu)$, and $N_p(f)$ or $\|f\|_p$ instead of $N_p(f, \mu)$.

In case $p = 1$, the space $\mathscr{L}_E^1$ defined here is equal to the space of the μ-integrable functions defined in § 8 (§ 8, proposition 20).

If $E = R$ we shall write $\mathscr{L}^p(\mu)$ instead of $\mathscr{L}_R^p(\mu)$.

We extend the preceding definition for functions defined only almost everywhere and for functions $f: T \to \bar{R}$ which are finite only almost everywhere.

We say that a function f defined almost everywhere on T with values in E or in $\bar{R}$ has the p-th power μ-integrable, if there exists a function f' in $\mathscr{L}_E^p$ respectively in $\mathscr{L}^p$, equal to f μ-almost everywhere; in this case we put $N_p(f) = N_p(f')$.

This definition depends only on f.

In the sequel we shall consider only functions defined and finite everywhere but most part of the results remain valid for functions which are defined or finite only almost everywhere.

Proposition 1. *The set $\mathscr{L}_E^p$ is a vector space.*

If $f \in \mathscr{L}_E^p$ and if α is a scalar, then αf is μ-measurable and $|\alpha f|^p = |\alpha|^p |f|^p \in \mathscr{L}^1$, whence $\alpha f \in \mathscr{L}_E^p$.

If $f, g \in \mathscr{L}_E^p$, then $f + g$ is μ-measurable and $\sup(|f|^p, |g|^p) \in \mathscr{L}^1$. From the inequality

$$(a + b)^p \leqq 2^p \sup(a^p, b^p), \quad \text{for} \quad a \geqq 0, b \geqq 0,$$

we deduce that

$$|f + g|^p \leqq (|f| + |g|)^p \leqq 2^p \sup(|f|^p, |g|^p) \in \mathscr{L}^1.$$

Since $|f + g|$ is μ-measurable, $|f + g|^p$ is μ-measurable and from the preceding inequality we deduce that $|f + g|^p \in \mathscr{L}^1$ (§ 8, proposition 19), therefore $f + g \in \mathscr{L}_E^p$.

Proposition 2. *We have $f \in \mathcal{L}^p_E$ if and only if f is μ-measurable and $|f| \in \mathcal{L}^p$. If $f \in \mathcal{L}^p_E$, then*

$$N_p(f) = N_p(|f|).$$

The proof is immediate.

Proposition 3. *If $f: T \to E$ is μ-measurable and if there exists a positive function $g \in \mathcal{L}^p$ such that $|f| \leqq g$ almost everywhere, then $f \in \mathcal{L}^p_E$.*

In fact, $|f|^p$ is μ-measurable and $|f|^p \leqq g^p$.
Since $g^p \in \mathcal{L}^1$ we deduce that $|f|^p \in \mathcal{L}^1$ (§ 8, proposition 19), whence $f \in \mathcal{L}^p_E$.

Proposition 4. *Let $f: T \to E$ be a μ-measurable function. If the set $A = \{t; f(t) \neq 0\}$ is μ-integrable and if there exists a μ-negligible set $N \subset A$ such that f is bounded on $A - N$ then $f \in \mathcal{L}^p_E$.*

In fact, if $|f(t)| \leqq \alpha$ for $t \in A - N$, then $|f|^p \leqq \alpha^p \varphi_A$ μ-almost everywhere. Since the function $\alpha^p \varphi_A$ is μ-integrable, the function $\alpha \varphi_A$ belongs to $\mathcal{L}^p$, therefore $f \in \mathcal{L}^p_E$.

Corollary 1. *Every μ-integrable step function $f: T \to E$ belongs to $\mathcal{L}^p_E$.*

Corollary 2. *Every μ-negligible function $f: T \to E$ belongs to $\mathcal{L}^p_E$.*

Proposition 5. *A function $f \in \mathcal{L}^p_E$ is μ-negligible if and only if $N_p(f) = 0$.*

The proof is immediate.

Proposition 6. *We have $f \in \mathcal{L}^p$ if and only if $f^+ \in \mathcal{L}^p$ and $f^- \in \mathcal{L}^p$.*

In fact, if $f \in \mathcal{L}^p$, then f is μ-measurable, whence f^+ and f^- are μ-measurable. Since $|f| \in \mathcal{L}^p$, from the inequalities $f^+ \leqq |f|$ and $f^- \leqq |f|$ we deduce that f^+ and f^- belong to $\mathcal{L}^p$.
Conversely, if f^+ and f^- belong to $\mathcal{L}^p$, then $f = f^+ - f^- \in \mathcal{L}^p$.

Proposition 7. *If $f, g \in \mathcal{L}^p$, then $\sup(f, g) \in \mathcal{L}^p$ and $\inf(f, g) \in \mathcal{L}^p$.*

In fact, $f + g$ and $f - g$ belong to $\mathcal{L}^p$, therefore $|f - g| \in \mathcal{L}^p$ and

$$\sup(f, g) = \frac{1}{2}(|f - g| + (f + g)) \in \mathcal{L}^p.$$

On the other hand, $-f$ and $-g$ belong to $\mathcal{L}^p$, therefore

$$\inf(f, g) = -\sup(-f, -g) \in \mathcal{L}^p.$$

Proposition 8. *If $f \in \mathcal{L}^p_E$ then the set $\{t; f(t) \neq 0\}$ has σ-finite measure.*

In fact, $\{t; f(t) \neq 0\} = \{t; |f(t)|^p \neq 0\}$. Since $|f|^p \in \mathcal{L}^1$, we can use the proposition 9, § 8.

Corollary. *If $f \in \mathcal{L}^p_E$, then the set $\{t; f(t) \neq 0\}$ can be covered by a μ-negligible set and a sequence of sets of the clan $\mathscr{C}$.*

Proposition 9. *If $f \in \mathcal{L}_E^p$, then, for every $\alpha > 0$, the set $\{t; |f(t)| \geqq \alpha\}$ is μ-integrable.*

In fact, $|f|^p \in \mathcal{L}^1$ and $\{t; |f(t)| \geqq \alpha\} = \{t; |f(t)|^p \geqq \alpha^p\}$. We use then the corollary 2 of the proposition 9, § 8.

2. THE INEQUALITIES OF HÖLDER AND MINKOWSKI

Let p and q be two numbers such that $1 \leqq p \leqq \infty$ and $1 \leqq q \leqq \infty$.

We say that p and q are *conjugate* to each other if

$$\frac{1}{p} + \frac{1}{q} = 1.$$

From this inequality we deduce that:

$$\begin{array}{lll} \text{if} & p = 1, & \text{then} \quad q = \infty; \\ \text{if} & p = \infty, & \text{then} \quad q = 1; \\ \text{if} & 1 < p < \infty, & \text{then} \quad 1 < q < \infty; \\ \text{if} & 1 \leqq p \leqq 2, & \text{then} \quad 2 \leqq q \leqq \infty; \\ \text{if} & p = 2, & \text{then} \quad q = 2; \end{array}$$

if $1 < p < \infty$, then the inequality $\frac{1}{p} + \frac{1}{q} = 1$ is equivalent to each of the following equalities:

$$p + q = pq, \quad (p - 1)\,q = p, \quad q = \frac{p}{p-1}.$$

Lemma 1. *Let $p > 1$ and $q > 1$ be such that $\frac{1}{p} + \frac{1}{q} = 1$. For every numbers a, b such that $0 \leqq a \leqq \infty$ and $0 \leqq b \leqq \infty$ we have*

$$ab \leqq \frac{a^p}{p} + \frac{b^q}{q}.$$

If $a = 0$ or if $b = 0$, then $ab = 0$ and the inequality is verified. If $a = \infty$ or if $b = \infty$, the inequality is also verified. Assume then that $0 < a < \infty$ and $0 < b < \infty$. The function $\varphi(x) = \frac{x^p}{p} + \frac{x^{-q}}{q}$ defined for $x > 0$ is derivable and the derivative is positive for $x > 1$ and negative for $x < 1$. Hence its minimum value for $x > 0$ is $\varphi(1) = 1$. Writing the inequality $1 \leqq \varphi(x)$ for $x = a^{\frac{1}{q}} b^{-\frac{1}{p}}$ we obtain

$$1 \leqq \frac{a^{p-1}}{bp} + \frac{a^{q-1}}{aq},$$

since $\frac{p}{q} = p - 1$ and $\frac{q}{p} = q - 1$. Multiplying by ab we obtain the desired inequality.

Proposition 9. *Let $1 \leqq p \leqq \infty$ and $1 \leqq q \leqq \infty$ be such that $\frac{1}{p} + \frac{1}{q} = 1$ and let $f \geqq 0$ and $g \geqq 0$ be two positive functions defined on T. If $f \in \mathscr{L}^p$ and $g \in \mathscr{L}^q$ then $fg \in \mathscr{L}^1$ and*

$$\int fg \, d\mu \leqq N_p(f) \, N_q(g).$$

This inequality is called *Hölder's inequality*.

If $p = 1$ and $q = \infty$, the proposition was already proved (§ 9, proposition 15). Consider then $1 < p < \infty$ and $1 < q < \infty$.

If, for example, $N_p(f) = 0$, then f is μ-negligible, whence fg is μ-negligible. It follows that $fg \in \mathscr{L}^1$ and $\int fg \, d\mu = 0$ and the inequality is proved. The case $N_q(g) = 0$ leads to the same conclusion.

Assume now that $N_p(f) > 0$ and $N_q(g) > 0$. Since f^p and g^q are μ-measurable, the functions $f = (f^p)^{\frac{1}{p}}$ and $g = (g^q)^{\frac{1}{q}}$ are μ-measurable, therefore fg is μ-measurable. If for every $t \in T$ we write the inequality $a \leqq \frac{a^p}{p} + \frac{b^q}{q}$ for

$$a = \frac{f(t)}{N_p(f)} \quad \text{and} \quad b = \frac{g(t)}{N_q(g)}$$

we deduce that

$$\frac{fg}{N_p(f) \, N_q(g)} \leqq \frac{f^p}{p \int f^p \, d\mu} + \frac{g^q}{q \int g^q \, d\mu} \in \mathscr{L}^1,$$

therefore $fg \in \mathscr{L}^1$ (§ 8, proposition 19). By integration we deduce that

$$\frac{\int fg \, d\mu}{N_p(f) \, N_q(g)} \leqq \frac{1}{p} + \frac{1}{q} = 1,$$

therefore

$$\int fg \, d\mu \leqq N_p(f) \, N_q(g).$$

Remark. The preceding proposition remain valid for functions $f, g \colon T \to \bar{R}_+$ which are finite only almost everywhere.

Corollary 1. *Let E, F, G be three Banach spaces, $(x, y) \to xy$ a bilinear mapping of $E \times F$ into G such that $|xy| \leqq |x|\,|y|$, and $1 \leqq p \leqq \infty$ and $1 \leqq q \leqq \infty$ two numbers such that $\frac{1}{p} + \frac{1}{q} = 1$. If $f \in \mathscr{L}_E^p(\mu)$ and $g \in \mathscr{L}_F^q(\mu)$, then $fg \in \mathscr{L}_G^1(\mu)$ and*

$$\left|\int fg\, d\mu\right| = \int |f|\,|g|\, d\mu \leqq N_p(f)\, N_q(g).$$

In fact, f and g are μ-measurable and the mapping $(x, y) \to xy$ is continuous, therefore fg is μ-measurable. On the other hand $|f| \in \mathscr{L}^p$ and $|g| \in \mathscr{L}^q$, therefore $|f|\,|g| \in \mathscr{L}^1$. From the inequality $|fg| \leqq |f|\,|g|$ we deduce that $fg \in \mathscr{L}_G^1$ and

$$\left|\int fg\, d\mu\right| \leqq \int |fg|\, d\mu \leqq \int |f|\,|g|\, d\mu \leqq N_p(f)\, N_q(g).$$

Corollary 2. *Let E be a Banach space. If $f \in \mathscr{L}_E^p$ and $f' \in \mathscr{L}_q^{E'}$, then $\langle f, f'\rangle \in \mathscr{L}^1$ and*

$$\left|\int \langle f, f'\rangle\, d\mu\right| \leqq \int |\langle f, f'\rangle|\, d\mu \leqq N_p(f)\, N_q(f').$$

Corollary 3. *Let E be a Banach space. If $f \in \mathscr{L}_E^p$ and $\varphi \in \mathscr{L}^q$, then $f\varphi \in \mathscr{L}_E^1$ and*

$$\left|\int f\varphi\, d\mu\right| \leqq \int |f|\,|\varphi|\, d\mu \leqq N_p(f)\, N_q(\varphi).$$

Proposition 10. *If $1 \leqq p < \infty$, $\frac{1}{p} + \frac{1}{q} = 1$, and if $f \in \mathscr{L}_E^p$, then $|f|^{p-1} \in \mathscr{L}^q$.*

In fact, f is μ-measurable, therefore $|f|$ is μ-measurable and $|f|^{p-1}$ is μ-measurable. On the other hand, if $1 < p < \infty$, then

$$(|f|^{p-1})^q = |f|^p \in \mathscr{L}^1,$$

whence $|f|^{p-1} \in \mathscr{L}^q$. If $p = 1$, then $|f(t)|^{p-1} \equiv 1$, whence $|f|^{p-1} \in \mathscr{L}^\infty$.

Corollary. *Let $1 \leqq p < \infty$ and $\frac{1}{p} + \frac{1}{q} = 1$. We have $f \in \mathscr{L}_E^p(\mu)$ if and only if $|f|^{p-1} f \in \mathscr{L}_E^1(\mu)$.*

In fact, if $f \in \mathscr{L}_E^p$, then $|f|^{p-1} \in \mathscr{L}^q$. By corollary 3 of the proposition 9 we have $|f|^{p-1} f \in \mathscr{L}^1$. Conversely, if $|f|^{p-1} f \in \mathscr{L}_E^1$, then $|f|^p = \big||f|^{p-1} f\big| \in \mathscr{L}^1$. On the other hand, since $g = |f|^{p-1} f$ is μ-measurable and since $f(t) = g(t)\,|f(t)|^{1-p}$ if $g(t) \neq 0$ and $f(t) = g(t)$ if $g(t) = 0$, we deduce that f is μ-measurable, therefore $f \in \mathscr{L}_E^p$.

Proposition 11. *Let $1 \leqq p \leqq \infty$. If $f, g \in \mathscr{L}_E^p$, then*

$$N_p(f + g) \leqq N_p(f) + N_p(g).$$

This inequality is called *Minkowski's inequality.*

If $p = 1$ or if $p = \infty$, the inequality was already remarked. Consider now the case $1 < p < \infty$. We have

$$|f + g|^p = |f + g|^{p-1}\, |f + g| \leqq |f + g|^{p-1}\, |f| + |f + g|^{p-1}\, |g|.$$

Since $f + g \in \mathscr{L}_E^p$, we have $|f + g|^{p-1} \in \mathscr{L}^q$, whence, using proposition 9, we deduce that

$$|f + g|^{p-1} |f| \in \mathscr{L}^1 \quad \text{and} \quad |f + g|^{p-1}|g| \in \mathscr{L}^1,$$

therefore

$$\int |f + g|^p \, d\mu \leqq \int |f| \, |f + g|^{p-1} \, d\mu + \int |g| \, |f + g|^{p-1} \, d\mu.$$

Using Hölder's inequality we obtain

$$\int |f| \, |f + g|^{p-1} \, d\mu \leqq N_p(f) \left(\int |f + g|^p \, d\mu \right)^{\frac{1}{q}}$$

and

$$\int |g| \, |f + g|^{p-1} \, d\mu \leqq N_p(g) \left(\int |f + g|^p \, d\mu \right)^{\frac{1}{q}},$$

whence

$$\int |f + g|^p \, d\mu \leqq (N_p(f) + N_p(g)) \left(\int |f + g|^p \, d\mu \right)^{\frac{1}{q}}.$$

Since

$$\left(\int |f + g|^p \, d\mu \right)^{1 - \frac{1}{q}} = \left(\int |f + g|^p \, d\mu \right)^{\frac{1}{p}} = N_p(f + g)$$

we deduce

$$N_p(f + g) \leqq N_p(f) + N_p(g).$$

3. CONVERGENCE IN MEAN OF ORDER p

In this section we shall suppose that $1 \leqq p < \infty$. In this case N_p is a *semi-norm on* $\mathscr{L}_E^p$. The equality $N_p(\alpha f) = |\alpha| \, N_p(f)$ is immediate, and $N_p(f + g) \leqq N_p(f) + N_p(g)$ is Hölder's inequality.

We shall consider on $\mathscr{L}_E^p$ the topology defined by the semi-norm N_p. This topology is called the topology of the *convergence in mean of order p*. If we denote by $\mathscr{N}_E^\infty$ the set of the μ-negligible functions $f\colon T \to E$, then the quotient space $\mathscr{L}_E^p / \mathscr{N}_E^\infty$ is denoted by L_E^p. To say that a sequence (f_n) of $\mathscr{L}_E^p$ converges in $\mathscr{L}_E^p$ to a function $f \in \mathscr{L}_E^p$ means that

$$\lim_{n \to \infty} N_p(f_n - f) = 0, \quad \text{i.e.} \quad \lim_{n \to \infty} \int |f_n - f|^p \, d\mu = 0.$$

To say that a sequence (f_n) is a Cauchy sequence in $\mathscr{L}_E^p$ means that

$$\lim_{n,m \to \infty} N_p(f_n - f_m) = 0, \quad \text{i.e.} \quad \lim_{n,m \to \infty} \int |f_n - f_m|^p \, d\mu = 0.$$

Proposition 12. *If the sequence (f_n) converges in $\mathscr{L}_E^p$ to a function $f \in \mathscr{L}_E^p$, then*

$$\lim_{n\to\infty} N_p(f_n) = N_p(f).$$

We use the inequality

$$|N_p(f_n) - N_p(f)| \leqq N_p(f_n - f).$$

Proposition 13. *Let E and F be two Banach spaces and $\boldsymbol{u}$: $E \to F$ a continuous linear mapping. If $f \in \mathscr{L}_E^p$ then $\boldsymbol{u} \circ f \in \mathscr{L}_F^p$ and*

$$N_p(\boldsymbol{u} \circ f) \leqq |\boldsymbol{u}|\, N_p(f).$$

In fact, f is μ-measurable, therefore $\boldsymbol{u} \circ f$ is μ-measurable. On the other hand, $|\boldsymbol{u} \circ f|^p \leqq |\boldsymbol{u}|^p\, |f|^p$ and $|f|^p$ is μ-integrable, whence $|\boldsymbol{u} \circ f|^p$ is μ-integrable, therefore $\boldsymbol{u} \circ f \in \mathscr{L}_F^p$. We have then

$$N_p(\boldsymbol{u} \circ f)^p = \int |\boldsymbol{u} \circ f|^p\, d\mu \leqq |\boldsymbol{u}|^p \int |f|^p\, d\mu = |\boldsymbol{u}|^p\, N_p(f)^p,$$

whence $N_p(\boldsymbol{u} \circ f) \leqq |\boldsymbol{u}|\, N_p(f)$.

Corollary 1. *If $f \in \mathscr{L}_E^p$, then for every $z \in E'$ we have $\langle f, z\rangle \in \mathscr{L}_C^p$ and*

$$N_p(\langle f, z\rangle) \leqq |z|\, N_p(f).$$

Corollary 2. *If $\varphi \in \mathscr{L}^p$ and $x \in E$, then $\varphi x \in \mathscr{L}_E^p$ and*

$$N_p(\varphi x) = |x|\, N_p(\varphi).$$

Theorem 1 (Lebesgue's dominated convergence theorem). *Let (f_n) be a sequence of $\mathscr{L}_E^p$ convergent μ-almost everywhere to a function f: $T \to E$. If there exists a function $g \geqq 0$ of $\mathscr{L}^p$ such that $|f_n| \leqq g$ μ-almost everywhere for each n, then $f \in \mathscr{L}_E^p$ and (f_n) converges to f in $\mathscr{L}_E^p$.*

In fact, $|f_n|^p$ converges μ-almost everywhere to $|f|^p$ and $|f_n|^p \leqq g^p$ μ-almost everywhere, for each n; since $g^p \in \mathscr{L}^1$, by Lebesgue's theorem for $\mathscr{L}^1$ we deduce that $|f|^p \in \mathscr{L}^1$; since f is μ-measurable, we deduce that $f \in \mathscr{L}_E^p$.

Passing to the limit in the inequalities $|f_n| \leqq g$ we deduce that we have also $|f| \leqq g$ μ-almost everywhere.

The sequence $(f_n - f)$ converges to 0 μ-almost everywhere and $|f_n - f| \leqq |f_n| + |f| \leqq 2g$, whence $|f_n - f|^p \leqq 2^p g^p$. Again by Lebesgue's theorem for $\mathscr{L}_E^1$ we deduce that $|f_n - f|^p$ converges to 0 in $\mathscr{L}_E^1$, i.e.

$$\lim_{n\to\infty} \int |f_n - f|^p\, d\mu = 0,$$

whence

$$\lim_{n\to\infty} N_p(f_n - f) = 0.$$

Theorem 2. *If* (f_n) *is an increasing sequence of positive functions of* $\mathscr{L}^p$ *and if* $\sup_n N_p(f_n) < \infty$, *then the function* $f = \sup_n f_n$ *has the p-th power* μ*-integrable, the sequence* (f_n) *converges to* f *in* $\mathscr{L}^p$, *and*

$$N_p\left(\sup_n f_n\right) = \sup_n N_p(f_n) = \lim_{n\to\infty} N_p(f_n).$$

In fact, (f_n^p) is an increasing sequence of positive integrable functions and $N_1(f_n^p) = N_p(f_n)^p$, whence $\sup_n N_1(f_n^p) < \infty$. Since $f^p = \sup_n f_n^p$, by the theorem 2, § 8, f^p is integrable and $N_1(f^p) = \sup_n N_1(f_n^p)$. It follows that f has the p-th power integrable and

$$N_p(f) = N_1(f^p)^{\frac{1}{p}} = \sup_n N_1(f_n^p)^{\frac{1}{p}} = \sup_n N_p(f_n).$$

Since $f_n \leqq f$ and $f \in \mathscr{L}^1$, by Lebesgue's theorem (f_n) converges to f in $\mathscr{L}^p$.

Corollary 1. *If* (f_n) *is a decreasing sequence of positive functions of* $\mathscr{L}^p$, *then the function* $f = \inf_n f_n$ *belongs to* $\mathscr{L}^p$, *the sequence* (f_n) *converges to* f *in* $\mathscr{L}^p$ *and we have*

$$N_p\left(\inf_n f_n\right) = \inf_n N_p(f_n) = \lim_{n\to\infty} N_p(f_n).$$

We apply the preceding proposition to the sequence $(f_1 - f_n)$.

Proposition 14. *Let* (f_n) *be a sequence of functions of* $\mathscr{L}_E^p$ *such that*

$$\sum_{n=1}^{\infty} N_p(f_n) < \infty.$$

Then

1. *The series* $\sum_{n=1}^{\infty} f_n(t)$ *is absolutely convergent* μ*-almost everywhere.*

2. *The function* $f(t) = \sum_{n=1}^{\infty} f_n(t)$ *(defined* μ*-almost everywhere) has the p-th power* μ*-integrable and*

$$N_p\left(\sum_{n=1}^{\infty} f_n\right) \leqq \sum_{n=1}^{\infty} N_p(f_n).$$

3. *The series* $\sum_{n=1}^{\infty} f_n$ *converges to* f *in mean of order p. More precisely, for every n we have*

$$N_p\left(f - \sum_{k\leqq n} f_k\right) \leqq \sum_{k>n} N_p(f_k).$$

If for every n we put

$$g_n(t) = \sum_{i=1}^{n} |f_i(t)| \quad \text{and} \quad g(t) = \sum_{i=1}^{\infty} |f_i(t)|,$$

then (g_n) is an increasing sequence of positive functions of $\mathcal{L}^p$ and we have $g = \sup_n g_n$ and

$$\sup_n N_p(g_n) \leqq \sup_n \sum_{i=1}^{n} N_p(f_i) = \sum_{i=1}^{\infty} N_p(f_i) < \infty .$$

It follows that g has the p-th power μ-integrable and that

$$N_p(g) \leqq \sum_{n=1}^{\infty} N_p(f_n) < \infty .$$

We deduce then that $g(t)$ is finite μ-almost everywhere, whence the series $\sum_{n=1}^{\infty} f_n(t)$ is absolutely convergent μ-almost everywhere. It follows then that this series is also convergent μ-almost everywhere. The function $f = \sum_{n=1}^{\infty} f_n$ is μ-measurable and $|f| \leqq g$, therefore f has the p-th power μ-integrable and

$$N_p(f) \leqq N_p(g) \leqq \sum_{n=1}^{\infty} N_p(f_n).$$

If for every n we apply the result just obtained to the series $f - \sum_{k \leqq n} f_k = \sum_{k > n} f_k$, we deduce that

$$N_p(f - \sum_{k \leqq n} f_k) = N_p(\sum_{k>n} f_k) \leqq \sum_{k>n} N_p(f_k),$$

and from this inequality it follows that the series $\sum_{n=1}^{\infty} f_n$ converges in mean of order p to f.

The proposition is thus completely proved.

Proposition 15. *If (f_n) is a Cauchy sequence in $\mathcal{L}_E^p$, then there exists a subsequence (f_{n_k}) converging almost everywhere and in mean of order p to a function $f \in \mathcal{L}_E^p$.*

For every $\varepsilon > 0$ there exists a number m_0 such that for $n \geqq m_0$ and $m \geqq m_0$ we have $N_p(f_n - f_m) < \varepsilon$. We can then find by induction a strictly increasing sequence (n_k) of integers such that $N_p(f_{n_{k+1}} - f_{n_k}) < \frac{1}{2^k}$ for every k. Then $\sum_{k=1}^{\infty} N_p(f_{n_{k+1}} - f_{n_k}) < \infty$.

By the preceding proposition, the series $\sum_{k=1}^{\infty} (f_{n_{k+1}} - f_{n_k})$ converges in mean of order p to a function $g \in \mathcal{L}_E^p$. For every i we have

$$\sum_{i=1}^{k-1} (f_{n_{i+1}} - f_{n_i}) = f_{n_k} - f_{n_1}.$$

It follows that the sequence $(f_{n_k} - f_1)_{1 \leqq k < \infty}$ converges in mean of order p to g, therefore the sequence $(f_{n_k})_{1 \leqq k < \infty}$ converges in mean of order p to $f = g + f_{n_1}$.

Theorem 3. *The space $\mathscr{L}_E^p$ is complete. The space L_E^p is a Banach space.*

Let (f_n) be a Cauchy sequence of $\mathscr{L}_E^p$. There exists then a subsequence (f_{n_k}) converging almost everywhere and in mean of order p to a function $f \in \mathscr{L}_E^p$. Since the Cauchy sequence (f_n) contains a subsequence converging in $\mathscr{L}_E^p$ to f, it follows that (f_n) itself converges in $\mathscr{L}_E^p$ to f.

Proposition 16. *If the sequence (f_n) converges in mean of order p to a function $f \in \mathscr{L}_E^p$, then there exists a subsequence (f_{n_k}) converging to f almost everywhere.*

In fact, by the proposition 15, there exists a sequence (f_{n_k}) converging almost everywhere and in mean of order p to a function $g \in \mathscr{L}_E^p$. Since (f_n) converges also to f in $\mathscr{L}_E^p$, we deduce that (f_{n_k}) converges to f in $\mathscr{L}_E^p$, therefore $N_p(f - g) = 0$, whence $f(t) = g(t)$ μ-almost everywhere. It follows then that (f_{n_k}) converges almost everywhere to f.

Proposition 17. *If (f_n) is a Cauchy sequence in $\mathscr{L}_E^p$ converging almost everywhere to a function $f: T \to E$, then $f \in \mathscr{L}_E^p$ and (f_n) converges in mean of order p to f.*

In fact, let (f_{n_k}) be a subsequence converging almost everywhere and in mean of order p to a function $g \in \mathscr{L}_E^p$. Since (f_{n_k}) converges also to f μ-almost everywhere, it follows that $f(t) = g(t)$ μ-almost everywhere, therefore $f \in \mathscr{L}_E^p$ and (f_{n_k}) converges in $\mathscr{L}_E^p$ to f. Since (f_n) is a Cauchy sequence containing a subsequence converging to f in $\mathscr{L}_E^p$ it follows that (f_n) converges in $\mathscr{L}_E^p$ to f.

Corollary. *If a sequence (f_n) of $\mathscr{L}_E^p$ converges in mean of order p to a function $f \in \mathscr{L}_E^p$ and converges almost everywhere to a function $g: T \to E$ then $f(t) = g(t)$ almost everywhere.*

Proposition 18. *Let E_0 be a dense subset of E. Then the set of the $\mathscr{C}$-step functions of the form $\sum \varphi_{A_i} x_i$ with $A_i \in \mathscr{C}$ and $x_i \in E_0$ is dense in $\mathscr{L}_E^p(\mu)$.*

We prove first that the space $\mathscr{E}_E(\mathscr{S})$ is dense in $\mathscr{L}_E^p$, where $\mathscr{S}$ is the semi-tribe generated by $\mathscr{C}$. Let $f \in \mathscr{L}_E^p$. The set $A = \{t; f(t) \neq 0\}$ has σ-finite measure. Since f is μ-measurable, there exists a μ-negligible set $N \subset A$ and a sequence (f_n) of $\mathscr{S}$-step functions converging to f on $A - N$ and such that $|f_n| \leq |f|$ for every n (§ 6, theorem 2). Using Lebesgue's theorem we deduce that (f_n) converges in $\mathscr{L}_E^p$ to f, whence $\mathscr{E}_E(\mathscr{S})$ is dense in $\mathscr{L}_E^p$.

We prove now that $\mathscr{E}_E(\mathscr{C})$ is dense in $\mathscr{E}_E(\mathscr{S})$ for the semi-norm N_p. Let $f = \sum_{i=1}^{n} \varphi_{A_i} x_i \in \mathscr{E}_E(\mathscr{S})$ with A_i disjoint and let $\varepsilon > 0$. Let $\|f\| = \sup_{1 \leq i \leq n} |x_i|$. For every i we can find a set $B_i \in \mathscr{C}$ such that $\mu(A_i \,\Delta\, B_i) < \dfrac{\varepsilon^p}{n^2 \|f\|^p}$ (§ 5, proposition 13). Put $C_1 = B_1$ and $C_k = B_k - \bigcup_{i<k} B_i$ for $2 \leq k \leq n$. The sets C_k belong to $\mathscr{C}$ and are mutually

disjoint. We shall prove that for every k we have $\mu(A_k \,\Delta\, C_k) < \dfrac{\varepsilon^p}{n\|f\|^p}$. In fact,

$$A_k - C_k = (A_k - B_k) \cup \Big(\bigcup_{i<k} B_i \cap A_k\Big)$$

and

$$C_k - A_k = (B_k - A_k) - \bigcup_{i<k} B_i \subset B_k - A_k.$$

Since the sets A_i are disjoint, we have $B_i \cap A_k \subset A_i \,\Delta\, B_i$, therefore

$$A_k \,\Delta\, C_k \subset (A_k \,\Delta\, B_k) \cup \Big(\bigcup_{i<k} B_i \cap A_k\Big) \subset \bigcup_{i \leqq k} (A_i \,\Delta\, B_i),$$

consequently

$$\mu(A_k \,\Delta\, C_k) \leqq \sum_{i \leqq k} \mu(A_i \,\Delta\, B_i) \leqq n \frac{\varepsilon^p}{n^2\|f\|^p} = \frac{\varepsilon^p}{n\|f\|^p}.$$

Consider now the function $g = \sum_{i=1}^{n} \varphi_{C_i} x_i \in \mathscr{E}_E(\mathscr{C})$. We have

$$N_p(f - g) = \left(\int \sum_{i=1}^{n} \varphi_{A_i \Delta C_i} |x_i|^p \, d\mu\right)^{\frac{1}{p}} = \left(\sum_{i=1}^{n} \mu(A_i \,\Delta\, C_i)\, |x_i|^p\right)^{\frac{1}{p}} < \varepsilon,$$

whence $\mathscr{E}_E(\mathscr{C})$ is dense in $\mathscr{E}_E(\mathscr{S})$. It follows then that $\mathscr{E}_E(\mathscr{C})$ is dense in $\mathscr{L}_E^p$.

If now, for every i, we take $y_i \in E_0$ with $\mu(C_i)\, |x_i - y_i|^p < \dfrac{\varepsilon^p}{n}$, then $h = \sum_{i=1}^{n} \varphi_{C_i} y_i$ is a $\mathscr{C}$-step function and we have

$$N_p(g - h) = \left(\int \sum_{i=1}^{n} \varphi_{C_i} |x_i - y_i|^p \, d\mu\right)^{\frac{1}{p}} = \left(\sum_{i=1}^{n} \mu(C_i)\, |x_i - y_i|^p\right)^{\frac{1}{p}} < \varepsilon,$$

therefore the functions $h = \sum \varphi_{C_i} y_i$ with $C_i \in \mathscr{C}$ and $y_i \in E_0$ are dense in $\mathscr{E}_E(\mathscr{C})$ and hence in $\mathscr{L}_E^p(\mu)$.

From the proof we deduce in particular:

Corollary 1. *The space $\mathscr{E}_E(\mathscr{C})$ is dense in $\mathscr{L}_E^p(\mu)$.*

Corollary 2. *If $\mathscr{C}$ is countable and if E is of countable type, then $\mathscr{L}_E^p(\mu)$ is of countable type.*

Corollary 3. *If $\mathscr{C}$ is countable, then $\mathscr{L}^p(\mu)$ is of countable type.*

Corollary 4. *For every function $f \in \mathscr{L}_E^p(\mu)$, there exists a sequence (f_n) of $\mathscr{C}$-step functions of $\mathscr{E}_E(\mathscr{C})$ converging to f μ-almost everywhere and in mean of order p.*

In fact, there exists a sequence (g_n) of $\mathscr{E}_E(\mathscr{C})$ converging to f in $\mathscr{L}_E^p$. By proposition 16, we can extract a sequence (g_{n_k}) converging to f almost everywhere. If we put $f_k = g_{n_k}$, the sequence (f_n) converges to f almost everywhere, and in $\mathscr{L}_E^p$.

Proposition 19. *If (f_n) is a sequence of $\mathscr{L}^p_E(\mu)$ converging uniformly to a function $f\colon T \to E$ and vanishing outside a μ-integrable set A, then $f \in \mathscr{L}^p_E(\mu)$ and (f_n) converges in mean of order p to f.*

Since $f_n(t) = 0$ for $t \notin A$ and every n, we have

$$N_p(f_n - f_m) = \left(\int_A |f_n - f_m|^p \, d\mu\right)^{\frac{1}{p}} \leqq \|f_n - f_m\| \, \mu(A)^{\frac{1}{p}},$$

whence (f_n) is a Cauchy sequence in $\mathscr{L}^p_E$. It follows that $f \in \mathscr{L}^p_E$ and that (f_n) converges in mean of order p to f.

Corollary. *Every totally measurable (with respect to $\Sigma(\mu)$) function $f\colon T \to E$ belongs to $\mathscr{L}^p_E$.*

The space L^p can be ordered by the relation $\tilde{f} \leqq \tilde{g}$ which means that $f(t) \leqq g(t)$ almost everywhere. This relation does not depend on the functions $f \in \tilde{f}$ and $g \in \tilde{g}$.

The theorem 4, § 8, can now be extended:

Theorem 4. *Let $H \subset L^p$ be a filtering (for $\leqq$) set of positive functions. The set H has a least upper bound in L^p if and only if $\sup\limits_{\tilde{f} \in H} \|\tilde{f}\|_p < \infty$. In this case $\sup H$ is the limit in L^p of the filter of the sections of H:*

$$\sup_{\tilde{f} \in H} \tilde{f} = \lim_{\tilde{f} \in H} \tilde{f}.$$

We remark first that if $\tilde{h} \leqq \tilde{f}$, then

$$(\|\tilde{f} - \tilde{h}\|_p) \leqq (\|\tilde{f}\|_p)^p - (\|\tilde{h}\|_p)^p.$$

In fact, from the inequality $a^p + b^p \leqq (a + b)^p$, for $a \geqq 0$ and $b \geqq 0$, we deduce that $(f - h)^p + h^p \leqq f^p$, whence $(f - h)^p \leqq f^p - h^p$, consequently, by integration, $N_p(f - h)^p \leqq N_p(f)^p - N_p(h)^p$.

The proof of the theorem is then the same as that of the theorem 4, § 8.

4. COMPUTATION OF THE SEMI-NORM N_p

Let E, F, G be three Banach spaces and $u\colon E \times F \to G$ a continuous bilinear mapping such that

$$|x| = \sup_{|y| \leqq 1} |u(x, y)|, \quad \text{for every} \quad x \in E.$$

Let $1 \leqq p \leqq \infty$ and $\dfrac{1}{p} + \dfrac{1}{q} = 1$.

Theorem 5. *For every function $f \in \mathscr{L}^p_E(\mu)$ we have*

$$N_p(f) = \sup \int |u(f, g)| \, d\mu = \sup \int |f| \, |g| \, d\mu,$$

where the supremum is taken for all the step functions $g \in \mathscr{E}_F(\mathscr{C})$ with $N_q(g) \leqq 1$.

If $f \in \mathscr{L}_E^p$ and $g \in \mathscr{E}_F(\mathscr{C})$ with $N_q(g) \leqq 1$, then from Hölder's inequality we deduce

$$\int |u(f, g)| \, d\mu \leqq \int |f| \, |g| \, d\mu \leqq N_p(f).$$

It remains to prove the inequality

$$N_p(f) \leqq \sup \int |u(f, g)| \, d\mu, \quad \text{for} \quad g \in \mathscr{E}_F(\mathscr{C}) \quad \text{with} \quad N_q(g) \leqq 1.$$

If $N_p(f) = 0$, this inequality is trivial. Assume then that $N_p(f) > 0$. We shall consider several cases:

1. We consider first the case where $p = 1$ and $f = \sum \varphi_{A_i} x_i \in \mathscr{E}_E(\mathscr{C})$ with A_i disjoint. Then $|f| = \sum \varphi_{A_i} |x_i| \in \mathscr{E}(\mathscr{C})$ and

$$N_1(f) = \int |f| \, d\mu = \sum \mu(A_i) \, |x_i|.$$

Let $\varepsilon > 0$. For each i we can find an element $y_i \in F$ with $|y_i| = 1$ such that $|u(x_i, y_i)| > (1 - \varepsilon) \, |x_i|$. The function $g = \sum \varphi_{A_i} y_i$ belongs to $\mathscr{E}_F(\mathscr{C})$ and we have

$$N_\infty(g) = \sup_i |y_i| = 1.$$

Then

$$u(f, g) = u(\sum \varphi_{A_i} x_i, \sum \varphi_{A_j} y_j) = \sum \varphi_{A_i} u(x_i, y_i)$$

and

$$|u(f, g)| = |\sum \varphi_{A_i} u(x_i, y_i)| = \sum \varphi_{A_i} |u(x_i, y_i)| \geqq \sum \varphi_{A_i} (1 - \varepsilon) \, |x_i|,$$

whence

$$\int |u(f, g)| \, d\mu \geqq (1 - \varepsilon) \sum \mu(A_i) \, |x_i| = (1 - \varepsilon) \, N_1(f),$$

therefore

$$\sup \int |u(f, g)| \, d\mu \geqq N_1(f), \quad \text{for} \quad g \in \mathscr{E}_F(\mathscr{C}) \quad \text{with} \quad N_\infty(g) = 1.$$

2. We consider then the case where $1 < p < \infty$ and $f = \sum \varphi_{A_i} x_i \in \mathscr{E}_E(\mathscr{C})$ with A_i disjoint and $N_p(f) = 1$. We have then

$$[N_p(f)]^p = \int |f|^p \, d\mu = \sum \mu(A_i) \, |x_i|^p = 1.$$

Let $\varepsilon > 0$. For each i there exists $z_i \in F$ with $|z_i| = 1$ and $|u(x_i, z_i)| \geqq (1 - \varepsilon) \, |x_i|$. Put $y_i = |x_i|^{p/q} \, z_i$. Then

$$|y_i|^q = |x_i|^p \quad \text{and} \quad |u(x_i, y_i)| \geqq (1 - \varepsilon) \, |x_i| \, |y_i|.$$

The function $g = \sum \varphi_{A_i} y_i$ belongs to $\mathscr{E}_F(\mathscr{C})$ and we have

$$N_q(g) = \left(\int \left|\sum \varphi_{A_i} y_i\right|^q d\mu\right)^{\frac{1}{q}} = \left(\int \sum \varphi_{A_i} |y_i|^q d\mu\right)^{\frac{1}{q}}$$

$$= \left(\sum \mu(A_i) |y_i|^q\right)^{\frac{1}{q}} = \left(\sum \mu(A_i) |x_i|^p\right)^{\frac{1}{q}} = 1.$$

Then

$$|u(f, g)| \geqq (1 - \varepsilon) \sum \varphi_{A_i} |x_i| \, |y_i|,$$

whence

$$\int |u(f, g)| \, d\mu \geqq (1 - \varepsilon) \sum \mu(A_i) |x_i| \, |y_i| = (1 - \varepsilon) \sum \mu(A_i) |x_i| \, |x_i|^{p/q}$$

$$= (1 - \varepsilon) \sum \mu(A_i) |x_i|^p = 1 - \varepsilon,$$

consequently

$$\sup \int |u(f, g)| \, d\mu \geqq 1, \quad \text{for} \quad g \in \mathscr{E}_F(\mathscr{C}) \quad \text{with} \quad N_q(g) = 1.$$

3. If $1 < p < \infty$ and $f = \sum \varphi_{A_i} x_i \in \mathscr{E}_E(\mathscr{C})$ with $N_p(f) = a > 0$, then $f_1 = \frac{1}{a} f \in \mathscr{E}_E(\mathscr{C})$ and $N_p(f_1) = \frac{1}{a} N_p(f) = 1$. If $g \in \mathscr{E}_F(\mathscr{C})$ and $N_q(g) = 1$, then

$$\int |u(f, g)| \, d\mu = \int |u(af_1, g)| \, d\mu = a \int |u(f_1, g)| \, d\mu,$$

therefore

$$\sup \int |u(f, g)| \, d\mu = a \sup \int |u(f_1, g)| \, d\mu \geqq a = N_p(f)$$

for $g \in \mathscr{E}_F(\mathscr{C})$ with $N_q(g) = 1$.

4. Consider now the case $1 \leqq p < \infty$, and $f \in \mathscr{L}_E^p$ with $N_p(f) > 0$. Let $\varepsilon > 0$. There exists a step function $f_1 \in \mathscr{E}_E(\mathscr{C})$ with $N_p(f - f_1) < \varepsilon$ and $N_p(f_1) > 0$. From 3 we deduce that there exists a function $g \in \mathscr{E}_F(\mathscr{C})$ with $N_q(g) = 1$ and

$$\int |u(f_1, g)| \, d\mu \geqq N_p(f_1) - \varepsilon \geqq N_p(f) - 2\varepsilon.$$

Since

$$\int |u(f - f_1, g)| \, d\mu \leqq N_p(f - f_1) \, N_q(g) < \varepsilon$$

we deduce that

$$\int |u(f, g)| \, d\mu = \int |u(f_1, g) + u(f - f_1, g)| \, d\mu$$

$$\geqq \int |u(f_1, g)| \, d\mu - \int |u(f - f_1, g)| \, d\mu \geqq N_p(f) - 3\varepsilon,$$

consequently

$$\sup \int |u(f, g)| \, d\mu \geqq N_p(f), \quad \text{for} \quad g \in \mathscr{E}_F(\mathscr{C}) \quad \text{with} \quad N_q(g) = 1.$$

5. We consider finally the case $p = \infty$ and $f \in \mathscr{L}_E^\infty(\mu)$ with $N_\infty(f) > 0$. Let $0 < \alpha < N_\infty(f)$. The set $B = \{t; |f(t)| > \alpha\}$ is μ-measurable and is not negligible. There exists then a μ-integrable and not negligible set $B' \subset B$. By the theorem 2, § 6, we can find a sequence (h_n) of μ-measurable step functions converging on B' to f. By Egorov's theorem, we can find a not negligible set $B'' \subset B'$ such that on B'' the sequence (h_n) converges uniformly to f.

Let $0 < \varepsilon < \alpha$; there exists a function $h = \sum_{i=1}^{n} \varphi_{A_i} x_i$ of the sequence (h_n) such that $|f(t) - h(t)| < \frac{\varepsilon}{2}$ for every $t \in B''$. There exists at least one of the sets $A_1, A_2, \ldots, A_n$, say A_j, such that the set $A = A_j \cap B''$ is not negligible.

Let $x \in f(A)$. Then we have $|x| > \alpha$ (since $A \subset B$) and $|f(t) - x| < \varepsilon$ for every $t \in A$. Let $y \in F$ be such that $|y| = 1$ and $|u(x, y)| \geqq (1 - \varepsilon)\,|x|$.

The function $g_1 = \dfrac{\theta}{\mu(A)} \varphi_A y$ with $0 < \theta < 1$ belongs to $\mathscr{E}_F(\mu)$ and we have $N_1(g_1) < 1$. Since $\mathscr{E}_E(\mathscr{C})$ is dense in $\mathscr{L}_E^1$, we can find a function $g \in \mathscr{E}_E(\mathscr{C})$ with $N_1(g_1 - g) < \min\left(\dfrac{\varepsilon}{N_\infty(f)}, N_1(g) - 1\right)$. Then $N_1(g) \leqq N_1(g - g_1) + N_1(g) < 1$ and

$$\int |u(f, g - g_1)|\, d\mu \leqq N_\infty(f)\, N_1(g - g_1) < \varepsilon.$$

We have then

$$\begin{aligned}
\int |u(f, g)|\, d\mu &\geqq \int |u(f, g_1)\, d\mu - \int |u(f, g - g_1)|\, d\mu \\
&\geqq \int |u(f, g_1)|\, d\mu - \varepsilon \\
&= \frac{\theta}{\mu(A)} \int_A |u(f, y)|\, d\mu - \varepsilon \\
&\geqq \frac{\theta}{\mu(A)} \int_A |u(x, y) + u(f - x, y)|\, d\mu - \varepsilon \\
&\geqq \frac{\theta}{\mu(A)} \int_A |u(x, y)|\, d\mu - \frac{\theta}{\mu(A)} \int_A |u(f - x, y)|\, d\mu - \varepsilon \\
&\geqq \frac{\theta}{\mu(A)} \int_A (1 - \varepsilon)\,|x|\, d\mu - \frac{\theta}{\mu(A)} \int_A |f - x|\,|y|\, d\mu - \varepsilon \\
&\geqq \theta(1 - \varepsilon)\,|x| - \frac{\theta}{\mu(A)} \int_A \varepsilon\, d\mu - \varepsilon \\
&\geqq (1 - \varepsilon)\,\theta\alpha - \theta\varepsilon - \varepsilon = \theta\alpha - \theta\varepsilon(\alpha + 1) - \varepsilon.
\end{aligned}$$

Taking the supremum for $g \in \mathscr{E}_E(\mathscr{C})$ with $N_1(g) \leqq 1$, and then letting $\theta \to 1$ and $\varepsilon \to 0$, we obtain

$$\sup \int |u(f, g)| \, d\mu \geqq \alpha, \quad \text{for} \quad g \in \mathscr{E}_F(\mathscr{C}) \quad \text{with} \quad N_1(g) \leqq 1.$$

Since $\alpha < N_\infty(f)$ is arbitrary, we deduce

$$\sup \int |u(f, g)| \, d\mu \geqq N_\infty(f), \quad \text{for} \quad g \in \mathscr{E}_F(\mathscr{C}) \quad \text{with} \quad N_1(g) = 1,$$

and the theorem is completely proved.

Remark. In the preceding theorem we can take the supremum for $g \in \mathscr{E}_F(\mathscr{C})$ with $N_q(g) < 1$ (instead of $N_q(g) \leqq 1$), or with $N_q(g) = 1$.

We can take also the supremum for $g \in \mathscr{L}_F^p$ (instead of $g \in \mathscr{E}_F(\mathscr{C})$) with $N_q(g) = 1$, or with $N_q(g) < 1$, or $N_q(g) \leqq 1$.

Corollary 1. *If $X = \mathscr{L}(E, F)$ and $U \in \mathscr{L}_X^p$, then*

$$N_p(U) = \sup \int |U(t) \, g(t)| \, d\mu = \sup \int |U(t)| \, |g(t)| \, d\mu$$

for $g \in \mathscr{E}_F(\mathscr{C})$ with $N_q(g) \leqq 1$.

Corollary 2. *If $f \in \mathscr{L}_E^p$, then*

$$N_p(f) = \sup \int |f(t) \, \varphi(t)| \, d\mu = \sup \int |f(t)| \, |\varphi(t)| \, d\mu$$

for $\varphi \in \mathscr{E}(\mathscr{C})$ with $N_q(\varphi) \leqq 1$.

In the case $F = E'$, the preceding theorem can be precised:

Theorem 6. *For every function $f \in \mathscr{L}_E^p$ we have*

$$N_p(f) = \sup \left| \int \langle f, g \rangle \, d\mu \right| = \sup \int |\langle f, g \rangle| \, d\mu = \sup \int |f| \, |g| \, d\mu$$

for $g \in \mathscr{E}_{E'}(\mathscr{C})$ with $N_q(g) = 1$.

For every function $f \in \mathscr{L}_{E'}^q$ we have

$$N_q(f) = \sup \left| \int \langle f, g \rangle \, d\mu \right| = \sup \int |\langle f, g \rangle| \, d\mu = \sup \int |f| \, |g| \, d\mu$$

for $g \in \mathscr{E}_E(\mathscr{C})$ with $N_p(g) = 1$.

For the first series of equalities we have to prove only the inequality

$$N_p(f) \leqq \sup \left| \int \langle f, g \rangle \, d\mu \right|, \quad \text{for} \quad g \in \mathscr{E}_{E'}(\mathscr{C}) \quad \text{with} \quad N_q(g) = 1.$$

For this purpose we consider the continuous bilinear functional $u(x, y) = \langle x, y \rangle$ on $E \times E'$ and we remark that for every $x \in E$ and every $\varepsilon > 0$ there exists $y \in E'$ with $|y| = 1$, such that $\langle x, y \rangle$ is *positive* and $\langle x, y \rangle \geqq (1 - \varepsilon)|x|$. We follow then the same lines of the proof of the inequality

$$N_p(\boldsymbol{f}) \leqq \sup \int |u(\boldsymbol{f}, \boldsymbol{g})| \, d\mu, \quad \text{for} \quad \boldsymbol{g} \in \mathscr{E}_{E'}(\mathscr{C}) \quad \text{with} \quad N_q(\boldsymbol{g}) = 1$$

in the theorem 5.

The second series of equalities is proved in the same way.

Corollary. *If $f \in \mathscr{L}_C^p(\mu)$, then*

$$N_p(f) = \sup \left| \int fg \, d\mu \right| = \sup \int |f| \, |g| \, d\mu$$

for $g \in \mathscr{E}_C(\mathscr{C})$ with $N_q(g) = 1$.

Theorem 7. *A μ-measurable function $\boldsymbol{f}$: $T \to E$ belongs to $\mathscr{L}_E^p(\mu)$ if and only if $u(\boldsymbol{f}, \boldsymbol{g})$ is μ-integrable, for every $\boldsymbol{g} \in \mathscr{L}_F^q(\mu)$.*

We know already that if $\boldsymbol{f} \in \mathscr{L}_E^p$ and $\boldsymbol{g} \in \mathscr{L}_F^q$ then $u(\boldsymbol{f}, \boldsymbol{g}) \in \mathscr{L}_G^1$.

Conversely, suppose that $\boldsymbol{f}$ is μ-measurable and that $u(\boldsymbol{f}, \boldsymbol{g}) \in \mathscr{L}_G^1$ for every $\boldsymbol{g} \in \mathscr{L}_F^q$. To show that $\boldsymbol{f} \in \mathscr{L}_E^p$, it is sufficient to prove that $|\boldsymbol{f}| \in \mathscr{L}^p$. We shall divide the proof into several parts.

a) If $A \subset T$ is a μ-measurable set with σ-finite measure, then $|\boldsymbol{f}| \varphi_A g$ is μ-integrable for every positive function $g \in \mathscr{L}^q$.

If $F = C$ this assertion is immediate. In fact, for every $x \in E$ and $\alpha \in C$ we have $|u(x, \alpha)| = |x| \, |\alpha|$; if $g \in \mathscr{L}^q$ and $g \geqq 0$, then $u(\boldsymbol{f}, g)$ is μ-integrable and $|u(\boldsymbol{f}, g)| = |\boldsymbol{f}| \, g$, therefore $|\boldsymbol{f}| \, g$ is μ-integrable.

Consider now the general situation. By the theorem 2, § 6, there exists a sequence $(\boldsymbol{f}_n)$ of μ-integrable step functions converging μ-almost everywhere on A to $\boldsymbol{f}$, and such that $|\boldsymbol{f}_n| \leqq |\boldsymbol{f}|$ for every n. By the corollary 1 of Egorov's theorem, § 6, there exists a μ-negligible set N such that $A - N$ is the union of a sequence (A_n) of disjoint μ-integrable sets such that on each A_n, the sequence $(\boldsymbol{f}_n)$ converges uniformly to $\boldsymbol{f}$.

Let B be one of the sets A_n and let $\varepsilon > 0$; there exists a function $\boldsymbol{f}_\varepsilon$ of the sequence $(\boldsymbol{f}_n)$ such that $|\boldsymbol{f}(t) - \boldsymbol{f}_\varepsilon(t)| < \frac{\varepsilon}{3}$ for every $t \in B$. Write $\boldsymbol{f}_\varepsilon(t) = \sum \varphi_{B_i} x_i$, where B_i are disjoint μ-integrable sets with union equal to B, and $x_i \in E$.

For each i there exists an element $y_i \in F$ such that $|y_i| = 1$ and $|x_i| < |u(x_i, y_i)| + \frac{\varepsilon}{3}$. The function $\boldsymbol{h}_B = \sum \varphi_{B_i} y_i$ is μ-measurable, and for every $t \in B$ we have $|\boldsymbol{h}_B(t)| = 1$ and

$$|\boldsymbol{f}_\varepsilon(t)| < \sum \varphi_{B_i}(t) \, |u(x_i, y_i)| + \frac{\varepsilon}{3} = |u(\sum \varphi_{B_i}(t) \, x_i, \sum \varphi_{B_i}(t) \, y_i)| + \frac{\varepsilon}{3}$$

$$= |u(\boldsymbol{f}_\varepsilon(t), \boldsymbol{h}_B(t))| + \frac{\varepsilon}{3}.$$

Then, for $t \in B$ we have

$$\begin{aligned}|f(t)| < |f_\varepsilon(t)| + \frac{\varepsilon}{3} < |u(f_\varepsilon(t), h_B(t))| + \frac{2\varepsilon}{3} \\ \leqq |u(f(t), h_B(t))| + |u(f_\varepsilon(t) - f(t), h_B(t)| + \frac{2\varepsilon}{3} \\ \leqq |u(f(t), h_B(t)| + \varepsilon,\end{aligned}$$

since

$$|u(f_\varepsilon(t) - f(t), h_B(t))| \leqq |f_\varepsilon(t) - f(t)|\,|h_B(t)| \leqq \frac{\varepsilon}{3}.$$

We have therefore

$$|f|\,\varphi_B \leqq |u(f, h_B)| + \varepsilon\varphi_B.$$

For each n, take now $\varepsilon_n = 2^{-n}\mu(A_n)^{-\frac{1}{p}}$ if $\mu(A_n) > 0$ and $\varepsilon_n = 2^{-n}$ if $\mu(A_n) = 0$. We find then a μ-integrable step function $h_n: T \to E$ such that for every $t \in A_n$ we have $|h_n(t)| = 1$ and

$$|f|\,\varphi_{A_n} \leqq |u(f, h_n)| + \varepsilon_n\varphi_{A_n}.$$

The function $h = \sum_{n=1}^{\infty} h_n$ is then μ-measurable, for every $t \in A - N$ we have $|h(t)| = 1$ and

$$|f|\,\varphi_{A-N} \leqq |u(f, h)| + \sum_{n=1}^{\infty} \varepsilon_n\varphi_{A_n}.$$

We remark that the function $\varphi = \sum_{n=1}^{\infty} \varepsilon_n\varphi_{A_n}$ belongs to $\mathscr{L}^p$. For every positive function $g \in \mathscr{L}^q$, the function φg is μ-integrable, and the function hg belongs to $\mathscr{L}^q_F$, therefore $u(f, hg)$ is μ-integrable. We have then

$$|f|\,\varphi_A g \leqq |u(f, hg)| + \varphi g \quad \mu\text{-almost everywhere}.$$

Since $|f|\,\varphi_A g$ is μ-measurable, it follows that it is μ-integrable.

b) If $A \subset T$ is a μ-measurable set with σ-finite measure, then we have

$$\sup \int_A |f|\, g\, d\mu = b < \infty, \quad \text{for} \quad g \in \mathscr{L}^q \quad \text{with} \quad N_q(g) \leqq 1.$$

In fact, if $b = \infty$, then for every n we can find a positive function $g_n \in \mathscr{L}^q$ with $N_q(g_n) \leqq 1$ and $\int_A |f|\, g_n\, d\mu \geqq n^3$. Since

$$\sum_{n=1}^{\infty} \frac{1}{n^2} N_q(g_n) \leqq \sum_{n=1}^{\infty} \frac{1}{n^2} < \infty,$$

the function

$$g'(t) = \sum_{n=1}^{\infty} \frac{1}{n^2} g_n(t)$$

is equal μ-almost everywhere to a function $g \in \mathscr{L}^q$, therefore $|f| \varphi_A g$ is μ-integrable. For every n we have $|f| \varphi_A g \geqq \frac{1}{n^2} |f| \varphi_A g_n$, μ-almost everywhere, therefore

$$\int_A |f| g \, d\mu \geqq \frac{1}{n^2} \int_A |f| g_n \, d\mu \geqq n,$$

whence $\int_A |f| g \, d\mu = \infty$, which is impossible. It follows that $b < \infty$.

c) If $A \subset T$ is a μ-measurable set with σ-finite measure, then $|f| \varphi_A \in \mathscr{L}^p$.

In fact, since $|f| \varphi_A$ is measurable we deduce (§ 6, theorem 2) that there exists a sequence (f_n) of positive μ-integrable step functions converging to $|f| \varphi_A$ μ-almost everywhere and such that $|f_n| \leqq |f| \varphi_A$ for every n. The μ-integrable step functions f_n belong also to $\mathscr{L}^p$, therefore

$$N_p(f_n) = \sup \int f_n g \, d\mu \leqq \sup \int_A |f| g \, d\mu = b < \infty,$$

where the supremum is taken for $g \in \mathscr{L}^q$ with $N_q(g) \leqq 1$. It follows that

$$\sup_n N_p(f_n) \leqq b < \infty .$$

From the corollary of the proposition 21, § 8, we deduce that the function $|f| \varphi_A$ belongs to $\mathscr{L}^p$.

d) If $1 \leqq p < \infty$, there exists a μ-measurable set $A \subset T$ with σ-finite measure such that $f = f\varphi_A$ μ-almost everywhere.

In fact, for every μ-integrable set $A \subset T$ we have $f\varphi_A \in \mathscr{L}^p$, i.e. $|f|^p \varphi_A \in \mathscr{L}^1$.

Put

$$\sup_A \int_A |f|^p \, d\mu = c, \quad \text{for } A \text{ } \mu\text{-integrable}.$$

There exists an increasing sequence (A_n) of μ-integrable sets such that

$$\sup_n \int_{A_n} |f|^p \, d\mu = c .$$

The set $A = \bigcup_{n=1}^{\infty} A_n$ has σ-finite measure, therefore $|f|^p \varphi_A$ is μ-integrable and $|f| \varphi_{A_n} \leqq |f| \varphi_A$ for every n, whence

$$c = \sup_n \int_{A_n} |f|^p \, d\mu \leqq \int_A |f|^p \, d\mu < \infty .$$

We have $f = f\varphi_A$ μ-almost everywhere. In fact, if A_0 is a μ-integrable set, disjoint of A, such that $|f(t)| > 0$ for $t \in A_0$, then

$$c + \int_{A_0} |f|^p \, d\mu = \sup_n \int_{A_n} |f|^p \, d\mu + \int_{A_0} |f|^p \, d\mu = \sup_n \int_{A_n \cup A_0} |f|^p \, d\mu \leqq c,$$

therefore $\int_{A_0} |f|^p \, d\mu = 0$, consequently A_0 is μ-negligible.

Since $f = f\varphi_A$ μ-almost everywhere and since $|f|\,\varphi_A \in \mathscr{L}^p$, it follows that $|f| \in \mathscr{L}^p$, therefore $f \in \mathscr{L}^p_E$.

e) If $p = \infty$, then $f \in \mathscr{L}^\infty_E$.

In fact, if $N_\infty(f) = \infty$, then for every n the μ-measurable set $B = \{t; |f(t)| > n\}$ is non negligible. If for every n we take a μ-integrable set $A_n \subset B_n$ with $\mu(A_n) > 0$, then the union $A = \bigcup_{n=1}^{\infty} A_n$ has σ-finite measure, therefore, by c), $|f|\,\varphi_A \in \mathscr{L}^\infty$. On the other hand, $N_\infty(f\varphi_A) \geqq N_\infty(f\varphi_{A_n}) \geqq n$ for every n, whence $N_\infty(f\varphi_A) = \infty$ and we get a contradiction. It follows that $N_\infty(f) < \infty$, whence $f \in \mathscr{L}^\infty_E$ and the theorem is completely proved.

Corollary 1. *Let $U: T \to X = \mathscr{L}(E, F)$ be a μ-measurable function. If the function $t \to U(t)f(t)$ is μ-integrable for every $f \in \mathscr{L}^q_E$, then $U \in \mathscr{L}^p_X$.*

Corollary 2. *Let $f: T \to E$ be a μ-measurable function. If the function $\langle f, f' \rangle$ is μ-integrable for every $f' \in \mathscr{L}^q_{E'}$, then $f \in \mathscr{L}^p_E$.*

Corollary 3. *Let $f': T \to E'$ be a μ-measurable function. If $\langle f, f' \rangle$ is μ-integrable for every $f \in \mathscr{L}^q_E$, then $f' \in \mathscr{L}^p_{E'}$.*

Corollary 4. *Let $f: T \to E$ be a function. If the function $f\varphi$ is μ-integrable for every real function $\varphi \in \mathscr{L}^q$, then $f \in \mathscr{L}^p_E$.*

In fact, f is μ-measurable, since for every μ-integrable set $A \subset T$ we have $\varphi_A \in \mathscr{L}^q$, whence $f\varphi_A \in \mathscr{L}^1$, therefore $f\varphi_A$ is μ-measurable.

Proposition 20. *Let $f: T \to E$ be a μ-measurable function. If for every $g \in \mathscr{L}^p_F$ the function $u(f, g)$ is μ-negligible, then f is μ-negligible.*

In fact, we have $f \in \mathscr{L}^q_E$ and

$$N_q(f) = \sup \int |u(f, g)| \, d\mu = 0, \quad \textit{for} \quad g \in \mathscr{L}^p_F \quad \textit{with} \quad N_p(g) \leqq 1.$$

Corollary 1. *Let $U: T \to \mathscr{L}(E, F)$ be a μ-measurable function. If the function $t \to U(t)f(t)$ is μ-negligible for every $f \in \mathscr{L}^p_E$, then U is μ-negligible.*

Corollary 2. *Let $f: T \to E$ (respectively $f': T \to E'$) be a μ-measurable function. If the scalar function $\langle f, f' \rangle$ is μ-negligible for every $f' \in \mathscr{L}^p_{E'}$ (respectively $f \in \mathscr{L}^p_E$), then f (respectively f') is μ-negligible.*

5. RELATIONS BETWEEN THE SPACES $\mathscr{L}^p_E$

Let μ be a *positive* measure on a clan $\mathscr{C}$, and let E be a Banach space.

Proposition 21.

a) *If* $1 \leqq r < p < s \leqq \infty$, *then* $\mathscr{L}^r_E \cap \mathscr{L}^s_E \subset \mathscr{L}^p_E$.

b) *If* $f: T \to E$ *is a* μ*-measurable function, then the set* $I_f = \{p;\ 1 \leqq p \leqq \infty, f \in \mathscr{L}^p_E\}$ *is either void or an interval.*

c) *The function* $p \to \log N_{1/p}(f)$ *is convex and the function* $p \to N_p(f)$ *is continuous on* I_f.

Let $1 \leqq r < p < s \leqq \infty$ and let $f \in \mathscr{L}^r_E \cap \mathscr{L}^s_E$. Suppose first that $s < \infty$. Then the functions $|f|^r$ and $|f|^s$ are μ-integrable.

There exists a number t such that $0 < t < 1$ and $p = tr + (1-t)s$. Put $\alpha = \frac{1}{t}$ and $\beta = \frac{1}{1-t}$. Then $1 < \alpha < \infty$, $1 < \beta < \infty$, $\frac{1}{\alpha} + \frac{1}{\beta} = 1$ and $p = \frac{r}{\alpha} + \frac{s}{\beta}$.

Since $|f|^r = |f|^{\frac{r}{\alpha}\alpha}$ and $|f|^s = |f|^{\frac{s}{\beta}\beta}$ are μ-integrable, it follows that $|f|^{\frac{r}{\alpha}} \in \mathscr{L}^\alpha$ and $|f|^{\frac{s}{\beta}} \in \mathscr{L}^\beta$, therefore $|f|^p = |f|^{\frac{r}{\alpha}}\,|f|^{\frac{s}{\beta}}$ is μ-integrable, i.e. $f \in \mathscr{L}^p_E$, and

$$\int |f|^p\, d\mu \leqq N_\alpha\left(|f|^{\frac{r}{\alpha}}\right) N_\beta\left(|f|^{\frac{s}{\beta}}\right)$$

$$= \left(\int |f|^r\, d\mu\right)^{\frac{1}{\alpha}} \left(\int |f|^s\, d\mu\right)^{\frac{1}{\beta}}.$$

Suppose now that $s = \infty$. Then $|f|^r$ is μ-integrable and $|f|$ is essentially bounded, whence $|f|^{p-r}$ is essentially bounded. It follows that the product $|f|^p = |f|^r\,|f|^{p-r}$ is μ-integrable, i.e. $f \in \mathscr{L}^p_E$ and we have

$$\int |f|^p\, d\mu \leqq N_1(|f|^r)\, N_\infty(|f|^{p-r})$$

$$= \int |f|^r\, d\mu\, N_\infty(f)^{p-r}.$$

Thus a) and b) are proved. Let us prove that $\log N_p(f)$ is convex as a function of $\frac{1}{p}$, i.e. that if $r, s, p \in I_f$ are such that

$$\frac{1}{p} = \frac{t}{r} + \frac{1-t}{s}, \quad \text{with} \quad 0 < t < 1,$$

then

$$\log N_p(f) \leqq t \log N_r(f) + (1-t) \log N_s(f).$$

We suppose first that $\infty \notin I_f$, whence $1 \leqq r < p < s < \infty$. Put $\alpha = \frac{r}{tp}$ and $\beta = \frac{s}{(1-t)p}$. Then $1 \leqq \alpha < \infty$, $1 \leqq \beta < \infty$ and $\frac{1}{\alpha} + \frac{1}{\beta} = 1$. Since $|f|^r$ and $|f|^s$ are μ-integrable, the functions $|f|^{\frac{r}{\alpha}\alpha}$ and $|f|^{\frac{s}{\beta}\beta}$ are μ-integrable, therefore $|f|^{\frac{r}{\alpha}} \in \mathscr{L}^\alpha$ and $|f|^{\frac{s}{\beta}} \in \mathscr{L}^\beta$. Then the product $|f|^{\frac{r}{\alpha}}|f|^{\frac{s}{\beta}} = |f|^{tp}|f|^{(1-t)p} = |f|^p$ is μ-integrable and

$$\int |f|^p \, d\mu \leqq N_\alpha\left(|f|^{\frac{r}{\alpha}}\right) N_\beta\left(|f|^{\frac{s}{\beta}}\right) = \left(\int |f|^r \, d\mu\right)^{\frac{1}{\alpha}} \left(\int |f|^s \, d\mu\right)^{\frac{1}{\beta}}$$

$$= \left(\int |f|^r \, d\mu\right)^{\frac{1}{r}tp} \left(\int |f|^s \, d\mu\right)^{\frac{1}{s}(1-t)p},$$

i.e.

$$N_p(f)^p \leqq N_r(f)^{tp} \, N_s(f)^{(1-t)p},$$

therefore

$$N_p(f) \leqq N_r(f)^t \, N_s(f)^{1-t},$$

consequently

$$\log N_p(f) \leqq t \log N_r(f) + (1-t) \log N_s(f).$$

If $\infty \in I_f$ and $s = \infty$, and if $\frac{1}{p} = \frac{t}{r} + \frac{1-t}{s} = \frac{t}{r}$, with $0 < t < 1$, then in the proof of a) we deduce that

$$\int |f|^p \, d\mu \leqq \int |f|^r \, d\mu \, N_\infty(f)^{p-r},$$

i.e.

$$N_p(f)^p \leqq N_r(f)^r \, N_\infty(f)^{p-r},$$

whence

$$N_p(f) \leqq N_r(f)^{\frac{r}{p}} N_\infty(f)^{\frac{p-r}{p}} = N_r(f)^t \, N_\infty(f)^{1-t},$$

consequently

$$\log N_p(f) \leqq t \log N_r(f) + (1-t) \log N_\infty(f).$$

From the convexity of $\log N_p(f)$ as a function of $\frac{1}{p}$ we deduce the continuity o $\log N_p(f)$ as a function of $\frac{1}{p}$, therefore as a function of p. Since $N_p(f) = \exp \log N_p(f)$ we deduce that $N_p(f)$ is continuous as a function of p and the proposition is completely proved.

Proposition 22. *Let $A \subset T$ be a μ-integrable set and $f\colon T \to E$ a μ-measurable function. Then the set $I_f = \{p;\ 1 \leqq p \leqq \infty, f\varphi_A \in \mathscr{L}_E^p\}$ is either void or an interval containing 1, and the function $p \to \mu(A)^{-\frac{1}{p}} N_p(f\varphi_A)$ is increasing on I_f.*

If $\mu(A) = 0$, the proposition is evident. Assume therefore that $0 < \mu(A) < \infty$. Suppose that $f\varphi_A \in \mathscr{L}_E^s$ and let $1 \leqq r < s$. If $s = \infty$, then $|f|\,\varphi_A$ is essentially bounded, therefore $|f|^r\,\varphi_A$ is essentially bounded; since A is μ-integrable, $|f|^r\varphi_A$ is μ-integrable, whence $f\varphi_A \in \mathscr{L}_E^r$.

If $s < \infty$, the set $B = \{t;\ t \in A, |f(t)| > 1\}$ is μ-measurable and contained in A, therefore B is μ-integrable. On the set $A - B$ the function f is bounded. Since $f\varphi_A \in \mathscr{L}_E^s$, we have $|f|^s\,\varphi_A \in \mathscr{L}^1$, therefore the function $|f|^s\,\varphi_B$ is μ-integrable. Since $|f|^r\,\varphi_B \leqq |f|^s\,\varphi_B$, the function $|f|^r\,\varphi_B$ is μ-integrable; since $|f|\,\varphi_{A-B}$ is bounded, the function $|f|^r\,\varphi_{B-A}$ is also bounded, consequently μ-integrable, therefore $f\varphi_A \in \mathscr{L}_E^r$.

It follows that I_f is an interval containing the point 1.

Suppose now that I_f is not void and does not reduce to $\{1\}$. Let $r, s \in I_f$ be such that $r < s$ and let p be such that

$$\frac{1}{r} = \frac{1}{s} + \frac{1}{p}.$$

Then $r \leqq p$. Put $\dfrac{1}{\alpha} = \dfrac{r}{s}$ and $\dfrac{1}{\beta} = \dfrac{r}{p}$. Then $1 \leqq \alpha \leqq \infty$, $1 \leqq \beta \leqq \infty$ and $\dfrac{1}{\alpha} + \dfrac{1}{\beta} = 1$. Moreover, $\alpha < s$, whence $\alpha \in I_f$.

From Hölder's inequality we deduce

$$\int |f|^r\,\varphi_A\,d\mu \leqq N_\alpha(|f|^r)\,N_\beta(\varphi_A),$$

whence

$$\left(\int |f|^r\,\varphi_A\,d\mu\right)^{\frac{1}{r}} \leqq N_\alpha(|f|^r)^{\frac{1}{r}}\,N_\beta(\varphi_A)^{\frac{1}{r}},$$

i.e.

$$N_r(f\varphi_A) \leqq N_\alpha(|f|^r)^{\frac{1}{r}}\,\mu(A)^{\frac{1}{\beta r}}.$$

If $s < \infty$, then $\alpha < \infty$, therefore

$$N_r(f\varphi_A) \leqq \left(\int |f|^{\alpha r}\,\varphi_A\,d\mu\right)^{\frac{1}{\alpha r}} \mu(A)^{\frac{1}{\beta r}},$$

consequently

$$\mu(A)^{-\frac{1}{r}}\,N_r(f\varphi_A) \leqq \mu(A)^{-\frac{1}{s}}\,N_s(f\varphi_A).$$

This equality remains valid also for $s = \infty$, because in this case $\alpha = \infty$ and $\beta = 1$, consequently

$$N_r(f\varphi_A) \leqq N_\infty(|f|^r \varphi_A)^{\frac{1}{r}} \mu(A)^{\frac{1}{r}} = N_\infty(f\varphi_A)\, \mu(A)^{\frac{1}{r}},$$

therefore

$$\mu(A)^{-\frac{1}{r}} N_r(f\varphi_A) \leqq N_\infty(f\varphi_A) = \mu(A)^{-\frac{1}{\infty}} N_\infty(f\varphi_A).$$

It follows that the function $p \to \mu(A)^{-\frac{1}{p}} N_p(f\varphi_A)$ is increasing, and the proposition is proved.

Corollary. *Suppose that the measure μ is bounded. Then:*

a) *If $1 \leqq r < s \leqq \infty$, then $\mathscr{L}^s_E \subset \mathscr{L}^r_E$ and the topology of $\mathscr{L}^s_E$ is finer than the topology of $\mathscr{L}^r_E$.*

b) *If $f: T \to E$ is a μ-measurable function, then the set $I_f = \{p;\, 1 \leqq p \leqq \infty, f \in \mathscr{L}^p_E\}$ is either void or an interval containing* 1.

c) *The function $p \to \mu(T)^{-\frac{1}{p}} N_p(f)$ is increasing on I_f.*

The statement concerning the topologies follows from c).

Proposition 23. *Let μ be a (discrete) measure such that every point of T has the measure* 1.

a) *If $1 \leqq r < s \leqq \infty$, then $\mathscr{L}^r_E \subset \mathscr{L}^s_E$ and the topology of $\mathscr{L}^r_E$ is finer than the topology of $\mathscr{L}^s_E$.*

b) *If $f: T \to E$ is a function, then the set $I_f = \{p;\, 1 \leqq p \leqq \infty, f \in \mathscr{L}^p_E\}$ is either void or is an interval containing ∞.*

c) *The function $p \to N_p(f)$ is decreasing on I_f.*

We remark that in this case every set is μ-measurable and every function $f: T \to E$ is μ-measurable.

Let $f \in \mathscr{L}^r_E$ and $1 \leqq r < s \leqq \infty$. If $s = \infty$, then $N_\infty(f) \leqq N_r(f)$. In fact, if $\alpha < N_\infty(f) = \|f\| = \sup_{t \in T} |f(t)|$, then there exists a point $t_0 \in T$ with $|f(t_0)| > \alpha$. Then

$$N_r(f) = \left(\int |f|^r \, d\mu\right)^{\frac{1}{r}} = \left(\sum_{t \in T} |f(t)|^r\right)^{\frac{1}{r}} \geqq (|f(t_0)|^r)^{\frac{1}{r}} = |f(t_0)| > \alpha,$$

whence $N_r(f) \geqq N_\infty(f)$.

Suppose now that $s < \infty$. We have $|f|^r \in \mathscr{L}^1$. From the first part of the proof we have $|f| \in \mathscr{L}^\infty$, whence $|f|^{s-r} \in \mathscr{L}^\infty$. It follows that the product $|f|^s = |f|^r |f|^{s-r}$ is μ-integrable whence $f \in \mathscr{L}^s_E$ and

$$\int |f|^s \, d\mu \leqq N_1(|f|^r)\, N_\infty(|f|^{s-r}).$$

But

$$N_\infty(|f|^{s-r}) = N_\infty(|f|^r)^{\frac{s-r}{r}} \leqq N_1(|f|^r)^{\frac{s-r}{r}},$$

whence

$$\int |f|^s \, d\mu \leqq N_1(|f|^r)\, N_1(|f|^r)^{\frac{s-r}{r}} = N_1(|f|^r)^{\frac{s}{r}} = \left(\int |f|^r \, d\mu\right)^{\frac{s}{r}},$$

consequently

$$\left(\int |f|^s \, d\mu\right)^{\frac{1}{s}} \leqq \left(\int |f|^r \, d\mu\right)^{\frac{1}{r}},$$

i.e. $N_s(f) \leqq N_r(f)$.

§ 13. LINEAR OPERATIONS ON $\mathscr{L}^p_E$

1. THE q-VARIATION

Let $\mathscr{C}$ be a clan, μ a positive (finite) measure on $\mathscr{C}$, X a Banach space, and $\boldsymbol{m}$ a set function defined on $\mathscr{C}$, with values in X or in $\bar{R}_+$, such that $\boldsymbol{m}(\emptyset) = 0$.

Let $1 \leqq q \leqq \infty$ and $\dfrac{1}{p} + \dfrac{1}{q} = 1$. For every set $A \subset T$ we put

$$\bar{\boldsymbol{m}}_q(A) = \sup \sum |\boldsymbol{m}(A_i)|\, |\alpha_i|,$$

where the supremum is taken for all the $\mathscr{C}$-step functions $\varphi = \sum \varphi_{A_i} \alpha_i$ of $\mathscr{E}(\mathscr{C}, A)$ with A_i disjoint, and $N_p(\varphi, \mu) \leqq 1$.

The set function $\bar{\boldsymbol{m}}_q$ is called the *q-variation* of $\boldsymbol{m}$.

The q-variation has the following properties:

1. $0 \leqq \bar{\boldsymbol{m}}_q(A) \leqq \infty$;

2. $\bar{\boldsymbol{m}}_q(\emptyset) = 0$;

3. $\bar{\boldsymbol{m}}_q(A) \leqq \bar{\boldsymbol{m}}_q(B)$ *if* $A \subset B$;

4. $\bar{\boldsymbol{m}}_q(A) = 0$ *if and only if* $\boldsymbol{m}(B) = 0$ *for every* $B \in \mathscr{C}$ *with* $B \subset A$;

5. *if for a set* $A \in \mathscr{C}$ *we have* $\mu(A) = 0$ *and* $\boldsymbol{m}(A) \neq 0$, *then* $\bar{\boldsymbol{m}}_q(A) = \infty$.

In fact, for every n we have $N_p(\varphi_A n) = 0$, therefore $\bar{\boldsymbol{m}}_q(A) \geqq |\boldsymbol{m}(A)|\, n$, consequently $\bar{\boldsymbol{m}}_q(A) = \infty$.

6. *If* $\mu(A) = 0$ *and* $\bar{\boldsymbol{m}}_q(A) < \infty$, *then* $\bar{\boldsymbol{m}}_q(A) = 0$.

In fact, for every $B \in \mathscr{C}$ with $B \subset A$ we have $\boldsymbol{m}(B) = 0$ (because if $\boldsymbol{m}(B) \neq 0$, then $\bar{\boldsymbol{m}}_q(A) \geqq \bar{\boldsymbol{m}}_q(B) = \infty$). We use then the property 4.

7. *We have* $\bar{\boldsymbol{m}} \leqq \bar{\boldsymbol{m}}_1$, *where* $\bar{\boldsymbol{m}}$ *is the usual variation of* $\boldsymbol{m}$ *defined in* § 3.

In fact, in the definition of $\bar{\boldsymbol{m}}_1(A)$ we take the supremum for $\varphi = \sum \varphi_{A_i} \alpha_i \in \mathscr{E}(\mathscr{C}, A)$ with A_i disjoint and $N_\infty(\varphi) \leqq 1$, i.e. $|\alpha_i| \leqq 1$ if $\mu(A_i) > 0$ and α_i arbitrary if $\mu(A_i) = 0$, while in the definition of $\bar{\boldsymbol{m}}(A)$ the supremum is taken for $|\alpha_i| = 1$.

8. *Let* $A \subset T$. *If* $\boldsymbol{m}(B) = 0$ *for every* $B \in \mathscr{C}$ *with* $B \subset A$ *and* $\mu(B) = 0$, *then* $\bar{\boldsymbol{m}}(A) = \bar{\boldsymbol{m}}_1(A)$.

In fact, in this case in the definition of $\bar{\boldsymbol{m}}_1(A)$ the supremum can be taken only for A_i with $\mu(A_i) > 0$.

In particular:

8′. *If* $\boldsymbol{m}$ *is absolutely continuous with respect to* μ, *then* $\bar{\boldsymbol{m}} = \bar{\boldsymbol{m}}_1$.

9. *For* $\varphi = \sum \varphi_{A_i} \alpha_i \in \mathscr{E}(\mathscr{C}, A)$ *with* A_i *disjoint we have*

$$\sum |\boldsymbol{m}(A_i)|\, |\alpha_i| \leqq \bar{\boldsymbol{m}}_q(A)\, N_p(\varphi)$$

except for the case where $\bar{\boldsymbol{m}}_q(A) = \infty$ *and* $N_p(\varphi) = 0$.

In particular:

9′. *For every* $A \in \mathscr{C}$ *we have*

$$|\boldsymbol{m}(A)| \leqq \bar{\boldsymbol{m}}_q(A)\, \mu(A)^{\frac{1}{p}}$$

except for the case where $\mu(A) = 0$ *and* $\boldsymbol{m}(A) \neq 0$.

10. *If* A *is* μ-*integrable with* $\mu(A) > 0$, *and if* $1 \leqq r \leqq s \leqq \infty$, *then*

$$\mu(A)^{-\frac{1}{r}}\, \bar{\boldsymbol{m}}_r(A) \leqq \mu(A)^{-\frac{1}{s}}\, \bar{\boldsymbol{m}}_s(A).$$

Consider the numbers r' and s' conjugate to r and s:

$$\frac{1}{r} + \frac{1}{r'} = 1, \quad \frac{1}{s} + \frac{1}{s'} = 1.$$

Since $r \leqq s$ we have $s' \leqq r'$. Then for every function $\varphi = \sum \varphi_{A_i} \alpha_i \in \mathscr{E}(\mathscr{C}, A)$ with A_i disjoint and $N_{r'}(\varphi) \leqq 1$ we have

$$\mu(A)^{-\frac{1}{s'}}\, N_{s'}(\varphi) \leqq \mu(A)^{-\frac{1}{r'}}\, N_{r'}(\varphi) \leqq \mu(A)^{-\frac{1}{r'}},$$

therefore $\left(\text{since } \frac{1}{r'} - \frac{1}{s'} = \frac{1}{s} - \frac{1}{r}\right)$

$$N_{s'}(\mu(A)^{\frac{1}{s}-\frac{1}{r}} \varphi) = \mu(A)^{\frac{1}{r'}-\frac{1}{s'}} N_{s'}(\varphi) \leqq 1.$$

Consequently,

$$\sum |m(A_i)| \, |\alpha_i| = \mu(A)^{\frac{1}{r}-\frac{1}{s}} \sum |m(A_i)| \, |\mu(A)^{\frac{1}{s}-\frac{1}{r}} \alpha_i| \leqq \mu(A)^{\frac{1}{r}-\frac{1}{s}} \, \bar{m}_s(A).$$

Hence

$$\bar{m}_r(A) \leqq \mu(A)^{\frac{1}{r}-\frac{1}{s}} \, \bar{m}_s(A),$$

therefore

$$\mu(A)^{-\frac{1}{r}} \bar{m}_r(A) \leqq \mu(A)^{-\frac{1}{s}} \bar{m}_s(A).$$

In particular:

11. *If A is μ-integrable and* $\frac{1}{p} + \frac{1}{q} = 1$, *then*

$$\bar{m}_1(A) \leqq \mu(A)^{\frac{1}{p}} \, \bar{m}_q(A) \leqq \bar{m}_\infty(A) \, \mu(A).$$

12. *We have* $\bar{m}_{1q} = \bar{m}_q$, *where* $\bar{m}_{1q}$ *is the q-variation of* $\bar{m}_1$.

Let $A \subset T$. If there exists $B \in \mathscr{C}$ with $B \subset A$, $\mu(B) = 0$ and $m(B) \neq 0$, then $\bar{m}_1(B) = \infty$, $\bar{m}_q(A) = \infty$ (property 5) and $\bar{m}_{1q}(B) = \infty$, therefore $\bar{m}_{1q}(A) = \bar{m}_q(A) = \infty$.

Assume therefore that $m(B) = 0$ for every set $B \in \mathscr{C}$ with $B \subset A$ and $\mu(B) = 0$. For every $\varphi = \sum \varphi_{A_i} \alpha_i \in \mathscr{E}(\mathscr{C}, A)$ with A_i disjoint and $N_p(\varphi) \leqq 1$ we have

$$\sum |m(A_i)| \, |\alpha_i| \leqq \sum \bar{m}_1(A_i) \, |\alpha_i| \leqq \bar{m}_{1q}(A),$$

therefore

$$\bar{m}_q(A) \leqq \bar{m}_{1q}(A).$$

If $\bar{m}_q(A) = \infty$, then $\bar{m}_{1q}(A) = \infty$, therefore $\bar{m}_q(A) = \bar{m}_{1q}(A)$.

If $\bar{m}_q(A) < \infty$, then for every $B \in \mathscr{C}$ with $B \subset A$ we have $\bar{m}_q(B) < \infty$, therefore $\bar{m}_1(B) < \infty$ (property 11).

Let then $\varphi = \sum_{i=1}^{n} \varphi_{A_i} \alpha_i \in \mathscr{E}(\mathscr{C}, A)$ with A_i disjoint and $N_p(\varphi) \leqq 1$. Let $\varepsilon > 0$. For each i there exists a finite family (B_{ij}) of disjoint sets of $\mathscr{C}$ contained in A_i, such that

$$\bar{m}(A_i) \leqq \sum_j |m(B_{ij})| + \frac{\varepsilon}{n|\alpha_i|}, \quad \text{if} \quad \alpha_i \neq 0,$$

and

$$\bar{m}(A_i) \leqq \sum_j |m(B_{ij})| + \frac{\varepsilon}{n}, \quad \text{if} \quad \alpha_i = 0.$$

Then, for every i

$$\overline{m}(A_i)\,|\alpha_i| \leqq \sum_j |m(B_{ij})|\,|\alpha_i| + \frac{\varepsilon}{n}.$$

Since $\overline{m}_1(A_i) = \overline{m}(A_i)$ and $N_p\left(\sum_{i,j} \varphi_{B_{ij}}\alpha_i\right) = N_p(\varphi) \leqq 1$, we deduce

$$\sum \overline{m}_1(A_i)\,|\alpha_i| \leqq \sum_{i,j} |m(B_{ij})|\,|\alpha_i| + \varepsilon \leqq \overline{m}_q(A) + \varepsilon,$$

therefore

$$\overline{m}_{1q}(A) \leqq \overline{m}_q(A) + \varepsilon,$$

consequently, ε being arbitrary, $\overline{m}_{1q}(A) \leqq \overline{m}_q(A)$, whence $\overline{m}_{1q}(A) = \overline{m}_q(A)$.

13. *If* $\boldsymbol{m}$ *is additive on* $\mathscr{C}$, *then* $\overline{m}_q$ *is subadditive on* $\mathfrak{C}(\mathscr{C})$; *if* $\boldsymbol{m}$ *is countably additive on* $\mathscr{C}$, *then* $\overline{m}_q$ *is countably subadditive on* $\mathfrak{C}(\mathscr{C})$.

Let (A_i) be a family of disjoint sets of $\mathfrak{C}(\mathscr{C})$ with union A (not necessarily in $\mathfrak{C}(\mathscr{C})$). We suppose that this family is finite if $\boldsymbol{m}$ is additive and that the family is countable if $\boldsymbol{m}$ is countably additive.

Let $\varphi = \sum \varphi_{B_j}\alpha_j \in \mathscr{E}(\mathscr{C}, A)$ with B_j disjoint and $N_p(\varphi) \leqq 1$. For each i the family $(A_i \cap B_j)_j$ consists of disjoint sets of $\mathscr{C}$ contained in A_i and $\sum_j \varphi_{A_i \cap B_j}|\alpha_j| \leqq \sum \varphi_{B_j}|\alpha_j|$, therefore $N_p\left(\sum_j \varphi_{A_i\cap B_j}\alpha_j\right) \leqq 1$, consequently

$$\sum_j |m(A_i \cap B_j)|\,|\alpha_j| \leqq \overline{m}_q(A_i).$$

On the other hand, for each j, the family $(A_i \cap B_j)_i$ consists of disjoint sets of $\mathscr{C}$, and its union is B_j, therefore

$$\sum_j |m(B_j)|\,|\alpha_j| = \sum_j \left|\sum_i m(A_i \cap B_j)\right| |\alpha_j|$$

$$\leqq \sum_i \sum_j |m(A_i \cap B_j)|\,|\alpha_j| \leqq \sum_i \overline{m}_q(A_i).$$

Consequently,

$$\overline{m}_q(A) \leqq \sum \overline{m}_q(A_i).$$

If now (A_i) is an arbitrary sequence of sets of $\mathfrak{C}(\mathscr{C})$, we define $A_1' = A_1$ and $A_i' = A_n - \bigcup_{i<n} A_i$ for $n \geqq 2$. Then the sets A_i' are disjoint, belong to $\mathfrak{C}(\mathscr{C})$, $A_n' \subset A_n$ for every n and $\bigcup A_i = \bigcup A_i'$, therefore

$$\overline{m}_q(\bigcup A_i) = \overline{m}_q(\bigcup A_i') \leqq \sum \overline{m}_q(A_i') \leqq \sum \overline{m}_q(A_i).$$

13′. *If* $\boldsymbol{m}$ *is additive on* $\mathscr{C}$, *then* $\overline{m}_1$ *is additive on* $\mathfrak{C}(\mathscr{C})$; *if* $\boldsymbol{m}$ *is countably additive on* $\mathscr{C}$, *then* $\overline{m}_1$ *is countably additive on* $\mathfrak{C}(\mathscr{C})$.

We have to prove that $\bar{m}_1$ is superadditive. Let A and B be two *disjoint* sets and choose an arbitrary number $\theta < \bar{m}_1(A) + \bar{m}_2(B)$. There exist two numbers α and β such that

$$\alpha < \bar{m}_1(A), \quad \beta < \bar{m}_1(B), \quad \text{and} \quad \alpha + \beta = \theta .$$

We find then a function $\varphi = \sum \varphi_{A_i}\alpha_i \in \mathscr{E}(\mathscr{C}, A)$ with A_i disjoint and $N_\infty(\varphi) \leqq 1$ (i.e. with $|\alpha_i| \leqq 1$ if $\mu(A_i) > 0$) such that

$$\alpha < \sum |\boldsymbol{m}(A_i)|\, |\alpha_i|$$

and a function $\psi = \sum \varphi_{B_j}\beta_j \in \mathscr{E}(\mathscr{C}, B)$ with B_j disjoint and $N_\infty(\psi) \leqq 1$ (i.e. with $|\beta_j| \leqq 1$ if $\mu(B_j) > 0$) such that

$$\beta < \sum |\boldsymbol{m}(B_j)|\, |\beta_j| .$$

The function $\varphi + \psi$ belongs to $\mathscr{E}(\mathscr{C}, A \cup B)$, and we have $N_\infty(\varphi + \psi) \leqq 1$, therefore

$$\theta = \alpha + \beta < \sum |\boldsymbol{m}(A_i)|\, |\alpha_i| + \sum |\boldsymbol{m}(B_j)|\, |\beta_j| \leqq \bar{m}_1(A \cup B) .$$

It follows that

$$\bar{m}_1(A \cup B) \leqq \bar{m}_1(A) + \bar{m}_1(B) .$$

We deduce easily that $\boldsymbol{m}$ is finitely superadditive and then superadditive.

14. *If* $\boldsymbol{m}$ *and* $\boldsymbol{n}$ *are two set functions defined on* $\mathscr{C}$ *with values in* X *or in* $\bar{R}_+$ *with* $\boldsymbol{m}(\emptyset) = 0$ *and* $\boldsymbol{n}(\emptyset) = 0$ *and if* α *is a scalar then*

$$\overline{(\boldsymbol{m} + \boldsymbol{n})}_q \leqq \bar{m}_q + \bar{n}_q \quad \textit{and} \quad \overline{(\alpha \boldsymbol{m})}_q = |\alpha|\, \bar{m}_q .$$

15. *Let* E, F *be two Banach spaces such that* $X \subset \mathscr{L}(E, F)$ *and* $\boldsymbol{m}: \mathscr{C} \to X$ *a set function with* $\boldsymbol{m}(\emptyset) = 0$. *Then for every set* $A \subset T$ *we have*

$$\bar{m}_q(A) = \sup \sum |\boldsymbol{m}(A_i)\, x_i| ,$$

where the supremum is taken for all the step functions $\boldsymbol{f} = \sum \varphi_{A_i} x_i \in \mathscr{E}_E(\mathscr{C}, A)$ *with* A_i *disjoint and* $N_p(\boldsymbol{f}) \leqq 1$.

Since $\sum |\boldsymbol{m}(A_i)\, x_i| \leqq \sum |\boldsymbol{m}(A_i)|\, |x_i|$ and $N_p(\sum \varphi_{A_i} x_i) = N_p(\sum \varphi_{A_i} |x_i|)$ for A_i disjoint, we deduce that

$$\sup \sum |\boldsymbol{m}(A_i)\, x_i| \leqq \bar{m}_q(A), \quad \text{for} \quad N_p(\sum \varphi_{A_i} x_i) \leqq 1 .$$

Conversely, if $\varphi = \sum_{i=1}^{n} \varphi_{A_i}\alpha_i \in \mathscr{E}(\mathscr{C}, A)$ with disjoint A_i and $N_p(\varphi) \leqq 1$, then for every $\varepsilon > 0$ and for every i we can find $y_i \in E$ with $|y_i| = 1$ and $|\boldsymbol{m}(A_i)|\, |\alpha_i| - \frac{\varepsilon}{n} \leqq |\boldsymbol{m}(A_i)\, \alpha_i y_i|$. Then $N_p(\sum \varphi_{A_i}\alpha_i y_i) = N_p(\varphi) \leqq 1$, therefore $\sum |\boldsymbol{m}(A_i)|\, |\alpha_i| - \varepsilon \leqq \sup \sum |\boldsymbol{m}(A_i)\, x_i|$, consequently

$$\bar{m}_q(A) \leqq \sup \sum |\boldsymbol{m}(A_i)\, x_i| , \quad \text{for} \quad N_p(\sum \varphi_{A_i} x_i) \leqq 1 .$$

2. THE q-SEMI-VARIATION

Let $\mathscr{C}$ be a clan, X a Banach space and $\boldsymbol{m}: \mathscr{C} \to X$ a set function with $\boldsymbol{m}(\emptyset) = 0$. Let E and F be two Banach spaces such that $X \subset \mathscr{L}(E, F)$. Let $1 \leqq q \leqq \infty$ and $\frac{1}{p} + \frac{1}{q} = 1$. For every set $A \subset T$ we put

$$\tilde{\boldsymbol{m}}_q(A) = \sup \left|\sum \boldsymbol{m}(A_i)\, x_i\right|$$

where the supremum is taken for all the step functions $\boldsymbol{f} = \sum \varphi_{A_i} x_i \in \mathscr{E}_E(\mathscr{C}, A)$ with A_i disjoint and $N_p(\boldsymbol{f}, \mu) \leqq 1$.

The set function $\tilde{\boldsymbol{m}}_q$ is called the q-semi-variation of $\boldsymbol{m}$.

We remark that the q-semi-variation depends essentially on the spaces E and F.

The q-semi-variation has the following properties analoguous to those of the q-variation:

1. $0 \leqq \tilde{\boldsymbol{m}}_q(A) \leqq \bar{\boldsymbol{m}}_q(A) \leqq \infty$;

2. $\tilde{\boldsymbol{m}}_q(\emptyset) = 0$;

3. $\tilde{\boldsymbol{m}}_q(A) \leqq \tilde{\boldsymbol{m}}_q(B)$ *if* $A \subset B$;

4. $\bar{\boldsymbol{m}}_q(A) = 0$ *if and only if* $\boldsymbol{m}(B) = 0$ *for every* $B \in \mathscr{C}$ *with* $B \subset A$, *i.e. if and only if* $\bar{\boldsymbol{m}}_q(A) = 0$.

In fact, if $\tilde{\boldsymbol{m}}_q(A) = 0$, then $\boldsymbol{m}(B) = 0$ for every $B \in \mathscr{C}$ with $B \subset A$, whence $\bar{\boldsymbol{m}}_q(A) = 0$; the converse implication follows from the property 1.

5. *If for a set* $A \in \mathscr{C}$ *we have* $\mu(A) = 0$ *and* $\boldsymbol{m}(A) \neq 0$, *then* $\tilde{\boldsymbol{m}}_q(A) = \infty$.

In fact, let $x \in E$ be such that $|x| = 1$ and $\boldsymbol{m}(A)\, x \neq 0$. Then for every n we have $N_p(\varphi_A n x) = 0$, therefore $\tilde{\boldsymbol{m}}_q(A) \geqq |\boldsymbol{m}(A)\, x|\, n$, consequently $\tilde{\boldsymbol{m}}_q(A) = \infty$.

6. *If* $\mu(A) = 0$ *and* $\tilde{\boldsymbol{m}}_q(A) < \infty$, *then* $\tilde{\boldsymbol{m}}_q(A) = 0$.

7. *We have* $\tilde{\boldsymbol{m}} \leqq \tilde{\boldsymbol{m}}_1$, *where* $\tilde{\boldsymbol{m}}$ *is the usual semi-variation of* $\boldsymbol{m}$ *defined in* § 4.

The same proof as for the corresponding property of $\bar{\boldsymbol{m}}_q$, using $x_i \in E$ instead of α_i.

8. *Let* $A \subset T$. *If* $\boldsymbol{m}(B) = 0$ *for every* $B \in \mathscr{C}$ *with* $B \subset A$ *and* $\mu(B) = 0$, *then* $\tilde{\boldsymbol{m}}(A) = \tilde{\boldsymbol{m}}_1(A)$.

In particular:

8'. *If* $\boldsymbol{m}$ *is absolutely continuous with respect to* μ, *then* $\tilde{\boldsymbol{m}} = \tilde{\boldsymbol{m}}_1$.

9. *If* $\boldsymbol{f} = \sum \varphi_{A_i} x_i \in \mathscr{E}_E(\mathscr{C}, A)$ *with* A_i *disjoint, then*

$$\left|\sum \boldsymbol{m}(A_i)\, x_i\right| \leqq \tilde{\boldsymbol{m}}_q(A)\, N_p(\boldsymbol{f})$$

except for the case where $\tilde{\boldsymbol{m}}_q(A) = 0$ *and* $N_p(\boldsymbol{f}) = 0$.

In particular:

9′. *For every $A \in \mathscr{C}$ we have*

$$|\boldsymbol{m}(A)| \leqq \tilde{\boldsymbol{m}}_q(A)\, \mu(A)^{\frac{1}{p}}$$

except for the case where $\mu(A) = 0$ and $\boldsymbol{m}(A) \neq 0$.

10. *If A is μ-integrable with $\mu(A) > 0$, and if $1 \leqq r \leqq s \leqq \infty$, then*

$$\mu(A)^{-\frac{1}{r}}\, \tilde{\boldsymbol{m}}_r(A) \leqq \mu(A)^{-\frac{1}{s}}\, \tilde{\boldsymbol{m}}_s(A).$$

The same proof as for the property 10 of the variation, taking $x_i \in E$ instead of α_i and $|\sum \boldsymbol{m}(A_i)\, x_i|$ instead of $\sum |\boldsymbol{m}(A_i)|\, |\alpha_i|$.

11. *If A is μ-integrable and $\dfrac{1}{p} + \dfrac{1}{q} = 1$, then*

$$\tilde{\boldsymbol{m}}_1(A) \leqq \mu(A)^{\frac{1}{p}}\, \tilde{\boldsymbol{m}}_q(A) \leqq \tilde{\boldsymbol{m}}_\infty(A)\, \mu(A).$$

12. *We have $\bar{\tilde{\boldsymbol{m}}}_{1q} = \tilde{\boldsymbol{m}}_q$, where $\bar{\tilde{\boldsymbol{m}}}_{1q}$ is the q-variation of $\tilde{\boldsymbol{m}}_1$.*

The proof is analoguous to that of the corresponding property of the q-variation, with obvious modifications, remarking that the q-variation and the q-semi-variation of $\tilde{\boldsymbol{m}}_1$ are equal.

13. *If $\boldsymbol{m}$ is additive, then $\tilde{\boldsymbol{m}}_q$ is subadditive; if $\boldsymbol{m}$ is countably additive, then $\tilde{\boldsymbol{m}}_q$ is countably subadditive.*

The same proof as for the property 13 of the q-variation, taking $x_j \in E$ instead of α_j and $|\sum \boldsymbol{m}(B_j)\, x_j|$ instead of $\sum |\boldsymbol{m}(B_j)|\, |\alpha_j|$.

14. *Let $\boldsymbol{m}, \boldsymbol{n}\colon \mathscr{C} \to \mathscr{L}(E, F)$ be two set functions and α a scalar. Then*

$$\widetilde{(\boldsymbol{m} + \boldsymbol{n})}_q \leqq \tilde{\boldsymbol{m}}_q + \tilde{\boldsymbol{n}}_q \quad \textit{and} \quad \widetilde{(\alpha \boldsymbol{m})}_q = |\alpha|\, \tilde{\boldsymbol{m}}_q.$$

15. *If $q = \infty$, or if $1 \leqq q \leqq \infty$ and $F = C$, then*

$$\tilde{\boldsymbol{m}}_q = \bar{\boldsymbol{m}}_q.$$

Suppose first that $F = C$. Let $A \subset T$ and let $\boldsymbol{f} = \sum \varphi_{A_i} x_i \in \mathscr{E}_E(\mathscr{C}, A)$ with A_i disjoint and $N_p(\boldsymbol{f}) \leqq 1$. Since for each i we have $\boldsymbol{m}(A_i)\, x_i \in C$, we can find a number $\theta_i \in C$ with $|\theta_i| = 1$ and $|\boldsymbol{m}(A_i)\, x_i| = \boldsymbol{m}(A_i)\, \theta_i x_i$. Then $\boldsymbol{g} = \sum \varphi_{A_i} \theta_i x_i \in \mathscr{E}_E(\mathscr{C}, A)$ and $N_p(\boldsymbol{g}) = N_p(\boldsymbol{f}) \leqq 1$, therefore

$$\sum |\boldsymbol{m}(A_i)\, x_i| = \sum \boldsymbol{m}(A_i)\, \theta_i x_i = \left|\sum \boldsymbol{m}(A_i)\, \theta_i x_i\right| \leqq \tilde{\boldsymbol{m}}_q(A),$$

consequently $\bar{\boldsymbol{m}}_q(A) \leqq \tilde{\boldsymbol{m}}_q(A)$. The converse inequality being true, we deduce $\bar{\boldsymbol{m}}_q(A) = \tilde{\boldsymbol{m}}_q(A)$.

Consider now the case $q = \infty$. Let $A \subset T$ and let $f = \sum \varphi_{A_i} \alpha_i \in \mathscr{E}(\mathscr{C}, A)$, with A_i disjoint and $|\alpha_i| \leqq 1$ if $\mu(A_i) > 0$. For each i we have $|\boldsymbol{m}(A_i)| \leqq \tilde{\boldsymbol{m}}_1(A)$, therefore, using the property 12,

$$\sum |\boldsymbol{m}(A_i)| \, |\alpha_i| \leqq \sum \tilde{\boldsymbol{m}}_1(A_i) \, |\alpha_i| \leqq \tilde{\boldsymbol{m}}_{1\infty}(A) = \tilde{\boldsymbol{m}}_{\infty}(A),$$

consequently $\overline{\boldsymbol{m}}_{\infty}(A) \leqq \tilde{\boldsymbol{m}}_{\infty}(A)$. The converse inequality is also true, therefore $\tilde{\boldsymbol{m}}_{\infty}(A) = \overline{\boldsymbol{m}}_{\infty}(A)$.

16. *If $1 < q \leqq \infty$, if $\boldsymbol{m}$ is additive and if $\tilde{\boldsymbol{m}}_q(A) < \infty$ (consequently if $\overline{\boldsymbol{m}}_q(A) < \infty$) for every $A \in \mathscr{C}$, then $\boldsymbol{m}$ is countably additive and absolutely continuous with respect to μ.*

The absolute continuity follows from the property 6: If A belongs to the semi-tribe $\mathscr{S}$ generated by $\mathscr{C}$ and $\mu(A) = 0$, then $\tilde{\boldsymbol{m}}_q(A) = 0$, therefore $\tilde{\boldsymbol{m}}_1(A) = 0$ (property 11), therefore $\tilde{\boldsymbol{m}}(A) = 0$ (property 7) and $\overline{\boldsymbol{m}}(A) = 0$.

Let now (A_i) be a sequence of disjoint sets of $\mathscr{C}$ with union $A \in \mathscr{C}$. From the property 9′ we deduce that for every n we have

$$\left|\boldsymbol{m}(A) - \sum_{i \leqq n} \boldsymbol{m}(A_i)\right| = \left|\boldsymbol{m}\left(\bigcup_{i>n} A_i\right)\right| \leqq \tilde{\boldsymbol{m}}_q(A) \, \mu\left(\bigcup_{i>n} A_i\right)^{\frac{1}{p}}.$$

Since μ is countably additive we have

$$\lim_{n \to \infty} \mu\left(\bigcup_{i>n} A_i\right) = 0,$$

therefore

$$\lim_{n \to \infty} \left|\boldsymbol{m}(A) - \sum_{i \leqq n} \boldsymbol{m}(A_i)\right| = 0,$$

i.e.

$$\boldsymbol{m}(A) = \sum_{i=1}^{\infty} \boldsymbol{m}(A_i).$$

Remark. If $\overline{\boldsymbol{m}}_1(A) < \infty$ for every $A \in \mathscr{C}$, we deduce only that $\boldsymbol{m}$ is absolutely continuous with respect to μ, therefore $\overline{\boldsymbol{m}}_1 = \overline{\boldsymbol{m}}$ but $\boldsymbol{m}$ is not necessarily countably additive.

For every $z \in F'$ consider the set function $\boldsymbol{m}_z \colon \mathscr{C} \to \mathscr{L}(E, C) = E'$ defined by the equality

$$\boldsymbol{m}_z(A)\, x = \langle \boldsymbol{m}(A)\, x, z \rangle, \quad \text{for} \quad A \in \mathscr{C} \quad \text{and} \quad x \in E.$$

For every set $A \in \mathscr{C}$ we have

$$|\boldsymbol{m}(A)| = \sup_{|z| \leqq 1} |\boldsymbol{m}_z(A)|.$$

In the sequel we shall consider $\dfrac{\boldsymbol{m}_z(A)}{\mu(A)} = 0$ if $\mu(A) = 0$ and $\boldsymbol{m}_z(A) = 0$, and $\dfrac{\boldsymbol{m}_z(A)}{\mu(A)} = \infty$ if $\mu(A) = 0$ and $\boldsymbol{m}(A) \neq 0$. We do the same convention concerning $\dfrac{\boldsymbol{m}(A)}{\mu(A)}$.

Proposition 1. *Let $A \subset T$. If $1 \leqq q < \infty$, we have*

$$\tilde{\boldsymbol{m}}_q(A) = \sup_{|z| \leqq 1} \sup \left(\sum \frac{|\boldsymbol{m}_z(A_i)|^q}{\mu(A_i)^{q-1}} \right)^{\frac{1}{q}},$$

$$\bar{\boldsymbol{m}}_q(A) = \sup \left(\sum \frac{|\boldsymbol{m}(A_i)|^q}{\mu(A_i)^{q-1}} \right)^{\frac{1}{q}},$$

where the supremum is taken for all the finite families (A_i) of disjoint sets of $\mathscr{C}$ contained in A, and

$$\tilde{\boldsymbol{m}}_\infty(A) = \sup_{|z| \leqq 1} \sup_{\substack{B \subset A \\ B \in \mathscr{C}}} \frac{|\boldsymbol{m}_z(B)|}{\mu(B)} = \sup_{\substack{B \subset A \\ B \in \mathscr{C}}} \frac{|\boldsymbol{m}(B)|}{\mu(B)} = \bar{\boldsymbol{m}}_\infty(A).$$

If there exists some set $B \in \mathscr{C}$ with $B \subset A$ such that $\mu(B) = 0$ and $\boldsymbol{m}(B) \neq 0$, then $\tilde{\boldsymbol{m}}_q(B) = \infty$, therefore $\tilde{\boldsymbol{m}}_q(A) = \bar{\boldsymbol{m}}_q(A) = \infty$. Since by the preceding convention we have $\dfrac{|\boldsymbol{m}(B)|}{\mu(B)} = \infty$ and $\dfrac{|\boldsymbol{m}_z(B)|}{\mu(B)} = \infty$ for some $z \in F'$ with $|z| \leqq 1$, we deduce that all the equalities of the proposition are verified.

Assume now that for every $B \in \mathscr{C}$ with $B \subset A$ and $\mu(B) = 0$ we have $\boldsymbol{m}(B) = 0$. In this case, in each equality we can take the supremum only for the sets A_i with $\mu(A_i) > 0$.

Let (A_i) be a finite family of disjoint sets of $\mathscr{C}$ contained in A with $\mu(A_i) > 0$, let $x_i \in E$ be such that $N_p(\sum \varphi_{A_i} x_i) \leqq 1$ and let $z \in F'$ with $|z| \leqq 1$. Then, using Hölder's inequality,

$$\begin{aligned}
|\langle \sum \boldsymbol{m}(A_i)\, x_i,\, z \rangle| &= |\sum \boldsymbol{m}_z(A_i)\, x_i| = \left| \sum \frac{\boldsymbol{m}_z(A_i)}{\mu(A_i)} x_i \mu(A_i) \right| \\
&= \left| \int \sum \varphi_{A_i} x_i \sum \varphi_{A_i} \frac{\boldsymbol{m}_z(A_i)}{\mu(A_i)}\, d\mu \right| \\
&\leqq N_p(\sum \varphi_{A_i} x_i)\, N_q \left(\sum \varphi_{A_i} \frac{\boldsymbol{m}_z(A_i)}{\mu(A_i)} \right) \\
&\leqq N_q \left(\sum \varphi_{A_i} \frac{\boldsymbol{m}_z(A_i)}{\mu(A_i)} \right).
\end{aligned}$$

If $q < \infty$ we have

$$N_q\left(\sum \varphi_{A_i} \frac{\boldsymbol{m}_z(A_i)}{\mu(A_i)}\right) = \left(\sum \frac{|\boldsymbol{m}_z(A_i)|^q}{\mu(A_i)^{q-1}}\right)^{\frac{1}{q}},$$

therefore, taking the supremum for $z \in F'$ with $|z| \leqq 1$ and for all the disjoint sets $A_i \in \mathscr{C}$ contained in A, we deduce

$$\tilde{\boldsymbol{m}}_q(A) \leqq \sup_{|z| \leqq 1} \sup \left(\sum \frac{|\boldsymbol{m}_z(A_i)|^q}{\mu(A_i)^{q-1}}\right)^{\frac{1}{q}}.$$

If $q = \infty$, we have

$$N_\infty\left(\sum \varphi_{A_i} \frac{\boldsymbol{m}_z(A_i)}{\mu(A_i)}\right) \leqq \sup_{B \subset A} \frac{|\boldsymbol{m}_z(B)|}{\mu(B)},$$

therefore, taking the supremum for $z \in F'$ with $|z| \leqq 1$ and for all the disjoint sets $A_i \in \mathscr{C}$ contained in A, we deduce

$$\tilde{\boldsymbol{m}}_q(A) \leqq \sup_{|z| \leqq 1} \sup \left(\sum \frac{|\boldsymbol{m}_z(A_i)|^q}{\mu(A_i)^{q-1}}\right)^{\frac{1}{q}}.$$

Starting from the inequalities

$$\sum |\boldsymbol{m}(A_i)\, x_i| \leqq \sum |\boldsymbol{m}(A_i)|\, |x_i| = \sum \frac{|\boldsymbol{m}(A_i)|}{\mu(A_i)} |x_i|\, \mu(A_i)$$
$$= \int \sum \varphi_{A_i} |x_i| \sum \varphi_{A_i} \frac{|\boldsymbol{m}(A_i)|}{\mu(A_i)}\, d\mu \leqq N_q\left(\sum \varphi_{A_i} \frac{|\boldsymbol{m}(A_i)|}{\mu(A_i)}\right)$$

we deduce in the same way that

$$\bar{\boldsymbol{m}}_q(A) \leqq \sup \left(\sum \frac{|\boldsymbol{m}(A_i)|^q}{\mu(A_i)^{q-1}}\right)^{\frac{1}{q}},$$

the supremum being taken for all the disjoint sets of $\mathscr{C}$ contained in A, and

$$\bar{\boldsymbol{m}}_\infty(A) \leqq \sup_{B \subset A} \frac{|\boldsymbol{m}(B)|}{\mu(B)}.$$

To prove the converse inequalities, consider first the case $1 \leqq q < \infty$ and let $(A_i)_{1 \leqq i \leqq n}$ be a family of disjoint sets of $\mathscr{C}$ contained in A with $\mu(A_i) > 0$, let $z \in F'$ with $|z| \leqq 1$ and let $\varepsilon > 0$. For every i we can find an element $x_i \in E$ such that

$$|x_i| = \left(\frac{|\boldsymbol{m}_z(A_i)|}{\mu(A_i)}\right)^{q-1}$$

and

$$|\boldsymbol{m}_z(A_i)|\, |x_i| - \frac{\varepsilon}{n} \leqq |\boldsymbol{m}_z(A_i)\, x_i| = \boldsymbol{m}_z(A_i)\, x_i = \langle \boldsymbol{m}(A_i)\, x_i, z \rangle.$$

Then

$$\sum \frac{|m_z(A_i)|^q}{\mu(A_i)^{q-1}} - \varepsilon = \sum |m_z(A_i)| \left(\frac{|m_z(A_i)|}{\mu(A_i)}\right)^{q-1} - \varepsilon$$

$$= \sum |m_z(A_i)|\,|x_i| - \varepsilon \leqq \sum \langle m(A_i)\, x_i, z\rangle$$

$$= \langle \sum m(A_i)\, x_i, z\rangle \leqq \left|\sum m(A_i)\, x_i\right|$$

$$\leqq \tilde{m}_q(A)\, N_p(\sum \varphi_{A_i} x_i) = \tilde{m}_q(A)\, (\sum \mu(A_i)\, |x_i|^p)^{\frac{1}{p}}$$

$$= \tilde{m}_q(A) \left(\sum \frac{|m_z(A_i)|^q}{\mu(A_i)^{q-1}}\right)^{\frac{1}{p}},$$

since $p(q-1) = q$; ε being arbitrary, we deduce that

$$\left(\sum \frac{|m_z(A_i)|^q}{\mu(A_i)^{q-1}}\right)^{\frac{1}{q}} \leqq \tilde{m}_q(A),$$

since $1 - \dfrac{1}{p} = \dfrac{1}{q}$, and we receive the desired inequality for $\tilde{m}_q(A)$.

Choosing the elements $x_i \in E$ such that

$$|x_i| = \left(\frac{|m(A_i)|}{\mu(A_i)}\right)^{q-1}$$

and

$$|m(A_i)|\,|x_i| - \frac{\varepsilon}{n} \leqq |m(A_i)\, x_i|$$

and starting from the inequalities

$$\sum \frac{|m(A_i)|^q}{\mu(A_i)^{q-1}} - \varepsilon = \sum |m(A_i)| \left(\frac{|m(A_i)|}{\mu(A_i)}\right)^{q-1} - \varepsilon$$

$$= \sum |m(A_i)|\,|x_i| - \varepsilon \leqq \sum |m(A_i)\, x_i| \leqq \bar{m}_q(A)\, N_p(\sum \varphi_{A_i} x_i)$$

$$= \bar{m}_q(A)\, (\sum \mu(A_i)\, |x_i|^p)^{\frac{1}{p}} = \bar{m}_q(A) \left(\sum \frac{|m(A_i)|^q}{\mu(A_i)^{q-1}}\right)^{\frac{1}{p}}$$

we deduce in the same way that

$$\left(\sum \frac{|m(A_i)|^q}{\mu(A_i)^{q-1}}\right)^{\frac{1}{q}} \leqq \bar{m}_q(A)$$

and we receive the desired inequality for $\bar{m}_q(A)$.

Finally for $q = \infty$, let $B \in \mathscr{C}$ be a set contained in A with $\mu(B) > 0$, let $x \in E$ with $|x| \leqq 1$, and let $z \in F'$ with $|z| \leqq 1$. Then

$$|\boldsymbol{m}_z(B)\,x| \leqq \tilde{\boldsymbol{m}}_\infty(B)\,N_1(\varphi_B x) = \tilde{\boldsymbol{m}}_\infty(B)\,\mu(B),$$

therefore

$$|\boldsymbol{m}_z(B)| \leqq \tilde{\boldsymbol{m}}_\infty(B)\,\mu(B) \leqq \tilde{\boldsymbol{m}}_\infty(A)\,\mu(B).$$

Consequently

$$|\boldsymbol{m}(B)| \leqq \tilde{\boldsymbol{m}}_\infty(A)\,\mu(B),$$

whence

$$\sup_{|z| \leqq 1} \sup_{B \subset A} \frac{|\boldsymbol{m}_z(B)|}{\mu(B)} = \sup_{B \subset A} \frac{|\boldsymbol{m}(B)|}{\mu(B)} \leqq \tilde{\boldsymbol{m}}_\infty(A) \leqq \bar{\boldsymbol{m}}_\infty(A).$$

The proposition is completely proved.

Corollary. *For every $A \subset T$ and $1 \leqq q \leqq \infty$ we have*

$$\tilde{\boldsymbol{m}}_q(A) = \sup_{|z| \leqq 1} \overline{(\boldsymbol{m}_z)}_q.$$

Proposition 2. *If $\boldsymbol{m}\colon \mathscr{C} \to \mathscr{L}(E, F)$ is an additive set function, if $1 \leqq q \leqq \infty$ and $\frac{1}{p} + \frac{1}{q} = 1$, then for every set $A \subset T$ we have*

$$\tilde{\boldsymbol{m}}_q(A) = \sup \left| \int \boldsymbol{f}\,d\boldsymbol{m} \right|, \quad \textit{for} \quad \boldsymbol{f} \in \mathscr{E}_E(\mathscr{C}, A) \quad \textit{with} \quad N_p(\boldsymbol{f}) \leqq 1.$$

In fact, for every function $\boldsymbol{f} = \sum \varphi_{A_i} x_i$ of $\mathscr{E}_E(\mathscr{C})$ we have

$$\int \boldsymbol{f}\,d\boldsymbol{m} = \sum \boldsymbol{m}(A_i)\,x_i.$$

Corollary 1. *If $\boldsymbol{m}\colon \mathscr{C} \to \mathscr{L}(E, F)$ is an additive set function, if $1 \leqq q \leqq \infty$ and $\frac{1}{p} + \frac{1}{q} = 1$, then for every function $\boldsymbol{f} \in \mathscr{E}_E(\mathscr{C}, A)$ we have*

$$\left| \int \boldsymbol{f}\,d\boldsymbol{m} \right| \leqq N_p(\boldsymbol{f})\,\tilde{\boldsymbol{m}}_q(A) \leqq \infty$$

and for every function $\varphi \in \mathscr{E}(\mathscr{C}, A)$ we have

$$\left| \int \varphi\,d\boldsymbol{m} \right| \leqq N_p(\varphi)\,\tilde{\boldsymbol{m}}_q(A) \leqq \infty.$$

The first inequality is evident. If $\varphi \in \mathscr{E}(\mathscr{C}, A)$, then for every $x \in E$ we have $\varphi x \in \mathscr{E}_E(\mathscr{C}, A)$, $\int \varphi x\,d\boldsymbol{m} = \int \varphi\,d\boldsymbol{m}\,x$ and $N_p(\varphi x) = N_p(\varphi)\,|x|$, therefore

$$\left| \int \varphi\,d\boldsymbol{m}\,x \right| \leqq |x|\,N_p(\varphi)\,\tilde{\boldsymbol{m}}_q(A),$$

consequently

$$\left|\int \varphi\, d\boldsymbol{m}\right| \leqq N_p(\varphi)\, \tilde{\boldsymbol{m}}_q(A).$$

In some cases we can extend the integral with respect to $\boldsymbol{m}$ from $\mathscr{E}_E(\mathscr{C})$ to $\mathscr{L}_E^p(\mu)$. We shall denote by $\mathscr{T}_{\sigma f}$ the tribe of the sets $A \subset T$ which are σ-finite with respect to μ.

Corollary 2. *Let* $1 \leqq q \leqq \infty$ *and* $\frac{1}{p} + \frac{1}{q} = 1$. *If* $\boldsymbol{m}\colon \mathscr{C} \to \mathscr{L}(E, F)$ *is an additive set function with finite variation* $|\boldsymbol{m}|$, *then for every function* $\boldsymbol{f} \in \mathscr{E}_E(\mathscr{C}, A)$ *we have*

$$\left|\int \boldsymbol{f}\, d\boldsymbol{m}\right| \leqq \int |\boldsymbol{f}|\, d|\boldsymbol{m}| \leqq N_p(\boldsymbol{f})\, \bar{\boldsymbol{m}}_q(A) \leqq \infty .$$

In fact, we have $|\boldsymbol{m}| \leqq \bar{\boldsymbol{m}}_1$ and the q-semi-variation of $\bar{\boldsymbol{m}}_1$ is equal to the q-variation $\bar{\boldsymbol{m}}_{1q}$ of $\bar{\boldsymbol{m}}_1$, therefore

$$\int |\boldsymbol{f}|\, d|\boldsymbol{m}| \leqq \int |\boldsymbol{f}|\, d\bar{\boldsymbol{m}}_1 \leqq N_p(\boldsymbol{f})\, \bar{\boldsymbol{m}}_{1q}(A) = N_p(\boldsymbol{f})\, \bar{\boldsymbol{m}}_q(A).$$

Proposition 3. *Let* $1 \leqq p \leqq \infty$ *and* $\frac{1}{p} + \frac{1}{q} = 1$. *Let* $\boldsymbol{m}\colon \mathscr{C} \to \mathscr{L}(E, F)$ *be a measure with* $\tilde{\boldsymbol{m}}_q(A) < \infty$ *for every set* $A \in \mathscr{T}_{\sigma f}$.

1\. *If* $(\boldsymbol{f}_n)$ *is a Cauchy sequence in* $\mathscr{L}_E^p$ *(or in* $\mathscr{L}^p$*) consisting of* $\mathscr{C}$*-step functions, then* $(\int \boldsymbol{f}_n\, d\boldsymbol{m})$ *is a Cauchy sequence in* F *(respectively in* $\mathscr{L}(E, F)$*).*

2\. *If* $(\boldsymbol{f}_n)$ *and* $(\boldsymbol{g}_n)$ *are two Cauchy sequences in* $\mathscr{L}_E^p$ *(or in* $\mathscr{L}^p$*) consisting of* $\mathscr{C}$*-step functions and converging* μ*-almost everywhere to the same function, then*

$$\lim_{n\to\infty} \int \boldsymbol{f}_n\, d\boldsymbol{m} = \lim_{n\to\infty} \int \boldsymbol{g}_n\, d\boldsymbol{m}.$$

Let $A \in \mathscr{T}_{\sigma f}$ be a set such that all the functions $\boldsymbol{f}_n$ and $\boldsymbol{g}_n$ vanish outside A. We have first

$$\left|\int \boldsymbol{f}_n\, d\boldsymbol{m} - \int \boldsymbol{f}_m\, d\boldsymbol{m}\right| = \left|\int (\boldsymbol{f}_n - \boldsymbol{f}_m)\, d\boldsymbol{m}\right| \leqq N_p(\boldsymbol{f}_n - \boldsymbol{f}_m)\, \tilde{\boldsymbol{m}}_q(A) < \infty ,$$

therefore $(\int \boldsymbol{f}_n\, d\boldsymbol{m})$ is a Cauchy sequence.

On the other hand, $(\boldsymbol{f}_n - \boldsymbol{g}_n)$ is a Cauchy sequence in $\mathscr{L}_E^p$ (or in $\mathscr{L}^p$) and converges μ-almost everywhere to 0, therefore $N_p(\boldsymbol{f}_n - \boldsymbol{g}_n) \to 0$. Then

$$\left|\int \boldsymbol{f}_n\, d\boldsymbol{m} - \int \boldsymbol{g}_n\, d\boldsymbol{m}\right| \leqq N_p(\boldsymbol{f}_n - \boldsymbol{g}_n)\, \tilde{\boldsymbol{m}}_q(A),$$

therefore the sequences $(\int \boldsymbol{f}_n\, d\boldsymbol{m})$ and $(\int \boldsymbol{g}_n\, d\boldsymbol{m})$ have the same limit.

The preceding proposition leads to the following

Definition 1. *Let* $1 \leqq p < \infty$ *and* $\frac{1}{p} + \frac{1}{q} = 1$. *Let* $\boldsymbol{m}: \mathscr{C} \to \mathscr{L}(E, F)$ *be a measure with* $\tilde{\boldsymbol{m}}_q(A) < \infty$ *for every set* $A \in \mathscr{T}_{\sigma f}$.

For every function f *of* $\mathscr{L}_E^p$ *(or of* $\mathscr{L}^p$*) we define the integral* $\int f\, d\boldsymbol{m}$ *by the equality*

$$\int f\, d\boldsymbol{m} = \lim_{n \to \infty} \int f_n\, d\boldsymbol{m},$$

where (f_n) *is an arbitrary Cauchy sequence in* $\mathscr{L}_E^p$ *(respectively in* $\mathscr{L}^p$*) consisting of* $\mathscr{C}$*-step functions and converging* μ*-almost everywhere to* f.

From this definition we deduce that the mapping $f \to \int f\, d\boldsymbol{m}$ of $\mathscr{L}_E^p(\mu)$ into F (respectively of $\mathscr{L}^p(\mu)$ into $\mathscr{L}(E, F)$) is linear and that for every μ-measurable set $A \subset T$ and every function f of $\mathscr{L}_E^p(\mu)$ or of $\mathscr{L}^p(\mu)$ vanishing outside A we have

$$\left| \int f\, d\boldsymbol{m} \right| \leqq N_p(f)\, \tilde{\boldsymbol{m}}_q(A).$$

Remark. If $q = 1$, we have defined in § 9 the integral of a μ-almost totally measurable function $f \in \mathscr{M}_E^\infty(\mathscr{C})$ with respect to an additive set function $\boldsymbol{m}: \mathscr{C} \to \mathscr{L}(E, F)$ with $\tilde{\boldsymbol{m}}_1(A) < \infty$ for $A \in \mathscr{C}$.

Proposition 4. *Let* $1 \leqq p < \infty$ *and* $\frac{1}{p} + \frac{1}{q} = 1$. *Let* $\boldsymbol{m}: \mathscr{C} \to \mathscr{L}(E, F)$ *be a measure with finite variation* $|\boldsymbol{m}|$, *absolutely continuous with respect to* μ. *If* $A \subset T$ *is* μ*-measurable and if* $\bar{\boldsymbol{m}}_q(A) < \infty$, *then* $\mathscr{L}_E^p(A, \mu) \subset \mathscr{L}_E^1(A, \boldsymbol{m})$ *and*

$$\left| \int f\, d\boldsymbol{m} \right| \leqq \int |f|\, d|\boldsymbol{m}| \leqq N_p(f)\, \bar{\boldsymbol{m}}_q(A), \quad \textit{for} \quad f \in \mathscr{L}_E^p(A, \mu).$$

Moreover, if $|\boldsymbol{m}| = g\mu$, *then* $g\varphi_A \in \mathscr{L}^q(\mu)$ *and*

$$\bar{\boldsymbol{m}}_q(A) = N_q(g\varphi_A, \mu).$$

Let $f \in \mathscr{L}_E^p(A, \mu)$. Let (f_n) be a sequence of $\mathscr{C}$-step functions of $\mathscr{E}_E(\mathscr{C}, A)$ converging to f μ-almost everywhere and in $\mathscr{L}_E^p(A, \mu)$. Since $\boldsymbol{m}$ is absolutely continuous with respect to μ, (f_n) converges to f $\boldsymbol{m}$-almost everywhere. For the step function $f_n - f_m$ we have

$$\int |f_n - f_m|\, d|\boldsymbol{m}| \leqq \bar{\boldsymbol{m}}_q(A)\, N_p(f_n - f_m, \mu),$$

therefore (f_n) is a Cauchy sequence in $\mathscr{L}_E^1(\boldsymbol{m})$. It follows that f is $\boldsymbol{m}$-integrable, i.e. $f \in \mathscr{L}_E^1(A, \boldsymbol{m})$. For every n we have

$$\left| \int f_n\, d\boldsymbol{m} \right| \leqq \int |f_n|\, d|\boldsymbol{m}| \leqq \bar{\boldsymbol{m}}_q(A)\, N_p(f_n).$$

Passing to the limit we obtain

$$\left|\int f\,dm\right| \leqq \int |f|\,d|m| \leqq \bar{m}_q(A)\,N_p(f).$$

Suppose now that $|m| = g\mu$. For every $\varphi \in \mathscr{L}^p(\mu)$ we have $\varphi\varphi_A \in \mathscr{L}^p(A, \mu)$, therefore $\varphi\varphi_A \in \mathscr{L}^1(A, |m|)$. Since $\varphi\varphi_A$ is $|m|$-integrable, $\varphi g \varphi_A$ is μ-integrable. It follows that $g\varphi_A \in \mathscr{L}^q(\mu)$ (§ 12, theorem 7) and

$$\int \varphi g \varphi_A\,d\mu = \int \varphi\varphi_A\,d|m| \leqq \bar{m}_q(A)\,N_p(\varphi).$$

Taking the supremum for $\varphi \in \mathscr{L}^p(\mu)$ with $N_p(\varphi) \leqq 1$ we obtain

$$N_q(g\varphi_A, \mu) \leqq \bar{m}_q(A).$$

On the other hand, if $\varphi = \sum \varphi_{A_i}x_i \in \mathscr{E}(\mathscr{C}, A)$ with A_i disjoint and $N_p(\varphi) \leqq 1$, then

$$\sum |m(A_i)|\,|x_i| \leqq \sum |m|\,(A_i)\,|x_i| = \int |\varphi|\,d|m|$$
$$= \int |\varphi|\,g\varphi_A\,d\mu \leqq N_p(\varphi)\,N_q(g\varphi_A) \leqq N_q(g\varphi_A),$$

therefore $\bar{m}_q(A) \leqq N_q(g\varphi_A)$, consequently

$$\bar{m}_q(A) = N_q(g\varphi_A).$$

Corollary. *If m is a measure with $\bar{m}_q(A) < \infty$ for every $A \in \mathscr{T}_{\sigma f}$, then $\mathscr{L}^p_E(\mu) \subset \mathscr{L}^1_E(m)$ and*

$$\left|\int f\,dm\right| \leqq \int |f|\,d|m| \leqq \bar{m}_q(A)\,N_p(f)$$

for every $A \in \mathscr{T}_{\sigma f}$ and $f \in \mathscr{L}^p_E(A, \mu)$.

3. LINEAR OPERATIONS ON $\mathscr{L}^p_E$

Let μ be a *positive measure* on T, E and F two Banach spaces. Consider the space $\mathscr{L}^p_E(\mu)$ with $1 \leqq p < \infty$. For every set $A \subset T$, denote by $\mathscr{L}^p_E(A, \mu)$ the space of the functions of $\mathscr{L}^p_E(\mu)$ vanishing outside A. For every μ-measurable set A, the space $\mathscr{E}_E(A, \mu)$ of the step functions of $\mathscr{E}_E(\mu)$ vanishing outside A is dense in $\mathscr{L}^p_E(A, \mu)$.

Let U: $\mathscr{L}^p_E \to F$ be a linear mapping. For every set $A \subset T$ denote by U_A the restriction of U to $\mathscr{L}^p_E(A, \mu)$ and put

$$\|U_A\|_p = \sup |U(f)|, \quad \text{for} \quad f \in \mathscr{L}^p_E(A, \mu) \quad \text{with} \quad N_p(f, \mu) \leqq 1,$$

and

$$|||U_A|||_p = \sup \sum |U(\varphi_{A_i}x_i)|,$$

the supremum being taken for all the step functions $f = \sum \varphi_{A_i} x_i \in \mathscr{E}_E(A, \mu)$, with A_i disjoint and $N_p(f, \mu) \leqq 1$.

Since for A μ-measurable the space $\mathscr{E}_E(A, \mu)$ is dense in $\mathscr{L}_E^p(A, \mu)$, we have

$$\|U_A\|_p = \sup \left|\sum U(\varphi_{A_i} x_i)\right|,$$

the supremum being taken for all the step functions $f = \sum \varphi_{A_i} x_i \in \mathscr{E}_E(A, \mu)$, with A_i disjoint and $N_p(f, \mu) \leqq 1$.

We deduce then that

$$\|U_A\|_p \leqq |||U_A|||_p \leqq \infty .$$

The condition $\|U_A\|_p < \infty$ means that U_A is continuous on $\mathscr{L}_E^p(A, \mu)$.

If $A \subset B$, then, evidently, $|||U_A|||_p \leqq |||U_B|||_p$.
We shall write $|||U|||_p$ instead of $|||U_T|||_p$ and $\|U\|_p$ instead of $\|U_T\|_p$.

Proposition 5. *If $p = 1$, or if $F = C$, we have*

$$\|U_A\|_p = |||U_A|||_p$$

for every μ-measurable set $A \subset T$.

We have to prove only that $|||U_A|||_p \leqq \|U_A\|_p$. If $\|U_A\|_p = \infty$ this inequality is verified. Suppose then that $\|U_A\|_p < \infty$.

Consider first the case $p = 1$ and let $f = \sum \varphi_{A_i} x_i \in \mathscr{E}_E(A, \mu)$ with disjoint A_i and $N_p(f, \mu) \leqq 1$. Since $|f| = \sum \varphi_{A_i} |x_i| \in \mathscr{E}(A, \mu)$ we have

$$N_1(f, \mu) = \int |f| \, d\mu = \sum \int \varphi_{A_i} |x_i| \, d\mu = \sum N_1(\varphi_{A_i} x_i),$$

therefore

$$\sum |U(\varphi_{A_i} x_i)| \leqq \sum \|U_A\|_1 \, N_1(\varphi_{A_i} x_i) = \|U_A\|_1 \, N_1(f, \mu) \leqq \|U_A\|_1 ,$$

consequently $|||U_A|||_1 \leqq \|U_A\|_1$.

Consider now the case $F = C$ and $1 \leqq p < \infty$ and let $f = \sum \varphi_{A_i} x_i \in \mathscr{E}_E(A, \mu)$ with disjoint A_i and $N_p(f, \mu) \leqq 1$. For every i we can find a complex number θ_i with $|\theta_i| = 1$ and

$$|U(\varphi_{A_i} x_i)| = \theta_i U(\varphi_{A_i} x_i) = U(\varphi_{A_i} \theta_i x_i).$$

Then we have $|f| = |\sum \varphi_{A_i} \theta_i x_i|$ and

$$\sum |U(\varphi_{A_i} x_i)| = U(\sum \varphi_{A_i} \theta_i x_i) \leqq \|U_A\|_p \, N_p(\sum \varphi_{A_i} \theta_i x_i, \mu) \leqq \|U_A\|_p ,$$

therefore $|||U_A|||_p \leqq \|U_A\|_p$.

Remark. If $1 < p < \infty$ and $F \neq C$ we can have $\|U_A\|_p < |||U_A|||_p$.

Example. Take $T = R$, μ Lebesgue's measure, $F = \mathscr{L}^p(\mu)$, and $U\colon \mathscr{L}^p(\mu) \to F$ the identical mapping $U(f) = f$. Let $A \subset R$ be a bounded interval with $\mu(A) > 1$.

We have evidently $\|U_A\|_p = 1$. We show now that $|||U_A|||_p = \infty$. In fact, for each natural number n choose n disjoint intervals $(A_i)_{1 \leqq i \leqq n}$ with $\mu(A_i) = \frac{1}{n}$ and n numbers $(x_i)_{1 \leqq i \leqq n}$ with $|x_i| = 1$. For the step function

$$f = \sum_{i=1}^{n} \varphi_{A_i} x_i$$

we have $N_p(f, \mu) = 1$ and

$$\sum_{i=1}^{n} |U(\varphi_{A_i} x_i)| = \sum_{i=1}^{n} N_p(\varphi_{A_i} x_i, \mu) = \sum_{i=1}^{n} \mu(A_i)^{\frac{1}{p}} |x_i| = n\left(\frac{1}{n}\right)^{\frac{1}{p}},$$

therefore $|||U_A|||_p \geqq n\left(\frac{1}{n}\right)^{\frac{1}{p}}$ for every n, consequently $|||U_A|||_p = \infty$.

Proposition 6. *For every μ-measurable set A and for every finite family (f_i) of $\mathscr{L}_E^p(A, \mu)$ with $|f_i|\,|f_j| = 0$ for $i \neq j$, we have*

$$\sum |U(f_i)| \leqq |||U_A|||_p \, \|\sum f_i\|_p$$

except for the case where $|||U_A|||_p = \infty$ and $\|\sum f_i\|_p = 0$.

If $U_A = 0$, then $U(f_i) = 0$ for every i and the inequality is verified. If $|||U_A|||_p = \infty$, the inequality is also verified.

Assume therefore that $0 < |||U_A|||_p < \infty$. Then $\|U_A\|_p < \infty$. Let (f_i) be a finite family of $\mathscr{L}_E^p(A, \mu)$ with $|f_i|\,|f_j| = 0$ if $i \neq j$ and $f = \sum f_i \in \mathscr{L}_E^p(A, \mu)$ and let $\varepsilon > 0$. There exists a μ-measurable step function $g \in \mathscr{L}_E^p(A, \mu)$ such that

$$\|f - g\|_p < \eta = \min\left(\varepsilon, \frac{\varepsilon}{n\|U_A\|}\right).$$

The sets $A_i = \{t; f_i(t) \neq 0\}$ are μ-measurable, disjoint, and contained in A; the functions $g_i = g\varphi_{A_i}$ are step functions of $\mathscr{L}_E^p(A, \mu)$ and we have

$$\|\sum f_i - \sum g_i\|_p \leqq \|f - g\|_p < \eta \leqq \varepsilon,$$

therefore

$$\|\sum g_i\|_p \leqq \|\sum f_i\|_p + \varepsilon.$$

On the other hand, for each i we have

$$\|f_i - g_i\|_p \leqq \|\sum f_i - \sum g_i\|_p < \eta < \frac{\varepsilon}{n\|U_A\|},$$

therefore

$$|U(f_i) - U(g_i)| \leqq \frac{\varepsilon}{n},$$

whence

$$|U(f_i)| \leqq |U(g_i)| + \frac{\varepsilon}{n}.$$

It follows that

$$\sum |U(f_i)| \leqq \sum |U(g_i)| + \varepsilon.$$

Each function g_i can be written

$$g_i = \sum_j \varphi_{A_{ij}} x_{ij}$$

with A_{ij} disjoint μ-measurable sets, and we have

$$\sum_{i,j} \varphi_{A_{ij}} x_{ij} = \sum_i g_i,$$

therefore

$$\left\|\sum_{i,j} \varphi_{A_{ij}} x_{ij}\right\|_p = \left\|\sum_i g_i\right\|_p \leqq \left\|\sum f_i\right\|_p + \varepsilon.$$

Then

$$\sum |U(f_i)| \leqq \sum |U(g_i)| + \varepsilon = \sum_i \left| U\left(\sum_j \varphi_{A_{ij}} x_{ij}\right)\right| + \varepsilon$$

$$\leqq \sum_{i,j} |U(\varphi_{A_{ij}} x_{ij})| + \varepsilon \leqq \left\|U_A\right\|_p \left\|\sum_{i,j} \varphi_{A_{ij}} x_{ij}\right\|_p + \varepsilon$$

$$\leqq \left\|U_A\right\|_p \left(\left\|\sum f_i\right\|_p + \varepsilon\right) + \varepsilon;$$

ε being arbitrary, we deduce that

$$\sum |U(f_i)| \leqq \left\|U_A\right\|_p \left\|\sum f_i\right\|_p.$$

Proposition 7. *For every μ-measurable set A we have:*

1. $\left\|U_A\right\|_p = \sup \sum |U(\varphi_{A_i} f)|$

for $f \in \mathscr{L}^p_E(A, \mu)$ with $N_p(f) \leqq 1$ and A_i disjoint μ-measurable sets.

2. $\left\|U_A\right\|_p = \sup \sum |U(\varphi_i x_i)|$

for $\varphi_i \in \mathscr{L}^p(A, \mu)$ with $N_p(\sum \varphi_i) \leqq 1$ and $\varphi_i \varphi_j = 0$ if $i \neq j$, and $x_i \in E$ with $|x_i| \leqq 1$.

3. $\left\|U_A\right\|_p = \sup \sum |U(\varphi_i f)|$

for $f \in \mathscr{L}^p_E(A, \mu)$ with $N_p(f) \leqq 1$, and φ_i real μ-measurable functions with $|\varphi_i| \leqq 1$ and $\varphi_i \varphi_j = 0$ if $i \neq j$.

4. $\left\|U_A\right\|_p = \sup \sum |U(f_i)|$

for $f_i \in \mathscr{L}^p_E(A, \mu)$ with $N_p(\sum f_i) \leqq 1$ and $|f_i|\,|f_j| = 0$ if $i \neq j$.

If we denote by $\mathscr{A}_A$ the set of the functions $\sum f_i$ for which the supremum is taken in each of these cases, we have $N_p(\sum f_i) \leqq 1$ and from the preceding proposition we deduce that

$$\sup \sum |U(f_i)| \leqq |||U_A|||, \quad \text{for} \quad \sum f_i \in \mathscr{A}_A.$$

On the other hand, $\mathscr{A}_A$ contains all the step functions $\sum \varphi_{A_i} x_i$ with A_i disjoint and $N_p(\sum \varphi_{A_i} x_i) \leqq 1$, therefore

$$|||U_A||| \leqq \sup \sum |U(f_i)|, \quad \text{for} \quad \sum f_i \in \mathscr{A}_A.$$

Remark. In each of these cases we have also

$$\|U_A\| = \sup |\sum U(f_i)|, \quad \text{for} \quad \sum f_i \in \mathscr{A}_A.$$

Proposition 8. *If L: $\mathscr{L}^p(\mu) \to R$ is a positive linear functional* (i.e. $L(\varphi) \geqq 0$ *for* $\varphi \geqq 0$ *μ-almost everywhere), then* $\|L\|_p < \infty$.

In fact, if $\|L\|_p = \infty$, we can find a sequence (φ_n) of functions $\varphi_n \geqq 0$ of $\mathscr{L}^p(\mu)$ with $N_p(\varphi_n, \mu) = 1$ and $L(\varphi_n) > n^3$ for every n. Then the function

$$\varphi = \sum_{n=1}^{\infty} \frac{1}{n^2} \varphi_n$$

is equal μ-almost everywhere to a function $\varphi \in \mathscr{L}^p(\mu)$ and we have $\varphi \geqq \dfrac{1}{n^2} \varphi_n$ μ-almost everywhere, therefore $L(\varphi) \geqq \dfrac{1}{n^2} L(\varphi_n) \geqq n$ for every n, whence $L(\varphi) = \infty$, which is impossible. It follows that $\|L\|_p < \infty$.

Theorem 1. *Let* $1 \leqq p < \infty$ *and* $\dfrac{1}{p} + \dfrac{1}{q} = 1$. *There is an isomorphism* $U \leftrightarrow \boldsymbol{m}$ *between the set of the linear mappings* U: $\mathscr{L}_E^p(\mu) \to F$ *with* $\|U_A\|_p < \infty$ *for* $A \in \mathscr{T}_{\sigma f}$, *and the set of the measures* $\boldsymbol{m}$: $\mathscr{C} \to \mathscr{L}(E, F)$ *with* $\tilde{\boldsymbol{m}}_q(A) < \infty$ *for* $A \in \mathscr{T}_{\sigma f}$, *given by the equality*

$$U(f) = \int f \, d\boldsymbol{m}, \quad \textit{for} \quad f \in \mathscr{L}_E^p.$$

Moreover, if U and $\boldsymbol{m}$ are in correspondence, then for every μ-measurable set $A \subset T$ we have

$$\|U_A\|_p = \tilde{\boldsymbol{m}}_q(A) \quad \textit{and} \quad |||U_A|||_p = \bar{\boldsymbol{m}}_q(A).$$

If $\boldsymbol{m}$: $\mathscr{C} \to \mathscr{L}(E, F)$ is a measure with $\tilde{\boldsymbol{m}}_q(A) < \infty$ for $A \in \mathscr{T}_{\sigma f}$, then the mapping U: $\mathscr{L}_E^p(\mu) \to F$ defined by

$$U(f) = \int f \, d\boldsymbol{m}, \quad \text{for} \quad f \in \mathscr{L}_E^p(\mu),$$

is linear. For every μ-measurable set $A \subset T$ and for every function $f = \sum \varphi_{A_i} x_i \in \mathscr{E}_E(\mathscr{C}, A)$ with A_i disjoint we have

$$|U(f)| = |\sum m(A_i)\, x_i|$$

and

$$\sum |U(\varphi_{A_i} x_i)| = \sum |m(A_i)\, x_i|,$$

therefore, taking the supremum for all the functions $f = \sum \varphi_{A_i} x_i \in \mathscr{E}_E(\mathscr{C}, A)$ with A_i disjoint and $N_p(f) \leqq 1$, we deduce

$$\|U_A\|_p = \tilde{m}_q(A) \quad \text{and} \quad |||U_A|||_p = \bar{m}_q(A).$$

In particular, $\|U_A\|_p < \infty$ for every set $A \in \mathscr{T}_{\sigma f}$.

Conversely, let $U\colon \mathscr{L}_E^p \to F$ be a linear mapping with $\|U_A\|_p < \infty$ for $A \in \mathscr{T}_{\sigma f}$. For every set $A \in \mathscr{C}$ the mapping $m(A)\colon E \to F$ defined by the equality

$$m(A)\, x = U(\varphi_A x), \quad \text{for} \quad x \in E,$$

is linear and continuous:

$$|m(A)\, x| = |U(\varphi_A x)| \leqq \|U_A\|_p\, N_p(\varphi_A x) = \|U_A\|_p\, |x|\, N_p(\varphi_A),$$

therefore $m(A) \in \mathscr{L}(E, F)$ and

$$|m(A)| \leqq \|U_A\|_p\, N_p(\varphi_A).$$

The mapping $m\colon \mathscr{C} \to \mathscr{L}(E, F)$ is additive and for every $\mathscr{C}$-step function $f = \sum \varphi_{A_i} x_i$ we have

$$U(f) = \sum U(\varphi_{A_i} x_i) = \sum m(A_i)\, x_i = \int f\, dm.$$

Let $A \subset T$ be a μ-measurable set. If in the equality

$$|U(\sum \varphi_{A_i} x_i)| = |\sum m(A_i)\, x_i|$$

we take the supremum for all the functions $f = \sum \varphi_{A_i} x_i \in \mathscr{E}_E(\mathscr{C}, A)$ with $N_p(f) \leqq 1$, we deduce

$$\|U_A\|_p = \tilde{m}_q(A).$$

In particular, for $A \in \mathscr{T}_{\sigma f}$ we deduce $\tilde{m}_q(A) < \infty$.

Let now $f \in \mathscr{L}_E^p(\mu)$ and let $A \in \mathscr{T}_{\sigma f}$ be such that f vanishes outside A. Let (f_n) be a sequence of $\mathscr{C}$-step functions vanishing outside A and converging to f in $\mathscr{L}_E^p$ and μ-almost everywhere. Then $U(f_n) \to U(f)$ and $\int f_n\, dm \to \int f\, dm$.

Since for every n we have

$$U(f_n) = \int f_n\, dm$$

we deduce that

$$U(f) = \int f\, dm.$$

Finally, the correspondence $\boldsymbol{m} \to U$ is evidently linear and one-to-one.

Corollary 1. *Let* $1 \leqq p < \infty$ *and* $\frac{1}{p} + \frac{1}{q} = 1$. *There exists an isomorphism* $U \leftrightarrow \boldsymbol{m}$ *between the set of the linear mappings* $U\colon \mathscr{L}_E^p(\mu) \to F$ *with* $|||U_A|||_p < \infty$ *for* $A \in \mathscr{T}_{\sigma f}$ *and the set of the measures* $\boldsymbol{m}\colon \mathscr{C} \to \mathscr{L}(E, F)$ *with* $\bar{\boldsymbol{m}}_q(A) < \infty$ *for* $A \in \mathscr{T}_{\sigma f}$, *given by the equality*

$$U(f) = \int f\, dm, \quad \textit{for} \quad f \in \mathscr{L}_E^p.$$

If U *and* $\boldsymbol{m}$ *are in correspondence, then* $\mathscr{L}_E^p(\mu) \subset \mathscr{L}_E^1(\boldsymbol{m})$ *and* $|||U_A|||_p = \bar{\boldsymbol{m}}_q(A)$ *for every* μ*-measurable set* $A \subset T$.

If μ *has the direct sum property, then* $|\boldsymbol{m}| = g\mu$ *and for every* μ*-measurable set* $A \subset T$ *with* $\bar{\boldsymbol{m}}_q(A) < \infty$ *we have* $\varphi_A g \in \mathscr{L}^p(\mu)$ *and* $|||U_A|||_p = N_q(g\varphi_A, \mu)$.

Corollary 2. *There exists an isomorphism* $U \leftrightarrow \boldsymbol{m}$ *between the set of the linear mappings* $U\colon \mathscr{L}_E^1(\mu) \to F$ *with* $\|U\|_1 < \infty$ *and the set of the vector measures* $\boldsymbol{m}\colon \mathscr{C} \to \mathscr{L}(E, F)$ *with finite variation* $|\boldsymbol{m}|$ *such that* $|\boldsymbol{m}| \leqq \alpha\mu$ *for some* α, *given by*

$$U(f) = \int f\, dm, \quad \textit{for} \quad f \in \mathscr{L}_E^1(\mu).$$

If μ *has the direct sum property, then* $|\boldsymbol{m}| = g\mu$ *with* $N_\infty(g, \mu) = \|U\|_1$.

Theorem 2. *Let* $1 \leqq p < \infty$ *and* $\frac{1}{p} + \frac{1}{q} = 1$. *For every linear mapping* $U\colon \mathscr{L}_E^p \to F$ *with* $\|U_A\|_p < \infty$ *for* $A \in \mathscr{T}_{\sigma f}$ *there exists a linear mapping* $U'\colon \mathscr{L}^p \to \mathscr{L}(E, F)$ *with* $\|U'_A\|_p < \infty$ *for* $A \in \mathscr{T}_{\sigma f}$ *and only one such that*

$$U(\varphi x) = U'(\varphi)\, x, \quad \textit{for} \quad \varphi \in \mathscr{L}^p(\mu) \quad \textit{and} \quad x \in E.$$

Moreover, for every μ*-measurable set* $A \subset T$ *we have*

$$\|U'_A\|_p \leqq \|U_A\|_p \quad \textit{and} \quad |||U'_A|||_p = \|U_A\|_p$$

and there exists a measure $\boldsymbol{m}\colon \mathscr{C} \to \mathscr{L}(E, F)$ *with* $\tilde{\boldsymbol{m}}_q(A) < \infty$ *for* $A \in \mathscr{T}_{\sigma f}$ *such that*

$$U(f) = \int f\, dm, \quad \textit{for} \quad f \in \mathscr{L}_E^p(\mu),$$

and

$$U(\varphi) = \int \varphi\, dm \quad \textit{for} \quad \varphi \in \mathscr{L}^p(\mu).$$

Let U: $\mathscr{L}_E^p \to F$ be a linear mapping with $\|U_A\|_p < \infty$ for $A \in \mathscr{T}_{\sigma f}$. Let $\boldsymbol{m}: \mathscr{C} \to \mathscr{L}(E, F)$ be the measure with $\tilde{\boldsymbol{m}}_q(A) < \infty$ for $A \in \mathscr{T}_{\sigma f}$ such that

$$U(f) = \int f\, d\boldsymbol{m}, \quad \text{for} \quad f \in \mathscr{L}_E^p(\mu).$$

Let now U': $\mathscr{L}^p \to \mathscr{L}(E, F)$ be the linear mapping defined by

$$U'(\varphi) = \int \varphi\, d\boldsymbol{m}, \quad \text{for} \quad \varphi \in \mathscr{L}^p.$$

For $\varphi \in \mathscr{L}^p$ and $x \in E$ we have

$$U(\varphi x) = \int \varphi x\, d\boldsymbol{m} = \int \varphi\, d\boldsymbol{m}\, x = U'(\varphi)\, x.$$

The uniqueness of U' is evident.

For a $\mathscr{C}$-step function $\varphi = \sum \varphi_{A_i} \alpha_i \in \mathscr{E}(\mathscr{C}, A)$ with A_i disjoint and $N_p(\varphi) \leqq 1$ and for every $x \in E$ with $|x| \leqq 1$ we have $N_p(\varphi x) = N_p(\varphi) \leqq 1$ and

$$\left|\sum U'(\varphi_{A_i}\alpha_i)\right| = \sup_{|x| \leqq 1} \left|\sum U'(\varphi_{A_i}\alpha_i)\, x\right| = \sup_{|x| \leqq 1} \left|\sum U(\varphi_{A_i}\alpha_i x)\right| \leqq \|U_A\|_p,$$

therefore $\|U'_A\|_p \leqq \|U_A\|_p$.

On the other hand

$$\sum \left|U'(\varphi_{A_i})\, \alpha_i\right| = \sum \left|\boldsymbol{m}(A_i)\right| \left|\alpha_i\right|,$$

therefore, taking the supremum for $\varphi = \sum \varphi_{A_i} \alpha_i \in \mathscr{E}(\mathscr{C}, A)$ with A_i disjoint and $N_p(\varphi) \leqq 1$, we obtain

$$|||U'_A|||_p = \bar{\boldsymbol{m}}_q(A) = |||U_A|||_p.$$

Remark. There are linear mappings U': $\mathscr{L}^p \to \mathscr{L}(E, F)$ with $\|U'_A\|_p < \infty$ for $A \in \mathscr{T}_{\sigma f}$, which do not correspond to any mapping U: $\mathscr{L}_E^p \to F$.

Theorem 3. *Let* $1 \leqq p < \infty$ *and* $\frac{1}{p} + \frac{1}{q} = 1$. *There exists an isomorphism* $U \leftrightarrow U'$ *between the set of the linear mappings* U: $\mathscr{L}_E^p \to F$ *with* $|||U_A|||_p < \infty$ *for* $A \in \mathscr{T}_{\sigma f}$ *and the set of the linear mappings* U': $\mathscr{L}^p \to \mathscr{L}(E, F)$ *with* $|||U'_A|||_p < \infty$ *for* $A \in \mathscr{T}_{\sigma f}$, *given by*

$$U(\varphi x) = U'(\varphi)\, x, \quad \textit{for} \quad \varphi \in \mathscr{L}^p \quad \textit{and} \quad x \in E.$$

If U *and* U' *are in correspondence, then*

$$|||U_A|||_p = |||U'_A|||_p, \quad \textit{for} \quad A \subset T,$$

and there exists a measure $\boldsymbol{m}: \mathscr{C} \to \mathscr{L}(E, F)$ *with* $\bar{\boldsymbol{m}}_q(A) < \infty$ *for* $A \in \mathscr{T}_{\sigma f}$ *such that*

$$U(f) = \int f\, d\boldsymbol{m}, \quad \text{for} \quad f \in \mathscr{L}^p_E,$$

$$U'(\varphi) = \int \varphi\, d\boldsymbol{m}, \quad \text{for} \quad \varphi \in \mathscr{L}^p,$$

and

$$|||U'_A|||_p = |||U_A|||_p = \bar{\boldsymbol{m}}_q(A), \quad \text{for} \quad A \subset T.$$

Let $U': \mathscr{L}^p \to \mathscr{L}(E, F)$ be a linear mapping with $|||U'_A|||_p < \infty$ for $A \in \mathscr{T}_{\sigma f}$. If we put $X = \mathscr{L}(E, F)$, we have $X = \mathscr{L}(R, X)$. By the theorem 1 to U' there corresponds a measure $\boldsymbol{m}: \mathscr{C} \to \mathscr{L}(R, X) = X = \mathscr{L}(E, F)$ with $\bar{\boldsymbol{m}}_q(A) = |||U'_A|||_p$ for every $A \subset T$, therefore with $\bar{\boldsymbol{m}}_q(A) < \infty$ for $A \in \mathscr{T}_{\sigma f}$, and we have

$$U'(\varphi) = \int \varphi\, d\boldsymbol{m}, \quad \text{for} \quad \varphi \in \mathscr{L}^p(\mu).$$

To $\boldsymbol{m}$ there corresponds a linear mapping $U: \mathscr{L}^p_E \to F$ with $|||U_A|||_p = \bar{\boldsymbol{m}}_q(A)$ for $A \subset T$ and

$$U(f) = \int f\, d\boldsymbol{m}, \quad \text{for} \quad f \in \mathscr{L}^p_E.$$

We have then

$$U(\varphi x) = \int \varphi x\, d\boldsymbol{m} = \int \varphi\, d\boldsymbol{m}\, x = U'(\varphi)\, x$$

for $\varphi \in \mathscr{L}^p$ and $x \in E$.

The correspondence $U' \to U$ is evidently linear and one-to-one.

4. THE GENERALIZED THEOREM OF LEBESGUE-NIKODYM

Let $\mathscr{C}$ be a clan, E and F two Banach spaces and Z a norming subspace of F'.

Theorem 4. *Let* $\boldsymbol{m}: \mathscr{C} \to \mathscr{L}(E, F)$ *be a measure with finite variation* μ. *If* μ *has the direct sum property, then there exists a function* $U_{\boldsymbol{m}}: T \to \mathscr{L}(E, Z')$ *having the following properties:*

1. $|U_{\boldsymbol{m}}(t)| = 1$ *μ-almost everywhere;*

2. $\langle U_{\boldsymbol{m}} f, z\rangle$ *is μ-integrable and*

$$\left\langle \int f\, d\boldsymbol{m}, z \right\rangle = \int \langle U_{\boldsymbol{m}}(t) f(t), z\rangle\, d\mu, \quad \text{for} \quad f \in \mathscr{L}^1_E(\boldsymbol{m}) \quad \text{and} \quad z \in Z;$$

3. *If ϱ is a lifting of $\mathscr{L}^{\infty}(\mu)$, we can choose U_m uniquely such that*

$$\varrho(U_m) = U_m.$$

4. *We can choose $U_m(t) \in \mathscr{L}(E, F)$ for every $t \in T$, in each of the following cases:*

a) $F = Z'$;

b) *there exists a family $\mathscr{A} \in C(\mu)$ such that, for every $A \in \mathscr{A}$ and every $x \in E$, the convex equilibrated cover of the set $\left\{\int_A \varphi x \, d\boldsymbol{m};\ \varphi \in \mathscr{E}(\mathscr{C}), \int_A |\varphi| \, d\mu \leqq 1\right\}$ is relatively compact in F for the topology $\sigma(F, Z)$;*

c) *for every $x \in E$, the convex equilibrated cover of the set $\{\int \varphi x \, d\boldsymbol{m};\ \varphi \in \mathscr{E}(\mathscr{C}), \int |\varphi| \, d\mu \leqq 1\}$ is relatively compact in F for the topology $\sigma(F, Z)$.*

If $\boldsymbol{m} = 0$ we take $U_m(t) = 0$ for every $t \in T$ and the theorem is proved. Suppose that $\boldsymbol{m} \neq 0$ and let ϱ be a lifting of $\mathscr{L}^{\infty}(\mu)$. For every $x \in E$ and $z \in Z$, the scalar set function $\boldsymbol{m}_{x,z}$ defined on $\mathscr{C}$ by the equality

$$\boldsymbol{m}_{x,z}(A) = \langle \boldsymbol{m}(A) x, z \rangle, \quad \text{for} \quad A \in \mathscr{C},$$

is a measure and we have

$$|\boldsymbol{m}_{x,z}| \leqq |x| \, |z| \, \mu.$$

From the Lebesgue-Nikodym theorem we deduce that there exists a scalar locally μ-integrable function $g_{x,z}$ such that

$$\boldsymbol{m}_{x,z} = g_{x,z}\mu.$$

Then $|\boldsymbol{m}_{x,z}| = |g_{x,z}| \, \mu$, hence $|g_{x,z}| \, \mu \leqq |x| \, |z| \, \mu$, therefore $|g_{x,z}(t)| \leqq |x| \, |z|$ μ-almost everywhere. It follows that $g_{x,z} \in \mathscr{L}^{\infty}(\mu)$. Modifying $g_{x,z}$ on a μ-negligible set we can realise

$$\varrho(g_{x,z}) = g_{x,z}.$$

Then

$$|g_{x,z}(t)| \leqq |x| \, |z|, \quad \text{for every} \quad t \in T.$$

Since the mapping $(x, z) \to \boldsymbol{m}_{x,z}$ of $E \times Z$ in the space of the scalar measures is bilinear and $\varrho(g_{x,z}) = g_{x,z}$, we deduce that the mapping $(x, z) \to g_{x,z}$ of $E \times Z$ into the space of the bounded μ-measurable scalar functions is bilinear, therefore, for every $t \in T$, the mapping $(x, z) \to g_{x,z}(t)$ is a bilinear functional on $E \times Z$.

For fixed $t \in T$ and $x \in E$, the mapping $g_x(t)$: $z \to g_{x,z}(t)$ is a continuous linear functional on Z, hence $g_x(t) \in Z'$ and we have

$$|g_x(t)| \leqq |x|.$$

For fixed $t \in T$, the mapping $U_m(t): x \to g_x(t)$ of E into Z' is linear and continuous, hence $U_m(t) \in \mathscr{L}(E, Z')$ and we have

$$|U_m(t)| \leqq 1.$$

Then

$$\langle U_m(t)\, x, z\rangle = g_{x,z}(t), \quad \text{for} \quad t \in T, \quad x \in E \quad \text{and} \quad z \in Z,$$

hence $\varrho(U_m) = U_m$. It follows first that

$$\langle \boldsymbol{m}(A)\, x, z\rangle = \int_A \langle U_m(t)\, x, z\rangle \, d\mu(t), \quad \text{for} \quad A \in \mathscr{C}, \quad x \in E \quad \text{and} \quad z \in Z,$$

and then

$$\left\langle \int \boldsymbol{f}\, d\boldsymbol{m}, z \right\rangle = \int \langle U_m(t)\, \boldsymbol{f}(t), z\rangle \, d\mu(t), \quad \text{for} \quad \boldsymbol{f} \in \mathscr{E}_E(\mathscr{C}) \quad \text{and} \quad z \in Z.$$

Let now $\boldsymbol{f} \in \mathscr{L}_E^1(\mu)$ and let $(\boldsymbol{f}_n)$ be a sequence of $\mathscr{E}_E(\mathscr{C})$ converging in mean and μ-almost everywhere to $\boldsymbol{f}$. From the inequality

$$|\langle U_m \boldsymbol{f}_{n+p}, z\rangle - \langle U_m \boldsymbol{f}_n, z\rangle| \leqq |\boldsymbol{f}_{n+p} - \boldsymbol{f}_n|\, |z|$$

we deduce that $(\langle U_m \boldsymbol{f}_n, z\rangle)$ is a Cauchy sequence in $\mathscr{L}^1(\mu)$ and converges μ-almost everywhere to $\langle U_m \boldsymbol{f}, z\rangle$. It follows that $\langle U_m \boldsymbol{f}, z\rangle$ is μ-integrable and

$$\lim_{n\to\infty} \int \langle U_m \boldsymbol{f}_n, z\rangle \, d\mu = \int \langle U_m \boldsymbol{f}, z\rangle \, d\mu, \quad \text{for} \quad z \in Z.$$

We have also

$$\lim_{n\to\infty} \int \boldsymbol{f}_n \, d\boldsymbol{m} = \int \boldsymbol{f}\, d\boldsymbol{m},$$

hence

$$\lim_{n\to\infty} \left\langle \int \boldsymbol{f}_n \, d\boldsymbol{m}, z \right\rangle = \left\langle \int \boldsymbol{f}\, d\boldsymbol{m}, z \right\rangle, \quad \text{for} \quad z \in Z.$$

From the equality

$$\left\langle \int \boldsymbol{f}_n \, d\boldsymbol{m}, z \right\rangle = \int \langle U_m \boldsymbol{f}_n, z\rangle \, d\mu, \quad \text{for every} \quad z \in Z \quad \text{and} \quad n,$$

we deduce by passing to the limit

$$\left\langle \int \boldsymbol{f}\, d\boldsymbol{m}, z \right\rangle = \int \langle U_m \boldsymbol{f}, z\rangle \, d\mu, \quad \text{for} \quad z \in Z.$$

We prove now that $|U_m(t)| = 1$, almost everywhere. By proposition 5, § 11, the function $t \to |U_m(t)|$ is μ-measurable; from the equality $|U_m(t)| \leqq 1$ we deduce that the function $|U_m|$ is locally μ-integrable. For every $A \in \mathscr{C}$, $x \in E$ and $z \in Z$ we have

$$|\langle \boldsymbol{m}(A)\, x, z\rangle| \leqq \int_A |x|\,|z|\,|U_m(t)|\, d\mu(t),$$

therefore, putting $\nu = |U_m|\,\mu$, we have

$$|\boldsymbol{m}(A)| \leqq \int_A |U_m(t)|\, d\mu(t) = \nu(A).$$

Since μ is the least positive measure verifying the inequality $|\boldsymbol{m}(A)| \leqq \mu(A)$ for $A \in \mathscr{C}$, we deduce that $\mu \leqq \nu$, hence $|U_m(t)| \geqq 1$ μ-almost everywhere, consequently

$$|U_m(t)| = 1 \quad \mu\text{-almost everywhere}.$$

It remains to prove the statement 4. The case $F = Z'$ is trivial. Suppose that the condition b) is verified. Let $A \in \mathscr{A}$ and $x \in E$ and denote by C the closure in the topology $\sigma(F, Z)$ of the convex equilibrated cover of the set $\left\{\int_A \varphi x\, d\boldsymbol{m};\ \varphi \in \mathscr{E}(\mathscr{C}),\ \int_A |\varphi|\, d\mu \leqq 1\right\}$. Then C is compact in F for the topology $\sigma(F, Z)$, hence C is compact in the algebraic dual Z^* of Z, for the topology $\sigma(Z^*, Z)$. There exists then a family $(z_i)_{i \in I}$ of elements of Z such that

$$C = \bigcap_{i \in I} \{y;\ y \in Z^*,\ |\langle y, z_i\rangle| \leqq 1\}.$$

For every $i \in I$ and $\varphi \in \mathscr{E}(\mathscr{C})$ with $\int_A |\varphi|\, d\mu \leqq 1$ we have

$$\left|\left\langle \int \varphi x\, d\boldsymbol{m}, z_i \right\rangle\right| = 1,$$

hence

$$\left|\int_A \langle U_m(t)\, x, z_i\rangle\, \varphi\, d\mu\right| \leqq 1,$$

consequently, for each $i \in I$ we have

$$|\langle U_m(t)\, x, z_i\rangle| \leqq 1 \quad \mu\text{-almost everywhere on } A.$$

We deduce that for every $t \in \varrho(A)$ and $i \in I$ we have

$$|\langle U_m(t)\, x, z_i\rangle| \leqq 1,$$

hence $U_m(t)\, x \in C \subset F$, for $t \in \bigcup_{A \in \mathscr{A}} \varrho(A)$, i.e. μ-almost everywhere.

If the condition c) is verified, then the condition b) is verified for every family $\mathscr{A} \in C(\mu)$. Thus the theorem is completely proved.

Remarks.

1°. The function U_m depends on the space Z. If we take $Z = F'$, then we have $U_m(t) \in \mathscr{L}(E, F'')$ for every $t \in T$.

If Z_1 and Z_2 are two norming subspaces of F' such that $Z_1 \subset Z_2$ and if $U_1: T \to \mathscr{L}(E, Z_1')$ and $U_2: T \to \mathscr{L}(E, Z_2')$ are the corresponding functions, then for every $t \in T$ and every $x \in E$, the functional $U_1(t)\,x \in Z_1'$ is the restriction to Z_1 of the functional $U_2'(t)\,x \in Z_2'$.

2°. If one of the conditions 4 is not verified, it may happen that U_m has not values in $\mathscr{L}(E, F)$.

Example. Let $T = [0, 1]$, μ the Lebesgue measure on T, $X = L^1(\mu)$, and the set function $\boldsymbol{m}: \mathscr{B} \to X$ defined by the equality

$$\boldsymbol{m}(A) = \tilde{\varphi}_A \in L^1(\mu), \quad \text{for} \quad A \in \mathscr{B},$$

where $\mathscr{B}$ is the semi-tribe of the Borel subsets of T (see § 14). We verify easily that $\boldsymbol{m}$ is additive. For every set $A \in \mathscr{B}$ we have $|\boldsymbol{m}(A)| = \|\tilde{\varphi}_A\|_1 = \mu(A)$, therefore $\boldsymbol{m}$ is countably additive, and with finite variation and we have $|\boldsymbol{m}| = \mu$. We shall prove that $\boldsymbol{m}$ cannot be represented as in the preceding theorem, by an integral with respect to μ, with $U_m(t) \in \mathscr{L}(E, F)$ for every $t \in T$.

Assume, by absurd, that there exists a function $U: T \to \mathscr{L}(R, X) = X = L^1(\mu)$ with $|U(t)| \equiv 1$, such that, putting $U_t = U(t)$,

$$\left\langle \int \varphi \, d\boldsymbol{m}, z \right\rangle = \int \langle U_t \varphi(t), z \rangle \, d\mu(t)$$

for every $\varphi \in L^1(\mu)$ and every $z \in Z = L^\infty(\mu)$. In particular, taking $\varphi = \varphi_A$ with $A \in \mathscr{B}$ we obtain

$$\int_A z(t)\, d\mu(t) = \langle \varphi_A, z \rangle = \left\langle \int \varphi_A \, d\boldsymbol{m}, z \right\rangle = \int \langle U_t \varphi_A(t), z \rangle \, d\mu(t)$$
$$= \int_A \langle U_t, z \rangle \, d\mu(t) = \int_A d\mu(t) \int U_t(s)\, z(s)\, d\mu(s).$$

Since $A \in \mathscr{B}$ is arbitrary, we deduce that

$$z(t) = \int U_t(s)\, z(s)\, d\mu(s) \quad \mu\text{-almost everywhere},$$

for every $z \in L^\infty(\mu)$.

Then taking $z = \varphi_{[p,q]}$ with p and q rational numbers in $[0, 1]$, we can find a μ-negligible set $N \subset [0, 1]$ such that for every $t \notin N$ and for every rational numbers $p, q \in [0, 1]$, we have

$$\int_{[p,q]} U_t(s)\, d\mu(s) = z(t) = \begin{cases} 1, & \text{if} \quad t \in [p, q], \\ 0, & \text{if} \quad t \notin [p, q]. \end{cases}$$

We deduce then that for $t \notin N$ and for every $\alpha, \beta \in [0, 1]$ we have

$$\int_{[\alpha,\beta]} U_t(s)\, d\mu(s) = \begin{cases} 1, & \text{if} \quad t \in [\alpha, \beta], \\ 0, & \text{if} \quad t \notin [\alpha, \beta]. \end{cases}$$

In fact, if $t \notin [\alpha, \beta]$ or if $t \in (\alpha, \beta)$, we take an increasing sequence $[p_n, q_n] \subset [\alpha, \beta]$ with $p_n \to \alpha$ and $q_n \to \beta$; if $t = \alpha$ or if $t = \beta$, we take a decreasing sequence $[\alpha_n, \beta_n] \supset [\alpha, \beta]$ with $\alpha_n \to \alpha$ and $\beta_n \to \beta$.

Since the intervals $[\alpha, \beta]$ of $[0, 1]$ generate the semi-tribe $\mathscr{B}$ we deduce that for $t \notin N$ and for every $A \in \mathscr{B}$ we have

$$\int_A U_t(s)\, d\mu(s) = \begin{cases} 1, & \text{if} \quad t \in A, \\ 0, & \text{if} \quad t \notin A. \end{cases}$$

It follows that for every $t \notin N$ we have $U_t(s) = 0$ μ-almost everywhere, therefore $|U_t(s)| = 0$ μ-almost everywhere, consequently $|U_t| = \|U_t\|_1 = 0$, and we get a contradiction.

3°. If Z' is of countable type (in particular if $F = C$) then $U_m: T \to \mathscr{L}(E, Z')$ is simply μ-measurable (§ 6, proposition 22). Then for every function $f \in \mathscr{L}^1_E(m)$ the function Uf is μ-measurable, hence μ-integrable and we have

$$\int f\, dm = \int U_m(t) f(t)\, d\mu(t), \quad \text{for} \quad f \in \mathscr{L}^1_E(m).$$

In particular

$$m(A)\, x = \int_A U_m(t)\, x\, d\mu(t), \quad \text{for} \quad A \in \Sigma(\mu) \quad \text{and} \quad x \in E.$$

4°. If there exists a countable set $H \subset \mathscr{L}(E, Z')$ such that $U_m(t) \in H$ μ-almost everywhere (in particular, if $\mathscr{L}(E, Z')$ is of countable type), then U_m is μ-measurable (§ 6, proposition 24). In this case, if we put $X = \mathscr{L}(E, Z')$ we have $U_m \in \mathscr{L}^\infty_X(\mu)$ and we have

$$\int \varphi\, dm = \int U_m(t)\, \varphi(t)\, d\mu(t), \quad \text{for} \quad \varphi \in \mathscr{L}^1(\mu).$$

In particular

$$m(A) = \int_A U_m(t)\, d\mu(t), \quad \text{for} \quad A \in \Sigma(\mu).$$

5°. If $F = C$, then $U_m: T \to \mathscr{L}(E, C) = E'$ and U_m is simply μ-measurable. If E' is of countable type, then U_m is μ-measurable, $U_m \in \mathscr{L}^\infty_{E'}(\mu)$ and

$$m(A) = \int_A U_m(t)\, d\mu(t), \quad \text{for} \quad A \in \Sigma(\mu).$$

6°. If $E = C$, then $U_m: T \to \mathscr{L}(C, Z') = Z'$ and

$$\left\langle \int \varphi \, d\boldsymbol{m}, z \right\rangle = \int \varphi(t) \langle U_m(t), z \rangle \, d\mu(t), \quad \text{for} \quad \varphi \in \mathscr{L}^1(\mu), z \in Z.$$

If, in addition, Z' is of countable type, then U_m is μ-measurable, $U_m \in \mathscr{L}_{Z'}^\infty(\mu)$ and

$$\int \varphi \, d\boldsymbol{m} = \int U_m(t) \varphi(t) \, d\mu(t), \quad \text{for} \quad \varphi \in \mathscr{L}^1(\mu),$$

and

$$\boldsymbol{m}(A) = \int_A U_m(t) \, d\mu(t), \quad \text{for} \quad A \in \Sigma(\mu).$$

We can give now a generalization of the theorem of Lebesgue-Nikodym.

Theorem 5. *Let ν be a scalar measure on $\mathscr{C}$ and $\boldsymbol{m}: \mathscr{C} \to \mathscr{L}(E, F)$ a measure with finite variation μ. If ν has the direct sum property and if $\boldsymbol{m}$ is absolutely continuous with respect to ν, then there exists a function $V_m: T \to \mathscr{L}(E, Z')$ having the following properties:*

1. *The function $|V_m|$ is locally ν-integrable and*

$$\int \varphi \, d\mu = \int |V_m| \, \varphi \, d|\nu|, \quad \textit{for} \quad \varphi \in \mathscr{L}^1(\mu);$$

2. *$\langle V_m f, z \rangle$ is ν-integrable and we have*

$$\left\langle \int f \, d\boldsymbol{m}, z \right\rangle = \int \langle V_m(t) f(t), z \rangle \, d\nu(t), \quad \textit{for} \quad f \in \mathscr{L}_E^1(\mu) \quad \textit{and} \quad z \in Z.$$

3. *If ϱ is a lifting of $\mathscr{L}^\infty(\nu)$, we can choose V_m uniquely ν-almost everywhere such that*

$$\varrho[V_m] = V_m.$$

If, in addition, there exists $\alpha > 0$ such that $\mu \leqq \alpha \, |\nu|$, then we can choose V_m uniquely such that $\varrho(V_m) = V_m$.

4. *We can choose $V_m(t) \in \mathscr{L}(E, F)$ for every $t \in T$, in each of the following cases:*

a) $F = Z'$;

b) *there exists a family $\mathscr{A} \in C(\nu)$ such that for every $A \in \mathscr{A}$ and $x \in E$, the convex equilibrated cover of the set $\left\{ \int_A \varphi x \, d\boldsymbol{m};\ \varphi \in \mathscr{E}(\mathscr{C}), \int_A |\varphi| \, d|\nu| \leqq 1 \right\}$ is relatively compact in F for the topology $\sigma(F, Z)$.*

b′) *the same statement as* b), *with $\mathscr{A} \in C(\mu)$ and with $\int |\varphi| \, d\mu \leqq 1$ instead of $\int_A |\varphi| \, d|\nu| \leqq 1$. In this case we have not necessarily $\varrho[V_m] = V_m$.*

c) *for every* $x \in E$, *the convex equilibrated cover of the set* $\{\int \varphi x \, d\boldsymbol{m}; \varphi \in \mathscr{E}(\mathscr{C}), \int |\varphi| \, d|\nu| \leqq 1\}$ *is relatively compact in* F *for the topology* $\sigma(F, Z)$.

c′) *the same condition as* c) *with* $\int |\varphi| \, d\mu \leqq 1$ *instead of* $\int |\varphi| \, d|\nu| \leqq 1$. *In this case we have not necessarily* $\varrho[V_{\boldsymbol{m}}] = V_{\boldsymbol{m}}$.

If $\nu = 0$, then $\boldsymbol{m} = 0$ and taking $V_{\boldsymbol{m}}(t) = 0$ for every $t \in T$, the theorem is proved. Suppose that $\nu \neq 0$. As μ is absolutely continuous with respect to $|\nu|$, there exists a locally ν-integrable function $g \geqq 0$ with $\mu = g\,|\nu|$, hence

$$\int \varphi \, d\mu = \int g\varphi \, d|\nu|, \quad \text{for} \quad \varphi \in \mathscr{L}^1(\mu).$$

By the corollary of the theorem of Lebesgue-Nikodym, § 10, there exists a locally ν-integrable scalar function h such that $|h(t)| = 1$, $\nu = h|\nu|$, and $|\nu| = \frac{1}{h}\nu$. The function $g\frac{1}{h}$ is then locally ν-integrable and we have $\mu = g\frac{1}{h}\nu$.

Let $U_{\boldsymbol{m}}: T \to \mathscr{L}(E, Z')$ be the function corresponding to $\boldsymbol{m}$ by the theorem 4 and put $V = U_{\boldsymbol{m}} g \frac{1}{h}$. As $|U_{\boldsymbol{m}}(t)| = 1$ μ-almost everywhere the function $|U_{\boldsymbol{m}}| - 1$ is μ-negligible, hence $(|U_{\boldsymbol{m}}| - 1)\, g$ is ν-negligible, therefore $|U_{\boldsymbol{m}}(t)|\, g(t) = g(t)$ ν-almost everywhere. It follows that $|V(t)| = g(t)$ ν-almost everywhere, hence $|V|$ is locally ν-integrable and

$$\int \varphi \, d\mu = \int |V|\, \varphi \, d|\nu|, \quad \text{for} \quad \varphi \in \mathscr{L}^1(\mu).$$

If $f \in \mathscr{L}^1_E(\mu)$ and $z \in Z$, the function $\langle U_{\boldsymbol{m}} f, z\rangle$ is μ-integrable, hence the function $\langle U_{\boldsymbol{m}} f, z\rangle g$ is ν-integrable and we have

$$\left\langle \int f \, d\boldsymbol{m}, z \right\rangle = \int \langle U_{\boldsymbol{m}} f, z\rangle \, d\mu = \int \langle U_{\boldsymbol{m}} f, z\rangle \, g \, d|\nu|$$
$$= \int \langle U_{\boldsymbol{m}} f, z\rangle \, g \frac{1}{h} \, d\nu = \int \langle V f, z\rangle \, d\nu .$$

Taking $V_{\boldsymbol{m}} = V$, the first two statements are proved.

Let now ϱ be a lifting of $\mathscr{L}^\infty(\nu)$. Since $|V|$ is μ-measurable, from the proposition 8, § 11, we deduce that there exists a function $V_{\boldsymbol{m}}: T \to \mathscr{L}^*(E, Z')$ with $\varrho[V_{\boldsymbol{m}}] = V_{\boldsymbol{m}}$, $V_{\boldsymbol{m}} \equiv V$ and $|V_{\boldsymbol{m}}(t)| \leqq |V(t)| < \infty$ for every $t \in T$. We deduce then that $V_{\boldsymbol{m}}(t) \in \mathscr{L}(E, Z')$ for every $t \in T$ and that $|V_{\boldsymbol{m}}|$ is μ-measurable (§ 11, proposition 5), hence $|V_{\boldsymbol{m}}|$ is locally ν-integrable. From the relation $V_{\boldsymbol{m}} \equiv V$ we deduce that $\langle V_{\boldsymbol{m}} f, z\rangle = \langle V f, z\rangle$ ν-almost everywhere for each $f \in \mathscr{L}^1_E(\boldsymbol{m})$ and $z \in Z$, hence

$$\left\langle \int f \, d\boldsymbol{m}, z \right\rangle = \int \langle V_{\boldsymbol{m}} f, z\rangle \, d\nu .$$

Taking $f = \varphi_A x$ with $A \in \mathscr{C}$ and $x \in E$ it follows that

$$|\langle \boldsymbol{m}(A)\, x, z\rangle| \leqq \int |V_m|\, \varphi_A\, |x|\, |z|\, d|\nu|, \quad \text{for every} \quad z \in Z.$$

Taking the supremum for $z \in Z$ with $|z| \leqq 1$ and $x \in E$ with $|x| \leqq 1$, we obtain

$$|\boldsymbol{m}(A)| \leqq \int_A |V_m|\, d|\nu|, \quad \text{for} \quad A \in \mathscr{C}.$$

It follows that $|\boldsymbol{m}| \leqq |V_m|\, |\nu| \leqq |V|\, |\nu| = \mu$, hence $\mu = |V_m|\, |\nu|$, therefore

$$\int \varphi\, d\mu = \int \varphi\, |V_m|\, d|\nu|, \quad \text{for} \quad \varphi \in \mathscr{L}^1(\mu).$$

Suppose now that $\mu \leqq \alpha|\nu|$ for some $\alpha > 0$. Then the function g belongs to $\mathscr{L}^\infty(\nu)$, hence $|V| \in \mathscr{L}^\infty(\nu)$. From the proposition 8, § 11, we deduce that there exists a function $V_m\colon T \to \mathscr{L}^*(E, Z')$ with $\varrho(V_m) = V_m$, $V_m \equiv V$ and $|V_m(t)| \leqq |V(t)|$ ν-almost everywhere. For every $x \in E$ with $|x| \leqq 1$ and $z \in Z$ with $|z| \leqq 1$ we have

$$\begin{aligned} |\langle V_m(t)\, x, z\rangle| &= \varrho(|\langle V_m x, z\rangle|)\,(t) = \varrho(|\langle V x, z\rangle|)\,(t) \\ &\leqq \varrho(|V|)\,(t) \leqq N_\infty(|V|, \nu) < \infty, \end{aligned}$$

hence $|V_m(t)| \leqq N_\infty(|V|) < \infty$, therefore $V_m(t) \in \mathscr{L}(E, Z')$ for every $t \in T$. We prove then that V_m has all the required properties as in the case $\varrho[V_m] = V_m$. In this way, the statement 3 is also proved.

It remains to prove the statement 4. The case $F = Z'$ is trivial. The case b) is proved as in the theorem 4 and c) implies b). In the case b′) we can take $U_m(t) \in \mathscr{L}(E, F)$ for every $t \in T$. Then $V(t) = U_m(t)\, g(t) \dfrac{1}{h(t)} \in \mathscr{L}(E, F)$ for every $t \in T$ and we can take $V_m = V$. But in this case we have not necessarily $\varrho[V_m] = V_m$. The case c′) implies b′).

The theorem is completely proved.

Remarks.

1°. The function V_m depends on the space Z.

2°. If one of the condition 4 is not verified, it is possible that V_m should not have values in $\mathscr{L}(E, F)$.

3°. If Z' is of countable type, then for every function $f \in \mathscr{L}^1_E(\mu)$ the function $t \to V_m(t) f(t)$ is ν-integrable and we have

$$\int f\, d\boldsymbol{m} = \int V_m(t) f(t)\, d\nu(t), \quad \text{for} \quad f \in \mathscr{L}^1_E(\mu).$$

In particular

$$\boldsymbol{m}(A)\, x = \int_A V_m(t)\, x\, d\nu(t), \quad \text{for} \quad A \in \Sigma(\mu) \quad \text{and} \quad x \in E.$$

4°. If there exists a countable set $H \subset \mathscr{L}(E, Z')$ with $V_m(t) \in \bar{H}$ ν-almost everywhere (in particular, if $\mathscr{L}(E, Z')$ is of countable type), then V_m is ν-measurable. In this case we have

$$\int \varphi \, dm = \int V_m(t) \varphi(t) \, d\nu(t), \quad \text{for} \quad \varphi \in \mathscr{L}^1(\mu).$$

In particular, V_m is locally ν-integrable and we have

$$m(A) = \int_A V_m(t) \, d\nu(t), \quad \text{for} \quad A \in \Sigma(\mu).$$

5°. If $F = C$ and if E' is of countable type, then V_m is locally ν-integrable and we have

$$\int \varphi \, dm = \int V_m(t) \varphi(t) \, d\nu(t), \quad \text{for} \quad \varphi \in \mathscr{L}^1(\mu).$$

6°. If $E = C$ and if Z' is of countable type, then V_m is locally ν-integrable.

7°. If E is of countable type and if there exists a countable norming set $S \subset Z$, then the function V_m is uniquely determined ν-almost everywhere by the equality

$$\left\langle \int f \, dm, z \right\rangle = \int \langle V_m(t) f(t), z \rangle \, d\nu, \quad \text{for} \quad f \in \mathscr{L}^1_E(m) \quad \text{and} \quad z \in Z.$$

In fact, if $V: T \to \mathscr{L}(E, Z')$ is another function verifying the preceding equalities, then we have

$$\int \langle [V_m(t) - V(t)] f(t), z \rangle \, d\nu = 0, \quad \text{for} \quad f \in \mathscr{L}^1_E(m) \quad \text{and} \quad z \in Z.$$

In particular, taking $f = \varphi_A x$ with $A \in \mathscr{C}$ and $x \in E$, we deduce

$$\int_A \langle [V_m(t) - V(t)] x, z \rangle \, d\nu = 0, \quad \text{for} \quad A \in \mathscr{C}, x \in E \quad \text{and} \quad z \in Z,$$

therefore

$$\langle [V_m(t) - V(t)] x, z \rangle = 0 \quad \nu\text{-almost everywhere}$$

for each $x \in E$ and $z \in Z$. Taking Z in the countable norming set $S \subset Z$, we deduce

$$[V_m(t) - V(t)] x = 0 \quad \nu\text{-almost everywhere}$$

for each $x \in E$; then taking x in a countable dense subset of E, we deduce that

$$V_m(t) - V(t) = 0 \quad \nu\text{-almost everywhere},$$

consequently $V_m(t) = V(t)$ ν-almost everywhere.

If E is not of countable type, or if F' has no countable norming subset, then V_m may be not uniquely determined only by the equality

$$\left\langle \int f\,dm, z \right\rangle = \int \langle V_m(t) f(t), z\rangle\,dv, \quad \text{for} \quad f \in \mathscr{L}_E^1(m) \quad \text{and} \quad z \in Z.$$

Examples.

1. Let $T = [0, 1]$, v the Lebesgue measure on T, $E = \mathscr{C}(T)$, where $\mathscr{C}(T)$ is the space of the real continuous functions on T, endowed with the norm

$$\|\varphi\| = \sup_{t \in T} |\varphi(t)|,$$

Z the space of the real functions z defined on T, such that

$$\|z\| = \sum_{t \in T} |z(t)| < \infty.$$

$F = Z'$ is then the space of the real functions z' on T such that

$$\|z'\| = \sup_{t \in T} |z'(t)| < \infty.$$

The space E is of countable type, but Z is not of countable type. If for every $t \in T$ we define $V(t): E \to F$ by the equality $V(t)\,\varphi = \varphi_{\{t\}}\varphi$ for $\varphi \in E$, then we have $|V(t)| = 1$ and

$$\langle z, V(t)\,\varphi\rangle = \langle z, \varphi_{\{t\}}\varphi\rangle = \sum_{s \in T} z(s)\,\varphi_{\{t\}}(s)\,\varphi(s) = z(t)\,\varphi(t).$$

Let $f \in \mathscr{L}_E^1(v)$ and $z \in F$ and for every $t \in T$ put $f(t) = \varphi_t \in E$. Then, for the measure $m = 0$ we have

$$\int \langle z, V(t) f(t)\rangle\,dv(t) = \int \langle z, V(t)\,\varphi_t\rangle\,dv(t)$$
$$= \int z(t)\,\varphi_t(t)\,dv(t) = 0 = \left\langle \int f\,dm, z \right\rangle.$$

On the other hand, for $U(t) \equiv 0$ we have also

$$\int \langle z, U(t) f(t)\rangle\,dv(t) = 0 = \left\langle \int f\,dm, z \right\rangle.$$

2. Let $T = [0, 1]$, v the Lebesgue measure, E the space of the real functions $\varphi: T \to R$ such that

$$\|\varphi\| = \sum_{t \in T} |\varphi(t)| < \infty,$$

$Z = \mathscr{C}(T)$, therefore $F = Z'$ is the space of the real regular Borel measure on T (see § 15 and § 19).

The space Z is of countable type but E is not of countable type.

For every $t \in T$ consider the linear mapping $V(t)\colon E \to F$ defined by the equality $V(t)\,\varphi = \varphi(t)\,\varepsilon_t$, for $\varphi \in E$, where ε_t is the measure with the total mass equal to 1 and concentrated in the point t. We have $|V(t)| = 1$ and $\langle z, V(t)\,\varphi\rangle = \langle z, \varphi(t)\,\varepsilon_t\rangle = z(t)\,\varphi(t)$ for $z \in Z$, and $\varphi \in E$. We verify easily that for $\boldsymbol{f} \in \mathscr{L}^1_E(\nu)$ and $z \in Z$ we have

$$\int \langle z, V(t)\boldsymbol{f}(t)\rangle\, d\nu(t) = \int \langle z, U(t)\boldsymbol{f}(t)\rangle\, d\nu(t) = 0,$$

where $\boldsymbol{m} = 0$ and $U(t) \equiv 0$.

The following theorem is in a certain sense the converse of the preceding theorem.

Theorem 6. *Let ν be a scalar measure on $\mathscr{C}$ and $U\colon T \to \mathscr{L}(E, F)$ a function such that $|U|$ is locally ν-integrable and the function $\langle Ux, z\rangle$ is ν-measurable for every $x \in E$ and $z \in Z$.*

Then the function $\langle U\boldsymbol{f}, z\rangle$ is ν-integrable for $\boldsymbol{f} \in \mathscr{L}^1_E(|U|\,|\nu|)$ and $z \in Z$ and there exists a measure $\boldsymbol{m}\colon \mathscr{C} \to \mathscr{L}(E, Z')$ with finite variation μ such that

$$\left\langle \int \boldsymbol{f}\, d\boldsymbol{m}, z \right\rangle = \int \langle U(t)\boldsymbol{f}(t), z\rangle\, d\nu, \quad \text{for} \quad \boldsymbol{f} \in \mathscr{L}^1_E(|U|\,|\nu|) \quad \textit{and} \quad z \in Z,$$

and

$$\int |\varphi|\, d\mu \leqq \int |U|\,|\varphi|\, d|\nu|, \quad \textit{for} \quad \varphi \in \mathscr{L}^1(|U|\,|\nu|).$$

The measure $\boldsymbol{m}$ has values in $\mathscr{L}(E, F)$ in each of the following cases:

a) $F = Z'$;

b) *for every $x \in E$ there exists a family $\mathscr{A} \in C(\nu)$ such that for every $A \in \mathscr{A}$ the convex equilibrated cover of the set $\{U(t)\,x;\ t \in A\}$ is relatively compact in F for the topology $\sigma(F, Z)$;*

c) *for every $x \in E$ the convex equilibrated cover of the set $\{U(t)\,x;\ t \in T\}$ is relatively compact in F for the topology $\sigma(F, Z)$;*

d) *the function $t \to U(t)\,x$ is ν-measurable for each $x \in E$; in particular F is of countable type.*

If ν has the direct sum property, we have the equality $\mu = |U|\,|\nu|$, hence

$$\int |\varphi|\, d\mu = \int |U|\,|\varphi|\, d|\nu|, \quad \textit{for} \quad \varphi \in \mathscr{L}^1(\mu),$$

in each of the following cases:

α) *There exists a lifting ϱ of $\mathscr{L}^\infty(\nu)$ such that $\varrho[U] = U$;*

β) *E is of countable type and there exists a countable norming set $S \subset Z$;*

γ) *E is of countable type and the function $t \to U(t)\,x$ is ν-measurable for every $x \in E$;*

δ) *the function U is ν-measurable (in this case ν may not have the direct sum property).*

For every $x \in E$ and $z \in Z$ the function $\langle Ux, z\rangle$ is locally ν-integrable, since it is ν-measurable and is dominated by the locally ν-integrable function $|U|$, i.e. $|\langle Ux, z\rangle| \leqq |x|\,|z|\,|U|$. Put

$$\boldsymbol{m}_{x,z}(A) = \int_A \langle Ux, z\rangle\, d\nu, \quad \text{for} \quad A \in \mathscr{C}, x \in E \quad \text{and} \quad z \in Z.$$

For fixed $A \in \mathscr{C}$ and $x \in E$, the mapping $\boldsymbol{m}_x(A)\colon z \to \boldsymbol{m}_{x,z}(A)$ is a continuous linear functional on Z:

$$|\boldsymbol{m}_{x,z}(A)| \leqq |x|\,|z| \int_A |U|\, d|\nu|,$$

therefore $\boldsymbol{m}_x(A) \in Z'$ and

$$|\boldsymbol{m}_x(A)| \leqq |x| \int_A |U|\, d|\nu|.$$

For fixed $A \in \mathscr{C}$, the mapping $\boldsymbol{m}(A)\colon x \to \boldsymbol{m}_x(A)$ of E into Z' is linear and continuous, therefore $\boldsymbol{m}(A) \in \mathscr{L}(E, Z')$ and

$$|\boldsymbol{m}(A)| \leqq \int_A |U|\, d|\nu| = \int_A d(|U|\,|\nu|).$$

The measure $\lambda = |U|\,|\nu|$ is positive and we have

$$|\boldsymbol{m}(A)| \leqq \lambda(A), \quad \text{for} \quad A \in \mathscr{C}.$$

We have also

$$\langle \boldsymbol{m}(A)\,x, z\rangle = \boldsymbol{m}_{x,z}(A) = \int_A \langle Ux, z\rangle\, d\nu, \quad \text{for} \quad A \in \mathscr{C}, x \in E \quad \text{and} \quad z \in Z.$$

From this last equality we deduce easily that the mapping $\boldsymbol{m}\colon \mathscr{C} \to \mathscr{L}(E, Z')$ is additive. From the inequality $|\boldsymbol{m}(A)| \leqq \lambda(A)$ for $A \in \mathscr{C}$ we deduce that $\boldsymbol{m}$ is countably additive and with finite variation μ and $\mu \leqq \lambda$. Then $\mathscr{L}^1(\lambda) \subset \mathscr{L}^1(\mu)$ and

$$\int |\varphi|\, d\mu \leqq \int |U|\,|\varphi|\, d|\nu|, \quad \text{for} \quad \varphi \in \mathscr{L}^1(\lambda).$$

We have also $\mathscr{L}_E^1(\lambda) \subset \mathscr{L}_E^1(\mu)$. For every step function $\boldsymbol{f} = \sum \varphi_{A_i} x_i$ of $\mathscr{E}_E(\mathscr{C})$ we have

$$\left\langle \int \boldsymbol{f}\, d\boldsymbol{m}, z \right\rangle = \sum \langle \boldsymbol{m}(A_i)\, x_i, z\rangle = \sum \int_{A_i} \langle Ux_i, z\rangle\, d\nu = \int \langle U\boldsymbol{f}, z\rangle\, d\nu,$$

for every $z \in Z$.

Let now $\boldsymbol{f} \in \mathscr{L}_E^1(\lambda)$ and let $(\boldsymbol{f}_n)$ be a sequence of step functions of the preceding form converging to $\boldsymbol{f}$ λ-almost everywhere and in the topology of $\mathscr{L}_E^1(\lambda)$. The function $|\boldsymbol{f}_n - \boldsymbol{f}|$ converges to 0 almost everywhere with respect to $\lambda = |U|\,|\nu|$, therefore the function $|U||f_n - f|$ converges to 0 almost everywhere with respect to $|\nu|$. From the inequality

$$|\langle Uf_n, z\rangle - \langle Uf, z\rangle| \leqq |U|\,|z|\,|f_n - f|$$

we deduce that $\lim_{n\to\infty} \langle U(t)f_n(t), z\rangle = \langle U(t)f(t), z\rangle$ ν-almost everywhere, for each $z \in Z$. On the other hand, from the inequality

$$\int |\langle U(f_n - f_m), z\rangle|\, d|\nu| \leqq |z| \int |f_n - f_m|\, d\lambda$$

we deduce that $(\langle Uf_n, z\rangle)$ is a Cauchy sequence in $\mathscr{L}^1(\nu)$. It follows that the function $\langle Uf, z\rangle$ is ν-integrable for each $z \in Z$ and that

$$\lim_{n\to\infty} \int \langle Uf_n, z\rangle\, d\nu = \int \langle Uf, z\rangle\, d\nu .$$

From the inequality $\mu \leqq \lambda$ we deduce also that f is μ-integrable and that (f_n) converges to f in $\mathscr{L}^1_E(\mu)$, therefore

$$\lim_{n\to\infty} \int f_n\, dm = \int f\, dm$$

and

$$\lim_{n\to\infty} \left\langle \int f_n\, dm, z \right\rangle = \left\langle \int f\, dm, z \right\rangle, \quad \text{for} \quad z \in Z .$$

For each step function f_n we have

$$\left\langle \int f_n\, dm, z \right\rangle = \int \langle Uf_n, z\rangle\, d\nu, \quad \text{for} \quad z \in Z .$$

Passing to the limit we obtain

$$\left\langle \int f\, dm, z \right\rangle = \int \langle Uf, z\rangle\, d\nu, \quad \text{for} \quad z \in Z .$$

Consider now the cases in which m has values in $\mathscr{L}(E, F)$. The case a) is trivial. Suppose now that U verifies the condition b). Let $x \in E$ and let $\mathscr{A} \in C(\mu)$ be a family verifying b). Let $B \in \mathscr{A}$. The closure C of the set $\{U(t)\,x;\ t \in B\}$ is compact in F for the topology $\sigma(F, Z)$. There exists then a family $(z_i)_{i\in I}$ of elements of Z such that

$$C = \bigcap_{i \in I} \{y;\ y \in Z^*,\ |\langle y, z_i\rangle| \leqq 1\} .$$

Then

$$|\langle U(t)\,x, z_i\rangle| \leqq 1, \quad \text{for} \quad i \in I \quad \text{and} \quad t \in A ,$$

hence

$$|\langle m(A)\,x, z_i\rangle| \leqq \int_A |\langle U(t)\,x, z_i\rangle|\, d|\nu| \leqq |\nu|\,(A),$$

consequently

$$m(A)\,x \in |\nu|\,(A)\,C \subset F.$$

It follows that $m(A)\,x \in F$ for every $A \in \mathscr{C}$ and every $x \in E$, hence $m(A) \in \mathscr{L}(E, F)$, for every $A \in \mathscr{C}$.

The case c) is proved in the same way with T instead of A (without supposing that ν has the direct sum property).

Consider now the case d). Then, for every set $A \in \mathscr{C}$ and every $x \in E$ the function $\varphi_A x$ is ν-integrable and we have

$$\langle m(A)\,x, z\rangle = \int_A \langle U(t)\,x, z\rangle\, d\nu = \left\langle \int_A U(t)\,x\, d\nu, z\right\rangle$$

for every $z \in Z$, hence

$$m(A)\,x = \int_A U(t)\,x\, d\nu \in F.$$

Consequently, $m(A) \in \mathscr{L}(E, F)$.

It remains to prove the equality $\mu = |U|\,|\nu|$.

We remark that the measure m is absolutely continuous with respect to ν, therefore, by theorem 5 there exists a function $V\colon T \to \mathscr{L}(E, F)$ such that $\mu = |V|\,|\nu|$ and

$$\left\langle \int f\, dm, z\right\rangle = \int \langle V(t)\,f(t), z\rangle\, d\nu(t), \quad \text{for} \quad f \in \mathscr{L}_E^1(m) \quad \text{and} \quad z \in Z.$$

In addition, if ϱ is a lifting of $\mathscr{L}^\infty(\nu)$ we can realise $\varrho[V] = V$; then we have also $\varrho[Vx] = Vx$ for every $x \in E$. We deduce that

$$\int_A \langle V(t)\,x, z\rangle\, d\nu(t) = \int_A \langle U(t)\,x, z\rangle\, d\nu(t)$$

for each $A \in \mathscr{C}$, $x \in E$ and $z \in Z$, therefore

$$\langle V(t)\,x, z\rangle = \langle U(t)\,x, z\rangle \quad \nu\text{-almost everywhere}$$

for each $x \in E$ and $z \in Z$, i.e. $V \equiv U$.

Suppose now the condition α): there exists a lifting ϱ of $\mathscr{L}^\infty(\nu)$ such that $\varrho[U] = U$. Then we choose V to have also $\varrho[V] = V$. Since $U \equiv V$ we deduce that $U(t) = V(t)$ ν-almost everywhere, therefore $\mu = |V|\,|\nu| = |U|\,|\nu|$.

Suppose now the condition β). Let (x_n) be a sequence dense in E. Then

$$\langle U(t)\,x_n, z\rangle = \langle V(t)\,x_n, z\rangle \quad \nu\text{-almost everywhere.}$$

Let $N(x_n, z)$ be the ν-negligible set on which the preceding equality is false. The set $N(x_n) = \bigcup_{s \in S} N(x_n, s)$ is ν-negligible and for $t \notin N(x_n)$ we have $V(t)\,x_n = U(t)\,x_n$. The set $N = \bigcup_{n=1}^{\infty} N(x_n)$ is ν-negligible and for $t \notin N$ we have $U(t) = V(t)$. Then $\mu = |V|\,|\nu| = |U|\,|\nu|$.

The case δ has already been considered (§ 10, theorem 6) without supposing that ν has the direct sum property.

Suppose now the condition γ). For every $x \in E$ the function $t \to U(t)x$ of T into F is ν-measurable and $|U(t)x| \leqq |U(t)|\,|x|$, hence Ux is locally ν-integrable, hence $\boldsymbol{m}_x = (Ux)\,\nu$ is a measure with finite variation μ_x and we have $\mu_x = |Ux|\,|\nu|$.

For every $\varphi \in \mathscr{L}^1(\mu_x)$ and $z \in Z$ we have

$$\left\langle \int \varphi\, d\boldsymbol{m}_x, z \right\rangle = \left\langle \int U(t)\,x\,\varphi(t)\,d\nu, z \right\rangle = \int \langle U(t)\,x\,\varphi(t), z\rangle\, d\nu .$$

On the other hand, $\varrho[Vx] = Vx$ and applying the part already proved of this theorem to the function $Vx: T \to Z' = \mathscr{L}(R, Z')$, we can find a measure $\boldsymbol{m}'_x: \mathscr{C} \to \mathscr{L}(R, Z')$ with finite variation μ'_x such that $\mu'_x = |Vx|\,|\nu|$ and

$$\left\langle \int \varphi\, d\boldsymbol{m}'_x, z \right\rangle = \int \langle V(t)\,x\,\varphi(t), z\rangle\, d\nu$$

$$= \int \langle U(t)\,x\,\varphi(t), z\rangle\, d\nu = \left\langle \int \varphi\, d\boldsymbol{m}_x, z \right\rangle$$

for $\varphi \in \mathscr{L}^1(\mu'_x)$ and $z \in Z$. It follows that $\boldsymbol{m}'_x(A) = \boldsymbol{m}_x(A)$ for $A \in \mathscr{C}$, hence $\boldsymbol{m}'_x = \boldsymbol{m}_x$, therefore $\mu'_x = \mu_x$, consequently $|Vx|\,|\nu| = |Ux|\,|\nu|$. We deduce that $|V(t)x| = |U(t)x|$ ν-almost everywhere. Let $N(x)$ be the ν-negligible set on which $|V(t)x| \neq |U(t)x|$. If (x_n) is a sequence dense in E, the set $N = \bigcup_{n=1}^{\infty} N(x_n)$ is ν-negligible and for $t \notin N$ we have $|V(t)\,x_n| = |U(t)\,x_n|$ for each n, hence $|V(t)| = |U(t)|$. It follows that $\mu = |V|\,|\nu| = |U|\,|\nu|$.

The theorem is completely proved.

Remark. The measure $\boldsymbol{m}$ depends on the space Z. If Z_1 and Z_2 are two norming subspaces of F' such that $Z_1 \subset Z_2$, and if $\boldsymbol{m}_1: \mathscr{C} \to \mathscr{L}(E, Z'_1)$ and $\boldsymbol{m}_2: \mathscr{C} \to \mathscr{L}(E, Z'_2)$ are the corresponding measures, then for every $A \in \mathscr{C}$ and every $x \in E$, the functional $\boldsymbol{m}_1(A)\,x \in Z'_1$ is the restriction to Z_1 of the functional $\boldsymbol{m}_2(A)\,x \in Z'_2$.

Theorem 7. *Let $\boldsymbol{m}$: $\mathscr{C} \to E$ be a measure with finite variation and g a scalar locally $\boldsymbol{m}$-integrable function. If the measure $\boldsymbol{m}$ has the direct sum property, then*

$$|g\boldsymbol{m}| = |g|\,|\boldsymbol{m}| .$$

If $\boldsymbol{m} = 0$ we have $g\boldsymbol{m} = 0$ and $|\boldsymbol{m}| = 0$ and the theorem is proved. Suppose now that $\boldsymbol{m} \neq 0$ and let ϱ be a lifting of $\mathscr{L}^\infty(|\boldsymbol{m}|)$. Considering $E \subset \mathscr{L}(E', R)$, there exists a function $U: T \to \mathscr{L}(E', R)$ such that $|U(t)| = 1$ $|\boldsymbol{m}|$-almost everywhere, $\varrho(U) = U$ and

$$\int f\,d\boldsymbol{m} = \int \langle U(t), f(t)\rangle\, d|\boldsymbol{m}|, \quad \text{for} \quad f \in \mathscr{E}_{E'}(\mathscr{C}).$$

There exists also a scalar function g' such that $g' \equiv g$ and $\varrho[g'] = g'$. Then g' is $|\boldsymbol{m}|$-measurable and $|g'| = |g|$, hence g' is locally $|\boldsymbol{m}|$-integrable. It follows that for the function $Ug': T \to \mathscr{L}(E', R)$, we have $\varrho[Ug'] = Ug'$ and $|U(t)\,g'(t)| = |g'(t)| = |g(t)|$ $|\boldsymbol{m}|$-almost everywhere, hence $|Ug'|$ is locally $|\boldsymbol{m}|$-integrable. By the theorem 6 there exists a measure $\boldsymbol{m}': \mathscr{C} \to \mathscr{L}(E', R)$ with $|\boldsymbol{m}'| = |Ug'|\,|\boldsymbol{m}|$, such that for every $f \in \mathscr{E}_E(\mathscr{C})$ we have

$$\int f\,d\boldsymbol{m}' = \int \langle U(t)\,g'(t), f(t)\rangle\, d|\boldsymbol{m}|.$$

For every $f \in \mathscr{E}_E(\mathscr{C})$ we have then

$$\int f\,d\boldsymbol{m}' = \int \langle U, g'f\rangle\, d|\boldsymbol{m}| = \int (g'f)\,d\boldsymbol{m} = \int f\,d(g'\boldsymbol{m}),$$

hence $\boldsymbol{m}' = g'\boldsymbol{m} = g\boldsymbol{m}$.

On the other hand, since $g\boldsymbol{m}$ is absolutely continuous with respect to $|\boldsymbol{m}|$, there exists a function $V: T \to \mathscr{L}(E', R)$, with $|V|$ locally $|\boldsymbol{m}|$-integrable, $\varrho[V] = V$, such that $|g\boldsymbol{m}| = |V|\,|\boldsymbol{m}|$ and

$$\int f\,d(g\boldsymbol{m}) = \int \langle V(t), f(t)\rangle\, d|\boldsymbol{m}|, \quad \text{for} \quad f \in \mathscr{E}_E(\mathscr{C}).$$

From the equality $\boldsymbol{m}' = g\boldsymbol{m}$ we deduce $|\boldsymbol{m}'| = |g\boldsymbol{m}|$; whence $|Ug'|\,|\boldsymbol{m}| = |V|\,|\boldsymbol{m}|$, therefore

$$|U(t)\,g'(t)| = |V(t)| \quad |\boldsymbol{m}|\text{-almost everywhere},$$

consequently

$$|g\boldsymbol{m}| = |V|\,|\boldsymbol{m}| = |Ug'|\,|\boldsymbol{m}| = |g|\,|\boldsymbol{m}|.$$

5. INTEGRAL REPRESENTATION OF LINEAR OPERATIONS ON $\mathscr{L}^p_E$

Let $\mathscr{C}$ be a clan, E and F two Banach spaces and Z a norming subspace of F'.

Theorem 8. *Let $1 \leqq p < \infty$ and $\frac{1}{p} + \frac{1}{q} = 1$. Let ν be a scalar measure on $\mathscr{C}$ with the direct sum property and $U: \mathscr{L}^p_E(\nu) \to F$ a linear mapping with $|||U_A|||_p < \infty$ for $A \in \mathscr{T}_{\sigma f}$. There exists then a function $G: T \to \mathscr{L}(E, Z')$ having the following properties:*

1. *For every ν-measurable set $A \subset T$ with $|||U_A|||_p < \infty$ we have $|G|\,\varphi_A \in \mathscr{L}^q(\nu)$ and*

$$N_q(G\varphi_A, \nu) = |||U_A|||_p.$$

2. *For every $f \in \mathscr{L}_E^p(\nu)$ and $z \in Z$, the function $\langle Gf, z\rangle$ is ν-integrable and we have*

$$\langle U(f), z\rangle = \int \langle G(t)f(t), z\rangle\, d\nu.$$

3. *If ϱ is a lifting of $\mathscr{L}^\infty(\nu)$, we can choose G uniquely ν-almost everywhere such that $\varrho[G] = G$.*

If, in addition, $p = 1$, we can choose G uniquely such that $\varrho(G) = G$.

4. *We can choose $G(t) \in \mathscr{L}(E, F)$ for every $t \in T$ in each of the following cases:*

a) $F = Z'$.

b) *There exists a family $\mathscr{A} \in C(\nu)$ such that for every $A \in \mathscr{A}$ and $x \in E$, the convex equilibrated cover of the set $\{U(\varphi x);\ \varphi \in \mathscr{E}(\mathscr{C}, A),\ \int |\varphi|\, d|\nu| \leqq 1\}$ is relatively compact in F for the topology $\sigma(F, Z)$.*

c) *For every $x \in E$, the convex equilibrated cover of the set $\{U(\varphi x);\ \varphi \in \mathscr{E}(\mathscr{C}),\ \int |\varphi|\, d|\nu| \leqq 1\}$ is relatively compact in F for the topology $\sigma(F, Z)$.*

Let $\boldsymbol{m}\colon \mathscr{C} \to \mathscr{L}(E, F)$ be the measure with $\bar{\boldsymbol{m}}_q(A) < \infty$ for $A \in \mathscr{T}_{\sigma f}$ corresponding to U by the corollary 1 of the theorem 1. We have therefore $\mathscr{L}_E^p(\nu) \subset \mathscr{L}_E^1(\boldsymbol{m})$ and

$$U(f) = \int f\, d\boldsymbol{m}, \quad \text{for} \quad f \in \mathscr{L}_E^p(\nu).$$

Moreover, $\boldsymbol{m}$ has finite variation $|\boldsymbol{m}|$, is absolutely continuous with respect to ν, therefore $|\boldsymbol{m}| = g\nu$, and for every ν-measurable set $A \subset T$ we have $g\varphi_A \in \mathscr{L}^q(\nu)$ and $N_q(g\varphi_A, \nu) = |||U_A|||_p$.

Let then $V_{\boldsymbol{m}}\colon T \to \mathscr{L}(E, Z')$ be the function corresponding to $\boldsymbol{m}$ and ν by theorem 5. We have $|\boldsymbol{m}| = |V_{\boldsymbol{m}}|\,|\nu|$, whence $|V_{\boldsymbol{m}}(t)| = g(t)$ ν-almost everywhere, therefore, if A is ν-measurable with $|||U_A|||_p < \infty$, then $|V_{\boldsymbol{m}}|\,\varphi_A \in \mathscr{L}^q$ and

$$N_q(V_{\boldsymbol{m}}\varphi_A, \nu) = N_q(g, \nu) = |||U_A|||_p.$$

If we take $G = V_{\boldsymbol{m}}$, then from the theorem 5 we deduce that G has all required properties.

Remarks.

1°. The function G corresponding to U depends on the space Z.

2°. If one of the conditions 4 is not verified it may happen that G has not values in $\mathscr{L}(E, F)$.

Example. Take $T = [0, 1]$, ν the Lebesgue measure, $E = R$, $F = L^1(\nu)$, and $U: \mathcal{L}^1(\nu) \to F$ the mapping defined by the equality

$$U(\varphi) = \tilde{\varphi}, \quad \text{for} \quad \varphi \in \mathcal{L}^1(\nu).$$

Then

$$U(\varphi) = \int \varphi \, d\boldsymbol{m}, \quad \text{for} \quad \varphi \in \mathcal{L}^1(\nu),$$

where $\boldsymbol{m}: \mathcal{B} \to F$ is the measure defined by the equality

$$\boldsymbol{m}(A) = \tilde{\varphi}_A \quad \text{for} \quad A \in \mathcal{B}$$

(here $\mathcal{B}$ is the semi-tribe of the Borel subsets of T).

Let $Z \subset F'$ be a norming subspace and $G: T \to \mathcal{L}(E, Z')$ the function corresponding to U by the theorem 8. Then $G = V_{\boldsymbol{m}}$, where $V_{\boldsymbol{m}}$ corresponds to $\boldsymbol{m}$ by the theorem 5. From the remark 2 following the theorem 5 we deduce that we cannot have $G(t) \in \mathcal{L}(E, F)$.

3°. If E is of countable type and if there exists a countable norming set $S \subset Z$, then G is uniquely determined ν-almost everywhere by the equality

$$\langle U(\boldsymbol{f}), z\rangle = \int \langle G(t)\boldsymbol{f}(t), z\rangle \, d\nu, \quad \text{for} \quad \boldsymbol{f} \in \mathcal{L}_E^p(\nu) \quad \text{and} \quad z \in Z.$$

But if E is not of countable type, or if there is no countable norming set $S \subset Z$, the preceding equality may not determine G uniquely ν-almost everywhere. (We take $U = 0$ and use the examples of the remark 7° following the theorem 5.)

4°. If Z' is of countable type, then for every function $\boldsymbol{f} \in \mathcal{L}_E^p(\nu)$ the function $G\boldsymbol{f}$ is ν-integrable and we have

$$U(\boldsymbol{f}) = \int G(t)\boldsymbol{f}(t) \, d\nu(t), \quad \text{for} \quad \boldsymbol{f} \in \mathcal{L}_E^p(\nu).$$

In particular

$$U(\varphi)x = \int G(t)\, x\, \varphi(t) \, d\nu(t), \quad \text{for} \quad \varphi \in \mathcal{L}^p(\nu) \quad \text{and} \quad x \in E.$$

5°. If there exists a countable set $H \subset \mathcal{L}(E, Z')$ with $G(t) \in \overline{H}$ ν-almost everywhere (in particular if $\mathcal{L}(E, Z')$ is of countable type), then G is ν-measurable. In this case, if we put $X = \mathcal{L}(E, Z')$ we have $G \in \mathcal{L}_E^q(\nu)$ and we have

$$U(\varphi) = \int G(t)\, \varphi(t) \, d\nu(t), \quad \text{for} \quad \varphi \in \mathcal{L}^p(\nu).$$

6°. If $F = C$, then

$$U(\boldsymbol{f}) = \int G(t)\boldsymbol{f}(t) \, d\nu(t), \quad \text{for} \quad \boldsymbol{f} \in \mathcal{L}_E^p(\nu).$$

If, in addition, E' is of countable type, then $G \in \mathscr{L}^p_{E'}(\nu)$ and we have

$$U(\varphi) = \int G(t)\,\varphi(t)\,d\nu(t), \quad \text{for} \quad \varphi \in \mathscr{L}^q(\nu).$$

7°. If $E = C$ and if Z' is of countable type, then $U \in \mathscr{L}^q_{Z'}(\nu)$ and we have

$$U(\varphi) = \int G(t)\,\varphi(t)\,d\nu(t), \quad \text{for} \quad \varphi \in \mathscr{L}^p(\nu).$$

Corollary 1. *If E' is of countable type, then the conjugate space of $\mathscr{L}^p_E(\nu)$, $1 \leqq p < \infty$, is isomorphic and isometric to the space $L^q_{E'}(\nu)$, $\frac{1}{p} + \frac{1}{q} = 1$.*

If E' is of countable type, E is also of countable type. If $\tilde{f}' \in L^q_{E'}(\nu)$, then

$$U(f) = \int \langle f(t), f'(t)\rangle\,d\nu(t), \quad \text{for} \quad f \in \mathscr{L}^p_E(\nu)$$

is a continuous linear functional on $\mathscr{L}^p_E(\nu)$ and we have $\|U\| = \|\tilde{f}'\|_q$.

Conversely, if U is a continuous linear functional, then U is of the preceding form with some function $f'\colon T \to E'$. Since E is of countable type then f' is uniquely determined ν-almost everywhere (remark 3° following the theorem 8), and since E' is of countable type, then $f' \in \mathscr{L}^q_{E'}(\nu)$ (remark 6° following the theorem 8). It follows that the equivalence class $\tilde{f}'$ is uniquely determined by U, and belongs to $L^q_{E'}(\nu)$.

Corollary 2. *If E is of countable type and reflexive, and if $1 < p < \infty$, then $L^p_E(\nu)$ is reflexive.*

Corollary 3. *We have $(L^1)' = L^\infty$, $(L^p)' = L^q$ and $(L^q)' = L^p$, if $1 < p < \infty$, $1 < q < \infty$ and $\frac{1}{p} + \frac{1}{q} = 1$.*

Remark. The conjugate space of L^∞ is isomorphic to the space of the real additive set functions on $\mathscr{C}$, with bounded variation and absolutely continuous with respect to ν (corollary 2 of the proposition 14, § 9). If such a set function is not countably additive, then it cannot be represented by the theorem of Lebesgue-Nikodym as an integral with respect to ν, therefore such a set function does not correspond to any function of $\mathscr{L}^1(\nu)$.

It follows that in general the conjugate space of L^∞ is not isomorphic to L^1.

The following theorem is in a certain sense the converse of the theorem 8.

Theorem 9. *Let $1 \leqq p < \infty$ and $\frac{1}{p} + \frac{1}{q} = 1$. Let ν be a scalar measure on $\mathscr{C}$ and $G\colon T \to \mathscr{L}(E, F)$ a function such that*

(i) $\quad |G|\,\varphi_A \in \mathscr{L}^p(\nu)$, *for every* $A \in \mathscr{T}_{\sigma f}$,

and such that the function $\langle Gf, z\rangle$ is ν-measurable for every $f \in \mathscr{L}^p_E(\nu)$ and $z \in Z$.

There exists then a linear mapping $U: \mathscr{L}_E^p(\nu) \to Z'$ *such that*

$$\langle U(f), z\rangle = \int \langle G(t)f(t), z\rangle \, d\nu, \quad \textit{for} \quad f \in \mathscr{L}_E^p(\nu) \quad \textit{and} \quad z \in Z,$$

and

$$|||U_A|||_p \leqq N_q(G\varphi_A, \nu)$$

for every ν*-measurable set* A *with* $|G| \, \varphi_A \in \mathscr{L}^q(\nu)$.

(ii) *We have* $U(f) \in F$ *for every* $f \in \mathscr{L}_E^p(\nu)$ *in each of the following cases:*

a) $F = Z'$;

b) *for every* $x \in E$ *there exists a family* $\mathscr{A} \in C(\nu)$ *such that for every* $A \in \mathscr{A}$ *the convex equilibrated cover of the set* $\{G(t)x; \, t \in A\}$ *is relatively compact in* F *for* $\sigma(F, Z)$;

c) *for every* $x \in E$ *the convex equilibrated cover of the set* $\{G(t)x; \, t \in T\}$ *is relatively compact in* F *for* $\sigma(F, Z)$;

d) *the function* $t \to G(t)x$ *is* ν*-measurable for each* $x \in E$; *in particular* F *is of countable type.*

(iii) *If* ν *has the direct sum property, we have*

$$|||U_A|||_p = N_q(G\varphi_A, \nu), \quad \textit{if } A \textit{ is } \nu\textit{-measurable and} \quad |G| \, \varphi_A \in \mathscr{L}^q(\nu),$$

in each of the following cases:

α) *There exists a lifting* ϱ *of* $\mathscr{L}^\infty(\nu)$ *such that* $\varrho[G] = G$;

β) *E is of countable type and there exists a countable norming set* $S \subset Z$;

γ) *E is of countable type and the function* $t \to G(t)x$ *is* ν*-measurable for every* $x \in E$;

δ) *the function G is* ν*-measurable (in this case* ν *may have not the direct sum property).*

We remark first that for each function $f \in \mathscr{L}_E^p(\nu)$ and each $z \in Z$ the function $\langle Gf, z\rangle$ is ν-integrable. In fact, let $A \in \mathscr{T}_{\sigma f}$ be a set such that f vanishes outside A. Then $|G| \, \varphi_A \in \mathscr{L}^p(\nu)$ and $|f| \in \mathscr{L}^q(\nu)$, therefore $|G| \, |f| = |G| \, \varphi_A \, |f| \in \mathscr{L}^1(\nu)$. On the other hand, $\langle Gf, z\rangle$ is ν-measurable and $|\langle Gf, z\rangle| \leqq |z| \, |G| \, |f|$, whence $\langle Gf, z\rangle$ is ν-integrable. Put

$$U_z(f) = \int \langle Gf, z\rangle \, d\nu.$$

The mapping $U(f): z \to U_z(f)$ is a continuous linear functional on Z:

$$|U_z(f)| \leqq |z| \int |G| \, |f| \, d|\nu|,$$

therefore $U(f) \in Z'$ and

$$|U(f)| \leqq \int |G| \, |f| \, d|\nu|.$$

The mapping $U: f \to U(f)$ of $\mathscr{L}_E^p(\nu)$ into Z' is linear and we have

$$\langle U(f), z\rangle = U_z(f) = \int \langle Gf, z\rangle \, d\nu,$$

for every $f \in \mathscr{L}_E^p(\nu)$ and $z \in Z$. Let A be a ν-measurable set such that $|G| \varphi_A \in \mathscr{L}^q$ and let $f = \sum \varphi_{A_i} x_i \in \mathscr{E}_E(\mathscr{C}, A)$ with A_i disjoint and $N_p(f) \leqq 1$. Then we have

$$\sum |U(\varphi_{A_i} x_i)| \leqq \sum \int |G| \varphi_{A_i} |x_i| \, d|\nu| = \int |G| \varphi_A \sum \varphi_{A_i} |x_i| \, d|\nu|$$

$$\leqq N_q(G\varphi_A) \, N_p(f) \leqq N_q(G\varphi_A),$$

whence

$$|||U_A|||_p \leqq N_q(G\varphi_A).$$

Let $\boldsymbol{m}: \mathscr{C} \to \mathscr{L}(E, Z')$ be the measure corresponding to U by the corollary 1 of the theorem 1, such that $\bar{\boldsymbol{m}}_q(A) = |||U_A|||_p$ for every ν-measurable set A and

$$U(f) = \int f \, d\boldsymbol{m}, \quad \text{for} \quad f \in \mathscr{L}_E^p(\nu),$$

therefore

$$\left\langle \int f \, d\boldsymbol{m}, z \right\rangle = \int \langle Gf, z\rangle \, d\nu, \quad \text{for} \quad f \in \mathscr{L}_E^p(\nu) \quad \text{and} \quad z \in Z.$$

If G verifies one of the conditions (ii), then by theorem 6, $\boldsymbol{m}$ is with values in $\mathscr{L}(E, F)$, therefore $U(f) \in \mathscr{L}(E, F)$ for every $f \in \mathscr{E}_E(\mathscr{C}, A)$ and then, passing to the limit for every $f \in \mathscr{L}_E^p(\nu)$.

Suppose now that G verifies one of the conditions (iii) and let $A \subset T$ be a ν-measurable set with $|G| \varphi_A \in \mathscr{L}^q(\nu)$. Then $\bar{\boldsymbol{m}}_q(A) = |||U_A|||_p < \infty$. By the theorem 6 we have $|\boldsymbol{m}| = |G| \, |\nu|$, whence, by proposition 4, we have $|\bar{\boldsymbol{m}}|_q(A) = N_q(G\varphi_A, \nu)$. Since $|\bar{\boldsymbol{m}}|_q = \bar{\boldsymbol{m}}_q$ (property 12 of the q-variation), we deduce that $|||U_A|||_p = \bar{\boldsymbol{m}}_q(A) = N_q(G\varphi_A, \nu)$.

The theorem is completely proved.

Remarks.

1°. The mapping U corresponding to G depends on the space Z.

2°. Instead of the condition (i) we can consider the weaker condition

(i′) $\quad |Gf| \in \mathscr{L}^1(\nu)$ for every $f \in \mathscr{L}_E^p(\nu)$.

We say that a mapping $\varrho: \mathscr{L}^p(\mu) \to \mathscr{L}^p(\mu)$ is a *linear lifting of* $\mathscr{L}^p(\mu)$ *if:*

(i) $\varrho(f) \sim f$;

(ii) $f \sim g$ *implies* $\varrho(f) = \varrho(g)$;

(iii) $f \geqq 0$ *implies* $\varrho(f) \geqq 0$;

(iv) $\varrho(\alpha f + \beta g) = \alpha\varrho(f) + \beta\varrho(g)$

(here $f \sim g$ means that $f(t) = g(t)$ μ-almost everywhere). We proved (§ 11, theorem 1) that if μ has the direct sum property and is $\neq 0$, then there exists a linear lifting ϱ of $\mathscr{L}^\infty(\mu)$ having in addition the following two properties:

(v) $\varrho(1) = 1$;

(vi) $\varrho(fg) = \varrho(f)\,\varrho(g)$.

Such a mapping was called a *lifting* of $\mathscr{L}^\infty(\mu)$.

For $1 \leqq p < \infty$ we have the following:

Proposition 9. *Suppose that μ is a positive finite measure with the direct sum property on $\mathscr{C}$ and that $\mu \neq 0$. If μ is non-atomic, then there is no linear lifting of the space $\mathscr{L}^p(\mu)$ with $1 \leqq p < \infty$.*

Suppose that there is such a linear lifting ϱ. Then for each $t \in T$ fixed, the mapping $f \to \varrho(f)(t)$ is a positive linear functional on $\mathscr{L}^p(\mu)$ and so, it is continuous (proposition 8). From the corollary 2 of the theorem 8 we deduce that there exists a function $g(t) \in \mathscr{L}^q$, $\dfrac{1}{p} + \dfrac{1}{q} = 1$, such that

$$\varrho(f)(t) = \int f\,g(t)\,d\mu, \quad \text{for} \quad f \in \mathscr{L}^p(\mu),$$

and

$$\|g(t)\|_q = \|\varrho(f)(t)\| = \sup\{|\varrho(f)(t)|;\ \|f\|_p \leqq 1\} < \infty.$$

Let $K \in \mathscr{C}$ be a set such that $0 < \mu(K) = a < \infty$, and for each n let $A_n = \{t;\ t \in K,$ $\|g(t)\|_q \leqq n\}$. Since $\|g(t)\|_q < \infty$ for each t, we must have $K = \bigcup_{n=1}^{\infty} A_n$. It follows that $\mu^*(A_{n_1}) \neq 0$ for some n_1. Let k be an integer verifying the inequality

$$k \geqq a(n_1 + 1)^p$$

and let $B_1, \ldots, B_k$ be k disjoint μ-measurable subsets of K whose union is K and such that $\mu(B_1) = \cdots = \mu(B_k) = \dfrac{a}{k}$.

Since $B_1, \ldots, B_k$ is a cover of A_{n_1}, we deduce that there exists at least one $j \in \{1, \ldots, k\}$, say $j = 1$, such that $\mu^*(A_{n_1} \cap B_1) \neq 0$. Consider now the set $B_1^* = \{t;\ \varrho(\varphi_{B_1})(t) = 1\}$; then $B_1^* \sim B_1$ and hence

$$\mu^*(A_{n_1} \cap B_1^*) \neq 0.$$

Define $f = (n_1 + 1)\,\varphi_{B_1}$. Since $k \geqq a(n + 1)^p$, we have

$$N_p(f) = (n_1 + 1)\,N_p(\varphi_{B_1}) = (n_1 + 1)\left(\frac{a}{k}\right)^{\frac{1}{p}} \leqq 1.$$

On the other hand, since $\mu^*(A_{n_1} \cap B_1^*) \neq 0$, we have $A_{n_1} \cap B_1^* \neq \emptyset$; but if $t \in A_{n_1} \cap B_1^*$, then

$$n_1 + 1 = \varrho((n_1 + 1)\,\varphi_{B_1})\,(t) = \varrho(f)\,(t) = \int fg(t)\,d\mu \leqq \|g(t)\|_q \leqq n_1 .$$

Hence we reached a contradiction and thus the proposition is completely proved.

Remark. In fact, from the proof we deduce that the conclusion of the preceding proposition remains valid if μ has the direct sum property, and there exists at least one set $K \in \mathscr{C}$ with $\mu(K) > 0$ having the Darboux property.

CHAPTER III

REGULAR MEASURES

§ 14. BOREL SETS. BOREL MEASURES

1. THE SEMI-TRIBE OF THE RELATIVELY COMPACT BOREL SETS

In the sequel T will mean a *locally compact space*.

We shall denote by $\mathscr{K}$ the *clan* generated by the *compact* sets, and by $\mathscr{B}$ the *semi-tribe* generated by the compact sets. We have $\mathscr{K} \subset \mathscr{B}$ and $\mathscr{B}$ is the semi-tribe generated by $\mathscr{K}$.

Since every set A of $\mathscr{B}$ is contained in the union of a *finite* family (K_i) of compact sets (§ 1, proposition 10) we deduce that every set $A \in \mathscr{B}$ is contained in a compact set, therefore $\mathscr{B}$ consists *of relatively compact* subsets of T. Since $\mathscr{B}$ is a semi-tribe, for every sequence (A_n) of sets of $\mathscr{B}$ contained in a compact set K we have $\bigcup_{n=1}^{\infty} A_n \in \mathscr{B}$.

$\mathscr{B}$ will be called the *semi-tribe of the relatively compact Borel subsets of T.*

We have $T \in \mathscr{B}$ if and only if T is compact. In this case $\mathscr{B}$ is a tribe.

Proposition 1. *If $\mathscr{C}$ is a clan containing all the compact subsets of a compact set K, then $\mathscr{C}$ contains all the open subsets of K.*

In fact, if $G \subset K$ is open, then $K - G$ is compact, and contained in K; hence $K - G \in \mathscr{C}$, therefore

$$G = K - (K - G) \in \mathscr{C}.$$

Corollary. *The clan $\mathscr{K}$ and the semi-tribe $\mathscr{B}$ contain all the relatively compact open subsets of T.*

In fact, if $G \subset T$ is a relatively compact open set, then $K = \bar{G}$ is compact. $\mathscr{K}$ and $\mathscr{B}$ contain all the open subsets of K, therefore they contain G.

Proposition 2. *If $\mathscr{C}$ is a clan containing all the open subsets of an open set G, then $\mathscr{C}$ contains all the compact subsets of G.*

In fact, if $K \subset G$ is compact, then $G - K$ is open and contained in G; hence $G - K \in \mathscr{C}$, therefore

$$K = G - (G - K) \in \mathscr{C}.$$

Corollary. *$\mathscr{K}$ is the clan generated by the relatively compact open sets and $\mathscr{B}$ is the semi-tribe generated by the relatively compact open sets.*

Let us denote by $\mathscr{G}$ the clan generated by the relatively compact open sets. By the corollary of proposition 1 we have $\mathscr{G} \subset \mathscr{K}$. On the other hand, every compact set K is contained in a relatively compact open set G, and $\mathscr{G}$ contains all the compact subsets of G; hence, by proposition 2, $\mathscr{G}$ contains K, therefore $\mathscr{G}$ contains the clan $\mathscr{K}$ generated by the compact sets. It follows that $\mathscr{K} = \mathscr{G}$.

We prove in the same manner the statement concerning $\mathscr{B}$.

We shall prove that the semi-tribe $\mathscr{B}$ can be obtained by other way.

For every compact set $K \subset T$ we shall denote by $\mathscr{B}_K$ the *tribe* generated by all the compact subsets $K' \subset K$.

The class of all the sets of $\mathscr{B}$ contained in K is a tribe which contains all the compact subsets $K' \subset K$, therefore $\mathscr{B}_K \subset \mathscr{B}$. It follows that all the sets of $\mathscr{B}_K$ are contained in K.

From proposition 1 we deduce that $\mathscr{B}_K$ contains all the open subsets $G \subset K$.

If for two compact sets K and K' we have $K \subset K'$, then $\mathscr{B}_K \subset \mathscr{B}_{K'}$. The family $(\mathscr{B}_K)$ is filtering for the relation of inclusion. We shall prove that the union of this family is equal to $\mathscr{B}$.

For every relatively compact open set $G \subset T$ we denote by $\mathscr{B}_G$ the *tribe* generated by the open subsets $G' \subset G$.

The class of all the sets of $\mathscr{B}$ contained in G is a tribe which contains all the open subsets $G' \subset G$, therefore $\mathscr{B}_G \subset \mathscr{B}$. It follows that all the sets of $\mathscr{B}_G$ are contained in G.

From proposition 2 we deduce that $\mathscr{B}_G$ contains all the compact sets $K \subset G$.

If $G \subset G'$, then $\mathscr{B}_G \subset \mathscr{B}_{G'}$.

Let K be a compact set and G be a relatively compact set. If $K \subset G$ then $\mathscr{B}_K \subset \mathscr{B}_G$ and if $G \subset K$ then $\mathscr{B}_G \subset \mathscr{B}_K$. We deduce that the union of the family $(\mathscr{B}_K)$ for K compact, is equal to the union of the family $(\mathscr{B}_G)$ for G open and relatively compact.

Lemma 1. *Let G be a relatively compact open set and $K \subset G$ be a compact set. Every set $E \in \mathscr{B}_G$ can be written uniquely in the form:*

$$E = A \cup B, \quad \textit{with} \quad A \in \mathscr{B}_K \quad \textit{and} \quad B \in \mathscr{B}_{G-K}.$$

Let us denote by Φ the class of the subsets of T of the form $A \cup B$ with $A \in \mathscr{B}_K$ and $B \in \mathscr{B}_{G-K}$.

Since $\mathscr{B}_K \subset \mathscr{B}_G$ and $\mathscr{B}_{G-K} \subset \mathscr{B}_G$ we deduce that $\Phi \subset \mathscr{B}_G$. We shall prove that Φ is a *tribe* which contains all the *open* subsets $G' \subset G$. It will follow then that $\Phi = \mathscr{B}_G$.

If $A \cup B$ and $A' \cup B'$ are two sets of Φ with $A, A' \in \mathscr{B}_K$ and $B, B' \in \mathscr{B}_{G-K}$, then $A - A' \in \mathscr{B}_K$ and $B - B' \in \mathscr{B}_{G-K}$, therefore

$$(A \cup B) - (A' \cup B') = (A - A') \cup (B - B') \in \Phi.$$

If $(A_n \cup B_n)$ is a sequence of sets of Φ with $A_n \in \mathscr{B}_K$ and $B_n \in \mathscr{B}_{G-K}$, then $\bigcup_{n=1}^{\infty} A_n \in \mathscr{B}_K$ and $\bigcup_{n=1}^{\infty} A_n \in \mathscr{B}_{G-K}$, therefore

$$\bigcup_{n=1}^{\infty} (A_n \cup B_n) = \left(\bigcup_{n=1}^{\infty} A_n\right) \cup \left(\bigcup_{n=1}^{\infty} B_n\right) \in \Phi,$$

hence Φ is a *tribe*.

If G' is an open subset of G, then $G' \cap (G - K)$ is open and contained in $G - K$, therefore $G' \cap (G - K) \in \mathscr{B}_{G-K}$; the set $K - G'$ is compact and contained in K, therefore $G' \cap K = K - (K - G') \in \mathscr{B}_K$. Then

$$G' = (G' \cap K) \cup (G' \cap (G - K)) \in \Phi.$$

It follows that $\Phi = \mathscr{B}_G$. If now

$$E = A \cup B$$

is a set of $\mathscr{B}_G$ with $A \in \mathscr{B}_K$ and $B \in \mathscr{B}_{G-K}$, then $A \subset K$ and $B \subset G - K$. Since K and $G - K$ are disjoint we deduce

$$E \cap K = A \quad \text{and} \quad E \cap (G - K) = B,$$

therefore the representation of $E \in \mathscr{B}_G$ as a union $E = A \cup B$ with $A \in \mathscr{B}_K$ and $B \in \mathscr{B}_{G-K}$ is unique.

Proposition 3. *If E is a subset of a compact set K and if E belongs to some tribe $\mathscr{B}_{K'}$, then $E \in \mathscr{B}_K$.*

Let $G \supset K' \cup K$ be a relatively compact open set. Since $\mathscr{B}_{K'} \subset \mathscr{B}_G$, we have $E \in \mathscr{B}_G$. From lemma 1 we deduce that $E = A \cup B$ with $A \in \mathscr{B}_K$ and $B \in \mathscr{B}_{G-K}$. But $B \cap K = \emptyset$, therefore

$$E = E \cap K = (A \cup B) \cap K = A \cap K = A,$$

hence $E \in \mathscr{B}_K$.

Proposition 4. *The semi-tribe $\mathscr{B}$ is equal to the union of the tribes $\mathscr{B}_K$, for all compact sets K.*

Let us denote by Φ the union of the tribes $\mathscr{B}_K$. Since the family $(\mathscr{B}_K)$ is filtering, Φ is a *clan* which contains all the compact sets, therefore $\Phi \subset \mathscr{B}$. We shall show that Φ is a *semi-tribe*. It will then follow that $\Phi = \mathscr{B}$.

Let (A_n) be a sequence of sets of Φ, and show that $\bigcap_{n=1}^{\infty} A_n \in \Phi$. For each n the set $B_n = \bigcap_{i=1}^{n} A_i$ belongs to Φ, and $\bigcap_{n=1}^{\infty} B_n = \bigcap_{n=1}^{\infty} A_n$. Let $K \supset B_1$ be a compact set. Since the sequence (B_n) is decreasing, we have $B_n \subset K$ for each n. From proposition 3 we deduce that $B_n \in \mathscr{B}_K$ for each n, therefore

$$\bigcap_{n=1}^{\infty} A_n = \bigcap_{n=1}^{\infty} B_n \in \mathscr{B}_K \subset \Phi,$$

hence Φ is a semi-tribe, and $\Phi = \mathscr{B}$.

Corollary. *The semi-tribe $\mathscr{B}$ is equal to the union of the tribes $\mathscr{B}_G$ for all relatively compact open sets G.*

Remarks.

1°. For every set $A \in \mathscr{B}$ we have $A \in \mathscr{B}_{\bar{A}}$.

2°. For every pair (K, K') of compact sets we have

$$\mathscr{B}_K \cap \mathscr{B}_{K'} = \mathscr{B}_{K \cap K'}.$$

3°. For every compact set $K \subset T$ we have

$$\mathscr{B}_K = \{A \mid A \subset K, A \in \mathscr{B}\} = \{A \cap K \mid A \in \mathscr{B}\}$$

and for every relatively compact open set $G \subset T$ we have

$$\mathscr{B}_G = \{A \mid A \subset G, A \in \mathscr{B}\} = \{A \cap G \mid A \in \mathscr{B}\}.$$

4°. The tribe $\mathscr{T}$ generated by the compact sets is generated also by the semi-tribe $\mathscr{B}$, therefore every set of $\mathscr{T}$ is the union of a sequence of sets of $\mathscr{B}$.

5°. Since the class of the compact sets is a lattice, we deduce that the clan $\mathscr{K}$ consists of all the finite unions $\bigcup_{i=1}^{n} (K_i - K_i')$ of *disjoint* differences of compact sets K_i and K_i' (§ 1, corollary of proposition 13).

We deduce in the same manner that $\mathscr{K}$ consists of all the finite unions $\bigcup_{i=1}^{n} (G_i - G_i')$ of disjoint differences of relatively compact open sets G_i and G_i'.

2. THE TRIBE OF THE BOREL SETS

We shall denote by $\mathcal{C}$ the class of all the sets $E \subset T$ which have the property that $A \cap E \in \mathscr{B}$ for every set $A \in \mathscr{B}$. Since $\mathscr{B}$ is a semi-tribe, it follows that $\mathcal{C}$ is a *tribe* which contains $\mathscr{B}$ and the whole space T.

The tribe $\mathcal{C}$ will be called the *tribe of the Borel subsets of T*.

The tribe $\mathcal{C}$ can be defined using only the compact sets.

Proposition 5. *We have $E \in \mathcal{T}$ if and only if $K \cap E \in \mathcal{B}$ for every compact set $K \subset T$.*

If $E \in \mathcal{T}$, we have evidently $E \cap K \in \mathcal{B}$ for every compact set K. Conversely, suppose that $E \cap K \in \mathcal{B}$ for every compact set $K \subset T$, and let $A \in \mathcal{B}$.

If we choose a compact set $K \supset A$, then

$$A \cap E = A \cap (K \cap E) \in \mathcal{B},$$

therefore $E \in \mathcal{T}$.

From this proposition we deduce

Corollary 1. *$\mathcal{T}$ contains all the open sets $G \subset T$.*

In fact, if $G \subset T$ is open, then for every compact set $K \subset T$ the set $K - G$ is compact and belongs to $\mathcal{B}$, therefore

$$K \cap G = K - (K - G) \in \mathcal{B},$$

hence $G \in \mathcal{T}$.

We deduce also:

Corollary 2. *$\mathcal{T}$ contains all the closed sets $F \subset T$.*

In fact, if F is closed, then $T - F$ is open, therefore $T - F \in \mathcal{T}$, hence

$$F = T - (T - F) \in \mathcal{T}.$$

3. BAIRE SETS

We shall denote by $\mathcal{K}_0$ the *clan* generated by the compact sets which are G_δ (countable intersections of open sets) and by $\mathcal{B}_0$ the *semi-tribe* generated by the compact sets which are G_δ.

We deduce that $\mathcal{B}_0 \subset \mathcal{B}$, hence the sets of $\mathcal{B}_0$ are relatively compact Borel sets. $\mathcal{B}_0$ will be called the *semi-tribe of the relatively compact Baire subsets of T.*

The tribe $\mathcal{T}_0$ of the sets $E \subset T$ which have the property that $E \cap A \in \mathcal{B}_0$ for every $A \in \mathcal{B}_0$ will be called the *tribe of the Baire subsets of T.*

We shall prove that every compact set $K \in \mathcal{B}_0$ is the intersection of a sequence of open sets of $\mathcal{B}_0$ and every open set $G \in \mathcal{B}_0$ is the union of a sequence of compact sets of $\mathcal{B}_0$.

In certain cases, every compact set is G_δ, therefore, in these cases we have $\mathcal{B}_0 = \mathcal{B}$.

Proposition 6. *If T has a countable base of open sets, then every compact set $K \subset T$ is G_δ.*

Let $\mathcal{G}$ be a countable base of open sets. The class $\mathcal{G}'$ of the finite unions of sets of $\mathcal{G}$ is also countable, therefore the sets of $\mathcal{G}'$ which cover a set $K \subset T$ can be arranged in a sequence (G_n).

Let $K \subset T$ be a compact set and U an open set containing K. The set U is the union of a certain family $(V_i)_{i \in I}$ of sets of $\mathscr{G}$. Since K is compact, K can be covered by a finite family $(V_i)_{i \in J}$. The union of this family is a set $G \in \mathscr{G}'$ and we have $K \subset G \subset U$. Since K is the intersection of all its open neighbourhoods, we deduce that $K = \bigcap_{n=1}^{\infty} G_n$, therefore K is G_δ.

Proposition 7. *If T is metrizable, then every compact set $K \subset T$ is G_δ.*

Let d be a distance on T compatible with the topology of T. For each point $x \in T$ and each natural number n, consider the open sphere $V_n(x)$ with centre x and radius $\frac{1}{n}$.

For each n choose a family of spheres $V_n(x)$ with $x \in K$ which cover K, and denote by U_n the union of this family. Then

$$K = \bigcap_{n=1}^{\infty} U_n.$$

In fact, let $x \in \bigcap_{n=1}^{\infty} U_n$. For each n we have $x \in U_n$, therefore we can find a point $x_n \in K$ such that $d(x, x_n) < \frac{1}{n}$. We obtain in this way a sequence (x_n) of points of K, converging to x, therefore $x \in K$, hence

$$\bigcap_{n=1}^{\infty} U_n \subset K.$$

The converse inclusion being evident, we deduce that

$$K = \bigcap_{n=1}^{\infty} U_n.$$

Remark. In the proof we used only the property that K is closed. Hence, in a metrizable space (not necessarily locally compact) every closed set is G_δ.

Corollary. *If T is a locally compact subspace of the euclidian space R^n, then every compact set $K \subset T$ is G_δ.*

Proposition 8. *If T has a countable base or if T is metrizable, then $\mathscr{K}_0 = \mathscr{K}$ and $\mathscr{B}_0 = \mathscr{B}$.*

The proof follows from propositions 6 and 7.

In particular, if T is a locally compact subspace of R^n the class of the Borel sets coincide with the class of the Baire sets.

Proposition 9. *Let $f: T \to R$ be a continuous function and $\alpha \in R$. The sets*

$$A_1 = \{t \mid f(t) \leqq \alpha\}, \quad A_2 = \{t \mid f(t) \geqq \alpha\}, \quad A_3 = \{t \mid f(t) = \alpha\}$$

are closed and G_δ, *and the sets*

$$B_1 = \{t \mid f(t) < \alpha\}, \quad B_2 = \{t \mid f(t) > \alpha\}, \quad B_3 = \{t \mid f(t) \neq \alpha\}$$

are open and F_σ.

From the continuity of f we deduce that the first three sets are closed and the other three sets are open. Since

$$A_1 = \{t \mid f(t) \leqq \alpha\} = \bigcap_{n=1}^{\infty} \left\{t \mid f(t) < \alpha + \frac{1}{n}\right\}$$

we deduce that A_1 is G_δ. From the equalities

$$\{t \mid f(t) \geqq \alpha\} = \{t \mid -f(t) \leqq -\alpha\}$$

and

$$\{t \mid f(t) = \alpha\} = \{t \mid f(t) \leqq \alpha\} \cap \{t \mid f(t) \geqq \alpha\}$$

we deduce that A_2 and A_3 are G_δ. Since

$$B_1 = \{t \mid f(t) < \alpha\} = \bigcup_{n=1}^{\infty} \left\{t \mid f(t) \leqq \alpha - \frac{1}{n}\right\}$$

we deduce that B_1 is F_σ. From the equalities

$$\{t \mid f(t) > \alpha\} = \{t \mid -f(t) < -\alpha\}$$

and

$$\{t \mid f(t) \neq \alpha\} = \{t \mid f(t) < \alpha\} \cup \{t \mid f(t) > \alpha\}$$

it follows that B_2 and B_3 are F_σ.

Proposition 10. *For every compact set* $K \subset T$ *which is* G_δ *there exists a continuous function* $f\colon T \to [0, 1]$ *such that*

$$K = \{t \mid f(t) = 1\}.$$

Let (G_n) be a sequence of open sets such that

$$K = \bigcap_{n=1}^{\infty} G_n.$$

For each n we can find a continuous function $f_n\colon T \to [0, 1]$ with $f_n(t) = 1$ for $t \in K$ and $f_n(t) = 0$ for $t \in T - G_n$.

The function

$$f(t) = \sum_{n=1}^{\infty} \frac{f_n(t)}{2^n}$$

is continuous on T and takes values in $[0, 1]$. If $t \in K$ then $f_n(t) = 1$ for every n, therefore $f(t) = 1$; conversely if $f(t) = 1$, then $f_n(t) = 1$ for every n, therefore $t \in G_n$ for every n, hence $t \in K$. It follows that $K = \{t \mid f(t) = 1\}$.

Proposition 11. *Let $K \subset T$ be a compact set and $G \supset K$ an open set. There exist a compact set $K_0 \in \mathscr{B}_0$ which is G_δ and an open set $G_0 \in \mathscr{B}_0$ which is F_σ, such that*

$$K \subset G_0 \subset K_0 \subset G.$$

Let U be a relatively compact open set such that $K \subset U \subset G$ and let $f: T \to [0, 1]$ be a continuous function with $f(t) = 1$ for $t \in K$ and $f(t) = 0$ for $t \notin U$.

The set $G_0 = \left\{t \mid f(t) > \frac{1}{2}\right\}$ is open and F_σ, and the set $K_0 = \left\{t \mid f(t) \geqq \frac{1}{2}\right\}$ is closed and G_δ, and we have

$$K \subset G_0 \subset K_0 \subset U \subset G.$$

Since U is relatively compact, G_0 and K_0 are relatively compact, hence K_0 is compact. The sets

$$C_n = \left\{t \mid f(t) \geqq \frac{1}{2} + \frac{1}{n}\right\}$$

are compact and G_δ and we have $G_0 = \bigcup_{n=1}^{\infty} C_n$, therefore $G_0 \in \mathscr{B}_0$.

Corollary 1. *The class of the compact neighbourhoods of a point $t \in T$ which are G_δ is a fundamental system of neighbourhoods of t.*

In fact, for every open neighbourhood V of t, we can find a compact set K_0 which is G_δ and an open set G_0 which is F_σ such that

$$t \in G_0 \subset K_0 \subset V.$$

It follows that K_0 is a neighbourhood of t contained in V.

Corollary 2. *The class of all open sets of $\mathscr{B}_0$ which are F_σ is a base of the topology of T.*

In fact, for every point $t \in T$ and every neighbourhood V of t, we can find an open set $G_0 \in \mathscr{B}_0$ which is F_σ such that $t \in G_0 \subset V$.

Proposition 12. *Let $\mathscr{G}$ be a base of open sets of the topology of T. Every semi-tribe $\mathscr{S}$ which contains $\mathscr{G}$ contains also $\mathscr{B}_0$.*

Let $K \subset T$ be a compact set which is G_δ:

$$K = \bigcap_{n=1}^{\infty} U_n,$$

where U_n are open sets. For each set U_n, there exists an open set G_n, union of a finite family of sets of $\mathscr{G}$, such that

$$K \subset G_n \subset U_n.$$

Then

$$K = \bigcap_{n=1}^{\infty} G_n .$$

Since every set G_n belongs to the semi-tribe $\mathscr{S}$, their intersection K belongs to $\mathscr{S}$. Hence $\mathscr{S}$ contains all the compact sets which are G_δ, therefore $\mathscr{S}$ contains the semi-tribe $\mathscr{B}_0$ generated by them.

Proposition 13. *Every compact set* $K \in \mathscr{B}_0$ *is* G_δ.

Let (K_n) be a sequence of compact sets which are G_δ, such that K belongs to the semi-tribe generated by the sets K_n (§ 1, proposition 11). For each n choose a continuous function $f_n \colon T \to [0, 1]$ such that $K_n = \{t \mid f_n(t) = 1\}$ (proposition 10). For each pair (t, s) of points of T put

$$d(t, s) = \sum_{n=1}^{\infty} \frac{1}{2^n} \left| f_n(t) - f_n(s) \right| .$$

We verify easily that d is a semi-distance on T:

$$d(t, t) = 0, \quad d(t, s) = d(s, t), \quad 0 \leqq d(t, s) \leqq d(t, u) + d(u, s).$$

Denote by $s \equiv t$ the relation $d(s, t) = 0$. Then $s \equiv t$ is an equivalence relation on T. Denote by $\dot{T}$ the quotient of T by this equivalence relation and by φ the canonical mapping of T onto $\dot{T}$ such that for each $t \in T$, $\varphi(t)$ is equal to the equivalence class $\dot{t}$ of t.

We verify easily that if for every pair (t, s) of points of T we put

$$\delta(\dot{t}, \dot{s}) = d(t, s)$$

then $\delta(\dot{t}, \dot{s})$ depends not on t and s, but only on the equivalence classes $\dot{t}$ and $\dot{s}$, and $\delta(\dot{t}, \dot{s})$ is a distance on $\dot{T}$. Consider on $\dot{T}$ the topology of metric space defined by the distance δ.

The canonical mapping $\varphi \colon T \to \dot{T}$ is then continuous for the initial topology on T. In fact, if $t_0 \in T$, we verify easily that the mapping $t \to d(t_0, t)$ is *continuous* on T, for the initial topology on T.

Let $E = \{\dot{t} \mid \delta(\dot{t}_0, \dot{t}) < r\}$ be an open neighbourhood of $\dot{t}_0$ in $\dot{T}$. Then $\overset{-1}{\varphi}(E) = \{t \mid d(t_0, t) < r\}$, and this set is open because $t \to d(t_0, t)$ is continuous. It follows that φ is itself continuous.

We remark that if $t \in K_n$ and $d(t, s) = 0$, then $\left| f_n(t) - f_n(s) \right| = 0$, therefore $f_n(s) = 0$, hence $s \in K_n$. It follows that every set K_n contains the whole class $\dot{t}$ of every point $t \in K_n$, hence $\overset{-1}{\varphi}(\varphi(K_n)) = K_n$.

The class of all the sets of the form $\overset{-1}{\varphi}(E)$ with $E \subset \dot{T}$ is a tribe which contains all the sets K_n, therefore it contains the semi-tribe generated by the sets K_n, hence it contains K. We deduce that K is of the form $K = \overset{-1}{\varphi}(C)$, with $C \subset \dot{T}$, therefore $\varphi(\overset{-1}{\varphi}(C)) = C$. Since $\overset{-1}{\varphi}(C) = K$ is compact and φ is continuous, the set $C = \varphi(K)$ is compact in the metric space $\dot{T}$, therefore C is G_δ.

Let (U_n) be a sequence of open sets of $\dot{T}$ such that

$$C = \bigcap_{n=1}^{\infty} U_n.$$

Since φ is continuous, the sets $G_n = \overset{-1}{\varphi}(U_n)$ are open and

$$K = \overset{-1}{\varphi}(C) = \overset{-1}{\varphi}\left(\bigcap_{n=1}^{\infty} U_n\right) = \bigcap_{n=1}^{\infty} \overset{-1}{\varphi}(U_n) = \bigcap_{n=1}^{\infty} G_n,$$

therefore K is G_δ.

Proposition 14. *Every compact set $K \in \mathscr{B}_0$ is the intersection of a sequence of open sets of $\mathscr{B}_0$ which are F_σ.*

Let $K \in \mathscr{B}_0$ be a compact set and let (U_n) be a sequence of open sets such that

$$K = \bigcap_{n=1}^{\infty} U_n.$$

For each n there exists an open set $G_n \in \mathscr{B}_0$ which is F_σ such that $K \subset G_n \subset U_n$. Then

$$K = \bigcap_{n=1}^{\infty} G_n.$$

Proposition 15. *Every open set $G \in \mathscr{B}_0$ is F_σ and is the union of a sequence of compact sets of $\mathscr{B}_0$.*

Let $G \in \mathscr{B}_0$ be an open set. By proposition 11 we can find a compact set $K \in \mathscr{B}_0$ such that $K \subset G$. Then $K - G$ is compact and belongs to $\mathscr{B}_0$, therefore there exists a sequence (G_n) of open sets of $\mathscr{B}_0$ which are F_σ (proposition 14) such that

$$K - G = \bigcap_{n=1}^{\infty} G_n.$$

For each n the set $K - G_n$ is compact and belongs to $\mathscr{B}_0$ and we have

$$G = K - (K - G) = K - \bigcap_{n=1}^{\infty} G_n = \bigcup_{n=1}^{\infty} (K - G_n).$$

Corollary. *$\mathscr{K}_0$ and $\mathscr{B}_0$ contain the same open sets and all their open sets are F_σ.*

In fact, let G be an open set of $\mathscr{B}_0$. By proposition 11, G is contained in a compact set $K \in \mathscr{B}_0$. Then $K - G$ is compact and belongs to $\mathscr{B}_0$. Since K and $K - G$ are G_δ, they belong to $\mathscr{K}_0$, therefore

$$G = K - (K - G) \in \mathscr{K}_0.$$

Proposition 16. *Every open set $G \in \mathscr{B}$ which is F_σ belongs to $\mathscr{B}_0$.*

In fact, since G is relatively compact, we can find a sequence (C_n) of compact sets such that $G = \bigcup_{n=1}^{\infty} C_n$. For each n we can find a compact set $K_n \in \mathscr{B}_0$ such that $C_n \subset K_n \subset G$ (proposition 11). It follows that

$$G = \bigcup_{n=1}^{\infty} K_n.$$

By proposition 11, the set $\bar{G}$ is contained in a compact set $K_0 \in \mathscr{B}_0$, therefore $K_n \subset K_0$ for every n. It follows that $G \in \mathscr{B}_0$.

Corollary. *The clan $\mathscr{K}_0$ (respectively the semi-tribe $\mathscr{B}_0$) is equal to the clan (respectively to the semi-tribe) generated by the relatively compact open sets which are F_σ.*

4. BOREL MEASURES. BAIRE MEASURES

Let X be a normed space.

Definition 1. *Any measure $\boldsymbol{m}$: $\mathscr{B} \to X$ defined on the semi-tribe of the relatively compact Borel sets will be called a Borel measure on T.*

If $\boldsymbol{m}$ and $\boldsymbol{n}$ are two Borel measures on T, with values in X, and if α is a scalar, then $\boldsymbol{m} + \boldsymbol{n}$ and $\alpha\boldsymbol{m}$ are also Borel measures.

Proposition 17. *Let $\boldsymbol{m}$ and $\boldsymbol{n}$ be two Borel measures on T. If $\boldsymbol{m}(K) = \boldsymbol{n}(K)$ for every compact set $K \subset T$, then $\boldsymbol{m} = \boldsymbol{n}$.*

In fact, the class $\mathscr{C}$ of the compact sets is a lattice. According to the corollary of the proposition 6, § 2, $\boldsymbol{m}$ and $\boldsymbol{n}$ coincide on $\mathscr{B}$.

Remarks.

1°. We can prove in the same manner that if $\boldsymbol{m}$ and $\boldsymbol{n}$ are two Borel measures on T such that $\boldsymbol{m}(G) = \boldsymbol{n}(G)$ for every open set $G \in \mathscr{B}$, then $\boldsymbol{m} = \boldsymbol{n}$.

2°. It is sufficient for a Borel measure with finite variation to be defined on the clan $\mathscr{K}$ only, because then it can be uniquely extended to a Borel measure (§ 5, theorem 3).

Definition 2. *Any measure $\boldsymbol{m}$: $\mathscr{B}_0 \to X$ defined on the semi-tribe of the relatively compact Baire sets will be called a Baire measure on T.*

If $\boldsymbol{m}$ and $\boldsymbol{n}$ are Baire measures on T and α is a scalar, then $\boldsymbol{m} + \boldsymbol{n}$ and $\alpha\boldsymbol{m}$ are Baire measures on T.

Proposition 18. *Let* $\boldsymbol{m}$ *and* $\boldsymbol{n}$ *be two Baire measures on* T. *If* $\boldsymbol{m}(K) = \boldsymbol{n}(K)$ *for every compact set* $K \in \mathscr{B}_0$, *then* $\boldsymbol{m} = \boldsymbol{n}$.

In fact, the class of the compact sets which are G_δ is a lattice which generates the semi-tribe $\mathscr{B}_0$.

Remark. It is sufficient for a Baire measure with finite variation to be defined on the clan $\mathscr{K}_0$ only, because then it can be uniquely extended to a Baire measure (§ 5, theorem 3).

5. INTEGRATION WITH RESPECT TO A BOREL MEASURE

Let E be a Banach space. The carrier (or support) of a function $f: T \to E$ is the smallest closed set F such that f is null outside F, i.e. F is the closure of the set $\{t; f(t) \neq 0\}$.

We shall prove that the continuous functions with compact carrier are integrable with respect to any Borel or Baire measure. We shall prove first the following:

Proposition 19. *Let* Φ *be a clan of subsets of* T *containing a fundamental system of neighbourhoods of every point* $t \in T$. *Let* $f: T \to E$ *be a function,* $K \subset T$ *a compact set, and* U *a neighbourhood of* K. *If the restriction of* f *to* K *is continuous, then there exists a sequence* (f_n) *of step functions of* $\mathscr{E}_E(\Phi)$ *vanishing outside* U *and converging uniformly to* f *on* K.

Let $\varepsilon > 0$. Since the restriction of f to K is continuous, for each point $t \in K$ we can find a neighbourhood $V_0 \in \Phi$ of t such that $V_0 \subset U$ and

$$|f(t) - f(t_0)| < \frac{\varepsilon}{2}, \quad \text{for every} \quad t \in V_0 \cap K.$$

If $t, t' \in V_0 \cap K$, then $|f(t) - f(t')| < \varepsilon$.

Since K is compact, we can find a finite family $V_1, \ldots, V_n$ of sets of Φ, contained in U, covering K with their interiors, such that for each i we have

$$|f(t) - f(t')| < \varepsilon, \quad \text{for every} \quad t, t' \in V_i \cap K.$$

Put $A_1 = V_1$ and

$$A_k = V_k - \bigcup_{i<k} A_i, \quad \text{for} \quad 1 < k \leqq n.$$

The sets A_k belong to Φ, are mutually disjoint and contained in U. We have

$$\bigcup_{i=1}^{n} A_i = \bigcup_{i=1}^{n} V_i \supset K$$

and $A_i \subset V_i$ for each i, therefore

$$|f(t) - f(t')| < \varepsilon, \quad \text{for every} \quad t, t' \in A_i \cap K.$$

For each i choose a point $t_i \in A_i \cap K$ and put $x_i = f(t_i)$. The Φ-step function

$$f_\varepsilon = \sum_{i=1}^{n} \varphi_{A_i} x_i$$

vanishes outside K and

$$|f(t) - f_\varepsilon(t)| < \varepsilon, \quad \text{for every} \quad t \in K.$$

In fact, if $t \in A_k \cap K$ for some k, then $f_\varepsilon(t) = \sum_{i=1}^{n} \varphi_{A_i}(t)\, x_i = x_k = f(t_k)$, therefore

$$|f(t) - f_\varepsilon(t)| = |f(t) - f(t_k)| < \varepsilon.$$

Taking $\varepsilon = 1, \frac{1}{2}, \ldots, \frac{1}{n}, \ldots$ we obtain a sequence (f_n) of Φ-step functions with carriers contained in U converging uniformly to f on K.

Corollary 1. *If the restriction of a function $f: T \to E$ to a compact $K \in \mathscr{K}$ (respectively $K \in \mathscr{K}_0$) is continuous, then there exists a sequence (f_n) of $\mathscr{K}$-step functions (respectively $\mathscr{K}_0$-step functions) vanishing outside K and converging uniformly to f on K.*

In view of the corollary 1 of the proposition 12, in the preceding proposition we can take $\Phi = \mathscr{K}_0$.

Let U be a relatively compact neighbourhood of K and let (g_n) be a sequence of $\mathscr{K}_0$-step functions vanishing outside U and converging uniformly to f on K.

If $K \in \mathscr{K}$ we take $f_n = g_n \varphi_K$ for every n and the first part of the corollary is proved.

Suppose now that $K \in \mathscr{K}_0$. Since the restriction f_K of f to K is continuous, f_K can be extended to a continuous function $g: T \to E$ vanishing outside U. Then the set $A = \{t; |g(t)| > 0\}$ is open F_σ (proposition 10) and relatively compact (contained in U), therefore $A \in \mathscr{K}_0$ (proposition 16). It follows that

$$B = \{t \in K; f(t) \neq 0\} = \{t; g(t) \neq 0\} = A \cap K \in \mathscr{K}_0.$$

Taking $f_n = g_n \varphi_B$ for every n, the second part of the corollary is also proved.

Corollary 2. *For every continuous function $f: T \to E$ with compact carrier K, there exists a sequence (f_n) of $\mathscr{K}_0$-step functions vanishing outside K and converging uniformly to f on T.*

Let U be a neighbourhood of K. Taking $\Phi = \mathscr{K}_0$ we can find a sequence (g_n) of $\mathscr{K}_0$-step functions vanishing outside U and converging uniformly to f on K. The set $A = \{t; f(t) \neq 0\}$ is open, F_σ (proposition 10) and relatively compact (contained in K), therefore $A \in \mathscr{K}_0$ (proposition 16). For every n we take $f_n = g_n \varphi_A$ and then (f_n) has all the required properties.

Proposition 20. *Let μ be a positive Borel measure and $f: T \to E$ a function. If for every compact $K \subset T$ and for every number $\varepsilon > 0$, there exists a compact $K' \subset K$*

with $\mu(K - K') < \varepsilon$ such that the restriction of f to K' is continuous, then f is μ-measurable.

Let K be a compact set. We can find, by induction, a sequence (K_n) of disjoint compact sets such that the set $N = K - \bigcup_{n=1}^{\infty} K_n$ is μ-negligible and such that the restriction of f to each K_n is continuous. By the corollary 1 of the proposition 19, $f\varphi_{K_n}$ is the limit of a sequence of $\mathscr{K}$-step functions, therefore $f\varphi_{K_n}$ is μ-measurable. From the equality

$$f\varphi_K(t) = \sum_{n=1}^{\infty} f\varphi_{K_n}(t) \quad \mu\text{-almost everywhere}$$

we deduce that $f\varphi_K$ is μ-measurable. Since every set $A \in \mathscr{B}$ is contained in a compact set K, we deduce that the function $f\varphi_A = f\varphi_K\varphi_A$ is μ-measurable. Then f is μ-measurable (§ 6, corollary of the theorem 2).

Remarks.

1°. We shall see (§ 15, theorem 3) that if μ is a *regular* Borel measure, then the condition stated in the preceding proposition is also sufficient for f to be μ-measurable.

2°. We can prove in the same manner that if μ is a positive Baire measure and if for every compact $K \in \mathscr{K}_0$ and every $\varepsilon > 0$ there exists a compact set $K' \in \mathscr{K}_0$ with $K' \subset K$ and $\mu(K' - K) < \varepsilon$, such that the restriction of f to K' is continuous, then f is μ-measurable.

Corollary. *A continuous function $f: T \to E$ is measurable with respect to every Borel or Baire measure.*

Proposition 21. *Let $1 \leqq p \leqq \infty$. A continuous function $f: T \to E$ with compact carrier belongs to the space $\mathscr{L}^p_E(\mu)$ for every Borel or Baire measure μ.*

Let μ be a Borel or Baire measure. We remark that f is bounded and μ-measurable, therefore $f \in \mathscr{L}^\infty_E(\mu)$. On the other hand, there exists a sequence (f_n) of $\mathscr{K}_0$-step functions vanishing outside the support of f and converging uniformly to f (corollary 2 of the proposition 19), therefore $f \in \mathscr{L}^p_E(\mu)$ for $1 \leqq p < \infty$ (§ 12, proposition 19).

Proposition 22. *Let $f: T \to E$ be a continuous function with compact carrier. For every Borel measures $\boldsymbol{m}, \boldsymbol{n}: \mathscr{B} \to \mathscr{L}(E, F)$ (or Baire measures $\boldsymbol{m}, \boldsymbol{n}: \mathscr{B}_0 \to \mathscr{L}(E, F)$) with finite variation and every scalars α, β we have*

$$\int f\, d(\alpha \boldsymbol{m} + \beta \boldsymbol{n}) = \alpha \int f\, d\boldsymbol{m} + \beta \int f\, d\boldsymbol{n}.$$

Let (f_n) be a sequence of step functions with carriers contained in the carrier of f, and converging uniformly to f. For each n we have

$$\int f_n \, d(\alpha \boldsymbol{m} + \beta \boldsymbol{n}) = \alpha \int f_n \, d\boldsymbol{m} + \beta \int f_n \, d\boldsymbol{n},$$

whence, for $n \to \infty$, we obtain

$$\int f \, d(\alpha \boldsymbol{m} + \beta \boldsymbol{n}) = \alpha \int f \, d\boldsymbol{m} + \beta \int f \, d\boldsymbol{n}.$$

Proposition 23. *The Borel sets are measurable with respect to every positive Borel measure* μ.

In fact, if E is a Borel set, then we have $E \cap A \in \mathscr{B} \subset \mathcal{T}(\mu)$ for every $A \in \mathscr{B}$, therefore $E \in \mathcal{T}(\mu)$ (§ 5, corollary 2 of the theorem 2).

Corollary. *The open and the closed sets are measurable with respect to every positive Borel measure.*

Remark. The Baire sets are measurable with respect to every Baire measure. But it may happen that some compact sets should not be measurable with respect to a Baire measure.

Example. Let E be a noncountable set with the discrete topology and let $T = E \cup \{\omega\}$ be the one-point compactification of E. The class $\mathscr{G}$ of the open sets of T consists of all the sets $A \subset E$ and all the sets $A \cup \{\omega\}$ with $A \subset E$ and $E - A$ finite. The class $\mathscr{C}$ of the compact sets of T consists of all the finite sets $A \subset E$ and all the sets $A \cup \{\omega\}$ with $A \subset E$ arbitrary. It follows that the tribe $\mathscr{B}$ of the Borel sets consists of all the subsets of T.

The class $\mathscr{C}_0$ of the compact sets which are G_δ consists of the finite sets $A \subset E$ and the sets $A \cup \{\omega\}$ with $A \subset E$ and $E - A$ at most countable. The tribe $\mathscr{B}_0$ of the Baire sets consists of all the sets $A \subset E$ which are at most countable, and all the sets $A \cup \{\omega\}$ with $A \subset E$ at most countable.

Consider the Baire measure μ defined for every set $A \in \mathscr{B}_0$ by $\mu(A) = 0$ if $\omega \notin A$ and $\mu(A) = 1$ if $\omega \in A$. In particular $\mu(T) = 1$. We have $\mu^*(\{\omega\}) = 1$ and $\mu^*(E) = 1$, because the only Baire set containing E is T. If the compact set $\{\omega\}$ were μ-measurable then E would be also μ-measurable and we should have $\mu(T) = \mu^*(E) + \mu^*(\{\omega\})$, i.e. $1 = 2$, which is impossible. It follows that $\{\omega\}$ is not μ-measurable.

§ 15. REGULAR MEASURES

In the definition of the Borel measures the presence of the topological structure of the space T is manifest only in the choice of the relatively compact Borel sets on which the measures are defined, but not in the values taken by these measures.

A stronger depedence on the topological structure of T is realized by the regular measures, which have the property to be continuous for a certain topology, defined by means of the compact sets and open sets, which, on their turn, characterize the topology of T.

1. TOPOLOGISATION OF $\mathscr{P}(T)$

For each pair (K, G) consisting of a compact set K and an open set G, we denote by $I(K, G)$ the class of all the subsets $A \subset T$ such that $K \subset A \subset G$. The class $I(K, G)$ will be called an *interval with origin K and extremity G.*

We have $I(K, G) = \emptyset$ if and only if $K \not\subset G$.

For two intervals $I(K, G)$ and $I(K', G')$ we have

$$I(K, G) \cap I(K', G') = I(K \cup K', G \cap G').$$

The class of all the intervals $I(K, G)$ is a base of a topology $\mathfrak{T}$ on $\mathscr{P}(T)$.

The topology induced by $\mathfrak{T}$ on any class $\mathscr{C} \subset \mathscr{P}(T)$ of subsets of T will be denoted also by $\mathfrak{T}$.

A class $\mathscr{C}$ of subsets of T is *dense* in $\mathscr{P}(T)$ for this topology, if every interval $I(K, G)$ contains at least a set of $\mathscr{C}$, i.e.:

$\mathscr{C}$ is dense in $\mathscr{P}(T)$ if and only if for every compact set $K \subset T$ and every open set $G \supset K$, there exists a set $A \in \mathscr{C}$ such that $K \subset A \subset G$.

Since every interval $I(K, G)$ contains K and G, it follows that *the class of all the compact sets* and *the class of all the open sets* are dense in $\mathscr{P}(T)$.

In particular, the clan $\mathscr{K}$ generated by the compact sets and the semi-tribe $\mathscr{B}$ are dense in $\mathscr{P}(T)$.

The class of all the *relatively compact* open sets is also dense in $\mathscr{P}(T)$, because in each nonvoid interval $I(K, G)$ there exists a relatively compact open set.

From the proposition 11, § 14, we deduce that the class of the compact sets which are G_δ, and the class of the relatively compact open sets which are F_σ, are dense in $\mathscr{P}(T)$.

It follows that the clan $\mathscr{K}_0$ generated by the compact sets which are G_δ and the semi-tribe $\mathscr{B}_0$ are dense in $\mathscr{P}(T)$.

2. REGULAR SET FUNCTIONS

Let $\mathscr{C}$ be a *class* of subsets of T, X a *normed* space, and $\boldsymbol{m}$: $\mathscr{C} \to X$ a set function.

Definition 1. *A set $A \in \mathscr{C}$ is said to be regular with respect to* $\mathbf{m}$, *if* $\mathbf{m}$ *is continuous in A for the topology* $\mathfrak{T}$, *i.e. if:*

for every number $\varepsilon > 0$, *there exist a compact set* $K \subset A$ *and an open set* $G \supset A$ *such that for every set* $A' \in \mathscr{C}$ *with* $K \subset A' \subset G$ *we have*

$$|\boldsymbol{m}(A) - \boldsymbol{m}(A')| < \varepsilon.$$

Since the class $\mathscr{C}$ is partially ordered by inclusion we can give a sense to right and left continuity.

Definition 2. *A set* $A \in \mathscr{C}$ *is said to be regular on the left with respect to* $\boldsymbol{m}$, *if* $\boldsymbol{m}$ *is continuous on the left in* A *for the topology* $\mathfrak{T}$, *i.e. if:*

for every number $\varepsilon > 0$, *there exists a compact set* $K \subset A$ *such that for every set* $A' \in \mathscr{C}$ *with* $K \subset A' \subset A$ *we have*

$$|\boldsymbol{m}(A) - \boldsymbol{m}(A')| < \varepsilon.$$

A set $A \in \mathscr{C}$ *is said to be regular on the right with respect to* $\boldsymbol{m}$ *if* $\boldsymbol{m}$ *is continuous on the right in* A *for the topology* $\mathfrak{T}$, *i.e. if:*

for every number $\varepsilon > 0$, *there exists an open set* $G \supset A$ *such that for every set* $A' \in \mathscr{C}$ *with* $A \subset A' \subset G$ *we have*

$$|\boldsymbol{m}(A) - \boldsymbol{m}(A')| < \varepsilon.$$

It follows from the properties of the continuity that if $\boldsymbol{m}'$ is the restriction of $\boldsymbol{m}$ to a subclass $\mathscr{C}' \subset \mathscr{C}$ and if a set $A \in \mathscr{C}'$ is regular with respect to $\boldsymbol{m}$, then A is regular with respect to $\boldsymbol{m}'$. The converse is not true.

From the definition 2 we deduce that every compact set $K \in \mathscr{C}$ is regular on the left, and that every open set $G \in \mathscr{C}$ is regular on the right.

We say that the set function $\boldsymbol{m}$ is regular (respectively regular on the left, regular on the right) on a subclass $\mathscr{C}' \subset \mathscr{C}$ if every set $A \in \mathscr{C}$ is regular (respectively regular on the left, regular on the right) with respect to $\boldsymbol{m}$, i.e. if $\boldsymbol{m}$ is continuous (respectively continuous on the left, continuous on the right) on $\mathscr{C}'$ for the topology $\mathfrak{T}$.

We remark that if $\boldsymbol{m}$ is regular on $\mathscr{C}'$ then the restriction $\boldsymbol{m}'$ of $\boldsymbol{m}$ to $\mathscr{C}'$ is also regular on $\mathscr{C}'$, but the converse is not true.

If $\boldsymbol{m}$ and $\boldsymbol{n}$ are two set functions defined on $\mathscr{C}$ with values in X and regular (respectively regular on the left, regular on the right) on a subclass $\mathscr{C}' \subset \mathscr{C}$ and if α is a scalar, then $\boldsymbol{m} + \boldsymbol{n}$ and $\alpha\boldsymbol{m}$ are regular (respectively regular on the left, regular on the right) on $\mathscr{C}'$.

From the preceding definitions it follows that if a set $A \in \mathscr{C}$ is regular, then A is regular on the left and on the right.

Since the class $\mathscr{C}$ is not totally ordered by inclusion, the union of the intervals $I(K, A)$ and $I(A, G)$ is different from $I(K, G)$. We may except that $\boldsymbol{m}$ can be continuous on the left and on the right in $A \in \mathscr{C}$, without being continuous in A.

However, we shall show that if $\boldsymbol{m}$ is an *additive* set function defined on a *clan* $\mathscr{C}$, then a set $A \in \mathscr{C}$ is regular with respect to $\boldsymbol{m}$ if and only if it is regular on the left and on the right with respect to $\boldsymbol{m}$.

In some cases the regularity on the left is equivalent to the regularity on the right. In the next sections we shall prove also that the regularity of $\boldsymbol{m}$ on a class is a consequence of its regularity on a smaller class.

3. REGULAR ADDITIVE SET FUNCTIONS ON A CLAN

Let $\mathscr{C}$ be a *clan* of subsets of T, X a *normed* space, and $\boldsymbol{m}\colon \mathscr{C} \to X$ an *additive* set function.

In this case, the regularity can be defined by the conditions stated in the following two propositions.

Proposition 1. *A set $A \in \mathscr{C}$ is regular with respect to $\boldsymbol{m}$ if and only if, for every number $\varepsilon > 0$, there exists a compact set $K \subset A$ and an open set $G \supset A$ such that for every set $B \in \mathscr{C}$ with $B \subset G - K$ we have $|\boldsymbol{m}(B)| < \varepsilon$.*

Suppose first that A is regular and let $\varepsilon > 0$. We can find a compact set $K \subset A$ and an open set $G \supset A$ such that if $A' \in \mathscr{C}$ and $K \subset A' \subset G$ we have

$$|\boldsymbol{m}(A) - \boldsymbol{m}(A')| < \frac{\varepsilon}{2}.$$

If $B \in \mathscr{C}$ and $B \subset G - K$, then

$$B = (A \cup B) - (A - B), \quad A - B \subset A \cup B$$

and

$$K \subset A \cup B \subset G, \quad K \subset A - B \subset G.$$

The sets $A \cup B$ and $A - B$ belong to $\mathscr{C}$, therefore

$$\begin{aligned} |\boldsymbol{m}(B)| &= |\boldsymbol{m}(A \cup B) - \boldsymbol{m}(A - B)| \\ &\leqq |\boldsymbol{m}(A \cup B) - \boldsymbol{m}(A)| + |\boldsymbol{m}(A) - \boldsymbol{m}(A - B)| < \varepsilon, \end{aligned}$$

hence the condition stated in the proposition is fulfilled.

Conversely, suppose this condition fulfilled and let $\varepsilon > 0$. Choose a compact set $K \subset A$ and an open set $G \supset A$ such that if $B \in \mathscr{C}$ and $B \subset G - A$, then $|\boldsymbol{m}(B)| < \frac{\varepsilon}{2}$.

If $A' \in \mathscr{C}$ and $K \subset A' \subset G$, then

$$A - A' \subset G - K, \quad A' - A \subset G - K$$

and

$$A' = (A \cap A') \cup (A' - A), \quad A - A' = A - (A \cap A').$$

The sets $A \cap A'$ and $A' - A$ are disjoint and belong to $\mathscr{C}$, therefore

$$\begin{aligned} |\boldsymbol{m}(A) - \boldsymbol{m}(A')| &= |\boldsymbol{m}(A) - \boldsymbol{m}(A \cap A') - \boldsymbol{m}(A' - A)| \\ &= |\boldsymbol{m}(A - A') - \boldsymbol{m}(A' - A)| \\ &\leqq |\boldsymbol{m}(A - A')| + |\boldsymbol{m}(A' - A)| < \varepsilon, \end{aligned}$$

hence A is regular.

Proposition 2.

a) *A set* $A \in \mathscr{C}$ *is regular on the left with respect to* $\boldsymbol{m}$ *if and only if, for every number* $\varepsilon > 0$, *there exists a compact set* $K \subset A$ *such that for every set* $B \in \mathscr{C}$ *with* $B \subset A - K$ *we have* $|\boldsymbol{m}(B)| < \varepsilon$.

b) *A set* $A \in \mathscr{C}$ *is regular on the right with respect to* $\boldsymbol{m}$ *if and only if, for every number* $\varepsilon > 0$, *there exists an open set* $G \supset A$ *such that for every set* $B \in \mathscr{C}$ *with* $B \subset G - A$ *we have* $|\boldsymbol{m}(B)| < \varepsilon$.

Suppose first that A is regular on the left and let $\varepsilon > 0$. Let $K \subset A$ be a compact set such that for $A' \in \mathscr{C}$ with $K \subset A' \subset A$ we have $|\boldsymbol{m}(A) - \boldsymbol{m}(A')| < \varepsilon$.
If $B \in \mathscr{C}$ and $B \subset A - K$, then $B = A - (A - B)$ and $K \subset A - B \subset A$, therefore

$$|\boldsymbol{m}(B)| = |\boldsymbol{m}(A) - \boldsymbol{m}(A - B)| < \varepsilon,$$

hence the condition stated in the proposition is fulfilled.
Conversely, suppose this condition fulfilled and let $\varepsilon > 0$. Choose a compact set $K \subset A$ such that if $B \in \mathscr{C}$ and $B \subset K - A$ then $|\boldsymbol{m}(B)| < \varepsilon$.
If $A' \in \mathscr{C}$ and $K \subset A' \subset A$, then $A - A' \subset A - K$, therefore

$$|\boldsymbol{m}(A) - \boldsymbol{m}(A')| = |\boldsymbol{m}(A - A')| < \varepsilon,$$

hence A is regular on the left.
The second part of the proposition is proved in the same manner, remarking that if $A \subset G$ and $B \subset G - A$, then $B = (A \cup B) - A$ and $A \subset A \cup B \subset G$, for the first implication, and taking $A' - A$ instead of $A - A'$ for the converse implication.

Corollary. *Let* μ *and* ν *be two additive positive set functions defined on* $\mathscr{C}$, *such that* $\mu \leqq \nu$. *If a set* $A \in \mathscr{C}$ *is regular (respectively regular on the left, regular on the right) with respect to* ν, *then* A *has the same property with respect to* μ.

Proposition 3. *A set* $A \in \mathscr{C}$ *is regular with respect to* $\boldsymbol{m}$ *if and only if it is regular on the left and on the right with respect to* $\boldsymbol{m}$.

As we have already remarked, if A is regular, then A is regular on the left and on the right (even if $\boldsymbol{m}$ is not additive and $\mathscr{C}$ is not a clan).
Conversely, suppose that A is regular on the left and on the right with respect to $\boldsymbol{m}$ and let $\varepsilon > 0$. Choose a compact set $K \subset A$ and an open set $G \supset A$ such that if $B \in \mathscr{C}$ and if $B \subset A - K$ or $B \subset G - A$, then $|\boldsymbol{m}(B)| < \frac{\varepsilon}{2}$. If $B \in \mathscr{C}$ and $B \subset G - K$, then

$$B = (B - A) \cup (B \cap A)$$

and

$$B - A \subset G - A, \quad B \cap A \subset A - K.$$

The sets $B - A$ and $B \cap A$ are disjoint and belong to $\mathscr{C}$, therefore

$$|\boldsymbol{m}(B)| = |\boldsymbol{m}(B - A) + \boldsymbol{m}(B \cap A)| \leqq |\boldsymbol{m}(B - A)| + |\boldsymbol{m}(B \cap A)| < \varepsilon,$$

hence, according to proposition 1, A is regular.

From this proposition we deduce that a compact set $K \in \mathscr{C}$ is regular if and only if K is regular on the right, and an open set $G \in \mathscr{C}$ is regular, if and only if G is regular on the left.

In certain special cases, the regularity is equivalent to the left regularity or to the right regularity.

Proposition 4. *Suppose that the clan $\mathscr{C}$ verifies the following condition:*

(*) *For every set $A \in \mathscr{C}$ there exists a set $A' \in \mathscr{C}$ such that $A \subset \operatorname{Int} A'$.*

Then $\boldsymbol{m}$ is regular on $\mathscr{C}$ if and only if $\boldsymbol{m}$ is regular on the left on $\mathscr{C}$.

From the proposition 3 we see that we have to prove only that if $\boldsymbol{m}$ is regular on the left, then $\boldsymbol{m}$ is regular on the right on $\mathscr{C}$.

Suppose then that $\boldsymbol{m}$ is regular on the left on $\mathscr{C}$. Let $A \in \mathscr{C}$ and $\varepsilon > 0$. Choose $A' \in \mathscr{C}$ with $A \subset \operatorname{Int} A'$. The set $A' - A$ belongs to $\mathscr{C}$, therefore $A' - A$ is regular on the left: we can find a compact set $K \subset A' - A$ such that if $B \in \mathscr{C}$ and $B \subset (A' - A) - K$, then $|\boldsymbol{m}(B)| < \varepsilon$. If we put $U = \operatorname{Int} A'$, the set $G = U - K$ is open,

$$A = U - (U - A) \subset U - K = G$$

and

$$G - A = (U - K) - A = (U - A) - K \subset (A' - A) - K.$$

If $B \in \mathscr{C}$ and $B \subset G - A$, then $B \subset (A' - A) - K$, therefore $|\boldsymbol{m}(B)| < \varepsilon$, hence A is regular on the right. It follows that A is regular with respect to $\boldsymbol{m}$.

The set $A \in \mathscr{C}$ being arbitrary, we deduce that $\boldsymbol{m}$ is regular on $\mathscr{C}$.

Corollary. *If every set of $\mathscr{C}$ is contained in an open set of $\mathscr{C}$ then $\boldsymbol{m}$ is regular on $\mathscr{C}$ if and only if it is regular on the left on $\mathscr{C}$.*

Proposition 5. *Suppose that the clan $\mathscr{C}$ consists of relatively compact sets and verifies the following condition:*

(**) *For every set $A \in \mathscr{C}$ there exists a set $A' \in \mathscr{C}$ such that $\bar{A} \subset A'$.*

Then $\boldsymbol{m}$ is regular on $\mathscr{C}$ if and only if $\boldsymbol{m}$ is regular on the right on $\mathscr{C}$.

We have to prove only that if $\boldsymbol{m}$ is regular on the right, then $\boldsymbol{m}$ is regular on the left.

Suppose then that $\boldsymbol{m}$ is regular on the right and let $A \in \mathscr{C}$ and $\varepsilon > 0$. Let $A' \in \mathscr{C}$ be such that $\bar{A} \subset A'$. The set $A' - A$ belongs to $\mathscr{C}$ whence it is regular on the right: there exists an open set $G \supset A' - A$ such that if $B \in \mathscr{C}$ and $B \subset G - (A' - A)$, then $|\boldsymbol{m}(B)| < \varepsilon$. The set $\bar{A}$ is compact, therefore the set $K = \bar{A} - G$ is compact and we have

$$K = \bar{A} - G = A - G \subset A$$

and
$$A - K = A - (A - G) = A \cap G \subset G - (A' - A).$$

If $B \in \mathscr{C}$ and $B \subset A - K$, then $B \subset G - (A' - A)$, therefore $|\boldsymbol{m}(B)| < \varepsilon$. It follows that A is regular on the left, therefore A is regular. Consequently, $\boldsymbol{m}$ is regular on $\mathscr{C}$.

Lemma 1. *If the clan $\mathscr{C}$ is dense in $\mathscr{P}(T)$ for the topology $\mathfrak{T}$ and if $\mathscr{C}$ consists of relatively compact sets, then the conditions* (*) *and* (**) *are verified.*

Let $A \in \mathscr{C}$. Since $\bar{A}$ is compact we can choose a relatively compact open set $U \supset \bar{A}$. If V is an arbitrary open set with $\bar{U} \subset V$ there exists a set $A' \in \mathscr{C}$ such that $\bar{U} \subset A' \subset V$, since $\mathscr{C}$ is dense in $\mathscr{P}(T)$. It follows that $\bar{A} \subset \operatorname{Int} A'$, consequently $A \subset \operatorname{Int} A'$ and $\bar{A} \subset A'$.

Proposition 6. *If the clan $\mathscr{C}$ is dense in $\mathscr{P}(T)$ for the topology $\mathfrak{T}$ and if $\mathscr{C}$ consists of relatively compact sets* (*in particular, if $\mathscr{C}$ is one of the clans $\mathscr{K}_0$ and $\mathscr{K}$ or one of the semi-tribes $\mathscr{B}_0$ and $\mathscr{B}$*), *then the following three conditions are equivalent:*

a) *$\boldsymbol{m}$ is regular on $\mathscr{C}$;*

b) *$\boldsymbol{m}$ is regular on the left on $\mathscr{C}$;*

c) *$\boldsymbol{m}$ is regular on the right on $\mathscr{C}$.*

4. SET FUNCTIONS REGULAR ON A SUBCLASS

Let $\mathscr{C}$ be a *clan* of subsets of T, X a *normed* space, and $\boldsymbol{m}\colon \mathscr{C} \to X$ an *additive* set function.

We shall show that the regularity of $\boldsymbol{m}$ on $\mathscr{C}$ can be deduced from the regularity of $\boldsymbol{m}$ on a smaller class.

Proposition 7. *If the sets $A_1, A_2, \ldots, A_n$ of $\mathscr{C}$ are disjoint and regular on the left* (*with respect to $\boldsymbol{m}$*), *then their union $A = \bigcup_{i=1}^{n} A_i$ is regular on the left.*

Let $\varepsilon > 0$. For each i there exists a compact set $K_i \subset A_i$ such that if $A_i' \in \mathscr{C}$ and $K_i \subset A_i' \subset A_i$, then
$$|\boldsymbol{m}(A_i) - \boldsymbol{m}(A_i')| < \frac{\varepsilon}{n}.$$
The set $K = \bigcup_{i=1}^{n} K_i$ is compact and $K \subset A$.

Let $A' \in \mathscr{C}$ be such that $K \subset A' \subset A$. If for every i we put $A_i' = A' \cap A_i$, the sets A_i' are disjoint sets of $\mathscr{C}$ and we have $A' = \bigcup_{i=1}^{n} A_i'$ and $K_i \subset A_i' \subset A_i$ for each i, therefore
$$|\boldsymbol{m}(A) - \boldsymbol{m}(A')| = \left|\sum_{i=1}^{n} \boldsymbol{m}(A_i) - \sum_{i=1}^{n} \boldsymbol{m}(A_i')\right| \leqq \sum_{i=1}^{n} |\boldsymbol{m}(A_i) - \boldsymbol{m}(A_i')| < \varepsilon,$$
hence A is regular on the left.

Remark. From the preceding proof we deduce the following result:

Let $\mathscr{A}$ be a class of subsets of T such that $A \cap B \in \mathscr{C}$ for every $A, B \in \mathscr{C}$ and let $\boldsymbol{m}: \mathscr{A} \to X$ be a finitely additive set function. If the sets $A_1, A_2, \ldots, A_n$ of $\mathscr{A}$ are disjoint and regular on the left, then their union is regular on the left.

In particular $\mathscr{A}$ can be a lattice or a semi-clan.

Corollary. *If $\mathscr{P}$ is a semi-clan generating the clan $\mathscr{C}$, and if $\boldsymbol{m}$ is regular on the left on $\mathscr{P}$, then $\boldsymbol{m}$ is regular on the left on $\mathscr{C}$.*

In fact, every set of $\mathscr{C}$ is the union of a finite family of disjoint sets of $\mathscr{P}$ (proposition 13, § 1).

Proposition 8. *Suppose that every relatively compact open set $U \in \mathscr{C}$ is contained in a compact set $C \in \mathscr{C}$.*

If $\boldsymbol{m}$ is regular (on the right) on the class of the compact sets of $\mathscr{C}$, then $\boldsymbol{m}$ is regular (on the left) on the class of the relatively compact open sets of $\mathscr{C}$.

Let $U \in \mathscr{C}$ be a relatively compact open set and let $\varepsilon > 0$. We can find a compact set $C \supset U$ of $\mathscr{C}$. Then $C - U$ is a compact set of $\mathscr{C}$, hence $C - U$ is regular (on the right): there exists an open set $G \supset C - U$ such that if $B \in \mathscr{C}$ and $B \subset G - (C - U)$, then $|\boldsymbol{m}(B)| < \varepsilon$. The set $K = C - G$ is compact, and we have

$$K = C - G \subset C - (C - U) = U$$

and

$$U - K = U - (C - G) = U \cap G \subset G - (C - U).$$

If $B \in \mathscr{C}$ is such that $B \subset U - K$, then $B \subset G - (C - U)$, therefore $|\boldsymbol{m}(B)| < \varepsilon$, hence U is regular (on the left).

Proposition 9. *Suppose that every compact set $C \in \mathscr{C}$ is contained in a relatively compact open set $U \in \mathscr{C}$. If $\boldsymbol{m}$ is regular (on the left) on the class of the relatively compact open sets of $\mathscr{C}$, then $\boldsymbol{m}$ is regular on the left on the class of the differences $C - D$ of compact sets $C, D \in \mathscr{C}$.*

Let C, D be two compact sets of $\mathscr{C}$.

We consider first the case $D \subset C$. Let $\varepsilon > 0$ and let $U \supset C$ be a relatively compact open set of $\mathscr{C}$. Then $U - D$ is a relatively compact open set of $\mathscr{C}$, hence $U - D$ is regular on the left: there exists a compact set $K \subset U - D$ such that if $B \in \mathscr{C}$ and $B \subset (U - D) - K$, then $|\boldsymbol{m}(B)| < \varepsilon$.

The set $C \cap K$ is compact and we have

$$C \cap K \subset C \cap (U - D) = C - D$$

and

$$(C - D) - (C \cap K) = (C - D) - K \subset (U - D) - K.$$

If $B \in \mathscr{C}$ is such that $B \subset (C - D) - (C \cap K)$, then $B \subset (U - D) - K$, therefore $|\boldsymbol{m}(B)| < \varepsilon$, hence $C - D$ is regular on the left.

If D is not contained in C, then $D \cap C$ is compact and $D \cap C \subset C$, therefore $C - (C \cap D)$ is regular on the left. From the equality

$$C - D = C - (C \cap D)$$

we deduce then that $C - D$ is regular on the left.

Remark. The preceding proposition remains valid for "open set" instead of "relatively compact open set".

Corollary. *Suppose that every compact set of $\mathscr{C}$ is contained in a relatively compact open set of $\mathscr{C}$ and that every relatively compact open set of $\mathscr{C}$ is contained in a compact set of $\mathscr{C}$. Then $\boldsymbol{m}$ is regular on the class of the compact sets of $\mathscr{C}$ if and only if $\boldsymbol{m}$ is regular on the class of the relatively compact open sets of $\mathscr{C}$.*

Proposition 10. *Suppose that $\mathscr{C}$ is generated by the class of its compact sets, and that every compact set of $\mathscr{C}$ is contained in an open set of $\mathscr{C}$. If $\boldsymbol{m}$ is regular on the class of the compact sets of $\mathscr{C}$, then $\boldsymbol{m}$ is regular on $\mathscr{C}$.*

As the clan $\mathscr{C}$ is generated by the class of its compact sets, every set of $\mathscr{C}$ is contained in a compact set of $\mathscr{C}$. From the proposition 8 we deduce that $\boldsymbol{m}$ is regular on the class of the open sets of $\mathscr{C}$.

By proposition 9, $\boldsymbol{m}$ is regular on the left on the class of the differences $C - D$ of compact sets $C, D \in \mathscr{C}$. Finally, by proposition 7, $\boldsymbol{m}$ is regular on the left on the class Φ of the finite unions $\bigcup_{i=1}^{n} (C_i - D_i)$ of disjoint differences $C_i - D_i$ of compact sets of $\mathscr{C}$. But the class of the compact sets of $\mathscr{C}$ is a lattice, therefore Φ is a clan containing the compact sets of $\mathscr{C}$ and contained in $\mathscr{C}$ (§ 1, corollary of proposition 13). If follows that $\Phi = \mathscr{C}$, therefore $\boldsymbol{m}$ is regular on the left on $\mathscr{C}$.

On the other hand, every set $A \in \mathscr{C}$ is contained in a compact set of $\mathscr{C}$, which is contained in an open set of $\mathscr{C}$. It follows that $\mathscr{C}$ verifies the condition (*) of proposition 4, and by this proposition we deduce that $\boldsymbol{m}$ is regular on $\mathscr{C}$.

Corollary. *If $\mathscr{C}$ is the clan generated by the compact sets (or by the compact sets which are G_δ) and if $\boldsymbol{m}$ is regular on the class of the compact sets (respectively on the class of the compact sets which are G_δ), then $\boldsymbol{m}$ is regular on $\mathscr{C}$.*

5. REGULAR POSITIVE SET FUNCTIONS

Let $\mathscr{C}$ be a *clan* of subsets of T and μ a *positive*, *finite* and *additive* set function defined on $\mathscr{C}$.

We begin with sufficient conditions of regularity expressed by means of the compact sets and the open sets *belonging* to $\mathscr{C}$.

Proposition 11. *Let A be a set of $\mathscr{C}$.*

a) *If*

$$\mu(A) = \sup_{K \subset A} \mu(K), \quad K \in \mathscr{C}, \quad \textit{compact},$$

then A is regular on the left.

b) *If*

$$\mu(A) = \inf_{G \supset A} \mu(G), \quad G \in \mathscr{C}, \quad \textit{open},$$

then A is regular on the right.

c) *If*

$$\mu(A) = \sup_{K \subset A} \mu(K) = \inf_{G \supset A} \mu(G), \quad K \in \mathscr{C}, \quad \textit{compact}, \quad G \in \mathscr{C} \quad \textit{open},$$

then A is regular.

In fact, if, for instance, condition a) is verified, then for every $\varepsilon > 0$ there exists a compact set $K \in \mathscr{C}$ such that $K \subset A$ and $\mu(A) \leqq \mu(K) + \varepsilon$. Then for every set $A' \in \mathscr{C}$ such that $K \subset A' \subset A$ we have

$$\mu(K) \leqq \mu(A') \leqq \mu(A) \leqq \mu(K) + \varepsilon,$$

therefore $|\mu(A) - \mu(A')| < \varepsilon$, hence A is regular on the left.

The other parts are proved in the same manner.

Remark. This proposition remains valid for an *increasing positive* and *finite* set function μ defined on an *arbitrary class* $\mathscr{C}$.

Corollary. *Every positive measure on a clan $\mathscr{C}$ containing $\mathscr{K}_0$ is regular on $\mathscr{K}_0$.*

Let μ be a positive measure on $\mathscr{C}$. Let K be a compact set which is G_δ. There exists then a sequence (G_n) of open sets of $\mathscr{K}_0$ with intersection equal to K (§ 14, proposition 14). We can take the sequence (G_n) to be decreasing. Since μ is countably additive, we have

$$\mu(K) = \inf_n \mu(G_n) = \inf_{G \supset K} \mu(G), \quad G \in \mathscr{C}, \text{ open},$$

therefore K is regular on the right and consequently K is regular.

From the corollary of the proposition 10 it follows that μ is regular on $\mathscr{K}_0$.

Remark. We shall prove (§ 16, corollary 1 of the proposition 1) that every positive Baire measure is regular.

The following lemma furnishes conditions equivalent with those of the preceding proposition.

Lemma 2. *Let A a be set of* $\mathscr{C}$.

a) *We have*

$$\mu(A) = \sup_{K \subset A} \mu(K), \quad K \in \mathscr{C}, \quad \textit{compact},$$

if and only if, for every $\varepsilon > 0$, *there exists a compact set* $K \in \mathscr{C}$ *such that* $K \subset A$ *and* $\mu(A - K) < \varepsilon$.

b) *We have*

$$\mu(A) = \inf_{G \supset A} \mu(G), \quad G \in \mathscr{C}, \quad \textit{open},$$

if and only if, for every $\varepsilon > 0$, *there exists an open set* $G \in \mathscr{C}$ *such that* $A \subset G$ *and* $\mu(G - A) < \varepsilon$.

c) *We have*

$$\mu(A) = \sup_{K \subset A} \mu(K) = \inf_{G \supset A} \mu(G), \quad K \in \mathscr{C}, \quad \textit{compact}, \quad G \in \mathscr{C}, \quad \textit{open},$$

if and only if, for every $\varepsilon > 0$, *there exist a compact set* $K \in \mathscr{C}$ *and an open set* $G \in \mathscr{C}$ *such that* $K \subset A \subset G$ *and* $\mu(G - K) < \varepsilon$.

These equivalences are immediate consequences of the fact that μ is *subtractive*.

If additional conditions on $\mathscr{C}$ are supposed, the regularity can be defined only by the aid of the compact sets, or of the open sets of $\mathscr{C}$.

Proposition 12. *Suppose that the clan* $\mathscr{C}$ *verifies the following condition:*

(*) *For every set* $A \in \mathscr{C}$ *there exists a set* $A' \in \mathscr{C}$ *such that* $A \subset \operatorname{Int} A'$.

If for every set $A \in \mathscr{C}$ *we have*

$$\mu(A) = \sup_{K \subset A} \mu(K), \quad K \in \mathscr{C}, \quad \textit{compact},$$

then μ *is regular on* $\mathscr{C}$.

In fact, by proposition 11, μ is regular on the left on $\mathscr{C}$, hence, by proposition 4, μ is regular on $\mathscr{C}$.

Corollary. *If every set of* $\mathscr{C}$ *is contained in an open set of* $\mathscr{C}$ *and if for every set* $A \in \mathscr{C}$ *we have*

$$\mu(A) = \sup_{K \subset A} \mu(K), \quad K \in \mathscr{C}, \quad \textit{compact},$$

then μ *is regular on* $\mathscr{C}$.

Proposition 13. *Suppose that the clan* $\mathscr{C}$ *consists of relatively compact sets and verifies the following condition:*

(**) *For every set* $A \in \mathscr{C}$ *there exists a set* $A' \in \mathscr{C}$ *such that* $\bar{A} \subset A'$.

If for every set $A \in \mathscr{C}$ we have

$$\mu(A) = \inf_{G \supset A} \mu(G), \quad G \in \mathscr{C}, \quad G \text{ open},$$

then μ is regular on $\mathscr{C}$.

In fact, by proposition 11, μ is regular on the right on $\mathscr{C}$ and by proposition 5, μ is regular on $\mathscr{C}$.

Proposition 14. *If the clan $\mathscr{C}$ is dense in $\mathscr{P}(T)$ for the topology $\mathfrak{T}$ and if $\mathscr{C}$ consists of relatively compact sets (in particular, if $\mathscr{C}$ is one of the clans $\mathscr{K}_0$ and $\mathscr{K}$ or one of the semi-tribes $\mathscr{B}_0$ and $\mathscr{B}$), then μ is regular on $\mathscr{C}$ in each of the following cases:*

a) *For every set $A \in \mathscr{C}$ we have*

$$\mu(A) = \sup_{K \subset A} \mu(K), \quad K \in \mathscr{C}, \quad \text{compact};$$

b) *for every set $A \in \mathscr{C}$ we have*

$$\mu(A) = \inf_{G \supset A} \mu(G), \quad G \in \mathscr{C}, \quad \text{open}.$$

In certain cases, the conditions stated in the proposition 11 are also sufficient for the corresponding regularity.

Proposition 15. *Let $A \in \mathscr{C}$ and suppose that for every compact set $C \subset A$ there exists a compact set $K \in \mathscr{C}$ such that $C \subset K \subset A$. Then A is regular on the left if and only if*

$$\mu(A) = \sup_{K \subset A} \mu(K), \quad K \in \mathscr{C}, \quad K \text{ compact}.$$

Suppose that A is regular on the left and let $\varepsilon > 0$. We can find a compact set $C \subset A$ such that if $B \in \mathscr{C}$ and $B \subset A - C$, then $\mu(B) < \varepsilon$. Let $K \in \mathscr{C}$ be a compact set such that $C \subset K \subset A$. Then $A - K \in \mathscr{C}$ and $A - K \subset A - C$, hence $\mu(A - K) < \varepsilon$. By lemma 2, the equality of the statement is verified. The converse implication follows from the proposition 11.

Corollary 1. *If $\mathscr{C}$ contains all the compact sets, then μ is regular on the left on $\mathscr{C}$ if and only if for every set $A \in \mathscr{C}$ we have*

$$\mu(A) = \sup_{K \subset A} \mu(K), \quad K \text{ compact}.$$

Corollary 2. *If $\mathscr{C}$ contains all the compact sets and verifies the following condition:*

(*) *For every set $A \in \mathscr{C}$ there exists a set $A' \in \mathscr{C}$ with $A \subset \operatorname{Int} A'$,*

then the following two conditions are equivalent:

a) *μ is regular on $\mathscr{C}$;*

b) *for every set* $A \in \mathscr{C}$ *we have*

$$\mu(A) = \sup_{K \subset A} \mu(K), \quad K \text{ compact}.$$

We use the propositions 4 and 15.

Corollary 3. *If* $\mathscr{C}$ *contains all the compact sets and if every set of* $\mathscr{C}$ *is contained in an open set of* $\mathscr{C}$, *the conditions* a) *and* b) *in the preceding corollary are equivalent.*

Proposition 16. *Let* $A \in \mathscr{C}$ *and suppose that for every open set* $U \supset A$ *there exists an open set* $G \in \mathscr{C}$ *such that* $A \subset G \subset U$. *Then* A *is regular on the right if and only if*

$$\mu(A) = \inf_{G \supset A} \mu(G), \quad G \in \mathscr{C}, \quad \text{open}.$$

The proof is similar to that of the preceding proposition.

Proposition 17. *If* $\mathscr{C}$ *contains all the compact sets and consists of relatively compact sets (in particular if* $\mathscr{C}$ *is equal to* $\mathscr{K}$ *or to* $\mathscr{B}$*), then the following three conditions are equivalent:*

a) μ *is regular on* $\mathscr{C}$;

b) *for every set* $A \in \mathscr{C}$ *we have*

$$\mu(A) = \sup_{K \subset A} \mu(K), \quad K \text{ compact};$$

c) $\mu(A) = \inf_{G \supset A} \mu(G)$, G *open and relatively compact.*

In fact, since $\mathscr{C}$ contains the compact sets, $\mathscr{C}$ is dense in $\mathscr{P}(T)$, therefore $\mathscr{C}$ verifies the conditions (*) and (**). It follows that the regularity of μ is equivalent to the left regularity and to the right regularity (proposition 6). On the other hand, the left regularity is equivalent to the condition b) (corollary of the proposition 15) and the right regularity is equivalent to the condition c) (proposition 16) since $\mathscr{C}$ contains all the relatively compact open sets (§ 14, proposition 1).

6. REGULAR SET FUNCTIONS WITH FINITE VARIATION

Let $\mathscr{C}$ be a *clan* of subsets of T, X a *normed space*, and $\boldsymbol{m}: \mathscr{C} \to X$ an *additive set function with finite variation* μ. We know then that μ is *positive* (finite) and *additive* on $\mathscr{C}$, and

$$|\boldsymbol{m}(A)| \leqq \mu(A), \quad \text{for every} \quad A \in \mathscr{C}.$$

Proposition 18. *If a set* $A \in \mathscr{C}$ *is regular (respectively regular on the left, regular on the right) with respect to* μ, *then* A *is regular (respectively regular on the left, regular on the right) with respect to* $\boldsymbol{m}$.

We apply propositions 1 and 2 and the inequality $|\boldsymbol{m}(B)| \leqq \mu(B)$ for $B \in \mathscr{C}$.

Corollary. *If μ is regular (regular on the left, on the right) on $\mathscr{C}$, then $\boldsymbol{m}$ is regular (regular on the left, on the right) on $\mathscr{C}$.*

The converse implication is not generally true. However for the left regularity we have

Proposition 19. *The set function $\boldsymbol{m}$ is regular on the left on $\mathscr{C}$ if and only if μ is regular on the left on $\mathscr{C}$.*

If μ is regular on the left, then from the preceding corollary we deduce that $\boldsymbol{m}$ is regular on the left.

Conversely, suppose that $\boldsymbol{m}$ is regular on the left on $\mathscr{C}$. Let $A \in \mathscr{C}$ and $\varepsilon > 0$. Let $(A_i)_{1 \leqq i \leqq n}$ be a finite family of disjoint sets of $\mathscr{C}$ contained in A, such that

$$\mu(A) < \sum_{i=1}^{n} |\boldsymbol{m}(A_i)| + \frac{\varepsilon}{2}.$$

For each i, we can find a compact set $K_i \subset A_i$ such that if $A_i' \in \mathscr{C}$ and $K_i \subset A_i' \subset A_i$, then $|\boldsymbol{m}(A_i) - \boldsymbol{m}(A_i')| < \dfrac{\varepsilon}{2n}$. The set $K = \bigcup_{i=1}^{n} K_i$ is compact and $K \subset A$. Let $A' \in \mathscr{C}$ be such that $K \subset A' \subset A$. For each i the set $A_i' = A' \cap A_i$ belongs to $\mathscr{C}$ and $K \subset A_i' \subset A_i$; the sets A_i' are disjoint, therefore

$$\begin{aligned}\mu(A) - \mu(A') &\leqq \sum_{i=1}^{n} |\boldsymbol{m}(A_i)| + \frac{\varepsilon}{2} - \sum_{i=1}^{n} |\boldsymbol{m}(A_i')| \\ &= \sum_{i=1}^{n} [|\boldsymbol{m}(A_i)| - |\boldsymbol{m}(A_i')|] + \frac{\varepsilon}{2} \\ &\leqq \sum_{i=1}^{n} |\boldsymbol{m}(A_i) - \boldsymbol{m}(A_i')| + \frac{\varepsilon}{2} < \varepsilon.\end{aligned}$$

It follows that A is regular on the left with respect to μ and hence μ is regular on the left on $\mathscr{C}$.

For the semi-variation we have a weaker result:

Proposition 20. *Let $\boldsymbol{m}\colon \mathscr{C} \to \mathscr{L}(E, F)$ be an additive set function with finite semi-variation $\tilde{\boldsymbol{m}}$. If $\boldsymbol{m}$ is regular on the left on $\mathscr{C}$, then $\tilde{\boldsymbol{m}}$ is regular on the left on $\mathscr{C}$.*

Let $A \in \mathscr{C}$ and $\varepsilon > 0$. We can find a family $(A_i)_{1 \leqq i \leqq n}$ of disjoint sets of $\mathscr{C}$ contained in A and a family $(x_i)_{1 \leqq i \leqq n}$ of elements of E such that $|x_i| \leqq 1$ and

$$\tilde{\boldsymbol{m}}(A) < \left| \sum_{i=1}^{n} \boldsymbol{m}(A_i)\, x_i \right| + \frac{\varepsilon}{2}.$$

Then we can find compact sets $K_i \subset A_i$ such that $|\boldsymbol{m}(A_i) - \boldsymbol{m}(A_i')| < \dfrac{\varepsilon}{2n}$ for $A_i' \in \mathscr{C}$ with $K_i \subset A_i' \subset A_i$.

If we put $K = \bigcup_{i=1}^{n} K_i$ and if $A' \in \mathscr{C}$ is such that $K \subset A' \subset A$, then putting $A'_i = A' \cap A_i$ we have

$$\tilde{m}(A) - \tilde{m}(A') \leqq |\sum m(A_i)\, x_i| + \frac{\varepsilon}{2} - |\sum m(A'_i)\, x_i|$$

$$\leqq \sum |m(A_i) - m(A'_i)| + \frac{\varepsilon}{2} < \varepsilon,$$

therefore A is regular on the left with respect to $\tilde{m}$.

Remarks.

1°. From the proof of the propositions 19 and 20 we deduce the following result:

Let $\mathscr{A}$ be a class with $\emptyset \in \mathscr{A}$ and $A \cap B \in \mathscr{A}$ for every $A, B \in \mathscr{A}$ and let $m: \mathscr{A} \to X = \mathscr{L}(E, F)$ be a finitely additive set function regular on the left. If m is with finite variation $\bar{m}$ (respectively with finite semi-variation $\tilde{m}$), then $\bar{m}$ (respectively $\tilde{m}$) is regular on the left on $\mathscr{C}$.

2°. The regularity on the right of m does not imply the regularity on the right of the semi-variation $\tilde{m}$.

3°. The converse of the proposition 20 is not true. The regularity of $\tilde{m}$ does not imply the regularity on the left or on the right of m.

Example. We take $E = l^1$ (the space of the real sequences (ξ_n) with $\|(\xi_n)\| = \sum |\xi_n| < \infty$) and $E = \mathscr{C}[0, 1]$ (the space of the continuous real functions f on $[0, 1]$ with norm $\|f\| = \sup_{x \in [0,1]} |f(x)|$). The conjugate space of l^1 is the space m of the bounded sequences (ξ_n) with norm $\|(\xi_n)\| = \sup_n |\xi_n|$ and the conjugate space of $\mathscr{C}[0, 1]$ in the space $\mathscr{M}[0, 1]$ of the real Borel measures μ on $[0, 1]$ with norm $\|\mu\| = |\mu|\,([0, 1])$ (see § 19, theorem 3, corollary 2).

We choose a sequence (y_n) of positive functions of $\mathscr{C}[0, 1]$ with $\|y_n\| \leqq 1$, such that the series $\sum y_n$ converges pointwise to a bounded function. Using the Lebesgue dominated convergence theorem we deduce that for every real Borel measure μ on $[0, 1]$ and for every set A of natural numbers, the series $\sum_{n \in A} y_n$ converges pointwise and lies in $\mathscr{L}^1(\mu)$ and we have

$$\sum_{n \in A} |\langle y_n, \mu \rangle| = \sum_{n \in A} \left| \int y_n \, d\mu \right| \leqq \sum_{n \in A} \int y_n \, d|\mu|$$

$$= \int \sum_{n \in A} y_n \, d|\mu| \leqq \left\| \sum_{n \in A} y_n \right\| \|\mu\|.$$

For every sequence $(\xi_n) \in l^1$ the series $\sum y_n \xi_n$ is absolutely convergent in $\mathscr{C}[0, 1]$, since

$$\sum \|y_n \xi_n\| \leqq \sum |\xi_n| < \infty.$$

Consider now the set N of the natural numbers endowed with the discrete topology and take T the one-point compactification of N, $T = N \cup \{\omega\}$. The semi-tribe $\mathscr{B}$ of the Borel sets consists of all the subsets of T. We define the function $\boldsymbol{m}: \mathscr{B} \to \mathscr{L}(E, F)$ by the following equalities: $\boldsymbol{m}(\emptyset) = 0$, $\boldsymbol{m}(\omega) = a \in \mathscr{L}(E, F)$ and

$$\boldsymbol{m}(A)(\xi_n) = \sum_{i \in A} y_i \xi_i, \quad \text{for} \quad (\xi_n) \in l^1 \quad \text{and} \quad A \subset N, A \neq \emptyset.$$

It is evident that $\boldsymbol{m}$ is *additive*. Moreover, if A is a nonvoid subset of N, we have

$$(1) \qquad |\boldsymbol{m}(A)| = \sup_{i \in A} \|y_i\|,$$

$$(2) \qquad \tilde{\boldsymbol{m}}(A) = \Big\| \sum_{i \in A} y_i \Big\|$$

and

$$(3) \qquad \bar{\boldsymbol{m}}(A) = \sum_{i \in A} \|y_i\|.$$

In fact,

$$|\boldsymbol{m}(A)| = \sup_{\sum|\xi_n| \leq 1} \boldsymbol{m}(A)(\xi_n)| = \sup_{\substack{\sum|\xi_n| \leq 1 \\ x \in [0,1]}} \Big| \sum_{i \in A} y_i(x)\, \xi_i \Big|$$

$$= \sup_{\substack{i \in A \\ x \in [0,1]}} |y_i(x)| = \sup_{i \in A} \|y_i\|.$$

Let now $(A_i)_{i \in I}$ be a finite family of disjoint subsets of A, $(\xi_n^i)_{i \in I}$ a family of sequences of l^1 with $\sum_n |\xi_n^i| \leqq 1$ and μ a real measure on $[0, 1]$ with $\|\mu\| \leqq 1$. Then

$$\Big| \sum_{i \in I} \langle \boldsymbol{m}(A_i)(\xi_n^i), \mu \rangle \Big| = \Big| \langle \sum_{i \in I} \sum_{j \in A_i} \langle y_j \xi_j^i, \mu \rangle \Big| \leqq \sum_i \sum_{j \in A_i} |\xi_j^i|\, |\langle y_j, \mu \rangle|$$

$$\leqq \sum_{j \in A} |\langle y_j, \mu \rangle| \leqq \Big\| \sum_{j \in A} y_j \Big\|,$$

consequently

$$\tilde{\boldsymbol{m}}(A) \leqq \Big\| \sum_{j \in A} y_j \Big\|.$$

On the other hand, taking $A_i = \{i\} \subset A$ for $i \in I$ and $\xi_j^i = \delta_j^i$ we have

$$\tilde{\boldsymbol{m}}(A) \geqq \sup_{\|\mu\| \leq 1} \Big| \sum_{i \in I} \langle y_i, \mu \rangle\, \xi_i^i \Big| = \sup_{\|\mu\| \leq 1} \Big| \langle \sum_{i \in I} y_i, \mu \rangle \Big| = \Big\| \sum_{i \in I} y_i \Big\|.$$

Taking then the supremum, for all the finite sets $I \subset A$ we obtain

$$\tilde{\boldsymbol{m}}(A) \geqq \Big\| \sum_{i \in A} y_i \Big\|$$

and the equality (2) is proved. From this equality we deduce that $\boldsymbol{m}$ has *finite semi-variation*. The equality (3) is proved in a similar way.

Choosing different sequences (y_n), we can prove many properties of $\boldsymbol{m}$ and $\boldsymbol{m}$:

1. If we take $y_n(x) = x^{n-1} - x^n$, and $\boldsymbol{m}(\omega) = 0$, then $\boldsymbol{m}$ is countably additive and regular, but $\tilde{\boldsymbol{m}}$ is not regular on the right in $\{\omega\}$.

We remark that $\|y_n\| \leqq \frac{1}{n}$, therefore $|\boldsymbol{m}(A)| \leqq \frac{1}{\inf A}$ for $A \subset N$.

a) $\boldsymbol{m}$ *is countably additive*: let (A_n) be a decreasing sequence with void intersection; if $A_p = \emptyset$ for some p, then $\tilde{\boldsymbol{m}}(A_n) = 0$ for $n \geqq p$; if all the sets A_n are nonvoid, then $\inf A_n \to \infty$ as $n \to \infty$, therefore $|\boldsymbol{m}(A_n)| \to 0$ as $n \to \infty$.

b) $\boldsymbol{m}$ *is regular:* let $A \subset T$ and $\varepsilon > 0$; let $n \in N$ be such that $\frac{1}{n} < \varepsilon$. We take $K = A \cap \{1, 2, \ldots, n\}$ and $G = A \cup \{n+1, n+2, \ldots, \omega\}$, therefore $G - K = \{n+1, n+2, \ldots\}$.

If $B \subset G - K$, then $\inf B > n$, therefore $|\boldsymbol{m}(B)| < \frac{1}{n} < \varepsilon$.

c) $\tilde{\boldsymbol{m}}$ *is not regular* (*on the right*) for the compact set $\{\omega\}$. Suppose on the contrary, that for every $\varepsilon > 0$, there exists an open set $G \ni \omega$ such that $\tilde{\boldsymbol{m}}(G) < \varepsilon$. It follows that for the sets $G_n = \{n+1, n+2, \ldots, \omega\}$ we have $\tilde{\boldsymbol{m}}(G_n) \to 0$ as $n \to \infty$. For fixed n and k take

$$A_1 = \{n+1\},\ A_2 = \{n+2\},\ \ldots,\ A_k = \{n+k\}$$

and

$$\xi_j^1 = \delta_j^{n+1},\ \xi_j^2 = \delta_j^{n+2},\ \ldots,\ \xi_j^k = \delta_j^{n+k}.$$

Then

$$\tilde{\boldsymbol{m}}(G_n) \geqq \left| \sum_{i=1}^{k} \boldsymbol{m}(A_i)(\xi_j^i) \right| = \left\| \sum_{i=n+1}^{n+k} y_i \right\|.$$

Since $\tilde{\boldsymbol{m}}(G_n) \to 0$, we deduce that the series $\sum y_i$ is uniformly convergent. But this is a contradiction, because $\sum_{i=1}^{n} y_i(x) = 1 - x^n$, therefore the series $\sum y_i$ converges pointwise to the discontinuous function y defined by $y(x) = 1$ for $x \neq 1$ and $y(1) = 0$. It follows that $\tilde{\boldsymbol{m}}$ is not regular on the right in $\{\omega\}$.

d) $\tilde{\boldsymbol{m}}$ *is regular* (*on the left*) for the open set N, but the regularity cannot be expressed as in proposition 2.

Suppose, by absurd, that for every $\varepsilon > 0$ there exists a compact set $K \subset N$ such that $\tilde{\boldsymbol{m}}(B) < \varepsilon$ if $B \subset N - K$. It follows that for the sets $B_n = \{n+1, n+2, \ldots\}$ we have $\tilde{\boldsymbol{m}}(B_n) \to 0$ as $n \to \infty$. Since $\tilde{\boldsymbol{m}}(\omega) = 0$, we have $\tilde{\boldsymbol{m}}(B_n) = \tilde{\boldsymbol{m}}(G_n)$, therefore $\tilde{\boldsymbol{m}}(G_n) \to 0$ as $n \to \infty$ and we get the same contradiction as in the preceding point.

2. If we take y_n continuous, equal to 0 outside the interval $\left[\frac{1}{n+1}, \frac{1}{n}\right]$ and linear on each half of this interval, with maximum equal to 1 and $|\boldsymbol{m}(\omega)| = 1$, then $\tilde{\boldsymbol{m}}$ is regular but $\boldsymbol{m}$ is not regular and is not countably additive.

We remark that $\|y_n\| = 1$ and $\|\sum_{i \in A} y_i\| = 1$ for every $A \subset N$.

a) $\tilde{\boldsymbol{m}}$ *is regular*. We have $\tilde{\boldsymbol{m}}(A) = 1$ for every set $A \subset T$, therefore $|\tilde{\boldsymbol{m}}(A) - \tilde{\boldsymbol{m}}(A')| = 0$ for every sets A and A', consequently $\tilde{\boldsymbol{m}}$ is regular.

b) $\boldsymbol{m}$ *is not regular*. In fact, if A is not closed and open at the same time, then for every compact set $K \subset A$ and every open set $G \supset A$ we have $G - K \neq \emptyset$, therefore if $B \neq \emptyset$ and $B \subset G - K$ we have $|\boldsymbol{m}(B)| = 1$, consequently $\boldsymbol{m}$ is not regular for A.

c) $\boldsymbol{m}$ *is not countably additive*. In fact, if (A_n) is a sequence of nonvoid sets with void intersection, we have $|\boldsymbol{m}(A_n)| = 1$, therefore the sequence $(\boldsymbol{m}(A_n))$ does not converge to 0, consequently $\boldsymbol{m}$ is not countably additive.

d) the regularity of $\tilde{\boldsymbol{m}}$ cannot be expressed as in the proposition 1. The proof is the same as for the point b) with $\tilde{\boldsymbol{m}}$ instead of $\boldsymbol{m}$.

As for the regularity we have to ask some restrictive conditions on $\mathscr{C}$:

Proposition 21. *Suppose that the clan $\mathscr{C}$ verifies the following condition:*

(*) *For every set $A \in \mathscr{C}$ there exists a set $A' \in \mathscr{C}$ with $A \subset \operatorname{Int} A'$.*

Then $\boldsymbol{m}$ is regular on $\mathscr{C}$ if and only if its variation μ is regular on $\mathscr{C}$.

In fact, in this case the regularity is equivalent to the left regularity (proposition 4).

Corollary 1. *Suppose that every set of $\mathscr{C}$ is contained in an open set of $\mathscr{C}$. Then $\boldsymbol{m}$ is regular on $\mathscr{C}$ if and only if μ is regular on $\mathscr{C}$.*

Corollary 2. *Suppose that $\mathscr{C}$ is dense in $\mathscr{P}(T)$ and consists of relatively compact sets. Then $\boldsymbol{m}$ is regular on $\mathscr{C}$ if and only if its variation μ is regular on $\mathscr{C}$.*

In fact, by lemma 1, $\mathscr{C}$ verifies the condition (*) of the proposition 21.

Proposition 22. *If $\mathscr{C}$ is the clan $\mathscr{K}$ or the semi-tribe $\mathscr{B}$, then $\boldsymbol{m}$ is regular on $\mathscr{C}$ if and only if μ is regular on $\mathscr{C}$.*

For *scalar* measures on a *semi-tribe* we can drop the condition (*) in the proposition 21.

Proposition 23. *Let $\mathscr{S}$ be a semi-tribe and μ a real measure on $\mathscr{S}$. A set $A \in \mathscr{S}$ is regular (respectively regular on the left, regular on the right) with respect to μ, if and only if A is regular (respectively regular on the left, regular on the right) with respect to μ^+ and μ^-.*

Suppose that A is regular with respect to μ and let $\varepsilon > 0$. There exists a compact set $K \subset A$ and an open set $G \supset A$ such that if $B \in \mathscr{S}$ and $B \subset G - A$, then $|\mu(B)| < \varepsilon$. Let $B \in \mathscr{S}$ with $B \subset G - K$. Consider the Hahn decomposition (§ 3, theorem 1) $B = B^+ \cup B^-$, where B^+ is essentially positive and B^- is essentially negative with respect to μ. Then $B^+, B^- \in \mathscr{S}$, $B^+ \subset B \subset G - K$ and $B^- \subset B \subset G - K$, therefore

(§ 3, proposition 15)

$$\mu^+(B) = \mu(B^+) < \varepsilon \quad \text{and} \quad \mu^-(B) = \mu(B^-) < \varepsilon,$$

consequently A is regular with respect to μ^+ and to μ^-.

The converse implication follows from $\mu = \mu^+ - \mu^-$.

The parts concerning the regularity on the left and on the right are proved in the same way.

Proposition 24. *Let $\mathscr{S}$ be a semi-tribe and μ a scalar measure on $\mathscr{S}$. A set $A \in \mathscr{S}$ is regular (respectively regular on the left, regular on the right) with respect to μ, if and only if A is regular (respectively regular on the left, regular on the right) with respect to $|\mu|$.*

Suppose that A is regular with respect to μ. If μ is real valued, then A is regular with respect to μ^+ and μ^-, therefore A is regular with respect to $|\mu| = \mu^+ + \mu^-$.

If μ is complex valued, then $\mu = \mu_1 + i\mu_2$, where μ_1 and μ_2 are real valued measures on $\mathscr{S}$. From the inequalities

$$|\mu_i(B)| \leqq |\mu(B)|, \quad i = 1, 2, \quad \text{for} \quad B \in \mathscr{S},$$

we deduce that A is regular with respect to μ_1 and μ_2, therefore A is regular with respect to $|\mu_1|$ and $|\mu_2|$. From the inequality

$$|\mu| \leqq |\mu_1| + |\mu_2|$$

we deduce that A is regular with respect to $|\mu|$.

The converse implication is evident (proposition 18). The parts concerning the one-sided regularity are proved in the same way.

Corollary. *A scalar measure μ on a semi-tribe $\mathscr{S}$ is regular on a class $\mathscr{C} \subset \mathscr{S}$ if and only if $|\mu|$ is regular on $\mathscr{C}$.*

For the regular set functions defined on $\mathscr{B}$, the variation and the semi-variation can be defined by the aid of the compact sets only.

Proposition 25. *If $\boldsymbol{m}: \mathscr{B} \to X = \mathscr{L}(E, F)$ is a regular set function, then for every set $A \subset T$ we have*

$$\overline{\boldsymbol{m}}(A) = \sup \sum |\boldsymbol{m}(K_i)| = \sup \sum |\boldsymbol{m}(K_i)\, x_i|$$

and

$$\tilde{\boldsymbol{m}}(A) = \sup \left|\sum \boldsymbol{m}(K_i)\, x_i\right|,$$

where the supremum is taken for all the finite families (K_i) of disjoint compact sets contained in A, and all the finite families (x_i) of elements of E with $|x_i| \leqq 1$.

For every set $A \in \mathscr{B}$ we have

$$|\boldsymbol{m}(A)| \leqq \sup_{K \subset A} |\boldsymbol{m}(K)|, \quad K \text{ compact}.$$

In fact, since $\boldsymbol{m}$ is regular, for every $\varepsilon > 0$ there exists a compact set $K \subset A$ such that $|\boldsymbol{m}(A) - \boldsymbol{m}(K)| < \varepsilon$, therefore $|\boldsymbol{m}(A)| \leqq |\boldsymbol{m}(K)| + \varepsilon$.

We can then apply the proposition 5, § 3, and the corollary of the proposition 6, § 4.

7. INTEGRATION WITH RESPECT TO REGULAR MEASURES

Let μ be a *regular positive Borel measure*. In particular, μ can be the variation of a regular Borel measure $\boldsymbol{m}: \mathscr{B} \to X$.

Proposition 26. *For every set $A \subset T$ we have*

$$\bar{\mu}(A) = \sup_{K \subset A} \mu(K), \quad K \textit{ compact}.$$

Let $\varepsilon > 0$ and $B \in \mathscr{B}$ such that $B \subset A$. We can find a compact set $K \subset B$ with $\mu(B) < \mu(K) + \varepsilon$. Then

$$\bar{\mu}(A) = \sup_{B \subset A} \mu(B) \leqq \sup_{K \subset A} \mu(K) + \varepsilon,$$

hence, ε being arbitrary,

$$\bar{\mu}(A) \leqq \sup_{K \subset A} \mu(K)$$

and thus

$$\bar{\mu}(A) = \sup_{K \subset A} \mu(K), \quad K \text{ compact}.$$

Proposition 27. *For every μ-measurable set $E \in \mathcal{C}(\mu)$ we have*

$$\mu^*(E) = \sup_{K \subset E} \mu(K), \quad K \textit{ compact}.$$

In fact, since μ is defined on the semi-tribe $\mathscr{B}$, we have $\bar{\mu}^*(E) = \mu^*(E)$ for every $E \in \mathcal{C}(\mu)$ (§ 5, proposition 7, with $\mathscr{S} = \mathscr{B}$).

Corollary. *For every μ-integrable set E and for every $\varepsilon > 0$ there exists a compact set $K \subset E$ such that $\mu(E - K) < \varepsilon$.*

Proposition 28. *Every μ-integrable set E is the union of a sequence (K_n) of disjoint compact sets and a μ-negligible set N.*

We take $K_1 \subset E$ such that $\mu(E - K_1) < 1$ and then, by induction, we take $K_n \subset E - \bigcup_{i<n} K_i$ such that $\mu\left(E - \bigcup_{i \leqq n} K_i\right) < \frac{1}{n}$. Then we take $N = E - \bigcup_{i=1}^{\infty} K_i$.

Proposition 29. *If $\mathscr{C}$ is a class of μ-integrable sets dense in $\mathscr{P}(T)$, then for every μ-integrable set E and for every $\varepsilon > 0$ there exists a set $A \in \mathscr{C}$ such that*

$$\mu(E \,\Delta\, A) < \varepsilon.$$

Let $K \subset E$ be a compact set such that $\mu(E - K) < \frac{\varepsilon}{2}$. Let then $G \supset K$ be a relatively compact open set such that $\mu(G - K) < \frac{\varepsilon}{2}$. There exists a set $A \in \mathscr{C}$ with $K \subset A \subset G$.

The sets $E - A$ and $A - E$ are μ-integrable and contained respectively in $E - K$ and $G - K$, therefore

$$\mu(E \,\Delta\, A) = \mu(E - A) + \mu(A - E) \leqq \mu(E - K) + \mu(G - K) < \varepsilon.$$

Corollary. *For every μ-integrable set E and for every $\varepsilon > 0$ there exist a compact set K which is G_δ and a relatively compact open set G which is F_σ such that*

$$\mu(E \,\Delta\, K) < \varepsilon \quad \textit{and} \quad \mu(E \,\Delta\, G) < \varepsilon.$$

Proposition 30. *If $\mathscr{C}$ is a subclass of $\mathscr{B}$ containing the compact sets, then*

$$\overline{\boldsymbol{m}}_{\mathscr{C}} = \overline{\boldsymbol{m}}.$$

In fact, let $A \in \mathscr{B}$ and $\varepsilon > 0$. There exists a compact set $K \subset A$ such that $|\boldsymbol{m}(A) - \boldsymbol{m}(K)| < \varepsilon$, whence $|\boldsymbol{m}(A)| < |\boldsymbol{m}(K)| + \varepsilon$. It follows that

$$|\boldsymbol{m}(A)| \leqq \sup_{K \subset A} |\boldsymbol{m}(K)|, \quad K \text{ compact}.$$

We can then apply the proposition 5, § 3.

Remarks.

1°. The conclusion $\overline{\boldsymbol{m}}_{\mathscr{C}} = \overline{\boldsymbol{m}}$ remains valid if $\boldsymbol{m}$ is a set function regular on the left on $\mathscr{B}$ or on a class containing $\mathscr{C}$.

2°. If $\mathscr{C}$ is a subclass of $\mathscr{B}_0$ containing the compact sets which are G_δ, and if $\boldsymbol{m}$ is a Baire measure with finite variation then $\overline{\boldsymbol{m}}_{\mathscr{C}} = \overline{\boldsymbol{m}}$. In fact, we shall see (§ 16, proposition 1) that we can define the regularity by means of the compact sets which are G_δ.

Proposition 31. *The class Φ of the μ-measurable sets $A \in \mathfrak{T}(\mu)$ with*

$$\mu^*(A) = \inf_{G \supset A} \mu^*(G) < \infty, \quad G \textit{ open},$$

is a semi-tribe and μ^* is regular on Φ.

a) We remark that for the sets $A \in \mathfrak{T}(\mu)$ we have

$$\mu^*(A) = \bar{\mu}(A) = \sup_{K \subset A} \mu(K), \quad K \text{ compact}.$$

It follows that for every set $A \in \Phi$ we have

$$\mu^*(A) = \sup_{K \subset A} \mu^*(K) = \inf_{G \supset A} \mu^*(G), \quad K \text{ compact}, G \text{ open},$$

therefore μ^* is regular on Φ. Hence, a set $A \in \mathfrak{C}(\mu)$ belongs to Φ if and only if, for every $\varepsilon > 0$, there exist a compact set $K \subset A$ and an open set $G \supset A$ such that $\mu^*(G) - \mu^*(K) < \varepsilon$, i.e. such that $\mu^*(G - K) < \varepsilon$.

b) We remark then that Φ contains all the open sets $G \subset T$ with $\mu^*(G) < \infty$ – because μ^* is increasing – and all the compact sets $K \subset T$ – because μ is regular on $\mathscr{B}$ –, therefore

$$\mu(K) = \inf_{G \supset K} \mu(G), \quad G \in \mathscr{B}, \text{ open}.$$

We have to prove now that Φ is a semi-tribe.

c) If $A_1, A_2 \in \Phi$, then $A_1 - A_2 \in \Phi$ and $A_1 \cup A_2 \in \Phi$.

Let $\varepsilon > 0$. We can find two compact sets $K_1 \subset A_1$ and $K_2 \subset A_2$ and two open sets $G_1 \supset A_1$ and $G_2 \supset A_2$ such that

$$\mu^*(G_1 - K_1) < \frac{\varepsilon}{2} \quad \text{and} \quad \mu^*(G_2 - K_2) < \frac{\varepsilon}{2}.$$

The set $K = K_1 - G_2$ is compact, the set $G = G_1 - K_2$ is open, $K \subset A_1 - A_2 \subset G$, and

$$G - K \subset (G_1 - K_1) \cup (G_2 - K_2),$$

therefore

$$\mu^*(G - K) \leqq \mu^*(G_1 - K_1) + \mu^*(G_2 - K_2) < \varepsilon,$$

hence $A_1 - A_2 \in \Phi$.

On the other hand, the set $K' = K_1 \cup K_2$ is compact, the set $G' = G_1 \cup G_2$ is open, $K' \subset A_1 \cup A_2 \subset G'$ and

$$G' - K' \subset (G_1 - K_1) \cup (G_2 - K_2),$$

therefore

$$\mu^*(G' - K') \leqq \mu^*(G_1 - K_1) + \mu^*(G_2 - K_2) < \varepsilon,$$

hence $A_1 \cup A_2 \in \Phi$.

d) *If* (A_i) *is a sequence of sets of* Φ *contained in a set of* Φ, *then* $\bigcup_{i=1}^{\infty} A_i \in \Phi$.

Since every set of Φ is contained in an open set of finite outer measure, we can find an open set U with $\mu^*(U) < \infty$ and $A_i \subset U$ for every i.

We put $B_1 = A_1$ and $B_n = A_n - \bigcup_{i<n} B_i$ for $n \geqq 2$. The sets B_n are *disjoint*, belong to Φ, are contained in U, and

$$\bigcup_{n=1}^{\infty} B_n = \bigcup_{n=1}^{\infty} A_n = A.$$

Let $\varepsilon > 0$. For each i we can find a compact set $K_i \subset B_i$ and an open set $G_i \supset B_i$ such that

$$\mu^*(G_i - K_i) < \frac{\varepsilon}{2^{i+1}}.$$

We can choose the sets G_i included in U. Then the set $G = \bigcup_{i=1}^{\infty} G_i$ is open and $\mu^*(G) \leqq \mu^*(U) < \infty$.

The sets K_i are disjoint, therefore

$$\sum_{i=1}^{\infty} \mu(K_i) = \mu^*\left(\bigcup_{i=1}^{\infty} K_i\right) \leqq \mu^*(G) < \infty,$$

whence

$$\sum_{i=1}^{\infty} \mu^*(G_i) = \sum_{i=1}^{\infty} \mu^*(G_i - K_i) + \sum_{i=1}^{\infty} \mu(K_i) < \frac{\varepsilon}{2} + \sum_{i=1}^{\infty} \mu(K_i) < \infty.$$

If n is a number such that

$$\sum_{i>n} \mu^*(G_i) < \frac{\varepsilon}{2},$$

then the set $K = \bigcup_{i=1}^{n} K_i$ is compact, we have $K \subset A \subset G$ and

$$G - K \subset \bigcup_{i \leqq n} (G_i - K_i) \cup \left(\bigcup_{i>n} G_i\right),$$

whence

$$\mu^*(G - K) \leqq \sum_{i \leqq n} \mu^*(G_i - K_i) + \sum_{i>n} \mu^*(G_i) < \varepsilon,$$

consequently $A \in \Phi$. It follows that Φ is a semi-tribe.

Remark. If for every set $A \subset T$ we put

$$\mu^{**}(A) = \inf_{G \supset A} \mu^*(G), \quad G \text{ open},$$

then μ^{**} is positive, countably subadditive on $\mathscr{P}(T)$, and countably additive on $\mathcal{T}(\mu)$. We have

$$\mu^*(A) \leqq \mu^{**}(A), \quad \text{for} \quad A \in \mathcal{T}(\mu),$$

and

$$\mu^*(A) = \mu^{**}(A), \quad \text{for} \quad A \in \Phi$$

$\left(\text{and even for } A = \bigcup_{n=1}^{\infty} A_n \text{ with } A_n \in \Phi\right).$

We can prove that if $\mu^{**}(A) < \infty$, then $\mu^*(A) = \mu^{**}(A)$, but we may have $\mu^*(A) = 0$ and $\mu^{**}(A) = \infty$.

Proposition 32. *The set $\mathscr{A}$ of the $\mathscr{K}$-step functions of the form $f = \sum \varphi_{K_i} x_i$ with K_i disjoint compact sets and $x_i \in E$, is dense in $\mathscr{L}^p_E(\mu)$ for $1 \leqq p < \infty$.*

We know that the set $\mathscr{E}_E(\mathscr{B})$ of the $\mathscr{B}$-step functions is dense in $\mathscr{L}^p_E(\mu)$. It will be sufficient to show that the set $\mathscr{A}$ is dense in $\mathscr{E}_E(\mathscr{B})$ for the semi-norm N_p.

Let $g = \sum_{i=1}^{n} \varphi_{E_i} x_i$ be a function of $\mathscr{E}_E(\mathscr{B})$ with E_i disjoint and $x_i \neq 0$ for each i and let $\varepsilon > 0$.

For each i there exists a compact set $K_i \subset E_i$ with

$$\mu(E_i - K_i) < \frac{\varepsilon^p}{n|x_i|^p}.$$

The compact sets K_i are disjoint, the function $f = \sum_{i=1}^{n} \varphi_{K_i} x_i$ belongs to $\mathscr{E}_E(\mathscr{K})$ and

$$|f - g| = \sum_{i=1}^{n} \varphi_{E_i - K_i} |x_i|,$$

since the sets $E_i - K_i$ are disjoint. Then

$$N_p(f - g) = \left(\int |f - g|^p \, d\mu\right)^{\frac{1}{p}} = \left(\sum_{i=1}^{n} \mu(E_i - K_i) |x_i|^p\right)^{\frac{1}{p}} < \varepsilon.$$

It follows that $\mathscr{A}$ is dense in $\mathscr{E}_E(\mathscr{B})$, whence $\mathscr{A}$ is dense in $\mathscr{L}^p_E(\mu)$.

Corollary 1. *The set $\mathscr{A}'$ of the $\mathscr{K}$-step functions of the form $f = \sum \varphi_{G_i} x_i$ with G_i disjoint open sets of $\mathscr{K}$ and $x_i \in E$, is dense in $\mathscr{L}^p_E(\mu)$ for $1 \leqq p < \infty$.*

In fact, let $g = \sum_{i=1}^{n} \varphi_{K_i} x_i$ be a $\mathscr{K}$-step function with K_i *disjoint* compact sets and $x_i \neq 0$ for every i and let $\varepsilon > 0$. Since μ is regular, and K_i are disjoint, we can find disjoint open sets $G_1, \ldots, G_n$ such that for every i we have $K_i \subset G_i$ and

$$\mu(G_i - K_i) < \frac{\varepsilon^p}{n|x_i|^p}.$$

We prove then as in the preceding proposition that for the function $f = \sum_{i=1}^{n} \varphi_{G_i} x_i$ we have $N_p(f - g) < \varepsilon$, therefore, by the preceding proposition, $\mathscr{A}'$ is dense in $\mathscr{L}^p_E(\mu)$.

Corollary 2. *If $\mathscr{C}$ is a class of μ-integrable sets dense in $\mathscr{P}(T)$, then the set $\mathscr{E}_E(\mathscr{C})$ is dense in $\mathscr{L}^p_E(\mu)$, for $1 \leqq p < \infty$.*

Let $g = \sum_{i=1}^{n} \varphi_{G_i} x_i$ be a step function with G_i disjoint open sets of $\mathscr{K}$ and $x_i \neq 0$, and let $\varepsilon > 0$. For each i let $K_i \subset G_i$ be a compact set such that

$$\mu(G_i - K_i) < \frac{\varepsilon^p}{n|x_i|^p}.$$

Since $\mathscr{C}$ is dense in $\mathscr{P}(T)$ for each i there exists a set $A_i \in \mathscr{C}$ with $K_i \subset A_i \subset G_i$.

Then

$$\mu(G_i - A_i) < \frac{\varepsilon^p}{n|x_i|^p},$$

and for the function $f = \sum_{i=1}^{n} \varphi_{A_i} x_i$ of $\mathscr{E}_E(\mathscr{C})$ we have $N_p(f - g) < \varepsilon$, therefore, by the preceding corollary, $\mathscr{E}_E(\mathscr{C})$ is dense in $\mathscr{L}_E^p(\mu)$.

Remark. If $\mathscr{C}$ is a class of μ-integrable sets dense in $\mathscr{P}(T)$ we can prove directly that $\mathscr{E}_E(\mathscr{C})$ is dense in $\mathscr{L}_E^1(\mu)$.

In fact, let $f = \sum_{i=1}^{n} \varphi_{E_i} x_i$ be a function of $\mathscr{E}_E(\mathscr{B})$ with $x_i \neq 0$ and let $\varepsilon > 0$.

Using the proposition 29, for each i we can find a set $A_i \in \mathscr{C}$ with

$$\mu(E_i \,\Delta\, A_i) < \frac{\varepsilon}{n\,|x_i|}.$$

The function $g = \sum_{i=1}^{n} \varphi_{A_i} x_i$ belongs to $\mathscr{E}_E(\mathscr{C})$ and

$$|f - g| = \left| \sum_{i=1}^{n} (\varphi_{E_i} - \varphi_{A_i})\, x_i \right| \leqq \sum_{i=1}^{n} |\varphi_{E_i} - \varphi_{A_i}|\, |x_i| = \sum_{i=1}^{n} \varphi_{E_i \Delta A_i} |x_i|,$$

therefore

$$\int |f - g|\, d\mu \leqq \sum_{i=1}^{n} \mu(E_i \,\Delta\, A_i)\, |x_i| < \varepsilon,$$

consequently $\mathscr{E}_E(\mathscr{C})$ is dense in $\mathscr{E}_E(\mathscr{B})$, whence it is dense in $\mathscr{L}_E^1(\mu)$.

Corollary 3. *The set of the step functions of $\mathscr{E}_E(\mathscr{K}_0)$ of the form $f = \sum \varphi_{K_i} x_i$ with K_i compact and G_δ, and the set of the step functions of $\mathscr{E}_E(\mathscr{K}_0)$ of the form $f = \sum \varphi_{G_i} x_i$ with G_i relatively compact, open and F_σ, are dense in $\mathscr{L}_E^p(\mu)$ for $1 \leqq p < \infty$.*

Proposition 33. *The space $\mathscr{K}_E(T)$ of the continuous functions $f\colon T \to E$ with compact carrier is dense in $\mathscr{L}_E^p(\mu)$ for $1 \leqq p < \infty$.*

Let $g = \sum_{i=1}^{n} \varphi_{K_i} x_i$ be a step function with K_i compact and disjoint and $x_i \neq 0$ and let $\varepsilon > 0$.

We can find disjoint open sets $G_1, \ldots, G_n$ such that for every i we have $K_i \subset G_i$ and

$$\mu(G_i - K_i) < \frac{\varepsilon^p}{n\,|x_i|^p}.$$

For each i let $\varphi_i\colon T \to [0, 1]$ be a continuous function with compact carrier contained in G_i and equal to 1 on K_i. Then $\varphi_i - \varphi_{K_i} \leqq \varphi_{G_i - K_i}$.

The function $f = \sum_{i=1}^{n} \varphi_i x_i$ belongs to $\mathscr{K}_E(T)$ and we have

$$N_p(f - g) = \left(\int \left|\sum_{i=1}^{n} (\varphi_i - \varphi_{K_i}) x_i\right|^p d\mu\right)^{\frac{1}{p}} \leqq \left(\int \sum_{i=1}^{n} (\varphi_i - \varphi_{K_i}) |x_i|^p d\mu\right)^{\frac{1}{p}}$$

$$\leqq \left(\sum_{i=1}^{n} \mu(G_i - K_i) |x_i|^p\right)^{\frac{1}{p}} < \varepsilon,$$

therefore $\mathscr{K}_E(T)$ is dense in $\mathscr{L}_E^p(\mu)$.

Remark. From the proof of the preceding proposition it follows that the set of the linear combinations $\sum \varphi_i x_i$ with $\varphi_i \in \mathscr{K}_+(T)$ and $x_i \in E$ is dense in $\mathscr{L}_E^p(\mu)$. Moreover

Proposition 34. *The set of the functions $\sum \varphi_i x_i$ (finite sum) with $\varphi_i \in \mathscr{K}_+(T)$, $\varphi_i \leqq 1$, $x_i \in E$ and $\varphi_i \varphi_j = 0$ for $i \neq j$, is dense in $\mathscr{L}_E^p(\mu)$, for $1 \leqq p < \infty$.*

Proposition 35. *Let E, F be two Banach spaces, $\boldsymbol{m}$ and $\boldsymbol{n}$ two regular Borel measures with finite variation, with values in $\mathscr{L}(E, F)$. Then we have $\boldsymbol{m} = \boldsymbol{n}$ if and only if*

$$\int f\, d\boldsymbol{m} = \int f\, d\boldsymbol{n}, \quad \textit{for every} \quad f \in \mathscr{K}_E(T).$$

If $\boldsymbol{m} = \boldsymbol{n}$, then evidently $\int f\, d\boldsymbol{m} = \int f\, d\boldsymbol{n}$, for every $f \in \mathscr{K}_E(T)$. Conversely, suppose that

$$\int f\, d\boldsymbol{m} = \int f\, d\boldsymbol{n}, \quad \text{for every} \quad f \in \mathscr{K}_E(T).$$

We have $|\boldsymbol{m}| \leqq |\boldsymbol{m}| + |\boldsymbol{n}|$ and $|\boldsymbol{n}| \leqq |\boldsymbol{m}| + |\boldsymbol{n}|$, therefore

$$\mathscr{L}_E^1(|\boldsymbol{m}| + |\boldsymbol{n}|) \subset \mathscr{L}_E^1(\boldsymbol{m}) \cap \mathscr{L}_E^1(\boldsymbol{n}).$$

We have also

$$\left|\int f\, d\boldsymbol{m}\right| \leqq \int |f|\, d|\boldsymbol{m}| \leqq \int |f|\, d(|\boldsymbol{m}| + |\boldsymbol{n}|),$$

$$\left|\int f\, d\boldsymbol{n}\right| \leqq \int |f|\, d|\boldsymbol{n}| \leqq \int |f|\, d(|\boldsymbol{m}| + |\boldsymbol{n}|),$$

therefore the linear mappings $f \to \int f\, d\boldsymbol{m}$ and $f \to \int f\, d\boldsymbol{n}$ of $\mathscr{L}_E^1(|\boldsymbol{m}| + |\boldsymbol{n}|)$ into F are continuous.

On the other hand, $|\boldsymbol{m}|$ and $|\boldsymbol{n}|$ are regular, therefore $|\boldsymbol{m}| + |\boldsymbol{n}|$ is regular, hence $\mathscr{K}_E(T)$ is dense in $\mathscr{L}_E^1(|\boldsymbol{m}| + |\boldsymbol{n}|)$.

Since these two mappings coincide on the dense subspace $\mathcal{K}_E(T)$, they coincide on the whole space $\mathcal{L}^1_E(|\boldsymbol{m}| + |\boldsymbol{n}|)$. In particular, if $A \in \mathcal{B}$ and $x \in E$, then $\varphi_A x \in \mathcal{L}^1_E(|\boldsymbol{m}| + |\boldsymbol{n}|)$, therefore

$$\int \varphi_A x \, d\boldsymbol{m} = \int \varphi_A x \, d\boldsymbol{n},$$

hence

$$\boldsymbol{m}(A)\, x = \boldsymbol{n}(A)\, x .$$

It follows that $\boldsymbol{m}(A) = \boldsymbol{n}(A)$ for every $A \in \mathcal{B}$, therefore $\boldsymbol{m} = \boldsymbol{n}$.

Proposition 36. *Let $U\colon \mathcal{M}_E(\mathcal{B}) \to F$ be a linear mapping with $\|U_A\| < \infty$ for $A \in \mathcal{B}$ and let $\boldsymbol{m}\colon \mathcal{B} \to \mathcal{L}(E, F)$ be the additive set function with finite variation $\overline{\boldsymbol{m}}$ such that*

$$U(f) = \int f \, d\boldsymbol{m}, \quad \textit{for} \quad f \in \mathcal{M}_E(\mathcal{B}).$$

If $\boldsymbol{m}$ is regular, then for every set $A \in \mathcal{C}(\mathcal{B})$ we have:

(1) $\quad |\!|\!| U_A |\!|\!| = \sup \sum |U(\varphi_{K_i} x_i)| \quad$ *(finite sums)*

for K_i disjoint compact sets contained in A and $x_i \in E$ with $|x_i| \leqq 1$;

(2) $\quad |\!|\!| U_A |\!|\!| = \sup \sum |U(\varphi_{A_i} f)|$

for $f \in \mathcal{K}_E(T, A)$ with $\|f\| \leqq 1$ and A_i disjoint sets of $\mathcal{C}(\mathcal{B})$ (respectively A_i disjoint compact sets);

(3) $\quad |\!|\!| U_A |\!|\!| = \sup \sum |U(\varphi_i f)|$

for $f \in \mathcal{K}_E(T, A)$ with $\|f\| \leqq 1$ and for $\varphi_i \in \mathcal{M}(\mathcal{B})$ with $|\varphi_i| \leqq 1$ and $\varphi_i \varphi_j = 0$ if $i \neq j$;

(4) $\quad |\!|\!| U_A |\!|\!| = \sup \sum |U(\varphi_i f)|$

for $f \in \mathcal{M}_E(\mathcal{C}, A)$ with $\|f\| \leqq 1$ and $\varphi_i \in \mathcal{K}(T)$ with $|\varphi_i| \leqq 1$ and $\varphi_i \varphi_j = 0$ if $i \neq j$;
For every open set $G \subset T$ we have

(5) $\quad |\!|\!| U_G |\!|\!| = \sup \sum |U(\varphi_i x_i)|$

for $\varphi_i \in \mathcal{K}(T, G)$ with $|\varphi_i| \leqq 1$ and $\varphi_i \varphi_j = 0$ if $i \neq j$ and for $x_i \in E$ with $|x_i| \leqq 1$;

(6) $\quad |\!|\!| U_G |\!|\!| = \sup \sum |U(\varphi_i f)|$

for $f \in \mathcal{K}_E(T, G)$ with $\|f\| \leqq 1$ and $\varphi_i \in \mathcal{K}(T)$ with $|\varphi_i| \leqq 1$ and $\varphi_i \varphi_j = 0$ if $i \neq j$;

(7) $\quad |\!|\!| U_G |\!|\!| = \sup \sum |U(f_i)|$

for $f_i \in \mathcal{K}_E(T, G)$ with $|f_i| \leqq 1$ and $|f_i|\,|f_j| = 0$ if $i \neq j$.

We have first (proposition 25)

$$\left\|\!\left| U_A \right|\!\right\| = \overline{m}(A) = \sup \sum \left| m(K_i) \right| = \sup \sum \left| m(K_i)\, x_i \right| = \sup \sum \left| U(\varphi_{K_i} x_i) \right|$$

for K_i disjoint compact sets contained in A and $|x_i| \leqq 1$.

If we denote by $\mathscr{A}_A$ the set of the functions $\sum f_i$ for which the supremum is taken in each of the seven cases, then we have

$$\sup \sum |U(f_i)| \leqq \left\|\!\left| U_A \right|\!\right\|, \quad \text{for} \quad \sum f_i \in \mathscr{A}_A.$$

In the cases 2 and 3 we remark that $\mathscr{A}_A$ contains all the functions $\sum \varphi_{K_i} x_i$ with K_i disjoint compact sets and $|x_i| \leqq 1$ for which the supremum is taken in the first case, therefore in the cases 2 and 3 we have also

$$\left\|\!\left| U_A \right|\!\right\| \leqq \sup \sum |U(f_i)|, \quad \text{for} \quad \sum f_i \in \mathscr{A}_A.$$

Consider now the case 4. Let $(K_i)_{1 \leqq i \leqq n}$ be a finite family of disjoint compact sets contained in A and let $\varepsilon > 0$.

Since m is regular, for each i there exists an open set $G_i \supset K_i$ of $\mathscr{B}$ such that $\overline{m}(G_i - K_i) < \dfrac{\varepsilon}{n}$. We can take the sets G_i to be disjoint. Take then a function $\varphi_i : T \to [0, 1]$ of $\mathscr{K}(T)$ with $\varphi_i(t) = 1$ for $t \in K_i$ and $\varphi_i(t) = 0$ for $t \notin G_i$. Then $\varphi_i - \varphi_{K_i} \leqq \varphi_{G_i - K_i}$, therefore if $(x_i)_{1 \leqq i \leqq n}$ are elements of E with $|x_i| \leqq 1$, we have

$$\begin{aligned} \left| \sum_{i=1}^{n} U(\varphi_{K_i} x_i) \right| - \sum_{i=1}^{n} |U(\varphi_i x_i \varphi_A)| &\leqq \left| \sum_{i=1}^{n} \int_A (\varphi_i - \varphi_{K_i})\, x_i \, dm \right| \\ &\leqq \sum_{i=1}^{n} \left| \int_A (\varphi_i - \varphi_{K_i})\, x_i \, dm \right| \\ &\leqq \sum_{i=1}^{n} \overline{m}(G_i - K_i) < \varepsilon, \end{aligned}$$

consequently

$$\left| \sum_{i=1}^{n} U(\varphi_{K_i} x_i) \right| \leqq \left| \sum_{i=1}^{n} U(\varphi_i x_i \varphi_A) \right| + \varepsilon.$$

Since $f = \sum \varphi_{G_i} \varphi_A x_i \in \mathscr{M}_E(\mathscr{C}, A)$ and $\|f\| \leqq 1$, taking the supremum we deduce

$$\|U_A\| \leqq \sup \left|\sum U(f_i)\right|, \quad \text{for} \quad \sum f_i \in \mathscr{A}_A.$$

We deduce in the same way that

$$\sum_{i=1}^{n} |U(\varphi_{K_i} x_i)| - \sum_{i=1}^{n} |U(\varphi_i x_i \varphi_A)| < \varepsilon,$$

consequently

$$\sum |U(\varphi_{K_i} x_i)| < \sum |U(\varphi_i x_i \varphi_A)| < \varepsilon,$$

therefore

$$\|U_A\| \leqq \sup \sum |U(f_i)|, \quad \text{for} \quad \sum f_i \in \mathscr{A}_A.$$

In the case 5 we take $A = G$ and all the open sets G_i contained in G and obtain the preceding inequalities.

Finally, in the cases 6 and 7 we remark that the corresponding sets $\mathscr{A}_G$ contain the set $\mathscr{A}_G$ of the case 5, therefore in the cases 6 and 7 we deduce also the preceding inequalities.

Remark. In each of the preceding cases, we have also

$$\|U_A\| = \sup |\sum U(f_i)|, \quad \text{for} \quad \sum f_i \in \mathscr{A}_A.$$

Proposition 37. *Let $\boldsymbol{m}$: $\mathscr{B} \to \mathscr{L}(E, F)$ be a regular additive set function, let $1 < q \leqq \infty$ and $\frac{1}{p} + \frac{1}{q} = 1$. For every μ-measurable set A we have*

$$\bar{\boldsymbol{m}}_q(A) = \sup \sum |\boldsymbol{m}(K_i)|\,|x_i| = \sup \sum |\boldsymbol{m}(K_i)\, x_i|$$

and

$$\tilde{\boldsymbol{m}}_q(A) = \sup |\sum \boldsymbol{m}(K_i)\, x_i|,$$

where the supremum is taken for all the functions $\sum \varphi_{K_i} x_i$ with K_i disjoint compact sets contained in A and $N_p(\sum \varphi_{K_i} x_i, \mu) \leqq 1$.

Let $f = \sum_{i=1}^{n} \varphi_{A_i} x_i$ be a step function with A_i disjoint sets of $\mathscr{B}$ and $N_p(f) \leqq 1$ and let $\varepsilon > 0$. For each i we can find a compact set $K_i \subset A_i$ such that

$$|\boldsymbol{m}(A_i) - \boldsymbol{m}(K_i)|\,|x_i| < \frac{\varepsilon}{n}.$$

Then

$$|\boldsymbol{m}(A_i)\, x_i - \boldsymbol{m}(K_i)\, x_i| < \frac{\varepsilon}{n},$$

therefore

$$|\boldsymbol{m}(A_i)\, x_i| \leqq |\boldsymbol{m}(K_i)\, x_i| + \frac{\varepsilon}{n} \leqq |\boldsymbol{m}(K_i)|\,|x_i| + \frac{\varepsilon}{n},$$

consequently

$$\sum |\boldsymbol{m}(A_i)\, x_i| \leqq \sum |\boldsymbol{m}(K_i)\, x_i| + \varepsilon \leqq \sum |\boldsymbol{m}(K_i)|\,|x_i| + \varepsilon.$$

Since

$$(\sum \mu(K_i)\,|x_i|^p)^{\frac{1}{p}} \leqq (\sum \mu(A_i)\,|x_i|^p)^{\frac{1}{p}} \leqq 1,$$

we deduce that

$$\bar{\boldsymbol{m}}_q(A) \leqq \sup \sum |\boldsymbol{m}(K_i)\, x_i| \leqq \sup \sum |\boldsymbol{m}(K_i)|\,|x_i|$$

for K_i disjoint compact sets contained in A and $N_p(\sum \varphi_{K_i} x_i, \mu) \leqq 1$.

The other inequality is evident.

The part concerning the semi-variation $\tilde{\boldsymbol{m}}_q$ follows from the fact that the set of the functions $\sum \varphi_{K_i} x_i$ with K_i disjoint compact sets contained in A is dense in $\mathscr{L}^p_E(A, \mu)$.

Proposition 38. *Let $U: \mathscr{L}^p_E(\mu) \to F$ be a linear mapping with $\|U_A\|_p < \infty$ for $A \in \mathscr{T}_{\sigma f}$. Then for every μ-measurable set A we have:*

(1) $\quad |||U_A|||_p = \sup \sum |U(\varphi_{K_i} x_i)|$

for K_i disjoint compact sets contained in A and $x_i \in E$ such that $N_p(\sum \varphi_{K_i} x_i) \leqq 1$;

(2) $\quad |||U_A|||_p = \sup \sum |U(\varphi_{A_i} f)|$

for $f \in \mathscr{K}_E(T, A)$ with $N_p(f) \leqq 1$ and A_i disjoint μ-measurable (or compact) sets;

(3) $\quad |||U_A|||_p = \sup \sum |U(\varphi_i f)|$

for $f \in \mathscr{K}_E(T, A)$ with $N_p(f) \leqq 1$ and φ_i μ-measurable functions with $|\varphi_i| \leqq 1$ and $\varphi_i \varphi_j = 0$ if $i \neq j$;

(4) $\quad |||U_A|||_p = \sup \sum |U(\varphi_i f)|$

for $f \in \mathscr{L}^p_E(A, \mu)$ with $N_p(f) \leqq 1$ and $\varphi_i \in \mathscr{K}(T)$ with $|\varphi_i| \leqq 1$ and $\varphi_i \varphi_j = 0$ if $i \neq j$.

For every open set G we have:

(5) $\quad |||U_G|||_p = \sup \sum |U(\varphi_i x_i)|$

for $\varphi_i \in \mathscr{K}(T, G)$ with $\varphi_i \varphi_j = 0$ if $i \neq j$ and $x_i \in E$ such that $N_p(\sum \varphi_i x_i) \leqq 1$;

(6) $\quad |||U_G|||_p = \sup \sum |U(\varphi_i f)|$

for $f \in \mathscr{K}_E(T, G)$ with $N_p(f) \leqq 1$ and $\varphi_i \in \mathscr{K}(T)$ with $|\varphi_i| \leqq 1$ and $\varphi_i \varphi_j = 0$ if $i \neq j$;

(7) $\quad |||U_G|||_p = \sup \sum |U(f_i)|$

for $f_i \in \mathscr{K}_E(T, G)$ with $N_p(\sum f_i) \leqq 1$ and $|f_i|\,|f_j| = 0$ if $i \neq j$.

If we denote by $\mathscr{A}_A$ the set of the functions $\sum f_i$ for which the supremum is taken in each of these cases, then we have

$$\sup \sum |U(f_i)| \leqq |||U_A|||_p, \quad \text{for} \quad \sum f_i \in \mathscr{A}_A.$$

We have to prove the converse inequality. In the first case we remark that $\mathscr{A}_A$ is dense in $\mathscr{L}^p_E(A, \mu)$ (proposition 32), therefore

$$\|U_A\|_p = \sup |\sum U(\varphi_{K_i} x_i)| \leqq \sup \sum |U(\varphi_{K_i} x_i)| \leqq |||U_A|||_p$$

for $\sum \varphi_{K_i} x_i \in \mathscr{A}_A$. If $\|U_A\|_p = \infty$, then the equality to be proved is verified. Assume therefore that $\|U_A\|_p < \infty$. Let $\sum_{i=1}^{n} \varphi_{A_i} x_i$ be a step function with A_i disjoint sets of $\mathscr{B}$ contained in A and $N_p(\sum \varphi_{A_i} x_i) \leqq 1$ and let $\varepsilon > 0$. For each i there exists a compact set $K_i \subset A_i$ such that

$$\mu(A_i - K_i)^p \, |x_i| \, \|U_A\|_p \leqq \frac{\varepsilon^p}{n}.$$

Then

$$N_p(\sum \varphi_{K_i} x_i) \leqq N_p(\sum \varphi_{A_i} x_i) \leqq 1,$$

whence $\sum \varphi_{K_i} x_i \in \mathscr{A}_A$. On the other hand

$$|U(\varphi_{A_i} x_i) - U(\varphi_{K_i} x_i)| \leqq \|U_A\|_p \, N_p(\varphi_{A_i} x_i - \varphi_{K_i} x_i)$$
$$\leqq \|U_A\|_p \, \mu(A_i - K_i)^p \, |x_i| < \frac{\varepsilon}{n},$$

therefore

$$|U(\varphi_{A_i} x_i)| \leqq |U(\varphi_{K_i} x_i)| + \frac{\varepsilon}{n},$$

consequently

$$\sum |U(\varphi_{A_i} x_i)| \leqq \sum |U(\varphi_{K_i} x_i)| + \varepsilon,$$

whence

$$|||U_A|||_p \leqq \sup \sum |U(\varphi_{K_i} x_i)|, \quad \text{for} \quad \sum \varphi_{K_i} x_i \in \mathscr{A}_A.$$

In the cases 2 and 3 we remark that the corresponding sets $\mathscr{A}_A$ contain all the functions which occur in the first case, consequently the preceding inequality remains valid also in the cases 2 and 3.

Consider now the case 4. Since the functions $\sum \varphi_i x_i$ with $\varphi_i \in \mathscr{K}(T)$, $\varphi_i \varphi_j = 0$ if $i \neq j$ and $N_p(\sum \varphi_i x_i) \leqq 1$ is dense in $\mathscr{L}_E^p(A, \mu)$ (proposition 34), we have

$$\|U_A\|_p \leqq \sup \sum |U(\varphi_i x_i)| \leqq \sup \sum |U(\varphi_i f)| \leqq |||U_A|||_p$$

for $\sum \varphi_i f \in \mathscr{A}_A$. If $\|U_A\|_p = \infty$, the equality 4 is verified. Suppose then that $\|U_A\|_p < \infty$. Let $\sum_{i=1}^{n} \varphi_{K_i} x_i$ be a step function with K_i compact disjoint sets contained in A and $N_p(\sum \varphi_{K_i} x_i) \leqq 1$ and let $\varepsilon > 0$. For each i there exists an open set $G_i \supset K_i$ of $\mathscr{B}$ such that

$$\mu(G_i - K_i)^{\frac{1}{p}} \, |x_i| \, \|U_A\|_p < \frac{\varepsilon}{n}.$$

We can take the sets G_i disjoint. We take then a function $\varphi_i \colon T \to [0, 1]$ of $\mathscr{K}(T, G_i)$ with $\varphi_i(t) = 1$ for $t \in K_i$ and we have $\varphi_i - \varphi_{K_i} \leqq \varphi_{G_i - K_i}$, therefore

$$|U(\varphi_{K_i} x_i) - U(\varphi_i x_i \varphi_A)| \leqq \|U_A\|_p \, N_p(\varphi_{K_i} x_i - \varphi_i x_i \varphi_A) \leqq \|U_A\|_p N_p(\varphi_{G_i - K_i} x_i)$$
$$\leqq \|U_A\|_p \, \mu(G_i - K_i)^{\frac{1}{p}} \, |x_i| < \frac{\varepsilon}{n},$$

consequently

$$|U(\varphi_{K_i} x_i)| \leqq |U(\varphi_i x_i \varphi_A)| + \frac{\varepsilon}{n},$$

whence

$$\sum \left|U(\varphi_{K_i} x_i)\right| \leqq \sum \left|U(\varphi_i x_i \varphi_A)\right| + \varepsilon .$$

It follows that

$$\left\|\left|U_A\right|\right\|_p \leqq \sup \sum \left|U(\varphi_i f)\right|, \quad \text{for} \quad \sum \varphi_i f \in \mathscr{A}_A .$$

In the case 5 we take $A = G$ and all the open sets G_i contained in G. Finally in the cases 6 and 7 we remark that the corresponding sets $\mathscr{A}_G$ contain all the functions $\sum \varphi_i x_i$ of the set A_G of the case 5.

Remark. In each of the preceding cases we have also

$$\left\|U_A\right\|_p = \sup \left|\sum U(f_i)\right|, \quad \text{for} \quad \sum f_i \in \mathscr{A}_A .$$

Theorem 1. *Let E, F and G be three Banach spaces and $u\colon E \times F \to G$ a continuous bilinear mapping such that*

$$|x| = \sup_{|y| \leqq 1} |u(x, y)| \quad \textit{for every } x \in E .$$

Let $1 \leqq p \leqq \infty$ *and* $\dfrac{1}{p} + \dfrac{1}{q} = 1$. *For every function* $f \in \mathscr{L}^p_E(\mu)$ *we have*

$$N_p(f) = \sup \int |u(f, g)| \, d\mu = \sup \int |f| \, |g| \, d\mu ,$$

where the supremum is taken for all the functions $g \in \mathscr{K}_F(T)$ *with* $N_q(g) \leqq 1$.

If $p > 1$, then $1 \leqq q < \infty$ and $\mathscr{K}_F(T)$ is dense in $\mathscr{L}^q_F$; since the supremum can be taken for all the step functions $g \in \mathscr{L}^q_F(\mu)$ with $N_q(g) \leqq 1$ (§ 12, theorem 5) we deduce that the supremum can be taken also for all $g \in \mathscr{K}_F(T)$ with $N_q(g) \leqq 1$.

Consider now the case $p = 1$ and assume that $f \in \mathscr{L}^1_E$ is a step function with $N_1(f) > 0$ (the case $N_1(f) = 0$ is trivial). Let $0 < \alpha < N_1(f)$. From the theorem 5, § 12 (remark), we deduce that there exists a step function $h = \sum_{i=1}^{n} \varphi_{A_i} y_i \in \mathscr{E}_F(\mu)$ with A_i disjoint μ-integrable sets, $y_i \neq 0$ and $N_\infty(h) < 1$ (i.e. $|y_i| < 1$ for every i) such that

$$\alpha < \int |u(f, h)| \, d\mu .$$

Let $\eta > 0$ be such that

$$m\eta \|f\| < \int |u(f, h)| \, d\mu - \alpha ,$$

where $\|f\| = \sup_{t \in T} |f(t)|$.

For every i there exist a compact set $K_i \subset A_i$ with $\mu(A_i - K_i) < \eta$, a relatively compact open set $U_i \supset K_i$ with $\mu(U_i - K_i) < \eta$ and a continuous function $\varphi_i: T \to [0, 1]$ with compact carrier, such that $\varphi_i(t) = 1$ for $t \in K_i$ and $\varphi_i(t) = 0$ for $t \in T - U_i$. Since the sets K_i are disjoint we can choose also the sets U_i disjoint. We have

$$\varphi_i \leqq \varphi_{U_i} = \varphi_{K_i} + \varphi_{U_i - K_i} \leqq \varphi_{A_i} + \varphi_{U_i - K_i},$$

whence

$$\int \varphi_i \, d\mu \leqq \mu(A_i) + \mu(U_i - K_i) \leqq \mu(A_i) + \eta.$$

The function $g = \sum_{i=1}^{n} \varphi_i y_i$ belongs to $\mathscr{K}_F(T)$ and we have $g(t) = h(t)$ for $t \in K = \bigcup_{i=1}^{n} K_i$ and $|g(t)| \leqq |y_i|$ for $t \in U_i$, therefore $N_\infty(g) = N_\infty(h) < 1$. We have then

$$\int_{T-K} |u(f, h)| \, d\mu \leqq \|f\| \sum \mu(A_i - K_i) \leqq n\eta \|f\| < \int |u(f, h)| \, d\mu - \alpha,$$

therefore

$$\int |u(f, g)| \, d\mu \geqq \int_K |u(f, g)| \, d\mu = \int_K |u(f, h)| \, d\mu$$

$$= \int |u(f, h)| \, d\mu - \int_{T-K} |u(f, h)| \, d\mu > \alpha.$$

It follows that

$$N_1(f) = \sup \int |u(f, g)| \, d\mu, \text{ for } g \in \mathscr{K}_F(T) \text{ with } N_\infty(g) < 1.$$

If $f \in \mathscr{L}_E^1(\mu)$ is arbitrary, for every $\varepsilon > 0$ we can find a step function $f_1 \in \mathscr{L}_E^1$ such that $N_1(f - f_1) < \varepsilon$ and then a function $g \in \mathscr{K}_F(T)$ with $N_\infty(g) < 1$ such that

$$\int |u(f_1, g)| \, d\mu \geqq N_1(f_1) - \varepsilon \geqq N_1(f) - 2\varepsilon.$$

Then

$$\int |u(f - f_1, g)| \, d\mu \leqq N_1(f - f_1) \, N_\infty(g) < \varepsilon,$$

therefore

$$\int |u(f, g)| \, d\mu = \int |u(f_1, g) + u(f - f_1, g)| \, d\mu$$

$$\geqq \int |u(f_1, g)| \, d\mu - \int |u(f - f_1, g)| \, d\mu \geqq N_1(f) - 3\varepsilon,$$

consequently

$$N_1(f) = \sup \int |u(f, g)| \, d\mu, \quad \text{for} \quad g \in \mathscr{K}_F(T) \quad \text{with} \quad N_\infty(g) \leqq 1.$$

If $F = F'$, we prove as for the theorem 6, § 12, the following

Theorem 2. *Let E be a Banach space, $1 \leqq p \leqq \infty$, and $\frac{1}{p} + \frac{1}{q} = 1$. For every function $f \in \mathscr{L}_E^p(\mu)$ we have*

$$N_p(f) = \sup \left| \int \langle f, g \rangle \, d\mu \right| = \sup \int |\langle f, g \rangle| \, d\mu = \sup \int |f| \, |g| \, d\mu$$

for $g \in \mathscr{K}_{E'}(T)$ with $N_q(g) \leqq 1$, and for every function $g \in \mathscr{L}_{E'}^p(\mu)$ we have

$$N_q(g) = \sup \left| \int \langle f, g \rangle \, d\mu \right| = \sup \int |\langle f, g \rangle| \, d\mu = \sup \int |f| \, |g| \, d\mu$$

for $f \in \mathscr{K}_E(T)$ with $N_q(f) \leqq 1$.

8. MEASURABLE FUNCTIONS

Let μ be a *positive regular* Borel measure and E a *metric* space. We shall see that the measurability can be defined by means of the continuity.

Lemma 3. *If $f: T \to E$ is a μ-measurable step function, then for every compact set $K \subset T$ and for every $\varepsilon > 0$, there exists a compact set $K' \subset K$ with $\mu(K - K') < \varepsilon$ such that the restriction of f to K' is continuous.*

Let $A_1, A_2, \ldots, A_n$ be the disjoint μ-measurable sets with union equal to T, such that f is constant on each A_i. Let K be a compact set and let $\varepsilon > 0$. The set $K \cap A_i$ is μ-integrable. Since μ is regular, there exists a compact set $K_i \subset K \cap A_i$ with $\mu(K \cap A_i) - \mu(K_i) < \frac{\varepsilon}{n}$. The function f is constant on each set K_i and the sets K_i are disjoint, whence the restriction of f to the union $K' = \bigcup_{i=1}^{n} K_i$ is continuous and we have

$$\mu(K - K') = \mu(K) - \mu(K') = \sum \mu(K \cap A_i) - \sum \mu(K_i) < \varepsilon.$$

Theorem 3 (Luzin). *A function $f: T \to E$ is μ-measurable if and only if, for every compact set $K \subset T$ and for every $\varepsilon > 0$, there exists a compact set $K' \subset K$ with $\mu(K - K') < \varepsilon$ such that the restriction of f to K' is continuous.*

Suppose that f is μ-measurable and let K be a compact set and $\varepsilon > 0$. There exists a μ-negligible set $N \subset K$ and a sequence (f_n) of μ-measurable step functions converging to f on $K - N$. According to the preceding lemma, for every n there exists a compact set $K_n \subset K$ with $\mu(K - K_n) < \frac{\varepsilon}{2^{n+1}}$ such that the restriction of f_n to K_n is continuous.

The set $K_0 = \bigcap_{n=1}^{\infty} K_n$ is compact, the restriction of all the functions f_n to K_0 are continuous and

$$\mu(K - K_0) \leqq \sum_{n=1}^{\infty} \mu(K - K_n) < \frac{\varepsilon}{2}.$$

According to the theorem of Egorov, § 6, there exists a μ-measurable set $A \subset K_0$ with $\mu(K_0 - A) < \frac{\varepsilon}{4}$, such that the sequence (f_n) converges uniformly on A to f. It follows that the restriction of the limit f to A is continuous. There exists then a compact set $K' \subset A$ with $\mu(A - K') < \frac{\varepsilon}{4}$. We have then $K' \subset K$ and

$$\mu(K - K') \leqq \mu(K - K_0) + \mu(K_0 - A) + \mu(A - K') < \varepsilon$$

and the restriction of f to K' is continuous.

Conversely, suppose that f verifies the condition of the theorem. We can find by induction a sequence (K_n) of disjoint compact sets such that the set $N = K - \bigcup_{n=1}^{\infty} K_n$ is μ-negligible and the restriction of f to each K_n is continuous. For each $i \leqq n$ there exists a finite partition of the set K_i consisting of μ-measurable sets A_{ij} such that the oscillation of f on each set A_{ij} is $\leqq \frac{1}{n}$. In each set A_{ij} choose a point t_{ij} and define the μ-measurable step function

$$g_n(t) = \begin{cases} f(t_{ij}), & \text{for} \quad t \in A_{ij}, \\ a \in E, & \text{for} \quad t \notin \bigcup_{i \leqq n} K_i. \end{cases}$$

Then the sequence (g_n) converges on K to f, whence f is μ-measurable.

The measurability can be expressed by means of the μ-integrable sets instead of compact sets.

Corollary 1. *If the function $f\colon T \to E$ is μ-measurable, then for every μ-integrable set $A \subset T$ and for every $\varepsilon > 0$ there exists a compact set $K' \subset A$ with $\mu(A - K') < \varepsilon$ such that the restriction of f to K' is continuous.*

In fact, if A is μ-integrable, we can find a compact set $K \subset A$ with $\mu(A - K) < \frac{\varepsilon}{2}$. We apply then the preceding theorem to find a compact set $K' \subset K$ with $\mu(K - K') < \frac{\varepsilon}{2}$ such that the restriction of f to K' is continuous and we have $\mu(A - K') < \varepsilon$.

Corollary 2. *Let $f\colon T \to E$ be a function. If for every compact set $K \subset T$ and for every $\varepsilon > 0$, there exists a μ-integrable set $A \subset K$ with $\mu(K - A) < \varepsilon$ such that the restriction of f to A is continuous, then f is μ-measurable.*

In fact, if K is compact, we apply the condition of this corollary with $\frac{\varepsilon}{2}$ instead of ε. Then we find a compact set $K' \subset A$ with $\mu(A - K') < \frac{\varepsilon}{2}$. Then $\mu(K - K') < \varepsilon$ and the restriction of f to K' is continuous, therefore f is μ-measurable.

Corollary 3. *A function f: $T \to E$ is μ-integrable if and only if for every μ-integrable set $A \subset T$ and for every $\varepsilon > 0$, there exists a μ-integrable set $A' \subset A$ with $\mu(A - A') < \varepsilon$ such that the restriction of f to A' is continuous.*

We can give now an equivalent condition of measurability using only the value 0 of the measure.

Proposition 39. *A function f: $T \to E$ is μ-measurable if and only if, for every compact set $K \subset T$ there exist a μ-negligible set $N \subset K$ and a sequence (K_n) of disjoint compact sets with $K - N = \bigcup_{n=1}^{\infty} K_n$ such that the restriction of f to each K_n is continuous.*

If f is μ-measurable, and K is compact, then using the corollary 1 of the theorem of Luzin we find $K_1 \subset K$ with $\mu(K - K_1) < 1$, and then, by induction, $K_n \subset K - \bigcup_{i<n} K_i$ with $\mu\left(K - \bigcup_{i \leqq n} K_i\right) < \frac{1}{n}$ such that the restriction of f to each K_n is continuous. Then the set $N = K - \bigcup_{i=1}^{\infty} K_i$ is μ-negligible.

Conversely, suppose that the condition of the proposition is verified. Then $\mu(K) = \sum_{n=1}^{\infty} \mu(K_n)$. If $\varepsilon > 0$, we can find an index n such that $\mu(K) - \sum_{i=1}^{n} \mu(K_i) < \varepsilon$. Then the set $K' = \bigcup_{i=1}^{n} K_i$ is compact, the restriction of f to K' is continuous, and $\mu(K - K') < \varepsilon$, therefore f is μ-measurable.

Remark. In the preceding proposition we can take μ-integrable sets A instead of K, or μ-integrable sets A_n instead of K_n, or only μ-integrable sets A and A_n instead of K and K_n.

The following proposition gives an equivalent condition of measurability using only the non null values of the measure.

Proposition 40. *A function f: $T \to E$ is μ-measurable if and only if for every compact set $K \subset T$ with $\mu(K) > 0$ there exists a compact set $K' \subset K$ with $\mu(K') > 0$ such that the restriction of f to K' is continuous.*

If f is μ-measurable and if $\mu(K) > 0$, then using the theorem of Luzin for $0 < \varepsilon < \mu(K)$ we can find a compact set $K' \subset K$ with $\mu(K - K') < \varepsilon$, therefore with $\mu(K') > \mu(K) - \varepsilon > 0$, such that the restriction of f to K' is continuous.

Conversely, suppose that the condition of the proposition is verified. We remark that in this condition we can take μ-integrable sets A with $\mu(A) > 0$ instead of compact sets K with $\mu(K) > 0$; in fact, since μ is regular, every μ-integrable set A with $\mu(A) > 0$ contains a compact set K with $\mu(K) > 0$.

Let K be a compact set. If $\mu(K) = 0$, the condition of the theorem of Luzin is verified, taking, for example, $K' = \{t_0\}$ with $t_0 \in K$. Suppose now that $\mu(K) > 0$. Consider the class Φ of all the compact sets $K' \subset K$ such that the restriction of f to K' is continuous and put $a = \sup \mu(K')$ for $K' \in \Phi$. There exists a sequence (K_n) of Φ such that $a = \sup_n \mu(K_n)$. The set $A = \bigcup_{n=1}^{\infty} K_n$ is μ-measurable and contained in K, therefore A is μ-integrable and we have $\mu(A) = \mu(K)$.

In fact, the set $A - K$ is μ-integrable and if we have $\mu(A - K) > 0$, there exists a compact set $K' \in \Phi$ with $\mu(K') = \alpha > 0$. The set K' is disjoint of all the sets K_n and if we put $K_n' = K_n \cup K'$ we have $K_n' \in \Phi$ and

$$\mu(K_n') = \mu(K_n) + \mu(K') = \mu(K_n') + \alpha,$$

therefore

$$\sup_n \mu(K_n') = \sup_n \mu(K_n) + \alpha = a + \alpha > 0$$

which is impossible. It follows that $\mu(A - K) = 0$. For every $\varepsilon > 0$ we find an index n such that $\mu(K) - \mu(K_n) < \varepsilon$ and the restriction of f to K_n is continuous, therefore f is μ-measurable.

Remark. In the preceding proposition we can take μ-integrable sets A instead of K, or μ-integrable sets A' instead of K'.

Definition 3. *We say that a class $\mathscr{L}$ of subsets of T is locally countable, if every point $t \in T$ possesses a neighbourhood V intersected by at most countably many sets of $\mathscr{L}$.*

From this definition it follows that if $\mathscr{L}$ is locally countable, the class of the sets $A \in \mathscr{L}$ which intersect a relatively compact set $E \subset T$ is at most countable, since the closure of E is compact and can be covered by a finite number of neighbourhoods, each of them intersected by countably many sets of $\mathscr{L}$.

Proposition 41. *Every positive regular Borel measure μ on T has the direct sum property. There exists a locally countable class $\mathscr{K}$ of disjoint compact sets such that $T - \bigcup_{K \in \mathscr{K}} K$ is μ-negligible.*

If $\mu = 0$, we take $\mathscr{K}$ consisting of a single compact nonvoid set $K \subset T$ and the proposition is proved in this case. Suppose now that $\mu \neq 0$. Consider the classes $\mathscr{L}$ of disjoint compact nonvoid sets $K \subset T$, such that for every set $K \in \mathscr{L}$ and every open set $U \subset T$ with $U \cap K \neq \emptyset$ we have $\mu(U \cap K) > 0$. The classes $\mathscr{L}$ form a part $\mathscr{F}$ of the set $\mathscr{P}(\mathscr{P}(T))$ that we consider ordered by inclusion.

The set $\mathscr{F}$ is not void. In fact, since $\mu \neq 0$, there exists at least a compact set $H \subset T$ with $\mu(H) > 0$. Let $\mathscr{U}$ be the class of all the open sets $U \subset T$ such that $H \cap U \neq \emptyset$ and $\mu(H \cap U) = 0$ and let U_0 be their union. The set U_0 is open and does not include H, because otherwise, H could be covered by a finite number of sets of $\mathscr{U}$ and we would have $\mu(H) = 0$.

The set $K = H - U_0$ is compact and we have $\mu(K) > 0$. In fact, if we had $\mu(K) = 0$, it would be an open set $G \supset K$ with $\mu(G) < \mu(H)$; then H could be covered by G and by a finite number of sets of $\mathscr{U}$ and we would have $\mu(H) = \mu(G \cap H) < \mu(H)$.

If U is an open set with $K \cap U \neq \emptyset$, then $\mu(K \cap H) > 0$. In fact, if we had $\mu(K \cap U) = 0$, then $\mu(H \cap U) = 0$; hence $U \subset G_0$, therefore $K \cap U = \emptyset$.

The class $\mathscr{L}$ consisting of the set K only belongs to $\mathscr{F}$, whence $\mathscr{F}$ is not void.

We verify easily that if $(\mathscr{L}_\alpha)_{\alpha \in A}$ is a totally ordered set of classes of $\mathscr{F}$, then the union $\mathscr{L} = \bigcup_{\alpha \in A} \mathscr{L}_\alpha$ belongs also to $\mathscr{F}$. The set $\mathscr{F}$ is therefore inductively ordered.

By Zorn's lemma, $\mathscr{F}$ has at least one maximal element. Let $\mathscr{K}$ be a maximal element of $\mathscr{F}$. The class $\mathscr{K}$ consists of disjoint compact nonvoid sets and for every $K \in \mathscr{K}$ and every open set U with $U \cap K \neq \emptyset$ we have $\mu(U \cap K) > 0$.

Let us prove that $\mathscr{K}$ has also the other properties of the proposition.

Let $t \in T$ and let U be a compact neighbourhood of t. For each finite family $K_i)_{1 \leqq i \leqq n}$ of sets of $\mathscr{K}$ which intersect V we have

$$\sum_{i=1}^{n} \mu(K_i \cap V) = \mu\left(V \cap \left(\bigcup_{i=1}^{n} K_i\right)\right) \leqq \mu(V),$$

since the sets K_i are disjoint. If we denote by $\mathscr{K}(V)$ the class of the sets $K \in \mathscr{K}$ with $K \cap V \neq \emptyset$, we have

$$\sum_{K \in \mathscr{K}(V)} \mu(K \cap V) \leqq \mu(V) < \infty .$$

Since $\mu(K \cap V) > 0$ for every $K \in \mathscr{K}(V)$, we deduce that $\mathscr{K}(V)$ is at most countable; hence $\mathscr{K}$ is locally countable.

It remains to show that $N = T - \bigcup_{K \in \mathscr{K}} K$ is μ-negligible. If not, there exists a compact set K' such that $N \cap K'$ is not μ-negligible. There exists a sequence (K_n) of sets of $\mathscr{K}$ which intersect K; hence

$$N \cap K' = K' - \bigcup_{n=1}^{\infty} (K_n \cap K),$$

therefore $N \cap K'$ is a relatively compact Borel set, consequently it is μ-integrable. There exists then at least one compact set $H \subset N \cap K'$ with $\mu(H) > 0$. We build as before a compact set $K \subset H$ such that for every open set U with $U \cap K \neq \emptyset$ we have $\mu(U \cap K) > 0$. Then the class $\mathscr{K} \cup \{K\}$ belongs to $\mathscr{F}$ which contradicts the fact that $\mathscr{K}$ is maximal in $\mathscr{F}$. It follows therefore that N is μ-negligible, and the proposition is completely proved.

Corollary. *If $\mu \neq 0$ is a positive regular Borel measure, then there exists a lifting of the space $\mathscr{L}^\infty(\mu)$.*

Remark. It follows that the Lebesgue-Nikodym theorem, the theorems of integral representation of the linear operations on $\mathscr{L}_E^p$ and all other theorems stated before for measures with direct sum property, are valid for regular Borel measures without any other specification.

Proposition 42. *Let E be a set and μ a regular positive measure on T. For each compact set $K \subset T$ let $g_K: T \to E$ be a function such that for each pair (K, K') of compact sets we have $g_K(t) = g_{K'}(t)$ μ-almost everywhere on $K \cap K'$. There exists then a function $g: T \to E$ such that for every compact sets $K \subset T$ we have*

$$g(t) = g_K(t) \quad \mu\text{-almost everywhere on } K.$$

If the functions g_K are μ-measurable, then g is μ-measurable.

In fact, μ has the direct sum property and we can apply the proposition 19, § 10.

§ 16. CONSTRUCTION AND EXTENSION OF REGULAR MEASURES

As we have already seen (§ 14, proposition 17), a Borel measure is perfectly determined by its values on the class of the compact sets, or on the class of the relatively compact open sets.

Now we ask whether a set function defined only on a sub-class of $\mathscr{B}$ (for example, only on the class of the compact sets or on the class of the relatively compact open sets) can be extended to a Borel measure on $\mathscr{B}$.

1. EXTENSION OF REGULAR SET FUNCTIONS

We extend first a set function, regular on a lattice of compact sets, to the semi-tribe generated by the lattice.

Theorem 1. *Let $\mathscr{L}$ be a lattice of compact sets, $\mathscr{G}$ a lattice of open sets and α a positive (finite) set function defined on $\mathscr{L}$. If:*

1. *$\mathscr{L}$ is dense in $\mathscr{P}(T)$;*

2. *α is increasing: $\alpha(K_1) \leqq \alpha(K_2)$, if $K_1 \subset K_2$;*

3. *α is subadditive: $\alpha(K_1 \cup K_2) \leqq \alpha(K_1) + \alpha(K_2)$;*

4. *α is additive: $\alpha(K_1 \cup K_2) = \alpha(K_1) + \alpha(K_2)$, if $K_1 \cap K_2 = \emptyset$;*

5. *for every set $K \in \mathscr{L}$ and every $\varepsilon > 0$, there exists an open set $G \in \mathscr{G}$ with $K \subset G$*

such that for every set $K' \in \mathscr{L}$ with $K \subset K' \subset G$ we have

$$\alpha(K') - \alpha(K) < \varepsilon;$$

6. *for every sets $K \in \mathscr{L}$ and $G \in \mathscr{G}$ we have*

$$K - G \in \mathscr{L} \quad \text{and} \quad G - K \in \mathscr{G};$$

then:

a) *α is countably additive;*

b) *α can be extended uniquely to a regular measure μ on the semi-tribe $\mathscr{S}$ generated by $\mathscr{L}$;*

c) *for every μ-measurable set $A \in \mathfrak{T}(\mu)$ we have*

$$\mu^*(A) = \sup_{K \subset A} \mu(K), \quad K \in \mathscr{L},$$

and for every set $A \in \mathscr{S}$ we have

$$\mu(A) = \inf_{G \supset A} \mu^*(G), \quad G \in \mathscr{G}.$$

The uniqueness of the extension follows from the corollary of the proposition 6, § 2.

Taking in the condition 3, $K_1 = \emptyset$, we deduce that $\alpha(\emptyset) = 0$. From the conditions 1 and 2 we deduce that $\alpha(K') \leqq \alpha(K \cup K') \leqq \alpha(K) + \alpha(K')$, therefore $\alpha(K) \geqq 0$, for every $K \in \mathscr{L}$. Thus, the positiveness of α is a consequence of the conditions 1 and 2.

Consider now the variation $\bar{\alpha}$ of α. Since α is additive on $\mathscr{L}$, for every set $A \subset T$ we have (§ 3, proposition 6)

$$\bar{\alpha}(A) = \sup_{\substack{K \subset A \\ K \in \mathscr{L}}} \alpha(K).$$

Since, in addition, α is increasing, we have

$$\bar{\alpha}(K) = \alpha(K), \quad \text{for} \quad K \in \mathscr{L},$$

therefore $\bar{\alpha}$ is an extension of α. It follows that $\bar{\alpha}$ is *positive*, increasing and super-additive (§ 3). We shall show that $\bar{\alpha}$ is countably additive and regular on $\mathscr{S}$, therefore the restriction μ of $\bar{\alpha}$ to $\mathscr{S}$ is the measure we need.

a) *For every compact set $K \in \mathscr{L}$ we have*

$$\bar{\alpha}(K) = \inf_{G \supset K} \bar{\alpha}(G), \quad G \in \mathscr{G}.$$

Let $K \in \mathscr{L}$ and $\varepsilon > 0$. According to the condition 4, there exists a relatively compact open set $G \in \mathscr{G}$ with $G \supset K$, such that for every compact set $K' \in \mathscr{L}$ with $K \subset K' \subset G$ we have

$$\alpha(K') - \alpha(K) < \varepsilon, \quad \text{i.e.} \quad \alpha(K') < \alpha(K) + \varepsilon.$$

The last inequality remains valid for every compact set $K' \in \mathscr{L}$ contained in G, therefore

$$\bar{\alpha}(G) \leqq \alpha(K) + \varepsilon,$$

whence

$$\bar{\alpha}(K) = \alpha(K) = \inf_{G \supset K} \bar{\alpha}(G), \quad G \in \mathscr{G}.$$

b) *$\bar{\alpha}$ is countably subadditive on the class of all the open sets.*

We remark first that if $K \subset G$, then $\alpha(K) \leqq \bar{\alpha}(G)$.

Consider first a finite family $G_1, \ldots, G_n$ of open sets and let G be their union. Take a compact set $K \in \mathscr{L}$ such that $K \subset G$. Since $\mathscr{L}$ is dense in $\mathscr{P}(T)$, for every point $x \in K$ there exists a compact neighbourhood $V \in \mathscr{L}$ of x, contained in one of the sets $G_1, \ldots, G_n$. The compact set K can be covered by a finite family (V_j) of such compact neighbourhoods. For each $i \leqq n$ we denote by K_i the union of those of the compact sets of the family (V_j) which are contained in G_i. The sets K_i belong to $\mathscr{L}$, $K_i \subset G_i$ and $K \subset \bigcup_{i=1}^{n} G_i$, therefore

$$\bar{\alpha}(K) \leqq \alpha\left(\bigcup_{i=1}^{n} K_i\right) \leqq \sum_{i=1}^{n} \alpha(K_i) \leqq \sum_{i=1}^{n} \bar{\alpha}(G_i),$$

whence, K being an arbitrary set of $\mathscr{L}$ contained in G,

$$\bar{\alpha}(G) \leqq \sum_{i=1}^{n} \bar{\alpha}(G_i).$$

Let now (G_i) be a sequence of open sets and let G be their union. Take a compact set $K \in \mathscr{L}$ such that $K \subset G$. Then K can be covered by a finite family $G_1, \ldots, G_n$ of sets of the sequence, therefore

$$\alpha(K) \leqq \bar{\alpha}\left(\bigcup_{i=1}^{n} G_i\right) \leqq \sum_{i=1}^{n} \bar{\alpha}(G_i) \leqq \sum_{i=1}^{\infty} \bar{\alpha}(G_i),$$

whence

$$\bar{\alpha}(G) \leqq \sum_{i=1}^{\infty} \bar{\alpha}(G_i),$$

consequently $\bar{\alpha}$ is countably subadditive on the class of the open sets.

Since $\bar{\alpha}$ is also countably superadditive, we deduce that

b′) *$\bar{\alpha}$ is countably additive on the class of all the open sets.*

c) *For every compact set $K \in \mathscr{L}$ and for every open set $G \supset K$ we have*

$$\bar{\alpha}(G - K) = \bar{\alpha}(G) - \bar{\alpha}(K).$$

Let $\varepsilon > 0$. From a) we deduce that there exists an open set $G' \supset K$ of $\mathscr{G}$ such that

$$\bar{\alpha}(G') < \alpha(K) + \varepsilon.$$

The set $G - K$ is open and $G = (G - K) \cup K \subset (G - K) \cup G'$. Since $\bar{\alpha}$ is increasing and subadditive on the class of the open sets, we have

$$\bar{\alpha}(G) \leqq \bar{\alpha}(G - K) + \bar{\alpha}(G') \leqq \bar{\alpha}(G - K) + \bar{\alpha}(K) + \varepsilon,$$

whence, ε being arbitrary,

$$\bar{\alpha}(G) \leqq \bar{\alpha}(G - K) + \bar{\alpha}(K).$$

On the other hand, $\bar{\alpha}$ is superadditive, therefore

$$\bar{\alpha}(G) \geqq \bar{\alpha}(G - K) + \bar{\alpha}(K),$$

whence

$$\bar{\alpha}(G) = \bar{\alpha}(G - K) + \bar{\alpha}(K),$$

therefore

$$\bar{\alpha}(G - K) = \bar{\alpha}(G) - \bar{\alpha}(K).$$

Now let us denote by Φ the class of all the sets $A \subset T$ such that $\bar{\alpha}(A) < \infty$ and

$$\bar{\alpha}(A) = \inf_{G \supset A} \bar{\alpha}(G), \quad G \in \mathscr{G}.$$

Since $\bar{\alpha}$ is increasing, the last equality is verified for the sets of $\mathscr{G}$. We deduce that an open set $G \in \mathscr{G}$ belongs to Φ if and only if $\bar{\alpha}(G) < \infty$. From a) we deduce that $\mathscr{L} \subset \Phi$.

Since for every set $A \in \Phi$ we have also

$$\bar{\alpha}(A) = \sup_{K \subset A} \bar{\alpha}(K), \quad K \in \mathscr{L},$$

we deduce that a set A belongs to Φ if and only if: *for every* $\varepsilon > 0$, *there exist a compact set* $K \in \mathscr{L}$ *and an open set* $G \in \mathscr{G}$ *such that* $K \subset A \subset G$ *and*

$$\bar{\alpha}(G) - \bar{\alpha}(K) < \varepsilon$$

or, according to c), such that

$$\bar{\alpha}(G - K) < \varepsilon.$$

We shall prove that Φ is a semi-tribe and that $\bar{\alpha}$ is countably additive on Φ. The preceding condition implies that $\bar{\alpha}$ is regular on Φ.

d) *If* $A_1, A_2 \in \Phi$, *then* $A_1 - A_2 \in \Phi$ *and* $A_1 \cup A_2 \in \Phi$.

Let $\varepsilon > 0$. We can find two compact sets K_1 and K_2 of $\mathscr{L}$ and two open sets G_1 and G_2 of $\mathscr{G}$ such that

$$K_i \subset A_i \subset G_i, \quad \bar{\alpha}(G_i) < \infty \quad \text{and} \quad \bar{\alpha}(G_i - K_i) < \frac{\varepsilon}{2} \quad \text{for} \quad i = 1, 2.$$

The set $K = K_1 - G_2$ is compact and belongs to $\mathscr{L}$, the set $G = G_1 - K_2$ is open and belongs to $\mathscr{G}$ and $\bar{\alpha}(G) \leqq \bar{\alpha}(G_1) < \infty$. On the other hand, we have

$K \subset A_1 - A_2 \subset G$ and

$$G - K \subset (G_1 - K_1) \cup (G_2 - K_2).$$

Since $G_1 - K_1$ and $G_2 - K_2$ are open and $\bar{\alpha}$ is subadditive on the class of the open sets, we deduce that

$$\bar{\alpha}(G - K) \leqq \bar{\alpha}(G_1 - K_1) + \bar{\alpha}(G_2 - K_2) < \varepsilon,$$

therefore $A_1 - A_2 \in \Phi$.

The set $K' = K_1 \cup K_2$ belongs to $\mathscr{L}$, the set $G' = G_1 \cup G_2$ belongs to $\mathscr{G}$ and we have $K' \subset A_1 \cup A_2 \subset G'$ and

$$G' - K' \subset (G_1 - K_1) \cup (G_2 - K_2),$$

therefore

$$\alpha(G' - K') < \varepsilon,$$

whence $A_1 \cup A_2 \in \Phi$.

e) *If* (A_i) *is a sequence of sets of* Φ *contained in a set of* Φ, *then* $\bigcup_{i=1}^{\infty} A_i \in \Phi$.

We put $B_1 = A_1$ and $B_n = A_n - \bigcup_{i<n} B_i$ for $n \geqq 2$. The sets B_n are *disjoint*, belong to Φ and

$$\bigcup_{n=1}^{\infty} B_n = \bigcup_{n=1}^{\infty} A_n = A.$$

Let B be a set of Φ containing all the sets A_n and let U be an open set of $\mathscr{G}$ with $\bar{\alpha}(U) < \infty$ such that $B \subset U$. Then $B_n \subset U$ for every n.

Let $\varepsilon > 0$. For each i we can find a compact set $K_i \in \mathscr{L}$ and an open set $G_i \in \mathscr{G}$ such that

$$K_i \subset A_i \subset G_i, \quad \bar{\alpha}(G_i) < \infty \quad \text{and} \quad \bar{\alpha}(G_i - K_i) < \frac{\varepsilon}{2^{i+1}}.$$

We can choose the sets G_i contained in U. Then the union G of the sets G_i is contained in U, therefore $\bar{\alpha}(G) \leqq \bar{\alpha}(U) < \infty$. The sets K_i are *disjoint*, therefore

$$\sum_{i=1}^{\infty} \bar{\alpha}(K_i) \leqq \bar{\alpha}\left(\bigcup_{i=1}^{\infty} K_i\right) \leqq \bar{\alpha}(G) < \infty,$$

whence

$$\sum_{i=1}^{\infty} \bar{\alpha}(G_i) = \sum_{i=1}^{\infty} \bar{\alpha}(G_i - K_i) + \sum_{i=1}^{\infty} \bar{\alpha}(K_i) < \varepsilon + \sum_{i=1}^{\infty} \bar{\alpha}(K_i) < \infty.$$

Let n be a natural number such that

$$\sum_{i>n} \bar{\alpha}(G_i) < \frac{\varepsilon}{2}.$$

The set $K = \bigcup_{i=1}^{n} K_i$ belongs to $\mathscr{L}$, and we have $K \subset A \subset G$ and

$$G - K \subset \bigcup_{i \leqq n} (G_i - K_i) \cup \left(\bigcup_{i > n} G_i\right),$$

therefore

$$\bar{\alpha}(G - K) \leqq \sum_{i \leqq n} \bar{\alpha}(G_i - K_i) + \sum_{i > n} \bar{\alpha}(G_i) < \varepsilon,$$

whence $A \in \Phi$.

From d) and e) we deduce that Φ is a semi-tribe containing $\mathscr{L}$, therefore $\mathscr{S} \subset \Phi$.

f) *$\bar{\alpha}$ is countably additive on Φ.*

Let (A_i) be a sequence of disjoint sets of Φ, whose union A belongs to Φ. Since $\bar{\alpha}$ is superadditive we have

$$\bar{\alpha}\left(\bigcup_{i=1}^{\infty} A_i\right) \geqq \sum_{i=1}^{\infty} \bar{\alpha}(A_i).$$

We have to prove the converse inequality. Let $\varepsilon > 0$. For each i there exists a set $G_i \supset A_i$ of $\mathscr{G}$ such that

$$\bar{\alpha}(G_i) < \bar{\alpha}(A_i) + \frac{\varepsilon}{2^i}.$$

We can choose the sets G_i such that their union G belongs to Φ (for example, contained in a set $U \in \mathscr{G}$ such that $A \subset U$ and $\bar{\alpha}(U) < \infty$). Since $\bar{\alpha}$ is countably subadditive on $\mathscr{G}$ we have

$$\bar{\alpha}\left(\bigcup_{i=1}^{\infty} A_i\right) \leqq \bar{\alpha}\left(\bigcup_{i=1}^{\infty} G_i\right) \leqq \sum_{i=1}^{\infty} \bar{\alpha}(G_i) \leqq \sum_{i=1}^{\infty} \bar{\alpha}(A_i) + \varepsilon,$$

whence, ε being arbitrary,

$$\bar{\alpha}\left(\bigcup_{i=1}^{\infty} A_i\right) \leqq \sum_{i=1}^{\infty} \bar{\alpha}(A_i).$$

g) *$\bar{\alpha}$ is complete on Φ.*

Let $A \in \Phi$ be a set with $\bar{\alpha}(A) = 0$ and let $B \subset A$. For every $\varepsilon > 0$ there exists a set $G \in \mathscr{G}$ such that $A \subset G$ and $\bar{\alpha}(G) < \varepsilon$. Since we have also $B \subset G$, we deduce that $B \in \Phi$ and $\bar{\alpha}(B) = 0$.

The restriction μ of $\bar{\alpha}$ to $\mathscr{S}$ is a regular measure extending α. For every set $A \in \mathscr{S}$ we have

$$\mu(A) = \inf_{G \supset A} \mu(G) < \infty, \quad G \in \mathscr{G},$$

and for every μ-measurable set $A \in \mathcal{T}(\mu)$ we have $\mu^*(A) = \bar{\alpha}(A)$. In fact (§ 5, proposition 7)

$$\mu^*(A) = \sup_{\substack{B \subset A \\ B \in \mathscr{S}}} \mu(B) = \sup_{\substack{B \subset A \\ B \in \mathscr{S}}} \sup_{\substack{K \subset B \\ K \in \mathscr{L}}} \alpha(K) = \sup_{\substack{K \subset A \\ K \in \mathscr{L}}} \alpha(K) = \bar{\alpha}(A).$$

The theorem is completely proved.

Remarks.

1°. The condition 4 implies that α is regular on $\mathscr{L}$.

2°. The open sets of $\mathscr{G}$ are μ-measurable. In fact, if $G \in \mathscr{G}$ and $K \in \mathscr{L}$, then $G \cap K = K - (K - G) \in \mathscr{C}$, where $\mathscr{C}$ is the clan generated by $\mathscr{L}$. If $A \in \mathscr{C}$, then

$$A = \bigcup_{i=1}^{n} (K_i - K_i'),$$

where K_i and K_i' belong to $\mathscr{L}$, therefore

$$G \cap A = \bigcup_{i=1}^{n} (K_i \cap G - K_i') \in \mathscr{C}.$$

It follows that $G \in \mathcal{T}(\mathscr{C}) \subset \mathcal{T}(\mu)$.

We state now the preceding theorem in two particular cases:

Corollary 1. *Let $\mathscr{C}_0$ be the lattice of the compact sets which are G_δ and α a positive (finite) set function defined on $\mathscr{C}_0$. If α is increasing, subadditive, additive and if: for every $K \in \mathscr{C}_0$ and every $\varepsilon > 0$ there exists an open set $G \supset K$ which is F_σ such that for every set $K' \in \mathscr{C}_0$ with $K \subset K' \subset G$ we have $\alpha(K') - \alpha(K) < \varepsilon$, then α is countably additive and can be uniquely extended to a Baire measure μ. For every μ-measurable set A we have*

$$\mu^*(A) = \sup_{K \subset A} \mu(K), \quad K \in \mathscr{B}_0, \text{ compact},$$

and for every set $A \in \mathscr{B}_0$ we have

$$\mu(A) = \inf_{G \supset A} \mu(G), \quad G \in \mathscr{B}_0, \text{ open}.$$

Remark. The hypotheses of the corollary imply that α is regular. We shall see (theorem 2), that the conclusion remains valid if α is increasing, subadditive, additive and regular (with arbitrary open sets G, not necessarily F_σ). We shall see also that in these conditions, α can be extended to a regular Borel measure.

Corollary 2. *If $\mathscr{C}$ is the lattice of all the compact sets and α is a positive, increasing, subadditive, additive and regular set function on $\mathscr{C}$, then α is countably additive and can be uniquely extended to a positive regular Borel measure μ. For every μ-measurable set A we have*

$$\mu^*(A) = \sup_{K \subset A} \mu(K), \quad K \in \mathscr{B}, \text{ compact},$$

and for every set $A \in \mathscr{B}$ we have

$$\mu(A) = \inf_{G \supset A} \mu(G), \quad G \in \mathscr{B}, \text{ open}.$$

Proposition 1. *Let $\mathscr{C}$ be a clan such that $\mathscr{K}_0 \subset \mathscr{C} \subset \mathscr{B}_0$ and X a Banach space. Every measure $\boldsymbol{m}$: $\mathscr{C} \to X$ with finite variation μ is regular. Moreover, for every set $A \in \mathcal{C}(\mu)$ we have*

$$\mu^*(A) = \sup_{K \subset A} \mu(K), \quad K \in \mathscr{C}, \textit{ compact},$$

and for every set $A \in \mathscr{T}(\mu)$ we have

$$\mu^*(A) = \inf_{G \supset A} \mu^*(G), \quad G \textit{ open and } F_\sigma.$$

Consider the lattice $\mathscr{L}$ of the compact sets of $\mathscr{C}$, the lattice $\mathscr{G}$ of the open sets of $\mathscr{C}$ and the restriction α of μ to $\mathscr{L}$. Since $\mathscr{K}_0$ and $\mathscr{B}_0$ have the same compact sets (§ 14, proposition 13) and the same open sets (§ 14, corollary of the proposition 15) we deduce that $\mathscr{L}$ consists of all the compact sets which are G_δ and $\mathscr{G}$ consists of all the relatively compact open sets which are F_σ. The set function α is positive, subadditive and additive on $\mathscr{L}$. Let $K \in \mathscr{L}$ and let (G_n) be a sequence of $\mathscr{G}$ with intersection equal to Φ (§ 14, proposition 14). We can take the sequence (G_n) to be decreasing. Since μ is countably additive, we have

$$\mu(K) = \inf_n \mu(G_n) = \inf_{G \supset K} \mu(G), \quad G \in \mathscr{G},$$

therefore α verifies all the conditions of the corollary 1 of the theorem 1. We can extend α to a positive regular measure μ_1 on $\mathscr{B}_0$. We remark that the semi-tribe generated by $\mathscr{C}$ is $\mathscr{B}_0$, therefore the sets of $\mathscr{B}_0$ are μ-integrable and we can consider the measure μ extended to $\mathscr{B}_0$. Since μ and μ_1 are equal on $\mathscr{L}$, it follows that $\mu = \mu_1$ (§ 2, corollary of the proposition 6), therefore μ is regular on $\mathscr{B}_0$, consequently μ is regular on $\mathscr{C}$. It follows then that $\boldsymbol{m}$ is also regular on $\mathscr{C}$.

Since $\mathscr{B}_0$ is the semi-tribe generated by $\mathscr{C}$ and μ_1 is the extension of μ from $\mathscr{C}$ to $\mathscr{B}_0$, we have $\mathscr{T}(\mu) = \mathscr{T}(\mu_1)$ and $\mathcal{C}(\mu) = \mathcal{C}(\mu_1)$. From the corollary 1 of the theorem 1 we deduce that for every set $A \in \mathcal{C}(\mu)$ we have

$$\mu^*(A) = \mu_1^*(A) = \sup_{K \subset A} \mu_1(K) = \sup_{K \subset A} \mu(K), \quad K \in \mathscr{L},$$

and that for every set $A \in \mathscr{B}_0$ we have

$$\mu(A) = \mu_1(A) = \inf_{G \supset A} \mu_1(G) = \inf_{G \supset A} \mu(G), \quad G \in \mathscr{G}.$$

If $A = \bigcup_{n=1}^{\infty} A_n \in \mathscr{T}_0$ with A_n disjoint sets of $\mathscr{B}_0$, then for every $\varepsilon > 0$ and for every n there exists an open set $G_n \in \mathscr{G}$ with $A_n \subset G_n$ and $\mu(G_n) < \mu(A_n) + \frac{\varepsilon}{2^n}$. Then $G = \bigcup_{n=1}^{\infty} G_n$ is open and F_σ and we have $A \subset G$ and

$$\mu^*(G) \leqq \sum \mu(G_n) \leqq \sum \mu(A_n) + \varepsilon = \mu(A) + \varepsilon,$$

therefore

$$\mu^*(A) = \inf_{G \supset A} \mu^*(G), \quad G \text{ open and } F_\sigma.$$

The proposition is completely proved.

Corollary 1. *Every Baire measure with finite variation (in particular every scalar Baire measure) is regular.*

Corollary 2. *If T has a countable base, or if T is metrizable (in particular if $T \subset R^n$), then every Borel measure with finite variation (in particular every scalar Borel measure) is regular.*

2. CONSTRUCTION OF REGULAR POSITIVE BOREL MEASURES

We show now that certain positive regular set functions defined on a lattice can be extended to regular Borel measures.

Theorem 2. *Let $\mathscr{L}$ be a lattice and α a positive (finite) set function defined on $\mathscr{L}$. If:*

1. *$\mathscr{L}$ is dense in $\mathscr{P}(T)$;*

2. *α is increasing;*

3. *α is subadditive;*

4. *α is additive;*

5. *α is regular;*

then:

a) *α is countably additive;*

b) *there exists a regular positive Borel measure μ and only one such that the sets of $\mathscr{L}$ are μ-integrable and*

$$\mu(A) = \alpha(A), \quad \textit{for} \quad A \in \mathscr{L};$$

c) *every set A of the semi-tribe $\mathscr{S}(\mathscr{L})$ is μ-integrable and*

$$\mu(A) = \sup_{K \subset A} \mu(K) = \inf_{G \supset A} \mu(G), \quad K \textit{ compact, } G \textit{ open;}$$

d) *for every compact set K we have*

$$\mu(K) = \inf_{A \supset K} \alpha(A), \quad A \in \mathscr{L},$$

and for every open set G we have

$$\mu^*(G) = \sup_{A \subset G} \alpha(A), \quad A \in \mathscr{L}.$$

For each compact set $K \subset T$ put

$$\beta(K) = \inf_{A \supset K} \alpha(A), \quad A \in \mathscr{L}.$$

We shall prove that the set function β defined on the lattice $\mathscr{C}$ of the compact sets, verifies the four conditions of theorem 1.

1. *β is increasing: $\beta(K_1) \leqq \beta(K_2)$ if $K_1 \subset K_2$.*

This property follows immediately from the definition of β.

2. *β is subadditive: $\beta(K_1 \cup K_2) \leqq \beta(K_1) + \beta(K_2)$.*

Let $\varepsilon > 0$. We can find two sets $A_1 \supset K_1$ and $A_2 \supset K_2$ of $\mathscr{L}$ such that

$$\alpha(A_1) < \beta(K_1) + \frac{\varepsilon}{2} \quad \text{and} \quad \alpha(A_2) < \beta(K_2) + \frac{\varepsilon}{2}.$$

Then $K_1 \cup K_2 \subset A_1 \cup A_2 \in \mathscr{L}$ and

$$\beta(K_1 \cup K_2) \leqq \alpha(A_1 \cup A_2) \leqq \alpha(A_1) + \alpha(A_2) \leqq \beta(K_1) + \beta(K_2) + \varepsilon,$$

hence, ε being arbitrary,

$$\beta(K_1 \cup K_2) \leqq \beta(K_1) + \beta(K_2).$$

3. *β is additive: $\beta(K_1 \cup K_2) = \beta(K_1) + \beta(K_2)$, if $K_1 \cup K_2 = \emptyset$.*

Since K_1 and K_2 are disjoint, there exist two disjoint relatively compact open sets $G_1 \supset K_1$ and $G_2 \supset K_2$. The lattice $\mathscr{L}$ being dense in $\mathscr{P}(T)$ we can find two sets $B_1, B_2 \in \mathscr{L}$ such that

$$K_1 \subset B_1 \subset G_1 \quad \text{and} \quad K_2 \subset B_2 \subset G_2.$$

The sets B_1 and B_2 are disjoint. Let $A \in \mathscr{L}$ be a set such that $A \supset K_1 \cup K_2$, and put $A_1 = A \cap B_1 \in \mathscr{L}$, $A_2 = A \cap B_2 \in \mathscr{L}$. We have $K_1 \subset A_1$, $K_2 \subset A_2$, $A_1 \cap A_2 = \emptyset$ and $A_1 \cup A_2 \subset A$. Using the properties of α we obtain

$$\beta(K_1) + \beta(K_2) \leqq \alpha(A_1) + \alpha(A_2) = \alpha(A_1 \cup A_2) \leqq \alpha(A).$$

The converse inequality is also true, therefore

$$\beta(K_1 \cup K_2) = \beta(K_1) + \beta(K_2).$$

4. *β is regular on the class of the compact sets.*

Let K be a compact set and let $\varepsilon > 0$. There exists a set $A \in \mathscr{L}$ such that $K \subset A$ and

$$\alpha(A) < \beta(K) + \frac{\varepsilon}{2}.$$

The set function α being regular, we can find a compact set $C \subset A$ and an open set $G \supset A$ such that if $A' \in \mathscr{L}$ and $C \subset A' \subset G$, then

$$|\alpha(A) - \alpha(A')| < \frac{\varepsilon}{2},$$

therefore

$$\alpha(A') \leqq \alpha(A) + \frac{\varepsilon}{2}.$$

Let now K' be a compact set such that $K \subset K' \subset G$. Choose a set $A' \in \mathscr{L}$ such that $C \cup K' \subset A' \subset G$. Then

$$\beta(K') \leqq \beta(C \cup K') \leqq \alpha(A') \leqq \alpha(A) + \frac{\varepsilon}{2} \leqq \beta(K) + \varepsilon,$$

therefore

$$\beta(K') - \beta(K) < \varepsilon,$$

hence β is regular on the class of the compact sets.

From theorem 1 we deduce that there exists a regular positive Borel measure μ on T such that for every compact set $K \subset T$ we have

$$\mu(K) = \beta(K).$$

We shall now show that every set $A \in \mathscr{L}$ is μ-integrable and that $\mu(A) = \alpha(A)$.

a) *For every set $A \in \mathscr{L}$ we have $\bar{\mu}(A) = \alpha(A)$, where $\bar{\mu}$ is the variation of μ.*

In fact (§ 15, proposition 26),

$$\bar{\mu}(A) = \sup_{K \subset A} \mu(K), \quad K \text{ compact},$$

and

$$\mu(K) = \beta(K) \leqq \alpha(A), \quad \text{if} \quad K \subset A,$$

therefore

$$\bar{\mu}(A) \leqq \alpha(A).$$

Let now $\varepsilon > 0$. Since α is regular, there exist a compact set $K \subset A$ and a relatively compact open set $G \supset A$ such that if $A' \in \mathscr{L}$ and $K \subset A' \subset G$, then

$$|\alpha(A) - \alpha(A')| < \frac{\varepsilon}{2},$$

hence

$$\alpha(A) < \alpha(A') + \frac{\varepsilon}{2}.$$

Choose a set $A_0 \in \mathscr{L}$ such that $K \subset A_0 \subset G$. We can find a set $A_1 \supset K$ of $\mathscr{L}$ such that

$$\alpha(A_1) < \beta(K) + \frac{\varepsilon}{2}.$$

Then $K \subset A_0 \cap A_1 \subset G$, $A_0 \cap A_1 \in \mathscr{L}$ and

$$\alpha(A) \leqq \alpha(A_0 \cap A_1) + \frac{\varepsilon}{2} \leqq \alpha(A_1) + \frac{\varepsilon}{2}$$

$$\leqq \beta(K) + \varepsilon = \mu(K) + \varepsilon \leqq \bar{\mu}(A) + \varepsilon,$$

hence, ε being arbitrary,

$$\alpha(A) \leqq \bar{\mu}(A),$$

therefore

$$\bar{\mu}(A) = \alpha(A).$$

b) *For every open set $G \subset T$ we have*

$$\mu^*(G) = \bar{\mu}(G) = \sup_{A \subset G} \alpha(A), \quad A \in \mathscr{L}.$$

In fact, $\mathscr{L}$ is dense in $\mathscr{P}(T)$, therefore for every compact set $K \subset G$ we can find a set $A \in \mathscr{L}$ such that $K \subset A \subset G$. It follows that

$$\bar{\mu}(K) \leqq \bar{\mu}(A) = \alpha(A) \leqq \bar{\mu}(G),$$

hence

$$\bar{\mu}(G) = \sup_{K \subset G} \bar{\mu}(K) \leqq \sup_{A \subset G} \alpha(A) \leqq \bar{\mu}(G) = \mu^*(G).$$

c) *For every set $A \in \mathscr{L}$ we have*

$$\bar{\mu}(A) = \inf_{G \supset A} \bar{\mu}(G), \quad G \text{ open}.$$

Let $\varepsilon > 0$ and $A \in \mathscr{L}$. Since α is regular, we can find a compact set $K \subset A$ and an open set $G \supset A$ such that if $A' \in \mathscr{L}$ and $K \subset A' \subset G$ then

$$|\alpha(A) - \alpha(A')| < \frac{\varepsilon}{2},$$

hence

$$\alpha(A') \leqq \alpha(A) + \frac{\varepsilon}{2}.$$

From b) we deduce that there exists a set $A_1 \in \mathscr{L}$ such that $A_1 \subset G$ and $\bar{\mu}(G) < \alpha(A_1) + \frac{\varepsilon}{2}$. Then $K \subset A \cup A_1 \subset G$ and $A \cup A_1 \in \mathscr{L}$, therefore

$$\alpha(A \cup A_1) \leqq \alpha(A) + \frac{\varepsilon}{2},$$

hence

$$\bar{\mu}(G) < \alpha(A_1) + \frac{\varepsilon}{2} \leqq \alpha(A \cup A_1) + \frac{\varepsilon}{2} \leqq \alpha(A) + \varepsilon.$$

It follows that

$$\bar{\mu}(A) = \alpha(A) = \inf_{G \supset A} \bar{\mu}(G), \quad G \text{ open}.$$

d) *Every set $A \in \mathscr{L}$ is μ-integrable and $\mu(A) = \alpha(A)$.*

In fact, for every set $A \in \mathscr{L}$ and every $\varepsilon > 0$, there exist a compact set $K \subset A$ and an open set $G \supset A$ with $\mu^*(G) < \infty$ such that

$$\mu(G) - \mu(K) < \varepsilon,$$

whence A is μ-integrable. In this case we have

$$\mu(A) = \bar{\mu}(A) = \alpha(A).$$

Since the class Φ of the μ-integrable sets A such that

$$\mu(A) = \sup_{K \subset A} \mu(K) = \inf_{G \supset A} \mu(G), \quad K \text{ compact, } G \text{ open,}$$

is a semi-tribe (§ 15, proposition 31) and contains $\mathscr{L}$, we deduce that $\mathscr{S} \subset \Phi$ and the theorem is completely proved.

Corollary 1. *By the conditions of the preceding theorem, α can be extended uniquely to a regular positive measure μ on the semi-tribe $\mathscr{S}$ generated by $\mathscr{L}$.*

In particular, $\mathscr{L}$ can be a clan. In this case we have a stronger result concerning vector set functions (see corollary 1 of the theorem 3).

Corollary 2. *Let $\mathscr{L}$ be a lattice containing the compact sets which are G_δ (or the relatively compact open sets which are F_σ) and such that $\mathscr{L} \subset \mathscr{B}$. Every positive (finite) increasing, subadditive, additive and regular set function α on $\mathscr{L}$ is countably additive and can be uniquely extended to a regular positive Borel measure μ.*

In fact, in this case $\mathscr{L}$ is dense in $\mathscr{P}(T)$.

In particular, $\mathscr{L}$ can be $\mathscr{K}_0$, $\mathscr{K}$ or $\mathscr{B}_0$. In these cases we have a stronger result for vector set functions (corollary 2 of the theorem 3).

3. CONSTRUCTION OF REGULAR BOREL VECTOR MEASURES

Theorem 3. *Let $\mathscr{C}$ be a clan, X a Banach space, and $\boldsymbol{m}: \mathscr{C} \to X$ a set function with finite variation μ. If:*

1. *$\mathscr{C}$ is dense in $\mathscr{P}(T)$;*

2. *$\boldsymbol{m}$ is additive;*

3. *μ is regular;*

then:

a) *$\boldsymbol{m}$ is countably additive;*

b) *there exists a regular Borel measure* $\boldsymbol{m}_1: \mathscr{B} \to X$ *with finite variation* μ_1 *and only one such that the sets of* $\mathscr{C}$ *are* μ_1*-integrable and*

$$\boldsymbol{m}_1(A) = \boldsymbol{m}(A), \quad \mu_1(A) = \mu(A), \quad \text{for} \quad A \in \mathscr{C};$$

c) *every* μ*-measurable set* A *of* $\mathscr{T}(\mu)$ *is* μ_1*-measurable and*

$$\mu^*(A) = \mu_1^*(A) = \sup_{K \subset A} \mu_1(K) = \inf_{G \supset A} \mu_1^*(G), \quad K \text{ compact, } G \text{ open;}$$

d) *for every compact set* K *we have*

$$\mu_1(K) = \inf_{A \supset K} \mu(A), \quad A \in \mathscr{C},$$

and for every open set G *we have*

$$\mu_1^*(G) = \sup_{A \subset G} \mu(A), \quad A \in \mathscr{C}.$$

Since $\mathscr{C}$ is a clan and μ is additive and positive, μ is also increasing and subadditive, therefore we can apply the theorem 2. Let μ_1 be the positive regular Borel measure corresponding to μ by this theorem. Then μ_1 verifies the condition d) and if $\Sigma(\mu_1)$ is the semi-tribe of the μ_1-integrable sets, then $\mathscr{C} \subset \Sigma(\mu_1)$ and $\mu_1(A) = \mu(A)$ for $A \in \mathscr{C}$.

Consider on $\Sigma(\mu_1)$ the topology $\mathcal{C}$ defined by the semi-distance

$$\varrho(A, B) = \mu_1(A \,\Delta\, B).$$

Since $\mathscr{C}$ is dense in $\mathscr{P}(T)$ for the topology $\mathcal{C}$, from the proposition 29, § 15, we deduce that $\mathscr{C}$ is dense in $\Sigma(\mu_1)$ for the semi-distance ϱ. Since $|\boldsymbol{m}(A)| \leqq \mu_1(A)$ for $A \in \mathscr{C}$, from the theorem 1, § 5, it follows that $\boldsymbol{m}$ can be extended to a measure $\boldsymbol{n}: \Sigma(\mu_1) \to X$ with finite variation ν, such that

$$|\boldsymbol{n}(A)| \leqq \mu_1(A), \quad \text{for} \quad A \in \Sigma(\mu_1),$$

and that ν is an extension of μ from $\mathscr{C}$ to $\Sigma(\mu_1)$. Since the continuous extension of μ is unique, we deduce that $\nu(A) = \mu_1(A)$ for $A \in \Sigma(\mu_1)$. If we denote by $\boldsymbol{m}_1$ the restriction of $\boldsymbol{n}$ to $\mathscr{B}$, then $\boldsymbol{m}_1$ is a Borel measure and from the inequality

$$|\boldsymbol{m}_1(A)| \leqq \mu_1(A), \quad \text{for} \quad A \in \mathscr{B},$$

we deduce that $\boldsymbol{m}_1$ is regular and with finite variation.

Since $\mathscr{B}$ is dense in $\mathscr{P}(T)$, $\mathscr{B}$ is dense in $\Sigma(\mu_1)$ for the semi-distance ϱ, therefore $\boldsymbol{n}$ is the only continuous extension of $\boldsymbol{m}_1$ from $\mathscr{B}$ to $\Sigma(\mu_1)$ and from the theorem 1, § 5, we deduce that the variation ν of $\boldsymbol{n}$ is the extension of the variation $|\boldsymbol{m}_1|$ of $\boldsymbol{m}_1$. But $\nu(A) = \mu_1(A)$ for $A \in \Sigma(\mu_1)$, therefore $|\boldsymbol{m}_1|(A) = \mu_1(A)$ for $A \in \mathscr{B}$, i.e. $|\boldsymbol{m}_1| = \mu_1$. It follows that the sets of $\mathscr{C}$ are $\boldsymbol{m}_1$-integrable and

$$\boldsymbol{m}_1(A) = \boldsymbol{n}(A) = \boldsymbol{m}(A), \quad \text{for} \quad A \in \mathscr{C}.$$

It remains to prove c).

We remark first that if $\mathscr{T}$ is the tribe generated by $\mathscr{C}$, then $\mathscr{T} \subset \mathcal{T}(\mu_1)$ and

$$\mu_1^*(A) = \mu^*(A), \quad \text{for} \quad A \in \mathscr{T}.$$

In fact, $\mathcal{T}(\mu_1)$ is a tribe containing $\mathscr{C}$, therefore $\mathcal{T}(\mu_1)$ contains also $\mathscr{T}$. On the other hand, μ^* and μ_1^* are countably additive on $\mathscr{T}$, and are equal on $\mathscr{C}$, therefore μ^* and μ_1^* are equal on $\mathscr{T}$ (§ 2, proposition 6).

If a set $A \in \mathscr{T}$ is μ-negligible, then A is also μ_1-negligible, therefore every subset of A is μ_1-negligible. We deduce that every μ-negligible set of $\mathscr{T}(\mu)$ is μ_1-negligible.

If follows that $\mathscr{T}(\mu) \subset \mathcal{T}(\mu_1)$ and for every $A \in \mathscr{T}(\mu)$ we have

$$\mu^*(A) = \mu_1^*(A) = \sup_{K \subset A} \mu_1(K), \quad K \text{ compact}.$$

In fact, every set $A \in \mathscr{T}(\mu)$ is of the form $A = B \cup N$ with $B \in \mathscr{T}$ and N μ-negligible, whence $B \in \mathcal{T}(\mu_1)$ and N is μ_1-negligible, therefore $A = B \cup N \in \mathcal{T}(\mu_1)$ and

$$\mu_1^*(A) = \mu_1^*(B) = \mu^*(B) = \mu^*(A).$$

From the theorem 2 we deduce that if A belongs to the semi-tribe $\mathscr{S}$ generated by $\mathscr{C}$, we have

$$\mu^*(A) = \mu_1^*(A) = \inf_{G \supset A} \mu_1^*(G), \quad G \text{ open}.$$

Let now $A \in \mathscr{T}$, and let (A_n) be a sequence of disjoint sets of $\mathscr{S}$ with union equal to A. If $\mu^*(A) = \infty$, then $\mu_1^*(G) = \infty$ for every open set $G \supset A$. Suppose that $\mu^*(A) < \infty$ and let $\varepsilon > 0$. For each i there exists an open set $G_i \supset A_i$ such that $\mu_1^*(G_i) < \mu_1^*(A_i) + \frac{\varepsilon}{2^i}$. Then $G = \bigcup_{i=1}^{\infty} G_i$ is open, $G \supset A$ and we have

$$\mu_1^*(G) \leqq \sum \mu_1^*(G_i) \leqq \sum \mu_1^*(A_i) + \varepsilon = \mu_1^*(A) + \varepsilon,$$

therefore

$$\mu_1^*(A) = \inf_{G \supset A} \mu_1^*(G), \quad G \text{ open}.$$

Remarks.

1°. The conclusions of the preceding theorem remain valid if we replace the condition 3 by the following two conditions:

3′. $\boldsymbol{m}$ is *regular;*

(*) *for every set* $A \in \mathscr{C}$ *there exists a set* $A' \in \mathscr{C}$ *with* $A \subset \operatorname{Int} A'$.

In fact, in this case μ is regular (§ 15, proposition 21).

The condition (*) can be replaced by one of the following conditions:

3″a) *every set of* $\mathscr{C}$ *is contained in an open set of* $\mathscr{C}$*;*

3″b) $\mathscr{C}$ *consists on relatively compact sets.*

In fact, since $\mathscr{C}$ is dense in $\mathscr{P}(T)$, the condition 3″b) implies (*) (§ 15, lemma 1).

2°. There are μ_1-measurable sets which are not μ-measurable (see the example at the end of the § 14).

Corollary 1. *By the conditions of the preceding theorem, $\boldsymbol{m}$ can be extended uniquely to a regular measure $\boldsymbol{m}_1$ with finite variation μ_1 on the semi-tribe $\mathcal{S}$ generated by $\mathcal{C}$. In this case μ_1 is the (unique) extension of μ.*

Corollary 2. *If $\mathcal{C}$ is a clan such that $\mathcal{K}_0 \subset \mathcal{C} \subset \mathcal{B}$, then every regular and additive set function $\boldsymbol{m}: \mathcal{C} \to X$ with finite variation μ is countably additive and can be extended uniquely to a regular Borel measure $\boldsymbol{m}_1: \mathcal{B} \to X$ with finite variation μ_1. In this case μ_1 is the extension of μ.*

In particular, we can take $\mathcal{C}$ to be $\mathcal{K}_0$, $\mathcal{K}$ or $\mathcal{B}_0$.

Corollary 3. *If $\mathcal{C}$ is a clan such that $\mathcal{K}_0 \subset \mathcal{C} \subset \mathcal{B}_0$, then every measure $\boldsymbol{m}: \mathcal{C} \to X$ with finite variation can be extended uniquely to a regular Borel measure $\boldsymbol{m}_1: \mathcal{B} \to X$ with finite variation μ_1 and μ_1 is the extension of μ.*

In fact, in this case $\boldsymbol{m}$ is regular (proposition 1).
In particular:

Corollary 4. *Every Baire measure $\boldsymbol{m}: \mathcal{B}_0 \to X$ with finite variation μ (in particular every scalar Baire measure $\boldsymbol{m}$) can be extended uniquely to a regular Borel measure $\boldsymbol{m}_1: \mathcal{B} \to X$ with finite variation μ_1. Then μ_1 is the extension of μ.*

Proposition 2. *If $\mathcal{C}$ is a clan such that $\mathcal{K}_0 \subset \mathcal{C} \subset \mathcal{B}_0$ and if $\boldsymbol{m}: \mathcal{C} \to X$ is a set function with finite variation, then the two following conditions are equivalent:*

a) *$\boldsymbol{m}$ is additive and regular;*

b) *$\boldsymbol{m}$ is countably additive.*

The implication a) $\Rightarrow$ b) follows from the corollary 2 of the theorem 3. The implication b) $\Rightarrow$ a) is stated in the proposition 1.

Corollary 5. *If T is of countable type or if T is metrizable (in particular if $T \subset R^n$), if $\mathcal{C}$ is a clan such that $\mathcal{K} \subset \mathcal{C} \subset \mathcal{B}$ and if $\boldsymbol{m}: \mathcal{C} \to X$ is a set function with finite variation, then the two following conditions are equivalent:*

a) *$\boldsymbol{m}$ is additive and regular;*

b) *$\boldsymbol{m}$ is countably additive.*

4. REGULARITY OF THE VECTOR MEASURES ON A SUBCLASS

In this section we deduce the regularity of a measure from its regularity on a subclass.

Proposition 3. *Let $\mathscr{L}$ be a lattice, $\mathscr{S}$ the semi-tribe generated by $\mathscr{L}$, and $\mathscr{C}$ a clan such that $\mathscr{L} \subset \mathscr{C} \subset \mathscr{S}$. Let X be a Banach space and $\boldsymbol{m}: \mathscr{C} \to X$ a measure with finite variation μ. If $\mathscr{L}$ is dense in $\mathscr{P}(T)$ and if the restriction α of μ to $\mathscr{L}$ is regular, then* **m** *and μ are regular on $\mathscr{C}$.*

In fact, α is increasing, subadditive, additive, and regular on $\mathscr{L}$, therefore, by the theorem 2, α can be extended to a regular measure μ_1 on $\mathscr{S}$. On the other hand, the sets of $\mathscr{S}$ are μ-integrable. The measures μ^* and μ_1 on $\mathscr{S}$ are equal on $\mathscr{L}$, therefore μ^* and μ_1 are equal on $\mathscr{S}$ (§ 2, corollary of the proposition 6). It follows that μ^* is regular on $\mathscr{S}$, therefore μ is regular on $\mathscr{C}$, consequently $\boldsymbol{m}$ is also regular on $\mathscr{C}$.

Corollary. *Let $\mathscr{L}$ be a lattice of compact sets, $\mathscr{S}$ the semi-tribe generated by $\mathscr{L}$, $\mathscr{C}$ a clan such that $\mathscr{L} \subset \mathscr{C} \subset \mathscr{S}$, and $\boldsymbol{m}: \mathscr{C} \to X$ a measure with finite variation μ. If $\mathscr{L}$ is dense in $\mathscr{P}(T)$ and if every set of $\mathscr{L}$ is the intersection of a sequence of open sets of $\mathscr{C}$, then* **m** *is regular on $\mathscr{C}$.*

Let K be a compact set of $\mathscr{L}$ and let (G_n) be a sequence of open sets of $\mathscr{C}$ such that $K = \bigcap_{n=1}^{\infty} G_n$. We can take the sequence (G_n) to be decreasing. Then

$$\mu(K) = \inf_n \mu(G_n) = \inf_{G \supset K} \mu(G), \quad G \in \mathscr{C}, \text{ open}.$$

From the proposition 11, § 15, it follows that μ is regular on $\mathscr{L}$, therefore, by proposition 3, μ is regular on $\mathscr{C}$, consequently $\boldsymbol{m}$ is regular on $\mathscr{C}$.

We can replace the regularity of the restriction of μ to $\mathscr{L}$ by the regularity of the restriction of $\boldsymbol{m}$ to $\mathscr{L}$ if we impose stronger conditions to $\mathscr{L}$.

Proposition 4. *Let $\mathscr{Q}$ be a clan, $\mathscr{S}$ the semi-tribe generated by $\mathscr{Q}$, $\mathscr{C}$ a clan such that $\mathscr{Q} \subset \mathscr{C} \subset \mathscr{S}$, and $\boldsymbol{m}: \mathscr{C} \to X$ a measure with finite variation μ. If $\mathscr{Q}$ is dense in $\mathscr{P}(T)$ and verifies the following condition:*

(*) *for every $A \in \mathscr{Q}$ there exists $A' \in \mathscr{Q}$ with $A \subset \operatorname{Int} A'$,*
and if the restriction of **m** *to $\mathscr{Q}$ is regular, then* **m** *is regular.*

In fact, in this case the restriction $\boldsymbol{n}$ of $\boldsymbol{m}$ to $\mathscr{Q}$ is regular and with finite variation ν and we have $\nu(A) \leqq \mu(A)$ for $A \in \mathscr{Q}$. By the corollary 1 of the theorem 3, $\boldsymbol{n}$ can be extended uniquely to a regular measure $\boldsymbol{m}_1: \mathscr{S} \to X$ with finite variation μ_1 and μ_1 is the extension of ν from $\mathscr{Q}$ to $\mathscr{S}$.

On the other hand, by the theorem 3, § 5, $\boldsymbol{m}$ can be extended to a measure $\boldsymbol{m}_2: \mathscr{S} \to X$ with finite variation μ_2 and $\mu_2^* = \mu^*$. Since $\boldsymbol{m}_1$ and $\boldsymbol{m}_2$ are countably additive on $\mathscr{S}$ and are equal on $\mathscr{Q}$, we deduce that $\boldsymbol{m}_1 = \boldsymbol{m}_2$ (§ 2, proposition 6). It follows that $\boldsymbol{m}_2$ is regular on $\mathscr{S}$, therefore its restriction $\boldsymbol{m}$ to $\mathscr{C}$ is regular on $\mathscr{C}$.

Corollary. *If* **m** *is a Borel measure with finite variation and if the restriction of* **m** *to the clan $\mathscr{K}$ generated by the compact sets is regular, then* **m** *is regular.*

We can take a *semi-clan* $\mathscr{P}$ instead of a *clan* $\mathscr{Q}$, if we ask that $\boldsymbol{m}$ (not only the restriction of $\boldsymbol{m}$ to $\mathscr{P}$) is regular on $\mathscr{P}$.

Proposition 5. *Let $\mathscr{P}$ be a semi-clan, $\mathscr{S}$ the semi-tribe generated by $\mathscr{P}$, $\mathscr{C}$ a clan such that $\mathscr{P} \subset \mathscr{C} \subset \mathscr{S}$, and $\boldsymbol{m}: \mathscr{C} \to X$ a measure with finite variation. If $\mathscr{P}$ is dense in $\mathscr{P}(T)$ and verifies the following condition:*

(*) *for every $A \in \mathscr{P}$ there exists a set $A' \in \mathscr{P}$ with $A \subset \operatorname{Int} A'$,*

and if $\boldsymbol{m}$ is regular on $\mathscr{P}$, then $\boldsymbol{m}$ is regular on $\mathscr{C}$.

In fact, if $\boldsymbol{m}$ is regular on $\mathscr{P}$, then $\boldsymbol{m}$ is regular on the left on $\mathscr{P}$, therefore $\boldsymbol{m}$ is regular on the left on the clan $\mathscr{Q}$ generated by $\mathscr{P}$ (corollary of the proposition 7, § 15). Since every set of $\mathscr{Q}$ is a finite union of sets of $\mathscr{P}$, we deduce that $\mathscr{Q}$ verifies also the condition (*). Since $\boldsymbol{m}$ is regular on the left on $\mathscr{Q}$, the restriction of $\boldsymbol{m}$ to $\mathscr{Q}$ is regular on the left, therefore the restriction of $\boldsymbol{m}$ to $\mathscr{Q}$ is regular (§ 15, proposition 4). Since $\mathscr{Q} \subset \mathscr{C} \subset \mathscr{S}$, we apply the proposition 3 and we deduce that $\boldsymbol{m}$ is regular on $\mathscr{C}$.

For *scalar* measures on a *semi-tribe* $\mathscr{S}$ we can take in the proposition 5 a lattice $\mathscr{L}$ instead of a semi-clan $\mathscr{P}$ and we can drop the condition (*).

Proposition 6. *Let $\mathscr{L}$ be a lattice, $\mathscr{S}$ the semi-tribe generated by $\mathscr{L}$ and μ a scalar measure on $\mathscr{S}$. If $\mathscr{L}$ is dense in $\mathscr{P}(T)$ and if μ is regular on $\mathscr{L}$, then μ is regular on $\mathscr{S}$.*

In fact, in this case the variation $|\mu|$ is also regular on $\mathscr{L}$ (§ 15, proposition 24) and we can apply the proposition 2.

Corollary. *If μ is a scalar Borel measure and if μ is regular on the lattice of the compact sets (or of the open sets of $\mathscr{B}$), then μ is regular.*

§ 17. STIELTJES MEASURES ON THE REAL LINE

1. FUNCTIONS WITH FINITE VARIATION

In this paragraph we shall suppose that T is an arbitrary *interval* (bounded or not) of the real line R, with the topology induced by the topology of R. Then T is a locally compact space. We shall suppose that the extremities of T are different. Let X be a *normed* space. Let $f: T \to X$ be a function and $[a, b]$ a compact interval of T. For each decomposition d:

$$a = x_0 < x_1 < \cdots < x_i < x_{i+1} < \cdots < x_n = b$$

of the interval $[a, b]$ consider the sum

$$V_d(f) = \sum_{i=0}^{n-1} |f(x_{i+1}) - f(x_i)|.$$

If d' is a decomposition finer than d (i.e. if $d \subset d'$) then $V_d(f) \leqq V_{d'}(f)$. Put

$$V_a^b(f) = \sup_d V_d(f),$$

where the supremum is taken for all the decomposition d of $[a, b]$. The number $V_a^b(f)$ is called the *variation* of f on the interval $[a, b]$.

The variation of f has the following properties:

1. $0 \leqq V_a^b(f) \leqq +\infty$; $V_a^b(f) = 0$ if and only if f is constant on $[a, b]$;

2. $V_a^b(\alpha f) = |\alpha| \, V_a^b(f)$;

3. $V_a^b(f + g) \leqq V_a^b(f) + V_a^b(g)$;

4. $V_{a'}^{b'}(f) \leqq V_a^b(f)$ if $[a', b'] \subset [a, b]$;

5. $V_a^b(f) + V_b^c(f) = V_a^c(f)$ if $a \leqq b \leqq c$;

6. $|f(b) - f(a)| \leqq V_a^b(f)$.

If the function f is real-valued and *increasing*, then

$$V_a^b(f) = f(b) - f(a).$$

The function f is said to be with *bounded variation* on $[a, b]$ if $V_a^b(f) < +\infty$.

The set of the functions $f\colon T \to X$ with bounded variation on $[a, b]$ is a vector space and $V_a^b(f)$ is a semi-norm on this space.

The function f is said to be *with finite variation* if $V_a^b(f) < +\infty$ for every compact interval $[a, b] \subset T$.

The set of the functions $f\colon T \to X$ with finite variation is a vector space.

Every real-valued and *monotone* function is with finite variation.

A function $f\colon T \to X$ with finite variation has one-sided limits in every point of T (if f is real-valued, the one-sided limits are finite) and the set of the points of T in which f is not continuous, is at most countable.

We put

$$a_0 = \inf T \quad \text{and} \quad b_0 = \sup T.$$

If $a_0 \in T$ we put $f(a_0 - 0) = f(a_0)$ and if $b_0 \in T$ we put $f(b_0 + 0) = f(b_0)$.

Let $f\colon T \to X$ be a function with *finite variation*. If $b \leqq a$ are two points of T we put

$$V_a^b(f) = -V_b^a(f).$$

Choose a fixed point $a \in T$ and consider the function

$$\varphi_a(t) = V_a^t(f).$$

The function φ_a has the following properties:

1. φ_a is real-valued and *increasing*;

2. φ_a is continuous on the left (on the right) in each point in which f is continuous on the left (on the right);

3. for every two points $a, b \in T$, the difference $\varphi_b - \varphi_a$ is constant:

$$\varphi_b - \varphi_a = V_a^b(f);$$

4. $\varphi_a(a) = 0$; $\varphi_a(t) \geqq 0$ if $t \geqq a$ and $\varphi_a(t) \leqq 0$ if $t \leqq a$;

5. $|f(a) - f(t)| \leqq |\varphi_a(t)|$.

From this last inequality we deduce, by passing to the limit:

6. $|f(a) - f(t-0)| \leqq |\varphi_a(t-0)|$,

$|f(a) - f(t+0)| \leqq \varphi_a(t+0)$.

2. STIELTJES MEASURES DEDUCED FROM FUNCTIONS WITH FINITE VARIATION

We shall denote by $\mathscr{I}$ the class of the intervals of the form $[a, b)$ and of the form $[a, b_0]$ contained in T.

If $b_0 \notin T$, then $\mathscr{I}$ consists only of the intervals of T of the form $[a, b)$.

We verify easily that $\mathscr{I}$ is a *semi-clan*. We shall denote by $\mathscr{C}$ the clan generated by $\mathscr{I}$.

The clan $\mathscr{C}$ consists of all the finite unions of disjoint intervals of $\mathscr{I}$ (§ 1, proposition 13).

We remark that if two intervals of $\mathscr{I}$ have in common an extremity, then their union is again an interval of $\mathscr{I}$. Hence, every nonvoid set A of $\mathscr{C}$ can be written uniquely as a finite union $A = \bigcup_{i=1}^{n} I_i$ of *disjoint nonvoid* intervals of $\mathscr{I}$ such that any two intervals I_i and I_j have in common no extremity.

We remind that an additive set function $\boldsymbol{m}: \mathscr{I} \to X$ can be extended uniquely to an additive set function $\boldsymbol{m}_1: \mathscr{C} \to X$ (§ 5, proposition 1) and that the variations of $\boldsymbol{m}$ and $\boldsymbol{m}_1$ are equal (§ 3, corollary 1 of proposition 4).

The Borel measures on T will be called *Stieltjes* measures.

The Stieltjes measures *with finite variation* are regular (§ 16, proposition 1). In particular, every *scalar* Stieltjes measure is regular.

We shall show that the Stieltjes measures with finite variation can be identified with the functions with finite variation.

Theorem 1. *For every function $f: T \to X$ with finite variation, there exists a Stieltjes measure $\boldsymbol{m}: \mathscr{B} \to X$ with finite variation and only one such that:*

for each interval $(a, b) \subset T$ with $a < b$ we have

$$\boldsymbol{m}((a, b)) = f(b-0) - f(a+0);$$

for every interval $[a, b] \subset T$ *we have*

$$\boldsymbol{m}([a, b]) = \boldsymbol{f}(b + 0) - \boldsymbol{f}(a - 0);$$

for every interval $[a, b) \subset T$ *we have*

$$\boldsymbol{m}([a, b)) = \boldsymbol{f}(b - 0) - \boldsymbol{f}(a - 0);$$

and for every interval $(a, b] \subset T$ *we have*

$$\boldsymbol{m}((a, b]) = \boldsymbol{f}(b + 0) - \boldsymbol{f}(a + 0).$$

Consider the semi-clan $\mathscr{I}$ of the intervals of T of the form $[a, b)$ and of the form $[a, b_0]$ if $b_0 \in T$.

For each interval $[a, b) \subset T$ put

$$\boldsymbol{m}([a, b)) = \boldsymbol{f}(b - 0) - \boldsymbol{f}(a - 0)$$

and if $b_0 \in T$, for each interval $[a, b_0] \subset T$ put

$$\boldsymbol{m}([a, b_0]) = \boldsymbol{f}(b_0) - \boldsymbol{f}(a - 0).$$

We verify easily that the set function $\boldsymbol{m}: \mathscr{I} \to X$ is *additive*.

Choose a fixed point $\alpha \in T$ and consider the variation

$$\varphi(t) = V_\alpha^t(\boldsymbol{f})$$

of $\boldsymbol{f}$. The function φ is increasing, and for two points $s < t$ of T we have

$$|\boldsymbol{f}(t) - \boldsymbol{f}(s)| \leqq \varphi(t) - \varphi(s).$$

Passing to the limit, we obtain successively, for $a, b \in T$:

$$|\boldsymbol{f}(b) - \boldsymbol{f}(a - 0)| \leqq \varphi(b) - \varphi(a - 0),$$

$$|\boldsymbol{f}(b - 0) - \boldsymbol{f}(a - 0)| \leqq \varphi(b - 0) - \varphi(a - 0).$$

For each interval $[a, b) \subset T$ put

$$\mu([a, b)) = \varphi(b - 0) - \varphi(a - 0)$$

and if $b_0 \in T$, for each interval $[a, b_0] \subset T$ put

$$\mu([a, b_0]) = \varphi(b_0) - \varphi(a - 0).$$

The set function μ defined on $\mathscr{I}$ is *additive* and *positive* (finite) and for every interval $I \in \mathscr{I}$ we have

$$|\boldsymbol{m}(I)| \leqq \mu(I).$$

Since $\mathscr{I}$ is a semi-clan, we can extend uniquely the set functions $\boldsymbol{m}$ and μ to *additive* set functions on the clan $\mathscr{C}$ generated by $\mathscr{I}$. We shall denote the extensions also by $\boldsymbol{m}$

respectively μ. For every set $A \in \mathscr{C}$ we have then

$$|\boldsymbol{m}(A)| \leqq \mu(A).$$

Since μ is finite on $\mathscr{C}$, it follows that $\boldsymbol{m}$ is with finite variation on $\mathscr{C}$.

We prove now that μ is regular on the left on $\mathscr{C}$.

Let $A = \bigcup_{i=1}^{n+1} I_i$ be a set of $\mathscr{C}$, where I_i are disjoint intervals of the form $I_i = [a_i, b_i)$ with $a_i < b_i$ for $1 \leqq i \leqq n$, and $I_{n+1} = \emptyset$ or $I_{n+1} = [a_{n+1}, b_0]$ if $b_0 \in T$. Let $\varepsilon > 0$. For $1 \leqq i \leqq n$ there exists a point $\beta_i \in [a_i, b_i)$ of continuity of φ, such that

$$\varphi(b_i - 0) - \varphi(\beta_i) < \frac{\varepsilon}{n}.$$

Put $K_i = [a_i, \beta_i]$ for $1 \leqq i \leqq n$ and $K_{n+1} = I_{n+1}$.

The set $K = \bigcup_{i=1}^{n+1} K_i$ is compact, $K \subset A$ and

$$A - K \subset \bigcup_{i=1}^{n} [\beta_i, b_i) \in \mathscr{C}.$$

For every set $B \in \mathscr{C}$ with $B \subset A - K$ we have

$$\mu(B) \leqq \mu(A - K) = \sum_{i=1}^{n} \mu([\beta_i, b_i))$$

$$= \sum_{i=1}^{n} (\varphi(b_i - 0) - \varphi(\beta_i - 0)) = \sum_{i=1}^{n} (\varphi(b_i - 0) - \varphi(\beta_i)) < \varepsilon,$$

therefore A is regular on the left with respect to μ. It follows that μ is regular on the left on $\mathscr{C}$.

From the inequality

$$|\boldsymbol{m}(A)| \leqq \mu(A), \quad \text{for} \quad A \in \mathscr{C},$$

we deduce that $\boldsymbol{m}$ is also regular on the left on $\mathscr{C}$.

Remark that each set $A \in \mathscr{C}$ is contained in an open set $G \in \mathscr{C}$ (G is open in the topology induced on T by the topology of R), hence the clan $\mathscr{C}$ verifies the condition (*) of proposition 4, § 15, therefore $\boldsymbol{m}$ and μ are regular on $\mathscr{C}$.

Remark also that the intervals of $\mathscr{I}$ form a base of the topology on T, therefore, for every compact set $K \subset T$ and every open set $G \supset K$ there exists a set $A \in \mathscr{C}$ such that $K \subset A \subset G$, hence $\mathscr{C}$ is dense in $\mathscr{P}(T)$.

According to theorem 3, § 16, $\boldsymbol{m}$ can be uniquely extended to a regular Borel measure with finite variation, defined on the semi-tribe $\mathscr{B}$ of the relatively compact Borel sets $A \subset T$.

The set function μ can also be extended to a regular positive Borel measure.

The extension of $\boldsymbol{m}$ and μ will be denoted also by $\boldsymbol{m}$ and μ. The variations of $\boldsymbol{m}$ on $\mathscr{C}$ and $\mathscr{B}$ are equal on $\mathscr{C}$.

For the variation $|\boldsymbol{m}|$ of $\boldsymbol{m}$ we have

$$|\boldsymbol{m}|(A) \leqq \mu(A), \quad \text{for} \quad A \in \mathscr{B}.$$

Let now $[a, b]$ be an interval of T with $b < b_0$.

Choosing a *decreasing* sequence (b_n) of points of T in which f is continuous, such that $b_n > b$ and $b_n \to b$, the corresponding sequence of intervals $([a, b_n))$ is *decreasing* and

$$[a, b] = \bigcap_{n=1}^{\infty} [a, b_n).$$

Since $\boldsymbol{m}$ is countably additive, we have

$$\boldsymbol{m}([a, b]) = \lim_{n\to\infty} \boldsymbol{m}([a, b_n)) = \lim_{n\to\infty} (f(b_n - 0) - f(a - 0))$$
$$= \lim_{n\to\infty} (f(b_n) - f(a - 0)) = f(b + 0) - f(a - 0).$$

Each interval $(a, b) \subset T$ with $a < b$ is of the form

$$(a, b) = \bigcup_{n=1}^{\infty} [a_n, b),$$

where (a_n) is a strictly decreasing sequence of points of T in which f is continuous, such that $a_n \to a$. Then

$$\boldsymbol{m}((a, b)) = \lim_{n\to\infty} \boldsymbol{m}([a_n, b)) = \lim_{n\to\infty} (f(b - 0) - f(a_n))$$
$$= f(b - 0) - f(a + 0).$$

An interval of the form $(a, b] \subset T$ can be written in the form

$$(a, b] = \bigcup_{n=1}^{\infty} [a_n, b],$$

where (a_n) is a strictly decreasing sequence of continuity points of f such that $a_n \to a$, therefore

$$\boldsymbol{m}((a, b]) = \lim_{n\to\infty} \boldsymbol{m}([a_n, b]) = \lim_{n\to\infty} (f(\quad + 0) - f(a_n))$$
$$= f(b + 0) - f(a + 0).$$

Remarks.

1°. It is sufficient to know the values of $\boldsymbol{m}$ only for the intervals of the form (a, b) with $a < b$, or only for the intervals $[a, b]$, or only for the intervals $[a, b)$, or only for the intervals $(a, b]$, and for the sets $\{a_0\}$, $\{b_0\}$, if a_0 and b_0 belong to T, because each of these classes together with $\{a_0\}$ and $\{b_0\}$ generate the semi-tribe $\mathscr{B}$.

2°. We can also prove the theorem in the following way: we show that $\boldsymbol{m}$ is *countably additive* on the semi-clan $\mathscr{I}$, hence on the *clan* $\mathscr{C}$, and that $\boldsymbol{m}$ is with finite variation on $\mathscr{I}$ hence also on $\mathscr{C}$. We remark then that the semi-tribe $\mathscr{B}$ is generated by $\mathscr{C}$ and applying the proposition 1, § 16, we see that $\boldsymbol{m}$ is regular, therefore, by theorem 3, § 16, $\boldsymbol{m}$ can be extended to a (regular) Borel measure with finite variation.

3°. The measure $\boldsymbol{m}$ corresponding to a function f with finite variation, depends only on the one-sided limits of f, and does not depend on the values of f in its points of discontinuity belonging to the *interior* of T.

If we modify f in the points of discontinuity belonging to Int T, in such a way that f *remains with finite variation*, then the corresponding measure is not changed.

We verify easily that if f is with finite variation and if we modify the values of f in the points of discontinuity different from a_0 and b_0, such that the new function f' is continuous on the left in these points, then f' is with finite variation, hence the measures corresponding to f and f' are equal.

Thus, we can always suppose that f is *continuous on the left* in all the points of T, except for b_0. In this case, if $b < b_0$ we have

$$\boldsymbol{m}((a, b)) = f(b) - f(a + 0),$$

$$\boldsymbol{m}([a, b]) = f(b + 0) - f(a),$$

$$\boldsymbol{m}([a, b)) = f(b) - f(a),$$

$$\boldsymbol{m}((a, b]) = f(b + 0) - f(a + 0).$$

If $b = b_0$, we put in the right hand member $b_0 - 0$ instead of b, and b_0 instead of $b + 0$.

4°. If two functions f and g, with finite variation, differ by a constant, then the corresponding measures are equal.

Hence, if we add a constant to a function f with finite variation such that the new function is null in a certain point $\alpha \in T$ given from advance, then the corresponding measure is not changed.

Conversely, if for two functions f and g with finite variation, *continuous on the right* in the interior of T, there corresponds the same measure $\boldsymbol{m}$, then the difference $f - g$ is constant.

5°. Let $f \colon T \to X$ be a function with finite variation, $\alpha \in T$ and $\varphi(t) = V_\alpha^t(f)$ the variation of f. If $\boldsymbol{m}$ is the measure corresponding to f and μ is the measure corresponding to φ and if f is *continuous on the left* in the interior of T, then μ is the variation of $\boldsymbol{m}$.

In fact, from the proof of the preceding theorem we deduce that $|\boldsymbol{m}| \leqq \mu$.

We shall show that $\mu(I) \leqq |\boldsymbol{m}|(I)$ for every interval $I \in \mathscr{I}$ and then it will follow that $\mu \leqq |\boldsymbol{m}|$.

Let $I = [a, b) \subset T$ and $\varepsilon > 0$. We have

$$\mu([a, b)) = \varphi(b) - \varphi(a) = V_a^b(f).$$

There exists a decomposition $d = (x_i)_{0 \leqq i \leqq n}$ of the interval $[a, b]$ such that

$$V_a^b(f) \leqq \sum_{i=0}^{n-1} |f(x_{i+1}) - f(x_i)| + \varepsilon.$$

But $f(x_{i+1}) - f(x_i) = \boldsymbol{m}([x_i, x_{i+1}))$, therefore

$$\mu([a, b)) \leqq \sum_{i=0}^{n-1} |\boldsymbol{m}([x_i, x_{i+1}))| + \varepsilon \leqq |\boldsymbol{m}|([a, b)) + \varepsilon,$$

hence, ε being arbitrary,

$$\mu([a, b)) \leqq |\boldsymbol{m}|([a, b)).$$

If $b_0 \in T$ and $I = [a, b_0]$ then

$$\mu([a, b_0]) = \varphi(b_0) - \varphi(a) = V_a^{b_0}(f).$$

There exists then a decomposition $d = (x_i)_{0 \leqq i \leqq n}$ of $[a, b_0]$ such that

$$V_a^{b_0}(f) \leqq \sum_{i=0}^{n-1} |f(x_{i+1}) - f(x_i)| + \varepsilon.$$

But $f(x_n) - f(x_{n-1}) = \boldsymbol{m}([x_{n-1}, b_0])$, therefore

$$\mu([a, b_0]) \leqq \sum_{i=0}^{n-2} |\boldsymbol{m}([x_i, x_{i+1}))| + |\boldsymbol{m}([x_{n-1}, b_0])| + \varepsilon \leqq |\boldsymbol{m}|([a, b_0]) + \varepsilon,$$

hence, ε being arbitrary,

$$\mu([a, b_0]) \leqq |\boldsymbol{m}|([a, b_0]).$$

Thus $\mu(I) \leqq |\boldsymbol{m}|(I)$ for every $I \in \mathscr{I}$, therefore $\mu \leqq |\boldsymbol{m}|$ and hence $\mu = |\boldsymbol{m}|$.

6°. If we take the real function $\varphi(t) = t$ for $t \in I$, the corresponding positive measure is the Lebesgue measure on I.

3. FUNCTIONS WITH FINITE VARIATION DEDUCED FROM STIELTJES MEASURES

Let $\boldsymbol{m}: \mathscr{B} \to X$ be a Stieltjes measure. We choose a point α in the interior of T and consider the function $f_\alpha: T \to X$ defined by the following equalities:

$$f_\alpha(b_0) = \boldsymbol{m}([\alpha, b_0]), \quad \text{if} \quad b_0 \in T,$$

$$f_\alpha(t) = \boldsymbol{m}([\alpha, t)), \quad \text{if} \quad \alpha \leqq t < b_0,$$

$$f_\alpha(t) = -\boldsymbol{m}([t, \alpha)), \quad \text{if} \quad a_0 \leqq t \leqq \alpha.$$

The function f_α has the following properties:

1. $f_\alpha(\alpha) = 0$.

In fact, $f_\alpha(\alpha) = \boldsymbol{m}([\alpha, \alpha)) = \boldsymbol{m}(\emptyset) = 0$.

2. *If* $\alpha, \beta \in T$, *then the difference* $f_\alpha - f_\beta$ *is constant.*

We suppose $\alpha < \beta$ and shall show that

$$f_\alpha(t) - f_\beta(t) \equiv \boldsymbol{m}([\alpha, \beta)).$$

If $\alpha < \beta \leqq t < b_0$, we have $[\alpha, t) \supset (\beta, t)$ and $[\alpha, t) - [\beta, t) = [\alpha, \beta)$, therefore

$$f_\alpha(t) - f_\beta(t) = \boldsymbol{m}([\alpha, t)) - \boldsymbol{m}([\beta, t)) = \boldsymbol{m}([\alpha, \beta)).$$

In the other cases, when $\alpha \leqq t \leqq \beta$ or $t \leqq \alpha \leqq \beta$ the proof is made in the same manner.

If $t = b_0$, we have $[\alpha, b_0] \supset [\beta, b_0]$ and $[\alpha, b_0] - [\beta, b_0) = [\alpha, \beta]$, therefore, in this case too we have

$$f_\alpha(b_0) - f_\beta(b_0) = \boldsymbol{m}([\alpha, b_0]) - \boldsymbol{m}([\beta, b_0]) = \boldsymbol{m}([\alpha, \beta)).$$

In the sequel we shall consider α fixed and we shall write f instead of f_α.

3. f *is continuous on the left in every point* $t < b_0$ *of* T.

Let (t_n) be an *increasing* sequence of points of T, convergent to t. Suppose first that $\alpha < t$; we can suppose then that $\alpha < t_n \leqq t$ for every n. The sequence of intervals $[\alpha, t_n)$ is increasing and their union is $[\alpha, t)$, therefore

$$\lim_{n\to\infty} \boldsymbol{m}([\alpha, t_n)) = \boldsymbol{m}([\alpha, t)),$$

hence

$$\lim_{n\to\infty} f(t_n) = f(t).$$

Suppose now that $t \leqq \alpha$. The sequence of intervals $[t_n, \alpha)$ is decreasing and their intersection is $[t, \alpha)$, therefore

$$\lim_{n\to\infty} \boldsymbol{m}([t_n, \alpha)) = \boldsymbol{m}([t, \alpha)),$$

hence

$$\lim_{n\to\infty} f(t_n) = f(t).$$

Since the increasing sequence (t_n) convergent to t is arbitrary, we deduce that f is continuous on the left in t.

4. *If $b_0 \in T$, then f has a limit on the left in b_0 and*

$$f(b_0 - 0) = \boldsymbol{m}([\alpha, b_0)).$$

Let (t_n) be an *increasing* sequence of points of T, convergent to b_0, such that $\alpha \leqq t_n < b_0$ for every n. The sequence of intervals $[\alpha, t_n)$ is increasing and their union is $[\alpha, b_0)$, therefore

$$\lim_{n\to\infty} \boldsymbol{m}([\alpha, t_n)) = \boldsymbol{m}([\alpha, b_0)).$$

5. *f has a limit on the right in every point $t < b_0$ of T.*

Let (t_n) be a decreasing sequence of points of T, convergent to t, such that $t < t_n$. Since $t < b_0$ we can suppose that $t_n < b_0$ for every n.

Suppose first that $\alpha \leqq t$. The sequence of intervals $[\alpha, t_n)$ is decreasing and their intersection is $[\alpha, t]$, therefore

$$\lim_{n\to\infty} \boldsymbol{m}([\alpha, t_n)) = \boldsymbol{m}([\alpha, t]),$$

hence

$$\lim_{n\to\infty} f(t_n) = \boldsymbol{m}([\alpha, t]).$$

Suppose now that $t < \alpha$. We can then suppose that $t_n < \alpha$ for every n. The sequence of intervals $[t_n, \alpha)$ is increasing and their union is (t, α), therefore

$$\lim_{n\to\infty} \boldsymbol{m}([t_n, \alpha)) = \boldsymbol{m}((t, \alpha)),$$

hence

$$\lim_{n\to\infty} f(t_n) = -\boldsymbol{m}((t, \alpha)).$$

The decreasing sequence (t_n) convergent to t being arbitrary, we deduce that

$$f(t + 0) = \boldsymbol{m}([\alpha, t]), \qquad \text{if} \quad \alpha \leqq t < b_0,$$

$$f(t + 0) = -\boldsymbol{m}((t, \alpha)), \quad \text{if} \quad a_0 \leqq t < \alpha.$$

We can now write for every $t \in T$

$$\boldsymbol{m}([\alpha, t)) = f(t + 0), \quad \text{for} \quad \alpha \leqq t \leqq b_0,$$

$$\boldsymbol{m}((t, \alpha)) = -f(t + 0), \quad \text{for} \quad a_0 \leqq t < \alpha.$$

6. *For every point $t \in T$ we have*

$$\boldsymbol{m}(\{t\}) = f(t+0) - f(t-0).$$

If $\alpha \leqq t \leqq b_0$, we have

$$\boldsymbol{m}(\{t\}) = \boldsymbol{m}([\alpha, t]) - \boldsymbol{m}([\alpha, t)) = f(t+0) - f(t-0).$$

If $a_0 \leqq t < \alpha$ we have

$$\boldsymbol{m}(\{t\}) = \boldsymbol{m}([t, \alpha)) - \boldsymbol{m}((t, \alpha)) = -f(t-0) + f(t+0).$$

Remark. f is continuous in t if and only if $\boldsymbol{m}(\{t\}) = 0$.

7. *If $a < b$ are two points of T, then*

$$\boldsymbol{m}([a, b)) = f(b-0) - f(a-0),$$

$$\boldsymbol{m}((a, b]) = f(b+0) - f(a+0),$$

$$\boldsymbol{m}((a, b)) = f(b-0) - f(a+0),$$

$$\boldsymbol{m}([a, b]) = f(b+0) - f(a-0).$$

Let us prove the first equality. Suppose first that $\alpha \leqq a < b \leqq b_0$. Then

$$\boldsymbol{m}([a, b)) = \boldsymbol{m}([\alpha, b)) - \boldsymbol{m}([\alpha, a)) = f(b-0) - f(a-0).$$

If $a_0 \leqq a \leqq \alpha \leqq b \leqq b_0$, then

$$\boldsymbol{m}([a, b)) = \boldsymbol{m}([a, \alpha)) + \boldsymbol{m}([\alpha, b)) = -f(a-0) + f(b-0)$$

and if $a_0 \leqq a \leqq b \leqq \alpha$, then

$$\boldsymbol{m}([a, b)) = \boldsymbol{m}([a, \alpha)) - \boldsymbol{m}([b, \alpha)) = -f(a-0) + f(b-0).$$

The other equalities are proved then using the equality

$$\boldsymbol{m}(\{t\}) = f(t+0) - f(t-0).$$

Remark. In the equalities 6 and 7 the point α does not appear any more.These equalities are true whatever be the chosen point α.

8. *Let $\boldsymbol{m}$ and $\boldsymbol{n}$ be two Stieltjes measures with values in X, f_m and f_n the corresponding functions (for the same point α). Then*

$$f_{m+n} = f_m + f_n$$

and

$$f_{cm} = cf_m, \quad c \text{ scalar}.$$

In fact, if $b_0 \in T$, then

$$f_{m+n}(b_0) = (\boldsymbol{m} + \boldsymbol{n})([\alpha, b_0]) = \boldsymbol{m}([\alpha, b_0]) + \boldsymbol{n}([\alpha, b_0]) = f_m(b_0) + f_n(b_0).$$

If $\alpha \leqq t < b_0$ we have

$$f_{m+n}(t) = (\boldsymbol{m} + \boldsymbol{n})([\alpha, t)) = \boldsymbol{m}([\alpha, t)) + \boldsymbol{n}([\alpha, t)) = f_m(t) + f_n(t),$$

and if $a_0 \leqq t \leqq \alpha$ we have

$$f_{m+n}(t) = -(\boldsymbol{m} + \boldsymbol{n})([t, \alpha)) = -\boldsymbol{m}([t, \alpha)) - \boldsymbol{n}([t, \alpha)) = f_m(t) + f_n(t).$$

We prove in the same manner that $f_{cm} = cf_m$.

9. *Let* $\boldsymbol{m}$ *and* $\boldsymbol{n}$ *be two Stieltjes measures on* T *with values in* X, f *and* g *the corresponding functions. If* $f = g$, *then* $\boldsymbol{m} = \boldsymbol{n}$.

In fact, for every interval $I \subset T$ we have

$$\boldsymbol{m}(I) = \boldsymbol{n}(I)$$

as we see easily using properties 6 an 7 and the equality $\boldsymbol{m}(\emptyset) = \boldsymbol{n}(\emptyset) = 0$.

Let G be a relatively compact *open* subset of T.

The set G can be written as the union of a sequence (I_n) of disjoint intervals of T, open in T; namely, if $a_0 \in G$, one of the intervals is of the form $[a_0, x)$, if $b_0 \in G$ one of the intervals is of the form $(b, b_0]$ and the other intervals are of the form (a, b). Then

$$\boldsymbol{m}(G) = \sum_{n=1}^{\infty} \boldsymbol{m}(I_n) = \sum_{n=1}^{\infty} \boldsymbol{n}(I_n) = \boldsymbol{n}(G).$$

Since the countably additive set functions $\boldsymbol{m}$ and $\boldsymbol{n}$ coincide on the relatively compact open sets, $\boldsymbol{m}$ and $\boldsymbol{n}$ coincide on $\mathscr{B}$ (§ 14, remark after proposition 17).

Remark. The mapping $\boldsymbol{m} \to f$ of the set of the Stieltjes measures on T with values in X, into the set of the functions $f\colon T \to X$ which are continuous on the left in the points $t < b_0$ of T and null in the same point α, is one-to-one.

10. *If* $\boldsymbol{m}$ *is a Stieltjes measure with finite variation, then* f *is with finite variation.*

Let μ be the variation of $\boldsymbol{m}$. Let $a < b$ be two points of T. Take a decomposition d:

$$a = x_0 < x_1 < \cdots < x_i < x_{i+1} < \cdots < x_n = b$$

of the interval $[a, b]$. If $b < b_0$ we have

$$V_d(f) = \sum_{i=0}^{n-1} |f(x_{i+1}) - f(x_i)| = \sum_{i=0}^{n-1} |f(x_{i+1} - 0) - f(x_i - 0)|$$

$$= \sum_{i=0}^{n-1} |\boldsymbol{m}([x_i, x_{i+1}))| \leqq \mu([a, b)) \leqq \mu([a, b]) < +\infty.$$

If $b = b_0$ then

$$\begin{aligned} V_d(f) &= \sum_{i=0}^{n-1} |f(x_{i+1}) - f(x_i)| \\ &= \sum_{i=0}^{n-2} |f(x_{i+1} - 0) - f(x_i - 0)| + |f(x_n + 0) - f(x_{n-1} - 0)| \\ &= \sum_{i=0}^{n-2} |\boldsymbol{m}([x_i, x_{i+1}))| + |\boldsymbol{m}([x_{n-1}, x_n])| \\ &\leqq \sum_{i=0}^{n-2} \mu([x_i, x_{i+1}]) + \mu([x_{n-1}, x_n]) = \mu([a, b_0]) < +\infty . \end{aligned}$$

The decomposition d being arbitrary, we have

$$V_a^b(f) \leqq \mu([a, b]).$$

Remarks.

1°. If m is a scalar Stieltjes measure, it is with finite variation, therefore f is with finite variation.

2°. The variation $V_a^b(f)$ is independent of the point α.

11. *If μ is a positive Stieltjes measure, then f is increasing.*

If $t_1 < t_2 < b_0$ we have

$$f(t_2) - f(t_1) = f(t_2 - 0) - f(t_1 - 0) = \mu([t_1, t_2)) \geqq 0.$$

If $t_1 < t_2 = b_0$, then

$$f(t_2) - f(t_1) = f(b_0) - f(t_1) = f(b_0 + 0) - f(t_1 - 0) = \mu([t_1, b_0]) \geqq 0.$$

Thus in all these cases we have $f(t_2) - f(t_1) \geqq 0$, hence f is increasing.

Remark. If μ is positive we have

$$V_a^b(f) = \mu([a, b)), \quad \text{if} \quad b < b_0,$$

and

$$V_a^{b_0}(f) = \mu([a, b_0]), \quad \text{if} \quad b_0 \in T.$$

§ 18. REDUCTION OF THE INTEGRATION IN ABSTRACT SPACES TO THE INTEGRATION IN LOCALLY COMPACT SPACES

1. THEOREM OF STONE

Theorem 1 (Stone). *For every set S and every clan $\mathscr{C}$ of subsets of S, there exists a totally disconnected, locally compact space T, such that $\mathscr{C}$ is isomorphic to the clan $\mathscr{D}$ of the open-compact subsets of T.*

Let us denote by Φ the set of the bases of filter[1]) consisting of sets of $\mathscr{C}$. Every set $A \neq \emptyset$ of $\mathscr{C}$ forms a base of filter, therefore $\{A\} \in \Phi$.

The set Φ is ordered by inclusion, and every totally ordered subclass $\Phi' \subset \Phi$ has a least upper bound in Φ. Indeed, the union of a totally ordered set of bases of filter of Φ is again a base of filter of Φ. By the theorem of Zorn, every base of filter of Φ is contained in a maximal base of filter of Φ. In particular, every set $A \neq \emptyset$ of $\mathscr{C}$ belongs to a maximal base of filter of Φ.

We shall denote by T the set of the maximal bases of filter of Φ. We remark that a maximal base of filter $t \in T$ has the following properties:

If $A \in t$ and if $A \subset B \in \mathscr{C}$, then $B \in t$; in particular, if (A_i) is a family of sets of t, then $\bigcup A_i \in t$.

If $A \in \mathscr{C}$ and $A \notin t$, then there exists a set $B \in t$ with $B \cap A = \emptyset$.

In particular, if (A_i) is a finite family of sets of t, then $\bigcap A_i \in t$.

For each set $A \in \mathscr{C}$ consider the subset $\varphi(A) \subset T$ defined by the equality

$$\varphi(A) = \{t \in T; A \in t\}.$$

The mapping φ of $\mathscr{C}$ in the class $\mathscr{P}(T)$ of the subsets of T has the following properties:

1. φ is one-to-one;

2. $\varphi(\emptyset) = \emptyset$;

3. $\varphi(A) \subset \varphi(B)$ if and only if $A \subset B$;

4. $\varphi(A \cup B) = \varphi(A) \cup \varphi(B)$;

5. $\varphi(A \cap B) = \varphi(A) \cap \varphi(B)$;

6. $\varphi(A - B) = \varphi(A) - \varphi(B)$.

Let us prove these properties. Let $A \neq B$ be two sets of $\mathscr{C}$. One of the sets $A - B$ and $B - A$ is nonvoid (otherwise we would have $A = B$). Suppose that $A - B \neq \emptyset$. There exists a maximal base of filter $t \in T$ such that $A - B \in t$. Then $B \notin t$ since $B \cap (A - B) = \emptyset$; on the other hand, $A \in t$, since $A \supset A - B$. It follows that $t \in \varphi(A)$ and $t \notin \varphi(B)$, therefore $\varphi(A) \neq \varphi(B)$, hence φ is one-to-one.

The void set $\emptyset \in \mathscr{C}$ does not belong to any base of filter, therefore $\varphi(\emptyset) = \emptyset$.

If $A \subset B$ and if $t \in \varphi(A)$, then $A \in t$, therefore $B \in t$, hence $t \in \varphi(B)$. It follows that $\varphi(A) \subset \varphi(B)$.

Conversely, if A is not contained in B we have $A - B \neq \emptyset$; there exists a maximal base of filter $t \in T$ such that $A - B \in t$. Then $A \in t$ (since $A \supset A - B$) and $B \notin t$

[1]) A class $\mathscr{B}$ of subsets of S is called a *base of filter*, if: 1. $\mathscr{B}$ is not void; 2. $\emptyset \notin \mathscr{B}$; 3. for any sets $A, B \in \mathscr{B}$, there exists $C \in \mathscr{B}$ such that $C \subset A \cap B$. It follows that every finite intersection of sets of $\mathscr{B}$ is nonvoid.

(since $(A - B) \cap B = \emptyset$). It follows that $t \in \varphi(A)$ and $t \notin \varphi(B)$, therefore $\varphi(A)$ is not contained in $\varphi(B)$.

We deduce that if $\varphi(A) \subset \varphi(B)$, then $A \subset B$.

Since $A \subset A \cup B$ and $B \subset A \cup B$, we deduce $\varphi(A) \subset \varphi(A \cup B)$ and $\varphi(B) \subset \varphi(A \cup B)$, therefore $\varphi(A) \cup \varphi(B) \subset \varphi(A \cup B)$.

In order to prove the converse inclusion, let $t \in \varphi(A \cup B)$, hence $A \cup B \in t$. If $A \notin t$ and $B \notin t$, there exist two sets $A', B' \in t$ with $A' \cap A = \emptyset$ and $B' \cap B = \emptyset$. Then for the set $C = A' \cap B' \in t$ we have $C \cap A = \emptyset$ and $C \cap B = \emptyset$, therefore $C \cap (A \cup B) = \emptyset$ and this is a contradiction.

It follows then that either $A \in t$ or $B \in t$. If, for example, $A \in t$, then $t \in \varphi(A)$, therefore $t \in \varphi(A) \cup \varphi(B)$, hence $\varphi(A \cup B) \subset \varphi(A) \cup \varphi(B)$ and thus

$$\varphi(A \cup B) = \varphi(A) \cup \varphi(B).$$

We prove now that $\varphi(A - B) = \varphi(A) - \varphi(B)$. If $t \in \varphi(A - B)$, then $A - B \in t$, therefore $A \in t$ (since $A \supset A - B$) and $B \notin t$ (since $(A - B) \cap B = \emptyset$). It follows that $t \in \varphi(A)$ and $t \notin \varphi(B)$, therefore $t \in \varphi(A) - \varphi(B)$, hence $\varphi(A - B) \subset \varphi(A) - \varphi(B)$.

Conversely, if $t \in \varphi(A)$ and $t \notin \varphi(B)$ then $A \in t$ and $B \notin t$. If $A - B \notin t$, then there exists $C \in t$ such that $C \cap (A - B) = \emptyset$; since $A \cap B \notin t$, we can choose the set C such that $C \cap A \cap B = \emptyset$, therefore $C \cap A = C \cap [(A - B) \cup (A \cap B)] = \emptyset$, and this is a contradiction. It follows that $A - B \in t$, therefore $t \in \varphi(A - B)$, hence $\varphi(A) - \varphi(B) \subset \varphi(A - B)$ and thus $\varphi(A - B) = \varphi(A) - \varphi(B)$.

The property 5 follows now from the equality $A \cap B = A - (A - B)$:

$$\varphi(A \cap B) = \varphi(A) - \varphi(A - B) = \varphi(A) - (\varphi(A) - \varphi(B)) = \varphi(A) \cap \varphi(B).$$

Let us denote by $\mathscr{D}$ the class of all the sets $\varphi(A) \subset T$ for $A \in \mathscr{C}$. From the preceding properties we deduce that $\mathscr{D}$ is a clan and that φ is an isomorphism of the clan $\mathscr{C}$ onto the clan $\mathscr{D}$.

We define now a topology on T.

Since the clan $\mathscr{D}$ contains the finite intersections of sets of $\mathscr{D}$, we deduce that $\mathscr{D}$ is a base of a topology $\mathfrak{T}$ on T, for which the open sets are arbitrary unions of sets of $\mathscr{D}$.

T is a separated space for this topology.

Let $t_1 \neq t_2$ be two points of T. There exists a set $A \in \mathscr{C}$ such that we have, for instance $A \in t_1$ and $A \notin t_2$; there exists then a set $B \in t_2$ with $A \cap B = \emptyset$. It follows that $t_1 \in \varphi(A)$, $t_2 \in \varphi(B)$ and

$$\varphi(A) \cap \varphi(B) = \varphi(A \cap B) = \emptyset.$$

But $\varphi(A)$ and $\varphi(B)$ are open, therefore T is separated.

The sets of $\mathscr{D}$ are compact.

For this purpose, take first a family $(A_\alpha)_{\alpha \in I}$ of sets of $\mathscr{C}$ such that $\bigcap_{\alpha \in J} \varphi(A_\alpha) \neq \emptyset$ for every finite subset $J \subset I$. It follows that $\bigcap_{\alpha \in J} A_\alpha \neq \emptyset$, therefore the family $(A_\alpha)_{\alpha \in I}$ is contained in a maximal base of filter $t \in T$, therefore $t \in \bigcap_{\alpha \in I} \varphi(A_\alpha)$.

Let now $A_0 \in \mathscr{C}$ and let $(F_i)_{i \in I}$ be an arbitrary family of closed sets of T, contained in $\varphi(A_0)$, such that $\bigcap_{i \in J} F_i \neq \emptyset$ for every finite subset $J \subset I$. Each set F_i is of the form

$$F_i = \bigcap_{\alpha} [\varphi(A_0) - \varphi(A_\alpha^i)] = \bigcap_{\alpha} \varphi(A_0 - A_\alpha^i)$$

with $A_\alpha^i \in \mathscr{C}$. In fact, $\varphi(A_0) - F_i$ is open, therefore it is of the form

$$\varphi(A_0) - F_i = \bigcup_{\alpha} \varphi(A_\alpha^i), \quad \text{with} \quad A_\alpha^i \in \mathscr{C}.$$

The double family $(\varphi(A_0 - A_\alpha^i))$ has the same intersection as (F_i) and the intersection of every finite subfamily is nonvoid. It follows that the intersection of the double family is nonvoid, therefore the intersection of the family (F_i) is nonvoid, hence the set $\varphi(A_0)$ is compact.

Every point $t \in T$ is contained in a set of the form $\varphi(A_0)$ which is at the same time compact and open.

It follows that every point possesses a compact neighbourhood, hence T is *locally compact*.

Since the space T has a base $\mathscr{D}$ consisting of open-closed sets, T is *totally disconnected*.

Every compact-open set $B \subset T$ belongs to $\mathscr{D}$.

In fact, B is open, therefore it is of the form

$$B = \bigcup_{\alpha} \varphi(A_\alpha), \quad \text{with} \quad A_\alpha \in \mathscr{C}.$$

B is compact, therefore there exists a finite family $(\varphi(A_\alpha))_{\alpha \in J}$ which covers B. Then

$$B = \bigcup_{\alpha \in J} \varphi(A_\alpha) = \varphi\left(\bigcup_{\alpha \in J} A_\alpha\right)$$

and $\bigcup_{\alpha \in J} A_\alpha \in \mathscr{C}$, therefore $B \in \mathscr{D}$.

Remarks.

1°. If $S \in \mathscr{C}$, then T is compact.

In fact, in this case S belongs to every maximal base of filter $t \in T$, therefore $t \in \varphi(S)$ for every $t \in T$, hence $T = \varphi(S)$.

2°. In the proof of the preceding theorem, it only seemed that we used the fact that the elements of $\mathscr{C}$ are *subsets* of a set S.

The theorem remains valid, with the same proof, if $\mathscr{C}$ is an arbitrary Boolean algebra with a smallest element $\emptyset$, with an order relation denoted by $\subset$ and with the operations $\sup(A, B) = A \cup B$ and $\inf(A, B) = A \cap B$. If the Boolean algebra has a greatest element, then T is compact.

3°. Every compact set $K \subset T$ is contained in a set $\varphi(A)$ of $\mathscr{D}$.

In fact, if for every $t \in K$ we choose a neighbourhood $\varphi(A_t)$ of t, we obtain a cover of K consisting of open sets of $\mathscr{D}$. We can find then a finite family which covers K:

$$K \subset \bigcup_{i=1}^{n} \varphi(A_i) = \varphi\left(\bigcup_{i=1}^{n} A_i\right).$$

Putting $A = \bigcup_{i=1}^{n} A_i$ we have $K \subset \varphi(A) \in \mathscr{D}$.

4^0. If $\varphi(A) = \bigcup_{i=1}^{\infty} \varphi(A_i)$ and if the sets A_i are mutually disjoint, then $A_i = \emptyset$ except for a finite set of indices.

In fact, $\varphi(A)$ is compact and the family $(\varphi(A_i))$ of open sets covers $\varphi(A)$. We can find then a finite family $(\varphi(A_i))_{i \in J}$ which covers $\varphi(A)$:

$$\varphi(A) = \bigcup_{i \in J} \varphi(A_i).$$

If $i \notin J$, then $\varphi(A_i) = \emptyset$.

5^0. We can prove that if T' is a locally compact space such that $\mathscr{C}$ is isomorphic with the clan $\mathscr{D}'$ of all compact-open subsets of T', then T and T' are homeomorphic.

2. THEOREM OF KAKUTANI

Theorem 2 (Kakutani). *Let T be a set, $\mathscr{C}$ a clan of subsets of T, X a Banach space, and $\boldsymbol{m}$: $\mathscr{C} \to X$ a measure with finite variation. Then there exists a locally compact space T' which is totally disconnected, and a regular Borel measure $\boldsymbol{m}'$ with finite variation on T', with values in X, and only one, such that for every pair (E, F) of Banach spaces with $X \subset \mathscr{L}(E, F)$ the spaces $L_E^p(\mathscr{C}, \boldsymbol{m})$ and $L_E^p(T', \boldsymbol{m}')$ are isomorphic and isometric for $1 \leqq p < \infty$. If two equivalence classes $\dot{\boldsymbol{f}} \in L_E^1(\mathscr{C}, \boldsymbol{m})$ and $\dot{\boldsymbol{f}}' \in L_E^1(T', \boldsymbol{m}')$ are in correspondence, then*

$$\int_T \boldsymbol{f}\, d\boldsymbol{m} = \int_T \boldsymbol{f}'\, d\boldsymbol{m}'.$$

We consider the space T' corresponding to T by the theorem of Stone, and the clan $\mathscr{C}'$ of the compact-open sets of T'. For every set $A' \in \mathscr{C}'$ which corresponds to the set $A \in \mathscr{C}$ we put

$$\boldsymbol{m}'(A') = \boldsymbol{m}(A).$$

We verify easily that $\boldsymbol{m}'$ is *additive* on $\mathscr{C}'$.

If μ is the variation of $\boldsymbol{m}$ and μ' is the variation of $\boldsymbol{m}'$, then we have

$$\mu'(A') = \mu(A), \quad \text{for} \quad A' \in \mathscr{C}',$$

because $\mathscr{C}$ and $\mathscr{C}'$ are isomorphic.

Since the clan $\mathscr{C}'$ consists of compact sets, $\boldsymbol{m}'$ and μ' are regular on the left; since $\mathscr{C}'$ consists of open sets, $\boldsymbol{m}'$ and μ' are regular on the right on $\mathscr{C}'$. It follows that $\boldsymbol{m}'$ and μ' are regular on $\mathscr{C}'$.

Since $\mathscr{C}'$ is dense in $\mathscr{P}(T)$, $\boldsymbol{m}'$ and μ' can be extended uniquely to regular Borel measures on T'. We denote the extensions of $\boldsymbol{m}'$ and μ' by the same characters, and μ' is still the variation of $\boldsymbol{m}'$, therefore

$$|\boldsymbol{m}'| = |\boldsymbol{m}|'.$$

The measures $\boldsymbol{m}$ and μ defined on $\mathscr{C}$ can be extended uniquely to the semi-tribe $\mathscr{S}$ generated by $\mathscr{C}$.

Consider now the spaces $\mathscr{L}^p_E(\boldsymbol{m})$ and $\mathscr{L}^p_E(\boldsymbol{m}')$. The sets of step functions $\mathscr{E}_E(\mathscr{C})$ and $\mathscr{E}_E(\mathscr{C}')$ are dense respectively in $\mathscr{L}^p_E(\boldsymbol{m})$ and $\mathscr{L}^p_E(\boldsymbol{m}')$.

To every step function $\boldsymbol{f} = \sum_i \varphi_{A_i} x_i$ of $\mathscr{E}_E(\mathscr{C})$ we put in correspondence the step function $\boldsymbol{f}' = \sum_i \varphi_{A_i'} x_i$ of $\mathscr{E}_E(\mathscr{C}')$. We verify easily that the mapping $\boldsymbol{f} \to \boldsymbol{f}'$ of $\mathscr{E}_E(\mathscr{C})$ onto $\mathscr{E}_E(\mathscr{C}')$ is linear. We have then

$$\int_{T'} \boldsymbol{f}' \, d\boldsymbol{m}' = \sum \boldsymbol{m}'(A_i')\, x_i = \sum \boldsymbol{m}(A_i)\, x_i = \int_T \boldsymbol{f}\, d\boldsymbol{m}.$$

On the other hand, taking the sets A_i to be disjoint, the sets A_i' are also disjoint, therefore $|\boldsymbol{f}'| = |\boldsymbol{f}|'$, hence

$$\int_{T'} |\boldsymbol{f}'|\, d|\boldsymbol{m}'| = \int_{T'} |\boldsymbol{f}|'\, d|\boldsymbol{m}|' = \int_T |\boldsymbol{f}|\, d|\boldsymbol{m}|.$$

We deduce that the correspondence $\boldsymbol{f} \to \boldsymbol{f}'$ is isometric for the semi-norms $N_1(\boldsymbol{f}, |\boldsymbol{m}|)$ and $N_1(\boldsymbol{f}', |\boldsymbol{m}'|)$, hence for the semi-norms $N_p(\boldsymbol{f}, |\boldsymbol{m}|)$ and $N_p(\boldsymbol{f}', |\boldsymbol{m}'|)$.

From this isomorphism we deduce the isomorphism $\dot{\boldsymbol{f}} \to \dot{\boldsymbol{f}}'$ between the sets of the equivalence classes $\dot{\boldsymbol{f}}$ and $\dot{\boldsymbol{f}}'$ of functions $\boldsymbol{f} \in \mathscr{E}_E(\mathscr{C})$ and $\boldsymbol{f}' \in \mathscr{E}_E(\mathscr{C}')$ in the spaces $L^p_E(\boldsymbol{m})$ and $L^p_E(\boldsymbol{m}')$.

The sets of equivalence classes of functions of $\mathscr{E}_E(\mathscr{C})$ and $\mathscr{E}_E(\mathscr{C}')$ are dense respectively in the spaces $L^p_E(\boldsymbol{m})$ and $L^p_E(\boldsymbol{m}')$. We deduce that we can extend the preceding isometry $\dot{\boldsymbol{f}} \to \dot{\boldsymbol{f}}'$ to an isometry between the whole spaces $L^p_E(\boldsymbol{m})$ and $L^p_E(\boldsymbol{m}')$.

Let now $\boldsymbol{f} \in \mathscr{L}^1_E(\boldsymbol{m})$. There exists a sequence $(\boldsymbol{f}_n)$ of functions of $\mathscr{E}_E(\mathscr{C})$ converging in mean to $\boldsymbol{f}$. Then

$$\lim_{n\to\infty} \int_T \boldsymbol{f}_n \, d\boldsymbol{m} = \int_T \boldsymbol{f}\, d\boldsymbol{m}$$

and

$$\lim_{n\to\infty} N_1(\boldsymbol{f}_n - \boldsymbol{f}, \boldsymbol{m}) = 0.$$

It follows that

$$\lim_{n\to\infty} N_1(\dot{f}_n - \dot{f}, m) = 0.$$

Let (f_n') be the corresponding sequence of step functions of $\mathscr{E}_E(\mathscr{C}')$. We have

$$\lim_{\substack{n\to\infty\\ m\to\infty}} N_1(f_n' - f_m', m') = \lim_{\substack{n\to\infty\\ m\to\infty}} N_1(f_n - f_m, m) = 0,$$

therefore (f_n') is a Cauchy sequence in $\mathscr{L}_E^1(m')$. This sequence has a limit $f' \in \mathscr{L}_E^1(m')$ and

$$\lim_{n\to\infty} \int_{T'} f_n' \, dm' = \int_{T'} f' \, dm'.$$

It follows that $\dot{f}'$ corresponds to $\dot{f}$ by the isometry between the spaces $L_E^1(m)$ and $L_E^1(m')$ and

$$\int_{T'} f' \, dm' = \lim_{n\to\infty} \int_{T'} f_n' \, dm' = \lim_{n\to\infty} \int_T f_n \, dm = \int_T f \, dm.$$

Remarks.

1°. The correspondence $m \to m'$ defined by the equality

$$m'(A') = m(A), \quad \text{for} \quad A' \in \mathscr{C}',$$

is linear and one-to-one.

2°. Kakutani [1] proved that every ordered Banach space which verifies certain additional conditions is isomorphic and isometric to a certain space $L^1(T, \mu)$ of real functions defined on a locally compact space T, integrable with respect to a measure μ.

§ 19. INTEGRAL REPRESENTATION OF LINEAR OPERATIONS ON $\mathscr{K}_E(T)$

1. THE SPACE $\mathscr{K}_E(T)$

Let T be a locally compact space and E a (real or complex) Banach space. We remind that the carrier of a function f: $T \to E$ is the closure of the set $\{t; f(t) \neq 0\}$. The space of the continuous functions f: $T \to E$ with compact carrier is denoted by $\mathscr{K}_E(T)$. If T is compact, then $\mathscr{K}_E(T) = \mathscr{C}_E(T)$, where $\mathscr{C}_E(T)$ is the space of the continuous functions f: $T \to E$.

For every set $A \subset T$ we denote by $\mathscr{K}_E(T, A)$ the space of the functions of $\mathscr{K}_E(T)$ vanishing outside A.

We shall consider on the space $\mathscr{K}_E(T)$ the topology of the uniform convergence defined by the norm

$$\|f\| = \sup_{t \in T} |f(t)|.$$

If $E = R$ we shall write $\mathscr{K}(T)$ and $\mathscr{K}(T, A)$ instead of $\mathscr{K}_R(T)$ and $\mathscr{K}_R(T, A)$. By $\mathscr{K}_+(T)$ we shall denote the subset of the positive functions of $\mathscr{K}(T)$.

Proposition 1. *If K is a compact set and G is an open set such that $K \subset G$, then every function $f \in \mathscr{K}_E(T, K)$ can be approximated uniformly by functions of the form $\sum \varphi_i x_i$ (finite sum) with $\varphi_i \in \mathscr{K}_+(T, G)$ and $x_i \in E$.*

Let $f \in \mathscr{K}_E(T, K)$ and let $\varepsilon > 0$. For every point $t \in K$ there exists an open neighbourhood V of t contained in G such that if $t' \in V$, then $|f(t) - f(t')| < \frac{\varepsilon}{2}$. Then

$$|f(t') - f(t'')| < \varepsilon, \quad \text{if} \quad t', t'' \in V.$$

Since K is compact, we can find a finite family (V_i) of open sets contained in G and covering K, such that for each i we have

$$|f(t') - f(t'')| < \varepsilon, \quad \text{if} \quad t', t'' \in V_i.$$

Let (φ_i) be a continuous partition of the unity subordinated to the family (V_i), i.e. $0 \leqq \varphi_i \leqq 1$, the carrier of φ_i is contained in V_i and we have

$$\sum \varphi_i(t) = 1 \quad \text{for} \quad t \in K \quad \text{and} \quad \sum \varphi_i(t) \leqq 1 \quad \text{for} \quad t \in T.$$

For each i take a point $t_i \in V_i$ and put $x_i = f(t_i)$. Then

$$\left\|\sum \varphi_i x_i - f\right\| < \varepsilon.$$

In fact, let $t \in T$; if $t \in V_i$ then $|x_i - f(t)| = |f(t_i) - f(t)| < \varepsilon$, and if $t \notin V_i$, then $\varphi_i(t) = 0$, therefore

$$\begin{aligned} \left|\sum \varphi_i(t)\, x_i - f(t)\right| &= \left|\sum \varphi_i(t)\, x_i - \sum \varphi_i(t) f(t)\right| \\ &\leqq \sum \varphi_i(t)\, |f(t_i) - f(t)| < \varepsilon \sum \varphi_i(t) \leqq \varepsilon. \end{aligned}$$

Corollary. *The space of the functions $\sum \varphi_i x_i$ with $\varphi_i \in \mathscr{K}_+(T)$ and $x_i \in E$ is dense in $\mathscr{K}_E(T)$.*

2. LINEAR OPERATIONS ON $\mathscr{K}_E(T)$

Let E and F be two Banach spaces and U: $\mathscr{K}_E(T) \to F$ a *linear operation.* For every set A we design by U_A the restriction of U to the space $\mathscr{K}_E(T, A)$ and put

$$(1) \qquad \|U_A\| = \sup |U(f)|, \quad \text{for} \quad f \in \mathscr{K}_E(T, A) \quad \text{with} \quad \|f\| \leqq 1,$$

and

$$(1') \qquad |||U_A||| = \sup \sum |U(f_i)|,$$

where the supremum is taken for all the finite families (f_i) of $\mathscr{K}_E(T, A)$ with $|f_i| \leqq 1$ and $|f_i|\,|f_j| = 0$ if $i \neq j$ (or with $\sum |f_i| \leqq \varphi_A$).

From this definition we deduce that

$$(2) \qquad |U(f)| \leqq \|U_A\|\,\|f\|, \quad \text{for} \quad f \in \mathscr{K}_E(T, A),$$

and

$$(2') \qquad \sum |U(f_i)| \leqq |||U_A|||\,\|\textstyle\sum f_i\|$$

for $f_i \in \mathscr{K}_E(T, A)$ with $|f_i|\,|f_j| = 0$ if $i \neq j$.

We have also

$$(3) \qquad \|U_A\| \leqq \|U_B\| \quad \text{and} \quad |||U_A||| \leqq |||U_B|||, \quad \text{if} \quad A \subset B,$$

and

$$(4) \qquad \|U_A\| \leqq |||U_A||| \leqq \infty.$$

If $F = C$, we have an equality:

Proposition 2. *If $U: \mathscr{K}_E(T) \to C$ is a linear functional, then for every set $A \subset T$ we have*

$$\|U_A\| = |||U_A||| \leqq \infty.$$

In fact, let (f_i) be a finite family of $\mathscr{K}_E(T, A)$ such that $|f_i| \leqq 1$ and $|f_i|\,|f_j| = 0$ if $i \neq j$. For each i there exists a scalar α_i such that $|\alpha_i| = 1$ and

$$|U(f_i)| = \alpha_i U(f_i) = U(\alpha_i f_i).$$

Then $g = \sum f_i \alpha_i \in \mathscr{K}_E(T, A)$ and $\|g\| = \|\sum f_i \alpha_i\| \leqq 1$ and we have

$$\sum |U(f_i)| = U(\textstyle\sum f_i \alpha_i) = |U(g)| \leqq \|U_A\|,$$

whence

$$|||U_A||| \leqq \|U_A\|, \quad \text{therefore} \quad \|U_A\| = |||U_A|||.$$

The number $\|U_A\|$ verifies also the equality

$$\|U_A\| = \sup |\textstyle\sum U(f_i)|$$

for $f_i \in \mathscr{K}_E(T, A)$ with $|f_i| \leqq 1$ and $|f_i|\,|f_j| = 0$ if $i \neq j$.

The following proposition gives another definition of $\|U_A\|$ and $|||U_A|||$.

Proposition 3. *If for every Borel set $A \in \mathscr{B}$ we have $\|U_A\| < \infty$, then for every set $A \subset T$ we have*

$$(5) \qquad \|U_A\| = \sup |\textstyle\sum U(\varphi_i f)|$$

and

(5′) $$|||U_A||| = \sup \sum |U(\varphi_i f)|,$$

where the supremum is taken for all the functions $f \in \mathcal{K}_E(T, A)$ *with* $|f| \leqq 1$ *and all the finite families* (φ_i) *of* $\mathcal{K}(T)$ *with* $|\varphi_i| \leqq 1$ *and* $\varphi_i \varphi_j = 0$ *if* $i \neq j$.

Let first $(f_i)_{1 \leqq i \leqq n}$ be a finite family of $\mathcal{K}_E(T, A)$ with $|f_i| \leqq 1$ and $|f_i|\,|f_j| = 0$ if $i \neq j$. Let $\varepsilon > 0$. Let $\eta > 0$ be such that $\eta \|U_A\| < \frac{\varepsilon}{n}$. For each i the set $K_i = \{t; f_i(t) \geqq \eta\}$ is compact and contained in the open set $G_i = \{t; f_i(t) \neq 0\}$. There exists a function $\varphi_i \colon T \to [0, 1]$ of $\mathcal{K}(T)$ with $\varphi_i(t) = 1$ for $t \in K_i$ and $\varphi_i(t) = 0$ for $t \notin G_i$. If we put $f = \sum_{i=1}^{n} f_i$ we have $f \in \mathcal{K}_E(T, A)$ and $f_i - \varphi_i f \in \mathcal{K}_E(T, A)$. Moreover, $\|f_i - \varphi_i f\| \leqq \eta \varphi_{G_i - K_i}$, therefore

$$|U(f_i) - U(\varphi_i f)| < \eta \|U_A\| < \frac{\varepsilon}{n},$$

whence

$$|U(f_i)| \leqq |U(\varphi_i f)| + \frac{\varepsilon}{n},$$

consequently

$$\sum |U(f_i)| \leqq \sum |U(\varphi_i f)| + \varepsilon.$$

It follows that

$$|||U_A||| \leqq \sup \sum |U(\varphi_i f)|.$$

The converse inequality is immediate.

The equality (5) is proved in the same way.

Remark. In the corollary of the theorem 2 we shall give another definition of $\|U_A\|$ and $|||U_A|||$.

The study of the operations $U \colon \mathcal{K}_E(T) \to F$ can be reduced to that of the operations $U' \colon \mathcal{K}(T) \to \mathcal{L}(E, F)$.

Theorem 1. *For every linear operation* $U \colon \mathcal{K}_E(T) \to F$ *with* $\|U_A\| < \infty$ *for* $A \in \mathcal{B}$, *there exists a linear operation* $U' \colon \mathcal{K}(T) \to \mathcal{L}(E, F)$ *with* $\|U'_A\| < \infty$ *for* $A \in \mathcal{B}$, *and only one such that*

$$U(\varphi x) = U'(\varphi)\, x, \quad \textit{for} \quad \varphi \in \mathcal{K}(T) \quad \textit{and} \quad x \in E.$$

The correspondence $U \to U'$ *is linear and one-to-one and for every Borel set* $A \in \mathcal{C}(\mathcal{B})$ *we have*

$$\|U'_A\| \leqq \|U_A\| \leqq \infty$$

and

$$|||U'_A||| = |||U_A||| \leqq \infty.$$

For every $\varphi \in \mathscr{K}(T)$ and $x \in E$ we have $\varphi x \in \mathscr{K}_E(T)$; we put

$$U'(\varphi)\,x = U(\varphi x).$$

For fixed $\varphi \in \mathscr{K}(T)$, vanishing outside a set $B \in \mathscr{B}$, the mapping $U'(\varphi)\colon x \to U'(\varphi)\,x$ of E into F is linear and continuous:

$$|U'(\varphi)\,x| = |U(\varphi x)| \leqq \|U_B\|\ \|\varphi\|\ |x|,$$

therefore $U'(\varphi) \in \mathscr{L}(E, F)$ and

$$|U'(\varphi)| \leqq \|U_B\|\ \|\varphi\|.$$

The mapping $U'\colon \varphi \to U'(\varphi)$ of $\mathscr{K}(T)$ into $\mathscr{L}(E, F)$ is linear.

Let now A be a set and prove that $\|U'_A\| \leqq \|U_A\|$. Let $\varphi \in \mathscr{K}(T, A)$ and let $B = \{t; \varphi(t) \neq 0\}$. Then B is open and relatively compact, whence $B \in \mathscr{B}$, and $B \subset A$, therefore

$$|U'(\varphi)| \leqq \|U_B\|\ \|\varphi\| \leqq \|U_A\|\ \|\varphi\|,$$

consequently

$$\|U'_A\| \leqq \|U_A\| \leqq \infty.$$

If $A \in \mathscr{B}$, then $\|U_A\| < \infty$, therefore $\|U'_A\| < \infty$.

Let us prove now that $|||U'_A||| = |||U_A|||$. Let $(\varphi_i)_{1 \leqq i \leqq n}$ be a family of functions of $\mathscr{K}(T, A)$ with $|\varphi_i| \leqq 1$ such that $\varphi_i \varphi_j = 0$ if $i \neq j$ and let $(\alpha_i)_{1 \leqq i \leqq n}$ be a family of scalars with $|\alpha_i| \leqq 1$. Let $\varepsilon > 0$. For each i there exists $x_i \in E$ with $|x_i| \leqq 1$ such that

$$|U'(\varphi_i \alpha_i)| < |U'(\varphi_i \alpha_i)\,x_i| + \frac{\varepsilon}{n}.$$

Then

$$\sum_{i=1}^{n} |U'(\varphi_i \alpha_i)| - \varepsilon \leqq \sum_{i=1}^{n} |U'(\varphi_i \alpha_i)\,x_i| = \sum_{i=1}^{n} |U(\varphi_i \alpha_i x_i)| \leqq |||U_A|||,$$

therefore $|||U'_A||| - \varepsilon \leqq |||U_A|||$, consequently, ε being arbitrary,

$$|||U_A||| \leqq |||U'_A|||.$$

On the other hand, if (φ_i) is a finite family of $\mathscr{K}(T, A)$ with $|\varphi_i| \leqq 1$ and $\varphi_i \varphi_j$ for $i \neq j$, and if (x_i) is a family of E with $|x_i| \leqq 1$, then

$$\sum |U(\varphi_i x_i)| = \sum |U'(\varphi_i)\,x_i| \leqq \sum |U'(\varphi_i)|\ |x_i| = \sum |U'(\varphi_i)\ |x_i|| \leqq |||U'_A|||,$$

therefore

$$|||U'_A||| \leqq |||U_A|||,$$

consequently

$$|||U'_A||| = |||U_A|||.$$

In order to prove the uniqueness of U' let $U'': \mathcal{K}(T) \to \mathcal{L}(E, F)$ be a linear mapping such that

$$U(\varphi x) = U''(\varphi)\, x, \quad \text{for} \quad \varphi \in \mathcal{K}(T) \quad \text{and} \quad x \in E.$$

Then $U'(\varphi)\, x = U''(\varphi)\, x$ for every $\varphi \in \mathcal{K}(T)$ and $x \in E$, therefore $U'(\varphi) = U''(\varphi)$ for every $\varphi \in \mathcal{K}(T)$, i.e. $U' = U''$.

It is easy to verify that the mapping $U \to U'$ is linear. In order to prove that this mapping is one-to-one, let $V: \mathcal{K}_E(T) \to F$ be a linear operation such that $\|V_A\| < \infty$ for $A \in \mathcal{B}$ and

$$V(\varphi x) = U'(\varphi x), \quad \text{for} \quad \varphi \in \mathcal{K}(T) \quad \text{and} \quad x \in E.$$

Let $f \in \mathcal{K}_E(T)$, let K be the carrier of f and let $G \supset K$ be an open set of $\mathcal{B}$. Let (f_n) be a sequence of functions of $\mathcal{K}_E(T, G)$ of the form $\sum \varphi_i x_i$ with $\varphi_i \in \mathcal{K}(T, G)$ and $x_i \in E$, converging uniformly to f. Then $U(f_n) = V(f_n)$ for every n. On the other hand, U and V are continuous on $\mathcal{K}_E(T, G)$, therefore

$$U(f) = \lim_{n \to \infty} U(f_n) = \lim_{n \to \infty} V(f_n) = V(f),$$

consequently $U = V$.

Remark. There are linear mappings $U': \mathcal{K}(T) \to \mathcal{L}(E, F)$ with $\|U'_A\| < \infty$ for $A \in \mathcal{B}$ which do not correspond to any linear mapping $U: \mathcal{K}_E(T) \to F$.

However, if U' is dominated (see definition 1), in particular if $F = C$ and $\|U_A\| < \infty$ for every $A \in \mathcal{B}$ (corollary 1 of the theorem 3) then U' can be obtained from a dominated linear mapping $U: \mathcal{K}_E(T) \to F$ (theorem 4).

3. DOMINATED OPERATIONS

Definition 1. *A linear mapping $U: \mathcal{K}_E(T) \to F$ is said to be dominated* (*or majored*) *if there exists a regular positive Borel measure v such that*

$$|U(f)| \leqq \int |f| \, dv, \quad \textit{for every} \quad f \in \mathcal{K}_E(T).$$

We say that U is dominated by v, or that v dominates U.

We shall see in theorem 2 that if U is dominated, there exists a least positive regular measure dominating U. We shall denote the least regular measure dominating U by μ_U.

We shall see also that the dominated operations can be defined by means of the positive linear functionals on $\mathcal{K}(T)$ (corollary of the theorem 6) or by the condition $|||U_A||| < \infty$ for $A \in \mathcal{B}$ (theorem 3).

The main result of this section is the following theorem which gives an integral representation of the dominated operations:

Theorem 2. *There exists an isomorphism $U \leftrightarrow \boldsymbol{m}$ between the set of the dominated linear operations $U: \mathscr{K}_E(T) \to F$ and the set of the regular Borel measures $\boldsymbol{m}: \mathscr{B} \to \mathscr{L}(E, F)$ with finite variation μ, given by the equality*

$$U(f) = \int f\, d\boldsymbol{m}, \quad \textit{for every} \quad f \in \mathscr{K}_E(T).$$

Moreover, if U and $\boldsymbol{m}$ are in correspondence, we have

$$\mu_U = \mu;$$

for every Borel set $A \in \mathcal{C}(\mathscr{B})$ we have

$$\|U_A\| \leqq \tilde{\boldsymbol{m}}(A) \quad \textit{and} \quad |||U_A||| \leqq \bar{\boldsymbol{m}}(A) = \mu^*(A),$$

and for every open set G we have

$$\|U_G\| = \tilde{\boldsymbol{m}}(G) \quad \textit{and} \quad |||U_G||| = \bar{\boldsymbol{m}}(G) = \mu^*(G).$$

Let first $\boldsymbol{m}: \mathscr{B} \to \mathscr{L}(E, F)$ be a regular Borel measure with finite variation μ and consider the space $\mathscr{M}_E(\mathscr{B})$ of the totally $\mathscr{B}$-measurable functions $f: T \to E$. By the corollary 2 of the proposition 19, § 14, we have $\mathscr{K}_E(T) \subset \mathscr{M}_E(\mathscr{B})$. By the theorem 1, § 9, there exists a linear mapping $U^*: \mathscr{M}_E(\mathscr{B}) \to F$ such that

$$U^*(f) = \int f\, d\boldsymbol{m}, \quad \text{for} \quad f \in \mathscr{M}_E(\mathscr{B}),$$

and such that

$$\|U^*_A\| = \tilde{\boldsymbol{m}}(A) \quad \text{and} \quad |||U^*_A||| = \bar{\boldsymbol{m}}(A)$$

for every set $A \in \mathcal{C}(\mathscr{B})$. The restriction U of U^* to $\mathscr{K}_E(T)$ verifies the equality

$$U(f) = \int f\, dm, \quad \text{for} \quad f \in \mathscr{K}_E(T).$$

For every set $A \in \mathcal{C}(\mathscr{B})$ we have then

$$\|U_A\| = \|U^*_A\| = \tilde{\boldsymbol{m}}(A)$$

and

$$|||U_A||| = |||U^*_A||| = \bar{\boldsymbol{m}}(A).$$

Since $\boldsymbol{m}$ is regular, for every open set G we have (§ 15, proposition 36)

$$\|U_G\| = \sup \left|\sum U(f_i)\right| = \sup \left|\sum U^*(f_i)\right| = \|U^*_G\| = \tilde{\boldsymbol{m}}(G)$$

and

$$|||U_G||| = \sup \sum |U(f_i)| = \sup \sum |U^*(f_i)| = |||U^*_G||| = \bar{\boldsymbol{m}}(G),$$

where the supremum is taken for all the finite families (f_i) of $\mathscr{K}_E(T, G)$ with $|f_i| \leqq 1$ and $|f_i|\,|f_j| = 0$ if $i \neq j$.

From the proposition 9, § 3, we deduce that $\bar{m} = \bar{\mu}$ and since μ is defined on a semi-tribe, we have $\mu^*(A) = \bar{\mu}(A)$ for every μ-measurable set A (§ 5, corollary 2 of the proposition 7). It follows that

$$|||U_A||| \leqq \mu^*(A), \quad \text{for} \quad A \in \mathcal{C}(\mathscr{B}),$$

and

$$|||U_G||| = \mu^*(G), \quad \text{for} \quad G \text{ open}.$$

From the equality

$$U(f) = \int f\, dm, \quad \text{for} \quad f \in \mathscr{K}_E(T),$$

we deduce that

$$|U(f)| \leqq \int |f|\, d\mu, \quad \text{for} \quad f \in \mathscr{K}_E(T),$$

therefore U is dominated by the regular measure μ.

The correspondence $m \to U$ is linear: from the proposition 35, § 15, we deduce that this correspondence is one-to-one. It remains to prove that every dominated linear operation U corresponds to some regular measure m with finite variation and that $\mu_U = |m|$.

Let $U: \mathscr{K}_E(T) \to F$ be a dominated linear operation and let ν be a positive regular Borel measure such that

$$|U(f)| \leqq \int |f|\, d\nu, \quad \text{for} \quad f \in \mathscr{K}_E(T).$$

From this inequality we deduce that U is continuous on $\mathscr{K}_E(T)$ for the topology of $\mathscr{L}^1_E(\nu)$. Since ν is regular, $\mathscr{K}_E(T)$ is dense in $\mathscr{L}^1_E(\nu)$ and the linear operation can be extended uniquely to a continuous linear mapping of $\mathscr{L}^1_E(\nu)$ into F, denoted also by U, and we have still

$$|U(f)| \leqq \int |f|\, d\nu, \quad \text{for} \quad f \in \mathscr{L}^1_E(\nu).$$

For every set $A \in \mathscr{B}$ and for every $x \in E$ we have $\varphi_A x \in \mathscr{L}^1_E(\nu)$. Put

$$m(A)\, x = U(\varphi_A x).$$

The mapping $m(A): x \to m(A)\, x$ of E into F is linear and continuous:

$$|m(A)\, x| = |U(\varphi_A x)| \leqq \int |\varphi_A x|\, d\nu = |x|\, \nu(A),$$

therefore $m(A) \in \mathscr{L}(E, F)$ and

$$|m(A)| \leqq \nu(A).$$

It is easy to verify that the set function $\boldsymbol{m}: \mathscr{B} \to \mathscr{L}(E, F)$ is additive. From the last inequality we deduce that $\boldsymbol{m}$ is regular, countably additive and with finite variation μ and that $\mu \leqq \nu$.

We show now that

$$U(f) = \int f\, d\boldsymbol{m}, \quad \text{for} \quad f \in \mathscr{L}^1_E(\nu).$$

For every step function

$$f = \sum \varphi_{A_i} x_i \in \mathscr{E}_E(\mathscr{B})$$

we have

$$U(f) = U(\sum \varphi_{A_i} x_i) = \sum U(\varphi_i x_i) = \sum \boldsymbol{m}(A_i)\, x_i = \int f\, d\boldsymbol{m}.$$

Since $\mu \leqq \nu$, we have $\mathscr{L}^1_E(\nu) \subset \mathscr{L}^1_E(\mu)$, therefore if $f \in \mathscr{L}^1_E(\nu)$ we have

$$\left|\int f\, d\boldsymbol{m}\right| \leqq \int |f|\, d\mu \leqq \int |f|\, d\nu,$$

whence the mapping $f \to \int f\, d\boldsymbol{m}$ of $\mathscr{L}^1_E(\nu)$ into F is continuous. Since the two linear mappings $\int f\, d\boldsymbol{m}$ and U of $\mathscr{L}^1_E(\nu)$ into F are continuous and coincide on the dense set $\mathscr{E}_E(\mathscr{B})$, we deduce that they coincide on the whole space:

$$U(f) = \int f\, d\boldsymbol{m}, \quad \text{for} \quad f \in \mathscr{L}^1_E(\nu).$$

This equality is valid, in particular, for $f \in \mathscr{K}_E(T)$.

Since ν is an arbitrary regular measure dominating U and $\mu \leqq \nu$, we deduce that μ is the smallest regular measure dominating U, i.e.

$$\mu_U = \mu.$$

Remark. From the preceding proof, with μ instead of ν, we deduce that

$$U(f) = \int f\, d\boldsymbol{m}, \quad \text{for} \quad f \in \mathscr{L}^1_E(\boldsymbol{m}).$$

Corollary. *If $U: \mathscr{K}_E(T) \to F$ is dominated, then for every open set G we have*

$$\|U_G\| = \sup \left|\sum U(\varphi_i x_i)\right|$$

and

$$|||U_G||| = \sup \sum |U(\varphi_i x_i)|,$$

where the supremum is taken for all the finite families (φ_i) of $\mathscr{K}(T, G)$ with $|\varphi_i| \leqq 1$ and $\varphi_i \varphi_j = 0$ if $i \neq j$, and for all the finite families (x_i) of E with $|x_i| \leqq 1$.

In fact, we can write

$$U(f) = \int f\,d\boldsymbol{m}, \quad \text{for} \quad f \in \mathscr{K}_E(T),$$

where $\boldsymbol{m}$ is a *regular* Borel measure and we apply then the proposition 36, § 15.

Theorem 3. *A linear mapping $U: \mathscr{K}_E(T) \to F$ is dominated if and only if*

$$|||U_A||| < \infty \text{ for every } A \in \mathscr{B}.$$

In this case we have $\mu_U(G) = |||U_G|||$ for every open set $G \in \mathscr{B}$.

If U is dominated, then from the theorem 2 we deduce that $|||U_A||| \leqq \mu^*(A) < \infty$ for every $A \in \mathscr{B}$.

Conversely, suppose that $|||U_A||| < \infty$ for every $A \in \mathscr{B}$ and let $U': \mathscr{K}(T) \to \mathscr{L}(E, F)$ be the linear mapping such that

$$U(\varphi x) = U'(\varphi)\,x, \quad \text{for} \quad \varphi \in \mathscr{K}(T) \quad \text{and} \quad x \in E.$$

We have $|||U'_A||| = |||U_A|||$ for $A \in \mathscr{B}$. We shall prove first that U' is dominated. For every open set $B \in \mathscr{B}$ put

$$\mu(G) = |||U'_G|||.$$

We shall show that the set function μ defined on the class $\mathscr{G}$ of the open sets of $\mathscr{B}$ verifies the conditions of the theorem 2, § 16, to be extended to a regular positive measure on $\mathscr{B}$. From the definition of μ we deduce immediately that μ is *increasing*:

1. $\mu(G') \leqq \mu(G'')$, if $G' \subset G''$.

Then μ is *subadditive*:

2. $\mu(G' \cup G'') \leqq \mu(G') + \mu(G'')$.

In fact, let $\varepsilon > 0$. There exists a finite family $(\varphi_i)_{1 \leqq i \leqq n}$ of $\mathscr{K}(T, G' \cup G'')$ with $|\varphi_i| \leqq 1$ and $\varphi_i\varphi_j = 0$ if $i \neq j$, such that

$$\mu(G' \cup G'') < \sum_{i=1}^{n} |U'(\varphi_i)| + \frac{\varepsilon}{2}.$$

Let $\eta > 0$ be a number such that $2n\eta\mu(G' \cup G'') < \varepsilon$. For each i the set $K_i = \{t;\ |\varphi_i(t)| \geqq \eta\}$ is compact and contained in $G' \cup G''$. There exists then a continuous partition of the unity $\psi'_i \in \mathscr{K}_+(T, G')$ and $\psi''_i \in \mathscr{K}_+(T, G'')$ such that $\psi'_i(t) + \psi''_i(t) = 1$ for $t \in K_i$ and $\psi'_i(t) + \psi''_i(t) \leqq 1$ for $t \in T$. Then $\|\varphi_i\psi'_i + \varphi_i\psi''_i - \varphi_i\| < \eta$, therefore $|U'(\varphi_i\psi'_i + \varphi_i\psi''_i) - U'(\varphi_i)| < \frac{\varepsilon}{2n}$, consequently

$$|U'(\varphi_i)| \leqq |U'(\varphi_i\psi'_i)| + |U'(\varphi_i\psi''_i)| + \frac{\varepsilon}{2n},$$

whence

$$\mu(G' \cup G'') \leqq \sum_{i=1}^{n} |U'(\varphi_i \psi_i')| + \sum_{i=1}^{n} |U'(\varphi_i \psi_i'')| + \varepsilon \leqq \mu(G') + \mu(G'') + \varepsilon;$$

ε being arbitrary, we deduce that

$$\mu(G' \cup G'') \leqq \mu(G') + \mu(G'').$$

The set function μ is *additive*:

3. $\mu(G' \cup G'') = \mu(G') + \mu(G'')$, if $G' \cap G'' = \emptyset$.

We have to prove that μ is superadditive. Let $\varepsilon > 0$. There exists a finite family (φ_i') of $\mathscr{K}(T, G')$ with $|\varphi_i'| \leqq 1$ and $\varphi_i'\varphi_j' = 0$ if $i \neq j$, such that

$$\mu(G') < \sum |U'(\varphi_i')| + \frac{\varepsilon}{2}$$

and a finite family (φ_i'') of $\mathscr{K}(T, G'')$ with $|\varphi_i''| \leqq 1$ and $\varphi_i''\varphi_j'' = 0$ if $i \neq j$, such that

$$\mu(G'') < \sum |U'(\varphi_i'')| + \frac{\varepsilon}{2}.$$

Then

$$\mu(G') + \mu(G'') < \sum |U'(\varphi_i')| + \sum |U'(\varphi_i'')| + \varepsilon \leqq \mu(G' \cup G'') + \varepsilon,$$

whence, ε being arbitrary,

$$\mu(G') + \mu(G'') \leqq \mu(G' \cup G'').$$

4. μ is *regular* on $\mathscr{G}$.

Let G be an open set of $\mathscr{B}$ and let $\varepsilon > 0$. There exists a finite family $(\varphi_i)_{1 \leqq i \leqq n}$ of $\mathscr{K}(T, G)$ with $|\varphi_i| \leqq 1$ and $\varphi_i\varphi_j = 0$ if $i \neq j$, such that

$$\mu(G) < \sum |U'(\varphi_i)| + \frac{\varepsilon}{2}.$$

Let $\eta > 0$ be a number such that $2n\eta\mu(G) < \varepsilon$. For each i the set

$$K_i = \{t; |\varphi_i(t)| \geqq \eta\}$$

is compact and contained in G. The set $K = \bigcup_{i=1}^{n} K_i$ is also compact and $K \subset G$.

Let now G' be an arbitrary open set such that $K \subset G' \subset G$ and prove that $\mu(G) < \mu(G') + \varepsilon$. Let $\varphi'\colon T \to [0, 1]$ be a continuous function such that $\varphi'(t) = 1$ for $t \in K$ and $\varphi'(t) = 0$ for $t \notin G'$. The function $\varphi_i\varphi'$ belongs to $\mathscr{K}(T, G')$ and we have $|\varphi_i\varphi'| \leqq 1$ and $\varphi_i\varphi'\varphi_j\varphi' = 0$ if $i \neq j$, therefore

$$\sum_{i=1}^{n} |U'(\varphi_i\varphi')| \leqq \mu(G').$$

On the other hand $\|\varphi_i\varphi' - \varphi_i\| < \eta$, therefore $|U'(\varphi_i\varphi') - U'(\varphi_i)| < \frac{\varepsilon}{2n}$, whence

$$|U'(\varphi_i)| \leqq |U'(\varphi_i\varphi')| + \frac{\varepsilon}{2n},$$

consequently

$$\mu(G) < \sum_{i=1}^{n} |U'(\varphi_i)| + \frac{\varepsilon}{2} \leqq \sum_{i=1}^{n} |U'(\varphi_i\varphi')| + \varepsilon \leqq \mu(G') + \varepsilon.$$

It follows that μ is regular on $\mathscr{G}$.

From the theorem 2, § 16, we deduce then that μ can be extended to a regular positive measure on $\mathscr{B}$, denoted also by μ.

We shall prove now that

$$|U'(\varphi)| \leqq \int |\varphi| \, d\mu, \quad \text{for} \quad \varphi \in \mathscr{K}(T).$$

Let first φ be a *positive* function of $\mathscr{K}(T)$ and let $\varepsilon > 0$. Let $0 = \alpha_0 < \alpha_1 < \cdots < \alpha_n = \|\varphi\|$ be such that $\alpha_i - \alpha_{i-1} < \varepsilon$ for $i = 1, 2, \ldots, n$. Put

$$G_i = \{t; \varphi(t) > \alpha_i\}, \quad \text{for} \quad i = 0, 1, 2, \ldots, n.$$

The sets G_i are open and $G_0 \supset G_1 \supset \cdots \supset G_n = \emptyset$. Let u be a positive function o $\mathscr{K}(T)$ such that $u(t) = 1$ for $t \in \bar{G}_0$.

Put

$$h_i = \frac{\varphi - \alpha_{i-1}u}{\alpha_i - \alpha_{i-1}}, \quad \text{for} \quad i = 1, 2, \ldots, n.$$

The functions h_i are continuous and we have

$$\begin{aligned} h_i(t) &> 1, && \text{for} \quad t \in G_i, \\ 0 < h_i(t) &\leqq 1, && \text{for} \quad t \in G_{i-1} - G_i, \\ h_i(t) &\leqq 0, && \text{for} \quad t \notin G_{i-1}. \end{aligned}$$

The functions $\varphi_i = \inf(1, \sup(0, h_i))$ belong to $\mathscr{K}(T)$ and we have

$$\varphi_i(t) = 1, \quad \text{for} \quad t \in G_i,$$

$$\varphi_i(t) = h_i(t) = \frac{\varphi(t) - \alpha_{i-1}}{\alpha_i - \alpha_{i-1}}, \quad \text{for} \quad t \in G_{i-1} - G_i,$$

$$\varphi_i(t) = 0, \quad \text{for} \quad t \notin G_{i-1}.$$

We have then

$$\varphi_n \leqq \varphi_{n-1} \leqq \cdots \leqq \varphi_1$$

and

$$\varphi_{G_i} \leqq \varphi_i \leqq \varphi_{G_{i-1}}, \quad \text{for} \quad i = 1, 2, \ldots, n.$$

We have also

$$\varphi = \sum_{i=1}^{n} (\alpha_i - \alpha_{i-1}) \varphi_i.$$

In fact, if $t \notin G_0$ we have $\varphi(t) = 0$ and $\varphi_i(t) = 0$ for $i = 1, 2, \ldots, n$; if $t \in G_{j-1} - G_j$, where $1 \leqq j \leqq n$, then

$$\varphi_i(t) = 1, \quad \text{for} \quad i = 1, 2, \ldots, j-1,$$

$$\varphi_j(t) = \frac{\varphi(t) - \alpha_{j-1}}{\alpha_j - \alpha_{j-1}},$$

$$\varphi_i(t) = 0, \quad \text{for} \quad i = j+1, \ldots, n,$$

therefore

$$\sum_{i=1}^{n} (\alpha_i - \alpha_{i-1}) \varphi_i(t) = \sum_{i=1}^{j-1} (\alpha_i - \alpha_{i-1}) + \varphi(t) - \alpha_{j-1} = \varphi(t).$$

We deduce then that

$$\begin{aligned} |U'(\varphi)| &\leqq \sum_{i=1}^{n} (\alpha_i - \alpha_{i-1}) |U(\varphi_i)| \leqq \sum_{i=1}^{n} (\alpha_i - \alpha_{i-1}) \mu(G_{i-1}) \\ &= \sum_{i=1}^{n} \alpha_i \mu(G_{i-1} - G_i) \leqq \sum_{i=1}^{n} (\alpha_{i-1} + \varepsilon) \mu(G_{i-1} - G_i) \\ &= \sum_{i=1}^{n} \alpha_{i-1} \mu(G_{i-1} - G_i) + \varepsilon \mu(G_0). \end{aligned}$$

For the function

$$\varphi_\varepsilon = \sum_{i=1}^{n} \varphi_{G_{i-1}-G_i} \alpha_{i-1}$$

we have $\varphi_\varepsilon \leqq \varphi$ and

$$\sum_{i=1}^{n} \alpha_{i-1} \mu(G_{i-1} - G_i) = \int \varphi_\varepsilon \, d\mu \leqq \int \varphi \, d\mu,$$

therefore

$$|U'(\varphi)| \leqq \int \varphi \, d\mu + \varepsilon \mu(G_0);$$

ε being arbitrary, we deduce that

$$|U'(\varphi)| \leqq \int \varphi \, d\mu.$$

If now $\varphi \in \mathscr{K}(T)$ then $\varphi = \varphi^+ - \varphi^-$ and $|\varphi| = \varphi^+ + \varphi^-$, therefore

$$|U'(\varphi)| \leqq |U'(\varphi^+)| + |U'(\varphi^-)| \leqq \int \varphi^+ \, d\mu + \int \varphi^- \, d\mu = \int |\varphi| \, d\mu,$$

i.e. U' is dominated.

Let $\boldsymbol{m}: \mathscr{B} \to \mathscr{L}(E, F)$ be the regular measure with finite variation corresponding to U' by the theorem 2:

$$U'(\varphi) = \int \varphi \, d\boldsymbol{m}, \quad \text{for} \quad \varphi \in \mathscr{K}(T),$$

and $|||U'_A||| \leqq \bar{\boldsymbol{m}}(A)$, for every set $A \in \mathscr{B}$.

Consider now the dominated linear mapping $V: \mathscr{K}_E(T) \to F$ corresponding to $\boldsymbol{m}$ by the theorem 2:

$$V(f) = \int f \, d\boldsymbol{m}, \quad \text{for} \quad f \in \mathscr{K}_E(T),$$

and

$$|||V_A||| \leqq \bar{\boldsymbol{m}}(A) < \infty, \quad \text{for every set} \quad A \in \mathscr{B}.$$

For $\varphi \in \mathscr{K}(T)$ and $x \in E$ we have

$$V(\varphi x) = \int \varphi x \, d\boldsymbol{m} = \int \varphi \, d\boldsymbol{m} \, x = U'(\varphi) \, x.$$

From the theorem 1 we deduce that $V = U$, therefore U is dominated.

Corollary 1. *A linear functional $U: \mathscr{K}_E(T) \to C$ is dominated if and only if $\|U_A\| < \infty$ for every set $A \in \mathscr{B}$.*

We use the proposition 2.

For the linear functionals, the theorem 2 can be stated as follows:

Corollary 2. *The equality*

$$U(f) = \int f \, d\boldsymbol{m}, \quad \textit{for} \quad f \in \mathscr{K}_E(T),$$

realizes an isomorphism between the set of the linear functionals $U: \mathscr{K}_E(T) \to C$ with $\|U_A\| < \infty$ for $A \in \mathscr{B}$ and the set of the regular measures $\boldsymbol{m}: \mathscr{B} \to E'$ with finite variation μ and we have

$$\mu_U = \mu,$$

$$\|U_A\| \leqq \mu^*(A), \quad \textit{for} \quad A \in \mathcal{C}(\mathscr{B}),$$

and

$$\|U_G\| = \mu^*(G), \quad \textit{for} \quad G \textit{ open}.$$

We can now precise the correspondence $U \to U'$ given in the theorem 1.

Theorem 4. *There exists an isomorphism $U \leftrightarrow U'$ between the space of the dominated linear operations $U\colon \mathcal{K}_E(T) \to F$ and the space of the dominated linear operations $U'\colon \mathcal{K}(T) \to \mathcal{L}(E, F)$, given by the equality*

$$U(\varphi x) = U'(\varphi)\, x, \quad \textit{for} \quad \varphi \in \mathcal{K}(T) \quad \textit{and} \quad x \in E.$$

If U and U' are in correspondence, then there exists a common regular measure $\boldsymbol{m}\colon \mathcal{B} \to \mathcal{L}(E, F)$ with finite variation such that

$$U(f) = \int f\, d\boldsymbol{m}, \quad \textit{for} \quad f \in \mathcal{K}_E(T),$$

and

$$U(\varphi) = \int \varphi\, d\boldsymbol{m}, \quad \textit{for} \quad \varphi \in \mathcal{K}(T),$$

and we have

$$\mu_U = \mu_{U'} = |\boldsymbol{m}|.$$

Let first $U\colon \mathcal{K}_E(T) \to F$ be a dominated linear mapping and let $\boldsymbol{m}\colon \mathcal{B} \to \mathcal{L}(E, F)$ be the regular measure with finite variation μ such that

$$U(f) = \int f\, d\boldsymbol{m}, \quad \text{for} \quad f \in \mathcal{K}_E(T).$$

Let $U'\colon \mathcal{K}(T) \to \mathcal{L}(E, F)$ be the linear mapping corresponding to U by the equality (theorem 1)

$$U(\varphi x) = U'(\varphi)\, x, \quad \text{for} \quad \varphi \in \mathcal{K}(T) \quad \text{and} \quad x \in E.$$

We know that the correspondence $U \to U'$ is linear and one-to-one. We have

$$U'(\varphi)\, x = U(\varphi x) = \int \varphi x\, d\boldsymbol{m} = \int \varphi\, d\boldsymbol{m}\, x$$

for every $x \in E$, therefore

$$U'(\varphi) = \int \varphi\, d\boldsymbol{m}, \quad \text{for every} \quad \varphi \in \mathcal{K}(T).$$

From this equality we deduce that U' is dominated and that

$$\mu_{U'} = \mu = \mu_U.$$

Conversely, let $U'\colon \mathcal{K}(T) \to X = \mathcal{L}(E, F)$ be a dominated linear mapping and let $\boldsymbol{m}\colon \mathcal{B} \to \mathcal{L}(R, X) = X$ be the regular measure corresponding to U' by the theorem 2.

If we put

$$U(f) = \int f\, d\boldsymbol{m}, \quad \text{for} \quad f \in \mathcal{K}_E(T),$$

then $U: \mathscr{K}_E(T) \to F$ is a dominated linear mapping and we have

$$U(\varphi x) = U'(\varphi)x, \quad \text{for} \quad \varphi \in \mathscr{K}(T) \quad \text{and} \quad x \in E.$$

We can give now a representation of a dominated operation U as an integral with respect to the positive measure μ_U.

Theorem 5. *Let $Z \subset F'$ be a norming space. For every dominated linear operation $U: \mathscr{K}_E(T) \to F$ there exists a function $G: T \to \mathscr{L}(E, Z')$ having the following properties:*

1. $|G(t)| = 1$ *μ_U-almost everywhere;*
2. $\langle Gf, z\rangle$ *is μ_U-integrable and*

$$\langle U(f), z\rangle = \int \langle G(t)f(t), z\rangle \, d\mu_U, \quad \textit{for} \quad f \in \mathscr{K}_E(T) \quad \textit{and} \quad z \in Z;$$

3. *if ϱ is a lifting of $\mathscr{L}^\infty(\mu_U)$, we can choose G uniquely such that*

$$\varrho(G) = G;$$

4. *we can choose $G(t) \in \mathscr{L}(E, F)$ for every $t \in T$ in each of the following cases:*

a) $F = Z'$;

b) *there exists a family $\mathscr{A} \in C(\mu_U)$ such that for every $A \in \mathscr{A}$ and every $x \in E$ the convex equilibrated cover of the set $\left\{U(\varphi x); \varphi \in \mathscr{K}(T), \int_A |\varphi| \, d\mu \leqq 1\right\}$ is relatively compact in F for the topology $\sigma(F, Z)$;*

c) *for every $x \in E$, the convex equilibrated cover of the set $\{U(\varphi x); \varphi \in \mathscr{K}(T), \int |\varphi| \, d\mu_U \leqq 1\}$ is relatively compact in F for $\sigma(F, Z)$.*

Let $\boldsymbol{m}: \mathscr{B} \to \mathscr{L}(E, F)$ be the regular measure corresponding to U by the theorem 2. The measure $|\boldsymbol{m}|$ is regular, therefore it has the direct sum property. Let then $U_{\boldsymbol{m}}: T \to \mathscr{L}(E, F)$ be the function corresponding to $\boldsymbol{m}$ by the theorem 4, § 13.

If we take $G = U_{\boldsymbol{m}}$, then G has all the required properties. The statement 4 is proved as in the theorem 4, § 13.

We have also a converse theorem:

Theorem 6. *Let $Z \subset F'$ be a norming space. Let μ be a scalar regular Borel measure and let $G: T \to \mathscr{L}(E, F)$ be a function such that $|G(t)| = 1$ μ-almost everywhere, and $\langle Gx, z\rangle$ is μ-measurable for every $x \in E$ and $z \in Z$. Then $\langle Gf, z\rangle$ is μ-integrable for every $f \in \mathscr{L}^1_E(\mu)$ and $z \in Z$, and there exists a dominated linear operation $U: \mathscr{K}_E(T) \to Z'$ such that*

$$\langle U(f), z\rangle = \int \langle G(t)f(t), z\rangle \, d\mu, \quad \textit{for} \quad f \in \mathscr{K}_E(T) \quad \textit{and} \quad z \in Z,$$

and

$$\mu_U \leqq |\mu|.$$

The operation U has values in F in each of the following cases:

a) $F = Z'$;

b) *for every $x \in E$ there exists a family $\mathscr{A} \in C(\mu)$ such that for every $A \in \mathscr{A}$ the convex equilibrated cover of the set $\{G(t)x;\ t \in A\}$ is relatively compact in F for $\sigma(F, Z)$;*

c) *for every $x \in E$ the convex equilibrated cover of the set $\{G(t)x;\ t \in T\}$ is relatively compact in F for $\sigma(F, Z)$;*

d) *for every $x \in E$ the function $t \to G(t)x$ is μ-measurable; in particular, F is of countable type.*

We have

$$\mu_U = |\mu|$$

in each of the following cases:

α) *there exists a lifting ϱ of $\mathscr{L}^\infty(\mu)$ such that $\varrho[G] = G$;*

β) *E is of countable type and there exists a countable norming set $S \subset Z$;*

γ) *E is of countable type and the function $t \to G(t)x$ is measurable for every $x \in E$;*

δ) *U is μ-measurable.*

We use the theorem 6, § 13, and the theorem 2.

4. POSITIVE FUNCTIONALS ON $\mathscr{K}(T)$

We say that a (not necessarily linear) functional L on $\mathscr{K}(T)$ or on $\mathscr{K}_+(T)$ is *positive* and we write $L \geqq 0$, if

$$L(f) \geqq 0, \quad \text{for every function} \quad f \geqq 0,$$

and that L is *increasing*, if

$$L(f) \leqq L(g), \quad \text{for} \quad f \leqq g.$$

If L and L' are two functionals on $\mathscr{K}(T)$ we write $L \leqq L'$, if $L' - L \geqq 0$, i.e. if

$$L(f) \leqq L'(f), \quad \text{for every function} \quad f \geqq 0.$$

Proposition 4. *An additive functional L on $\mathscr{K}(T)$ or on $\mathscr{K}_+(T)$ is positive if and only if it is increasing.*

Suppose that L is positive. If $f \leqq g$, then $g - f \geqq 0$, therefore $L(g - f) \geqq 0$. On the other hand, $g = (g - f) + f$, and L is additive, therefore $L(g) = L(g - f) + L(f)$, whence

$$L(f) \leqq L(g),$$

i.e. L is increasing.

Conversely, suppose that L is increasing. Since L is additive we have $L(0) = 0$. If $f \geqq 0$, then $L(f) \geqq L(0) = 0$, consequently, L is positive.

Proposition 5. *Every positive linear functional L on $\mathscr{K}(T)$ is dominated.*

Let $A \in \mathscr{B}$ and let $\varphi_0 \in \mathscr{K}(T)$ be a function such that $\varphi_0(t) = 1$ for $t \in \overline{A}$. Then for every function $f \in \mathscr{K}(T, A)$ we have

$$-\|f\| \varphi_0 \leqq f \leqq \|f\| \varphi_0 .$$

Since L is increasing, we have

$$-\|f\| L(\varphi_0) \leqq L(f) \leqq \|f\| L(\varphi_0),$$

therefore

$$|L(f)| \leqq \|f\| L(\varphi_0).$$

It follows that

$$\|L_A\| \leqq L(\varphi_0) < \infty,$$

consequently, by the corollary of the theorem 3, L is dominated.

The theorem 2 can be stated now for positive functionals:

Theorem 7 (Riesz, Kakutani). *There exists an isomorphism $L \leftrightarrow \mu$ between the set of the positive linear functionals $L: \mathscr{K}(T) \to R$ and the set of the positive regular measures $\mu: \mathscr{B} \to R_+$ given by the equality*

$$L(f) = \int f \, d\mu, \quad \textit{for} \quad f \in \mathscr{K}(T).$$

Moreover, if L and μ are in correspondence, we have

$$\|L_A\| \leqq \mu^*(A), \quad \textit{for} \quad A \in \mathfrak{C}(\mathscr{B}),$$

$$\|L_G\| = \mu^*(G), \quad \textit{for} \quad G \textit{ open},$$

and

$$\mu_L = \mu .$$

In fact, for a positive measure μ, we have

$$\mu^*(A) = \bar{\mu}(A) = \tilde{\mu}(A), \quad \text{for} \quad A \in \mathfrak{C}(\mathscr{B}).$$

Remarks.

1°. *L is continuous on $\mathscr{K}(T)$ if and only if the corresponding measure μ is bounded* (i.e. T is μ-integrable). In this case we have

$$\|L\| = \mu(T) = \|\mu\|.$$

2°. Extending L by continuity to $\mathscr{L}^1(\mu)$ we have

$$L(f) = \int f \, d\mu, \quad \text{for every} \quad f \in \mathscr{L}^1(\mu).$$

We give now a characterization of the dominated linear operations by means of the positive linear functionals.

Corollary. *A linear operation $U: \mathscr{K}_E(T) \to F$ is dominated if and only if there exists a positive linear functional L on $\mathscr{K}(T)$ such that*

$$|U(f)| \leqq L(|f|), \quad \textit{for} \quad f \in \mathscr{K}_E(T).$$

The positive linear functional corresponding to the measure μ_U will be denoted by $|U|$. Then $|U|$ is the smallest positive linear functional verifying the preceding inequality.

If we have

$$U(f) = \int f \, d\boldsymbol{m}, \quad \text{for} \quad f \in \mathscr{K}_E(T),$$

then $\mu_U = |\boldsymbol{m}|$, therefore

$$|U|(\varphi) = \int |\varphi| \, d|\boldsymbol{m}|, \quad \text{for} \quad \varphi \in \mathscr{K}(T).$$

We shall give a direct computation of the functional $|U|$ (theorem 7).

For this purpose, we need some more properties of the positive functionals.

Proposition 6. *Every positive and additive functional L on $\mathscr{K}(T)$ or on $\mathscr{K}_+(T)$ is homogeneous.*

a) We prove first that

$$L(\alpha f) = \alpha L(f), \quad \text{for} \quad \alpha \geqq 0 \quad \text{and} \quad f \in \mathscr{K}_+(T).$$

Let $f \in \mathscr{K}_+(T)$. For every natural number n we have

$$L(nf) = L(f + f + \cdots + f) = L(f) + L(f) + \cdots + L(f) = nL(f).$$

We have also

$$L(0f) = 0 = 0L(f).$$

For every rational number $r \geqq 0$ we have then

$$L(rf) = rL(f).$$

In fact, if $r = \frac{p}{q}$ where p and q are positive integral numbers and $q \neq 0$, we have

$$qL\left(\frac{p}{q}f\right) = L\left(q\frac{p}{q}f\right) = L(pf) = pL(f),$$

therefore

$$L\left(\frac{p}{q}f\right) = \frac{p}{q}L(f),$$

i.e.

$$L(rf) = rL(f).$$

Let now $\alpha \geqq 0$ be an arbitrary real number. There exist two sequences (r_n) and (s_n) of positive rational numbers converging to α such that

$$r_n \leqq \alpha \leqq s_n, \quad \text{for every } n.$$

Then

$$r_n f \leqq \alpha f \leqq s_n f,$$

therefore, L being increasing,

$$r_n L(f) = L(r_n f) \leqq L(\alpha f) \leqq L(s_n f) = s_n L(f).$$

Since

$$\lim_{n\to\infty} r_n L(f) = \lim_{n\to\infty} s_n L(f) = \alpha L(f)$$

we deduce

$$L(\alpha f) = \alpha L(f).$$

b) Suppose now that L is defined on $\mathscr{K}(T)$ and prove that

$$L(\alpha f) = \alpha L(f), \quad \text{for} \quad \alpha \in R \quad \text{and} \quad f \in \mathscr{K}(T).$$

We remark first that if $f, g \in \mathscr{K}(T)$, then

$$L(f - g) = L(f) - L(g).$$

In fact, $f = (f - g) + g$, therefore $L(f) = L(f - g) + L(g)$, whence $L(f - g) = L(f) - L(g)$. In particular,

$$L(-f) = -L(f), \quad \text{for} \quad f \in \mathscr{K}(T).$$

Let $f \in \mathscr{K}(T)$ and $\alpha \geqq 0$. Then $f^+, f^- \in \mathscr{K}_+(T)$ and we have $f = f^+ - f^-$, whence

$$L(\alpha f) = L(\alpha f^+) - L(\alpha f^-) = \alpha L(f^+) - \alpha L(f^-) = \alpha L(f^+ - f^-) = \alpha L(f).$$

If $\alpha \leqq 0$, then $-\alpha \geqq 0$ and we have

$$-\alpha L(f) = L(-\alpha f) = -L(\alpha f),$$

therefore

$$L(\alpha f) = \alpha L(f).$$

Proposition 7. *A linear functional on $\mathscr{K}(T)$ is uniquely determined by its values on $\mathscr{K}_+(T)$.*

In fact, let L and L' be two linear functionals on $\mathscr{K}(T)$ which coincide on $\mathscr{K}_+(T)$. Then for every function $f \in \mathscr{K}(T)$ we have $f = f^+ - f^-$ and

$$L(f) = L(f^+) - L(f^-) = L'(f^+) - L'(f^-) = L'(f),$$

whence $L = L'$.

Remark. From the preceding proof we deduce that every linear operation $U: \mathscr{K}(T) \to X$ is uniquely determined by its values on $\mathscr{K}_+(T)$.

A functional defined on $\mathscr{K}_+(T)$ is not always the restriction of a linear functional on $\mathscr{K}(T)$.

However, for positive and additive functionals we have

Proposition 8. *Every positive and additive functional L defined on the set* $\mathscr{K}_+(T)$ *can be uniquely extended to a positive linear functional on* $\mathscr{K}_+(T)$.

We remark first that if f_1, f_2, g_1, g_2 are functions of $\mathscr{K}_+(T)$ such that

$$f_1 - f_2 = g_1 - g_2,$$

then

$$f_1 + g_2 = f_2 + g_1,$$

therefore, L being additive on $\mathscr{K}_+(T)$,

$$L(f_1) + L(g_2) = L(f_2) + L(g_1),$$

hence

$$L(f_1) - L(f_2) = L(g_1) - L(g_2).$$

For every function $f \in \mathscr{K}(T)$ written in the form

$$f = f_1 - f_2,$$

where f_1 and f_2 are functions of $\mathscr{K}_+(T)$, we put

$$L'(f) = L(f_1) - L(f_2).$$

By the preceding remark L' is independent on the particular way in which f is written as a difference of two functions of $\mathscr{K}_+(T)$.

If $f \in \mathscr{K}_+(T)$, then $f = f - 0$, therefore

$$L'(f) = L(f) - L(0) = L(f),$$

hence L' is an extension of L. It follows then that L' is *positive*.

The functional L' is *additive*. If $f, g \in \mathscr{K}(T)$ and if

$$f = f_1 - f_2, \quad g = g_1 - g_2, \quad \text{with} \quad f_1, f_2, g_1, g_2 \in \mathscr{K}_+(T),$$

then

$$f + g = (f_1 + g_1) - (f_2 + g_2)$$

and $f_1 + g_1 \in \mathscr{K}_+(T), f_2 + g_2 \in \mathscr{K}_+(T)$. We deduce

$$L'(f + g) = L(f_1 + g_1) - L(f_2 + g_2)$$
$$= L(f_1) - L(f_2) + L(g_1) - L(g_2) = L'(f) + L'(g).$$

From the proposition 6 it follows that L is homogeneous, and from the proposition 7 it follows that L' is unique.

Let $U: \mathscr{K}_E(T) \to F$ be a linear mapping. For every function $\varphi \in \mathscr{K}_+(T)$ put

$$\|U_\varphi\| = \sup_{|f| \leqq \varphi} |U(f)|, \quad f \in \mathscr{K}_E(T)$$

and

$$|||U_\varphi||| = \sup_{\sum |f_i| \leqq \varphi} \sum |U(f_i)| \quad \text{(finite sums)}, \quad f_i \in \mathscr{K}_E(T).$$

From this definition we deduce that

$$|U(f)| \leqq \|U_{|f|}\|, \quad \text{for} \quad f \in \mathscr{K}_E(T)$$

and

$$\|U_\varphi\| \leqq |||U_\varphi|||, \quad \text{for} \quad \varphi \in \mathscr{K}_+(T).$$

If $F = C$, we have an equality:

Proposition 9. *If $U: \mathscr{K}_E(T) \to C$ is a linear functional, then for every $\varphi \in \mathscr{K}_+(T)$ we have*

$$\|U_\varphi\| = |||U_\varphi|||.$$

Let $\varphi \in \mathscr{K}_+(T)$ and $\sum |f_i| \leqq \varphi$ with $f_i \in \mathscr{K}_E(T)$. For each i there exists a number α_i with $|\alpha_i| = 1$ and $|U(f_i)| = \alpha_i U(f_i) = U(\alpha_i f_i)$. Then

$$\sum |f_i \alpha_i| \leqq \sum |f_i| \leqq \varphi$$

and

$$\sum |U(f_i)| = \sum U(f_i \alpha_i) = U(\sum f_i \alpha_i) \leqq \|U_\varphi\|,$$

therefore

$$|||U_\varphi||| \leqq \|U_\varphi\|.$$

Proposition 10. *A linear mapping $U: \mathscr{K}_E(T) \to F$ is dominated if and only if $|||U_\varphi||| < \infty$ for every $\varphi \in \mathscr{K}_+(T)$.*

In fact, if U is dominated and if $\varphi \in \mathscr{K}_+(T)$, then for every finite family (f_i) of $\mathscr{K}_E(T)$ with $\sum |f_i| \leqq \varphi$ we have

$$\sum |U(f_i)| \leqq \sum \int |f_i| \, d\mu_U = \int \sum |f_i| \, d\mu_U \leqq \int \varphi \, d\mu_U,$$

therefore

$$|||U_\varphi||| \leqq \int \varphi \, d\mu_U < \infty.$$

Conversely, suppose that $|||U_\varphi||| < \infty$ for every $\varphi \in \mathscr{K}_+(T)$, and let $A \in \mathscr{B}$. Let $\varphi \in \mathscr{K}_+(T)$ be such that $\varphi(t) = 1$ for $t \in A$. If (f_i) is a finite family of $\mathscr{K}_E(T, A)$ with $|f_i| \leqq 1$ and $|f_i| \, |f_j| = 0$ for $i \neq j$, then $\sum |f_i| \leqq \varphi_A \leqq \varphi$, therefore

$$\sum |U(f_i)| \leqq |||U_\varphi|||,$$

consequently

$$|||U_A||| \leqq |||U_\varphi||| < \infty.$$

From the theorem 3 we deduce that U is dominated.

We can give now a direct computation of the functional $|U|$.

Theorem 8. *If $U: \mathscr{K}_E(T) \to F$ is a dominated linear mapping, then for every function $\varphi \in \mathscr{K}_+(T)$ we have*

$$|U|(\varphi) = \sup_{\sum |f_i| \leqq \varphi} \sum |U(f_i)|, \quad f_i \in \mathscr{K}_E(T).$$

We shall prove that $\|U_\varphi\|$ is additive on $\mathscr{K}_+(T)$.

Let $\varphi', \varphi'' \in \mathscr{K}_+(T)$ and let $\varepsilon > 0$. There exist two families (f_i') and (f_j'') of $\mathscr{K}_E(T)$ with $\sum |f_i'| \leqq \varphi'$ and $\sum |f_j''| \leqq \varphi''$ such that

$$\|U_{\varphi'}\| < \sum |U(f_i')| + \frac{\varepsilon}{2},$$

$$\|U_{\varphi''}\| < \sum |U(f_j'')| + \frac{\varepsilon}{2}.$$

Then $\sum |f_i'| + \sum |f_j''| \leqq \varphi' + \varphi''$, therefore

$$\|U_{\varphi'}\| + \|U_{\varphi''}\| < \sum |U(f_i')| + \sum |U(f_j'')| + \varepsilon \leqq \|U_{\varphi'+\varphi''}\| + \varepsilon,$$

hence, ε being arbitrary,

$$\|U_{\varphi'}\| + \|U_{\varphi''}\| \leqq \|U_{\varphi'+\varphi''}\|.$$

In order to prove the converse inequality let $(f_i)_{1 \leqq i \leqq n}$ be a finite family of $\mathscr{K}_E(T)$ with $\sum |f_i| \leqq \varphi' + \varphi''$ and let $\varepsilon > 0$. Let $G = \{t; \varphi'(t) + \varphi''(t) > 0\}$ and let $\eta > 0$ be such that $n\eta \|U_G\| < \varepsilon$.

For each i the set $K_i = \{t; |f_i(t)| \geqq \eta\}$ is compact. Then the set $K = \bigcup_{i=1}^{n} K_i$ is compact and contained in the open set G. Let G_1 be an open set such that $K \subset G_1 \subset \bar{G}_1 \subset G$ and let $\psi: T \to [0, 1]$ be a function of $\mathscr{K}_+(T)$ with $\psi(t) = 1$ for $t \in K$ and vanishing outside G_1. Then the function

$$\chi(t) = \begin{cases} \dfrac{\psi(t)}{\varphi'(t) + \varphi''(t)}, & \text{if} \quad \varphi'(t) + \varphi''(t) \neq 0, \\ 0, & \text{if} \quad \varphi'(t) + \varphi''(t) = 0, \end{cases}$$

is continuous and vanishes outside G_1. The functions $\psi' = \chi\varphi'$ and $\psi'' = \chi\varphi''$ are then continuous, with compact carrier, and we have $\psi'(t) + \psi''(t) = 1$ for $t \in K$ and $\psi'(t) + \psi''(t) \leqq 1$ for $t \in T$. Then

$$\sum |f_i\psi'| = \sum |f_i| \, \psi' \leqq (\varphi' + \varphi'') \, \psi' \leqq \varphi'\psi \leqq \varphi'$$

and

$$\sum |f_i\psi''| = \sum |f_i| \, \psi'' \leqq (\varphi' + \varphi'') \, \psi'' \leqq \varphi''\psi \leqq \varphi''.$$

For every i we have

$$\|f_i\psi' + f_i\psi'' - f_i\| < \eta,$$

therefore

$$|U(f_i\psi' + f_i\psi'') - U(f_i)| < \frac{\varepsilon}{n},$$

consequently

$$|U(f_i)| \leqq |U(f_i\psi')| + |U(f_i\psi'')| + \frac{\varepsilon}{n},$$

whence

$$\sum |U(f_i)| \leqq \sum |U(f_i\psi')| + \sum |U(f_i\psi'')| + \varepsilon \leqq \|\|U_{\varphi'}\|\| + \|\|U_{\varphi''}\|\| + \varepsilon.$$

It follows that

$$\|\|U_{\varphi'+\varphi''}\|\| \leqq \|\|U_{\varphi'}\|\| + \|\|U_{\varphi''}\|\|,$$

hence

$$\|\|U_{\varphi'+\varphi''}\|\| = \|\|U_{\varphi'}\|\| + \|\|U_{\varphi''}\|\|,$$

i.e. $\|\|U_\varphi\|\|$ is additive and positive. Then it can be extended to a positive linear functional on $\mathscr{K}(T)$, denoted also by $\|\|U_\varphi\|\|$.

Let now $\varphi \in \mathscr{K}_+(T)$ and let (f_i) be a finite family of $\mathscr{K}_E(T)$ with $\sum |f_i| \leqq \varphi$. Then

$$\sum |U(f_i)| \leqq \sum \int |f_i| \, d\mu_U = \int \sum |f_i| \, d\mu_U \leqq \int \varphi \, d\mu_U = |U| (\varphi),$$

therefore

$$\|\|U_\varphi\|\| \leqq |U| (\varphi).$$

Let then ν be the positive regular Borel measure corresponding to $\|\|U_\varphi\|\|$ by the theorem of Kakutani and Riesz:

$$\|\|U_\varphi\|\| = \int \varphi \, d\nu, \quad \text{for} \quad \varphi \in \mathscr{K}(T).$$

From the definition of $\|\|U_\varphi\|\|$ we deduce that

$$|U(f)| \leqq \|\|U_{|f|}\|\| = \int |f| \, d\nu, \quad \text{for} \quad f \in \mathscr{K}_E(T),$$

hence U is dominated by ν, therefore $\mu_U \leqq \nu$. It follows that for every $\varphi \in \mathscr{K}_+(T)$ we have

$$|U| (\varphi) = \int \varphi \, d\mu_U \leqq \int \varphi \, d\nu = \|\|U_\varphi\|\|,$$

hence

$$|U| (\varphi) = \|\|U_\varphi\|\|, \quad \text{for} \quad \varphi \in \mathscr{K}_+(T),$$

and the theorem is completely proved.

Corollary. *If $U\colon \mathscr{K}_E(T) \to C$ is a dominated linear functional, then for every function $\varphi \in \mathscr{K}_+(T)$ we have*

$$|U|(\varphi) = \sup_{|f| \leqq \varphi} |U(f)|, \quad f \in \mathscr{K}_E(T).$$

Proposition 11. *A real linear functional $U\colon \mathscr{K}(T) \to R$ is dominated if and only if U is the difference of two positive linear functionals on $\mathscr{K}(T)$. More precisely, if U is dominated, then*

$$U^+ = \frac{1}{2}(|U| + U) \quad \textit{and} \quad U^- = \frac{1}{2}(|U| - U)$$

are positive linear functionals on $\mathscr{K}(T)$ and we have

$$U = U^+ - U^- \quad \textit{and} \quad |U| = U^+ + U^-.$$

If L_1 and L_2 are two positive linear functionals on $\mathscr{K}(T)$, and if $U = L_1 - L_2$, then L_1 and L_2 are dominated, therefore U is also dominated.

Conversely, suppose that U is dominated. Then

$$|U(\varphi)| \leqq |U|(\varphi), \quad \text{for} \quad \varphi \in \mathscr{K}_+(T),$$

therefore

$$-|U|(\varphi) \leqq U(\varphi) \leqq |U|(\varphi), \quad \text{for} \quad \varphi \in \mathscr{K}_+(T).$$

It follows then that

$$U^+(\varphi) \geqq 0 \quad \text{and} \quad U^-(\varphi) \geqq 0, \quad \text{for} \quad \varphi \in \mathscr{K}_+(T),$$

i.e. U^+ and U^- are positive. From the definition of U^+ and U^- we deduce immediately that $U = U^+ - U^-$ and $|U| = U^+ + U^-$.

Remarks.

1°. The positive linear functionals U^+ and U^- are called respectively the positive part and the negative part of U.

2°. The equality $U = U^+ - U^-$ is not the only way to write U as a difference of two positive functionals. In fact, if L is a positive linear functional, then $U^+ + L \geqq 0$ and $U^- + L \geqq 0$ and we have still

$$U = (U^+ + L) - (U^- + L).$$

5. CONTINUOUS LINEAR OPERATIONS

In this section we shall give an integral representation of linear functionals which are not dominated.

Theorem 9. *Let $Z \subset F'$ be a norming space. If $U\colon \mathscr{K}_E(T) \to F$ is a linear mapping with $\|U_A\| < \infty$ for $A \in \mathscr{B}$, then there exists an additive set function $\boldsymbol{m}\colon \mathscr{B} \to \mathscr{L}(E, Z')$*

with finite semi-variation such that

$$U(f) = \int f\, d\boldsymbol{m}, \quad \textit{for} \quad f \in \mathscr{K}_E(T).$$

Moreover, for every open set G we have

$$\|U_G\| = \tilde{\boldsymbol{m}}(G).$$

For every $z \in Z$, consider the linear functional U_z: $\mathscr{K}_E(T) \to C$ defined by the equality

$$U_z(f) = \langle U(f), z \rangle, \quad \text{for} \quad f \in \mathscr{K}_E(T).$$

For every set $A \in \mathscr{B}$ and for every function $f \in \mathscr{K}_E(T, A)$ we have

$$|U_z(f)| \leqq |U(f)|\, |z| \leqq \|U_A\|\, \|f\|\, |z|,$$

therefore

$$\|U_{zA}\| \leqq \|U_A\|\, |z| < \infty.$$

By the theorem 7, for each $z \in Z$ there exists a regular measure $\boldsymbol{m}_z$: $\mathscr{B} \to E'$ with finite variation μ_z such that

$$U_z(f) = \int f\, d\boldsymbol{m}_z, \quad \text{for} \quad f \in \mathscr{K}_E(T).$$

Moreover, if $A \in \mathscr{B}$ and if G is an open set of $\mathscr{B}$ such that $A \subset G$, then we have

$$|\boldsymbol{m}_z(A)| \leqq \mu_z(A) \leqq \mu_z(G) = \|U_{zG}\| \leqq \|U_G\|\, |z|.$$

For fixed $A \in \mathscr{B}$ and $x \in E$, the mapping $\boldsymbol{m}(A)\, x$: $z \to \boldsymbol{m}_z(A)\, x$ is a linear functional on Z; if $G \in \mathscr{B}$ is open and $A \subset G$, then

$$|\langle \boldsymbol{m}(A)\, x, z \rangle| = |\boldsymbol{m}_z(A)\, x| \leqq |\boldsymbol{m}_z(A)|\, |x| \leqq \|U_G\|\, |x|\, |z|,$$

therefore $\boldsymbol{m}(A)\, x \in Z'$ and

$$|\boldsymbol{m}(A)\, x| \leqq \|U_G\|\, |x|.$$

For fixed $A \in \mathscr{B}$ the mapping $\boldsymbol{m}(A)$: $x \to \boldsymbol{m}(A)\, x$ of E into Z' is linear and continuous, therefore $\boldsymbol{m}(A) \in \mathscr{L}(E, Z')$ and

$$|\boldsymbol{m}(A)| \leqq \|U_G\|, \quad \text{for } G \text{ open with} \quad A \subset G.$$

It is easy to verify that the mapping $\boldsymbol{m}$: $\mathscr{B} \to \mathscr{L}(E, Z')$ is additive. For every $z \in Z$ we have

$$\boldsymbol{m}_z(A)\, x = \langle \boldsymbol{m}(A)\, x, z \rangle, \quad \text{for} \quad x \in E \quad \text{and} \quad A \in \mathscr{B}.$$

If $A \in \mathscr{B}$, if $G \in \mathscr{B}$ is open and $A \subset G$, then (§ 4, proposition 5)

$$\tilde{\boldsymbol{m}}(A) = \sup_{|z| \leqq 1} \bar{\boldsymbol{m}}_z(A) \leqq \|U_G\| < \infty,$$

therefore $\boldsymbol{m}$ is with finite semi-variation. Since the set functions $\bar{\boldsymbol{m}}_z$ are countably additive, we deduce that $\tilde{\boldsymbol{m}}$ is countably subadditive on $\mathcal{C}(\mathscr{B})$ (§ 4, corollary of the proposition 5) and that for every $x \in E$ and every sequence (A_n) of disjoint sets of $\mathscr{B}$ with union in $\mathscr{B}$ we have

$$\boldsymbol{m}\left(\bigcup_{n=1}^{\infty} A_n\right) x = \sum_{n=1}^{\infty} \boldsymbol{m}(A_n)\, x.$$

Consider the space $\mathscr{M}_E(\mathscr{B})$ of the totally $\mathscr{B}$-measurable functions and the linear mapping $U^*\colon \mathscr{M}_E(\mathscr{B}) \to Z'$ defined by the equality

$$U^*(f) = \int f\, d\boldsymbol{m}, \quad \text{for} \quad f \in \mathscr{M}_E(\mathscr{B}).$$

We have

$$\|U_A^*\| = \tilde{\boldsymbol{m}}(A) < \infty, \quad \text{for} \quad A \in \mathscr{B}.$$

For every $f \in \mathscr{M}_E(\mathscr{B})$ and $z \in Z$ we have

$$\langle U(f), z\rangle = \int f\, d\boldsymbol{m}_z.$$

In fact, we verify easily this equality for step functions $f \in \mathscr{E}_E(\mathscr{B})$. If $f \in \mathscr{M}_E(\mathscr{B})$ and if f vanishes outside an open set $G \in \mathscr{B}$, there exists a sequence (f_n) of $\mathscr{E}_E(\mathscr{B}, G)$ converging uniformly to f. Then $U^*(f_n) \to U^*(f)$, therefore $\langle U^*(f_n), z\rangle \to \langle U^*(f), z\rangle$ for $z \in Z$. On the other hand, for each $z \in Z$ we have

$$\int f\, d\boldsymbol{m}_z = \lim_{n\to\infty} \int f_n\, d\boldsymbol{m}_z.$$

Passing to the limit in the equality

$$\langle U^*(f_n), z\rangle = \int f_n\, d\boldsymbol{m}_z$$

we obtain

$$\langle U^*(f), z\rangle = \int f\, d\boldsymbol{m}_z, \quad \text{for} \quad f \in \mathscr{M}_E(\mathscr{B}) \quad \text{and} \quad z \in Z.$$

We have also

$$\langle U(f), z\rangle = U_z(f) = \int f\, d\boldsymbol{m}_z, \quad \text{for} \quad f \in \mathscr{K}_E(T) \quad \text{and} \quad z \in Z,$$

therefore

$$\langle U(f), z\rangle = \langle U^*(f), z\rangle, \quad \text{for} \quad f \in \mathscr{K}_E(T) \quad \text{and} \quad z \in Z,$$

consequently

$$U(f) = U^*(f) = \int f\, d\boldsymbol{m}, \quad \text{for} \quad f \in \mathscr{K}_E(T).$$

Let now G be an open set. Then

$$\tilde{\boldsymbol{m}}(G) = \sup_{|z| \leqq 1} \bar{\boldsymbol{m}}_z(G) = \sup_{|z| \leqq 1} \|U_{zG}\| = \sup_{|z| \leqq 1} \sup_{|f| \leqq \varphi_G} |U_z(f)|$$

$$= \sup_{|f| \leqq \varphi_G} \sup_{|z| \leqq 1} |\langle U(f), z\rangle| = \sup_{|f| \leqq \varphi_G} |U(f)| = \|U_G\|.$$

Remark. The additive set function $\boldsymbol{m}$ may be neither countably additive, nor regular, nor with finite variation.

Example. Let $K = [0, 1]$ and $\mathscr{C}(K)$ the space of the real continuous functions on K. Take $F = \mathscr{C}(K)$ and consider the linear operation $U: \mathscr{C}(K) \to F$ defined by

$$U(f) = f, \quad \text{for} \quad f \in \mathscr{C}(K).$$

For every Borel set $A \subset K$ we have, evidently, $\|U_A\| = 1$; but for every open set $G \subset K$ we have $|||U_G||| = \infty$. In fact, for every n we can find a family of n functions $f_1, \ldots, f_n$ of $\mathscr{C}(K, G)$ with $\|f_i\| = 1$ and $|f_i|\,|f_j| = 0$ if $i \neq j$. Then

$$\sum |U(f_i)| = \sum \|f_i\| = n,$$

therefore $|||U_G||| > n$, consequently $|||U_G||| = \infty$.

The conjugate space of $\mathscr{C}(K)$ is isomorphe to the space $\mathscr{M}$ of the regular real Borel measures.

For every measure $\mu \in \mathscr{M}$ we have

$$U_\mu(f) = \langle U(f), \mu\rangle = \langle f, \mu\rangle = \int f\, d\mu.$$

On the other hand, by the preceding theorem, there exists an additive set function $\boldsymbol{m}: \mathscr{B} \to \mathscr{M}'$ with finite semi-variation, such that for every $\mu \in \mathscr{M}$, the set function $\boldsymbol{m}_\mu$ is a regular measure and we have

$$U_\mu(f) = \int f\, d\boldsymbol{m}_\mu, \quad \text{for} \quad f \in \mathscr{C}(K).$$

It follows that

$$\int f\, d\mu = \int f\, d\boldsymbol{m}_\mu, \quad \text{for} \quad f \in \mathscr{C}(K),$$

i.e. $\boldsymbol{m}_\mu = \mu$, for every $\mu \in \mathscr{M}$. For every set $A \in \mathscr{B}$ we have

$$|\boldsymbol{m}(A)| = \sup_{\|\mu\| \leqq 1} |\boldsymbol{m}_\mu(A)| = \sup_{\|\mu\| \leqq 1} |\mu(A)| = 1.$$

It follows that $\boldsymbol{m}$ cannot be regular and countably additive, and that $\bar{\boldsymbol{m}}(A) = \infty$, i.e. $\boldsymbol{m}$ has not finite variation. On the other hand,

$$\tilde{\boldsymbol{m}}(A) = \sup_{\|\mu\| \leqq 1} \bar{\boldsymbol{m}}_\mu(A) = \sup_{\|\mu\| \leqq 1} |\mu|\,(A) = 1.$$

§ 20. DISINTEGRATION OF MEASURES

The aim of this paragraph is to prove the theorem of disintegration (theorem 2). In order to do this, we need the notion of image of a measure and that of a strong lifting.

1. IMAGES OF MEASURES

Let T, S be two locally compact spaces, $\mathscr{B}(T)$, $\mathscr{B}(S)$ the corresponding semi-tribes of relatively compact Borel subsets.

Let X be a Banach space and $\boldsymbol{m}: \mathscr{B}(T) \to X$ a Borel measure with *finite variation* μ on T.

Let $p: T \to S$ be a *continuous* function.

We want to define a measure $\boldsymbol{n}: \mathscr{B}(S) \to X$ related in a natural way to the measure $\boldsymbol{m}$ and to the function p. It is natural to ask that a function $f: S \to R$ be $\boldsymbol{n}$-integrable if the composed function $f \circ p: T \to R$ is $\boldsymbol{m}$-integrable.

In particular, we want the function $f = \varphi_A$ with $A \in \mathscr{B}(S)$ to be $\boldsymbol{n}$-integrable, therefore we ask the sets $\overset{-1}{p}(A)$ with $A \in \mathscr{B}(S)$ to be $\boldsymbol{m}$-integrable.

Definition 1. *The continuous function $p: T \to S$ is called μ-proper if $\overset{-1}{p}(A)$ is μ-integrable for every set $A \in \mathscr{B}(S)$.*

We say also that p is $\boldsymbol{m}$-proper, if p is μ-proper.

Let $p: T \to S$ be a *continuous* $\boldsymbol{m}$-proper function. For every set $A \in \mathscr{B}(S)$ put

$$\boldsymbol{n}(A) = \boldsymbol{m}(\overset{-1}{p}(A))$$

and

$$\nu(A) = \mu(\overset{-1}{p}(A)).$$

It is easy to see that $\boldsymbol{n}: \mathscr{B}(S) \to X$ is countably additive, and that ν is positive and countably additive on $\mathscr{B}(S)$. Moreover, $\boldsymbol{n}$ has *finite variation*:

$$|\boldsymbol{n}(A)| = |\boldsymbol{m}(\overset{-1}{p}(A)| \leqq \mu(\overset{-1}{p}(A)) = \nu(A)$$

and we have $|\boldsymbol{n}| \leqq \nu$.

Definition 2. *The Borel measure $\boldsymbol{n}: \mathscr{B}(S) \to X$ defined by*

$$\boldsymbol{n}(A) = \boldsymbol{m}(\overset{-1}{p}(A)), \quad \textit{for} \quad A \in \mathscr{B}(S)$$

is called the image of $\boldsymbol{m}$ by the function p and is denoted by $p(\boldsymbol{m})$.

Then ν is denoted by $p(\mu)$, and the inequality $|\boldsymbol{n}| \leqq \nu$ is now written

$$|p(\boldsymbol{m})| \leqq p(|\boldsymbol{m}|).$$

Remark. This inequality may be stricte. Take, for example, $T = \{0, 1\}$, $S = \{0\}$, $p(0) = p(1) = 0$ and $\mu = \varepsilon_0 - \varepsilon_1$, where $\varepsilon_0(0) = 1$, $\varepsilon_0(1) = 0$, $\varepsilon_1(0) = 0$, $\varepsilon_1(1) = 1$. Then $|\mu| = \varepsilon_0 + \varepsilon_1$ and we have $p(\mu) = 0$, but $p(|\mu|) \neq 0$.

Proposition 1. *If* $\boldsymbol{m}$ *is regular, then* $\boldsymbol{n}$ *is regular.*

In fact, let $A \in \mathscr{B}(S)$ and $\varepsilon > 0$. The set $\overset{-1}{p}(A)$ is μ-integrable. Since μ is regular, there exists a compact set $K \subset \overset{-1}{p}(A)$ such that $\mu(\overset{-1}{p}(A)) - \mu(K) < \varepsilon$. Then $K' = p(K)$ is compact in S, and we have

$$K \subset \overset{-1}{p}(K') \subset \overset{-1}{p}(A),$$

therefore

$$\mu(\overset{-1}{p}(A)) - \mu(\overset{-1}{p}(K')) < \varepsilon,$$

consequently

$$\nu(A) - \nu(K') < \varepsilon.$$

It follows that ν is regular on the left, therefore ν is regular and then $\boldsymbol{n}$ is also regular.

Proposition 2. *If* μ *is bounded, then* ν *is bounded.*

In fact

$$\nu^*(S) = \sup_{A \in \mathscr{B}(S)} \nu(A) = \sup_{A \in \mathscr{B}(S)} \mu(\overset{-1}{p}(A)) \leqq \mu(T) < \infty.$$

We can extend the equality $\nu(A) = \mu(\overset{-1}{p}(A))$ for ν-integrable sets:

Proposition 3. *If a set* $A \subset S$ *is* ν*-integrable, then the set* $\overset{-1}{p}(A)$ *is* μ*-integrable and we have*

$$\nu(A) = \mu(\overset{-1}{p}(A)).$$

a) Consider first the tribe $\mathscr{T}(S)$ generated by $\mathscr{B}(S)$ and prove that if $A \in \mathscr{T}(S)$, then $\overset{-1}{p}(A)$ is μ-measurable and

$$\nu^*(A) = \mu^*(\overset{-1}{p}(A)).$$

In fact, there exists a sequence (A_n) of disjoint sets of $\mathscr{B}(S)$ with union equal to A, therefore

$$\overset{-1}{p}(A) = \bigcup_{n=1}^{\infty} \overset{-1}{p}(A_n).$$

The sets $\overset{-1}{p}(A_n)$ are disjoint and μ-integrable, consequently $\overset{-1}{p}(A)$ is μ-measurable, and

$$\mu^*(\overset{-1}{p}(A)) = \sum \mu(\overset{-1}{p}(A_n)) = \sum \nu(A_n) = \nu^*(A).$$

In particular, if $A \in \mathscr{T}(S)$ is ν-negligible, then $\overset{-1}{p}(A)$ is μ-negligible.

b) We prove now that if $N \subset S$ is ν-negligible, then $\overset{-1}{p}(N)$ is μ-negligible.

In fact, let $K \subset T$ be a compact set. Then $K' = p(K)$ is also compact in S, therefore $K' \cap N$ is ν-negligible and contained in a ν-negligible set $A \in \mathscr{T}(S)$. It follows that

$$K \cap \overset{-1}{p}(N) \subset \overset{-1}{p}(K') \cap \overset{-1}{p}(N) = \overset{-1}{p}(K' \cap N) \subset \overset{-1}{p}(A),$$

and $\overset{-1}{p}(A)$ is μ-negligible, therefore $K \cap \overset{-1}{p}(N)$ is μ-negligible, consequently $\overset{-1}{p}(A)$ is μ-negligible.

c) Let now $A \in \Sigma(\nu)$ be a ν-integrable set and prove that $\overset{-1}{p}(A)$ is μ-integrable and

$$\mu(\overset{-1}{p}(A)) = \nu(A).$$

We have $A = B \cup N$, where $B \in \mathscr{T}(S)$ and N is ν-negligible. Then $\overset{-1}{p}(B)$ is μ-measurable and $\overset{-1}{p}(N)$ is μ-negligible, therefore the set $\overset{-1}{p}(A) = \overset{-1}{p}(B) \cup \overset{-1}{p}(B)$ is μ-measurable and we have

$$\mu^*(\overset{-1}{p}(A)) = \mu^*(\overset{-1}{p}(B)) = \nu^*(B) = \nu(A),$$

whence $\overset{-1}{p}(A)$ is μ-integrable and

$$\mu(\overset{-1}{p}(A)) = \nu(A).$$

Theorem 1. *Let E and F be two Banach spaces such that $X \subset \mathscr{L}(E, F)$. If $f \in \mathscr{L}_E^1(S, \nu)$ then $f \circ p \in \mathscr{L}_E^1(T, \mu)$ and we have*

$$\int f \circ p \, d\boldsymbol{m} = \int f \, dp(\boldsymbol{m}).$$

Consider first a $\mathscr{B}(S)$-step function of the form $f = \sum \varphi_{A_i} x_i$ with $A_i \in \mathscr{B}(S)$ and $x_i \in E$. Then

$$f \circ p = \sum \varphi_{\overset{-1}{p}(A_i)} x_i,$$

and the sets $\overset{-1}{p}(A_i)$ are $\boldsymbol{m}$-integrable, therefore $f \circ p$ is $\boldsymbol{m}$-integrable and

$$\int f \circ p \, d\boldsymbol{m} = \sum \boldsymbol{m}(\overset{-1}{p}(A_i)) x_i = \sum \boldsymbol{n}(A_i) x_i = \int f \, d\boldsymbol{n}.$$

Let now $f \in \mathscr{L}^1_E(S, \nu)$. There exists a sequence (f_n) of $\mathscr{B}(S)$-step functions converging to f in $\mathscr{L}^1_E(S, \nu)$ and ν-almost everywhere. If $A \subset S$ is the ν-negligible set such that

$$f_n(s) \to f(s) \quad \text{for} \quad s \notin A,$$

then $\overset{-1}{p}(A)$ is μ-negligible and

$$(f_n \circ p)(t) \to (f \circ p)(t) \quad \text{for} \quad t \notin \overset{-1}{p}(A).$$

On the other hand, $(f_n \circ p)$ is a Cauchy sequence in $\mathscr{L}^1_E(T, \mu)$, since

$$\int |f_n \circ p - f_m \circ p| \, d\mu = \int |f_n - f_m| \circ p \, d\mu = \int |f_n - f_m| \, d\nu.$$

It follows that $f \circ p$ is μ-integrable and that $f_n \circ p \to f \circ p$ in $\mathscr{L}^1_E(T, \mu)$. For each n we have

$$\int f_n \circ p \, d\boldsymbol{m} = \int f_n \, d\boldsymbol{n},$$

therefore

$$\int f \circ p \, d\boldsymbol{m} = \int f \, d\boldsymbol{n}.$$

Remarks.

1°. If f is $\boldsymbol{n}$-integrable (but not ν-integrable) the function $f \circ p$ may be not $\boldsymbol{m}$-integrable.

2°. If $f: S \to E$ is locally ν-integrable and if $f \circ p$ is μ-integrable, then f is also ν-integrable.

In fact, we have

$$\int_{\overset{-1}{p}(A)} |f \circ p| \, d\mu = \int_A |f| \, d\nu, \quad \text{for} \quad A \in \mathscr{B}(S),$$

since $|f| \, \varphi_A$ is ν-integrable. This equality can be written

$$(|f \circ p|\mu)(\overset{-1}{p}(A)) = (|f|\nu)(A), \quad \text{for} \quad A \in \mathscr{B}(S),$$

therefore

$$p(|f \circ p| \, \mu) = |f| \, \nu.$$

Since $|f \circ p| \, \mu$ is bounded, the measure $|f| \, \nu$ is also bounded, therefore f is ν-integrable.

2. THE STRONG LIFTING PROPERTY

Let S be a locally compact space and $\nu \neq 0$ a *positive regular Borel measure* on S.

Definition 3. *A lifting ϱ of $\mathscr{L}^\infty(\nu)$ is called a strong lifting if*

$$\varrho(f) = f$$

for every continuous function $f \in \mathscr{L}^\infty(\nu)$.

Proposition 4. *A lifting ϱ of $\mathscr{L}^\infty(\nu)$ is a strong lifting if and only if $\varrho(U) \supset U$ for every open set $U \subset S$.*

Assume first that ϱ is a strong lifting and let $U \subset S$ be an open set. Consider the set $\mathscr{F}$ of the continuous functions $f\colon S \to R$ such that $0 \leqq f \leqq \varphi_U$. Then $\varphi_U = \sup_{f \in \mathscr{F}} f$. It follows that

$$\varrho(\varphi_U) \geqq \varrho(f) = f, \quad \text{for each} \quad f \in \mathscr{F},$$

therefore

$$\varrho(\varphi_U) \geqq \sup_{f \in \mathscr{F}} f = \varphi_U,$$

consequently $\varrho(U) \supset U$.

Conversely, suppose that $\varrho(U) \supset U$ for every open set $U \subset S$ and let $g\colon S \to R$ be a continuous bounded *positive* function. Consider the set $\mathscr{G}$ of all the functions $\alpha\varphi_U \leqq g$ with $\alpha \geqq 0$ and U open. It is easy to see that $g = \sup_{\alpha\varphi_U \in \mathscr{G}} \alpha\varphi_U$.

Then

$$\varrho(g) \geqq \alpha\varrho(\varphi_U) \geqq \alpha\varphi_U, \quad \text{for} \quad \alpha\varphi_U \in \mathscr{G},$$

therefore

$$\varrho(g) \geqq g.$$

Let now $f\colon S \to R$ be a continuous bounded function and let λ be a number such that $\lambda + f \geqq 0$ and $\lambda - f \geqq 0$. Since $\varrho(\lambda) = \lambda$, we deduce that

$$\lambda + \varrho(f) = \varrho(\lambda + f) \geqq \lambda + f$$

and

$$\lambda - \varrho(f) = \varrho(\lambda - f) \geqq \lambda - f,$$

therefore $\varrho(f) = f$.

Corollary. *A lifting ϱ of $\mathscr{L}^\infty(\nu)$ is a strong lifting, if and only if $\varrho(F) \subset F$ for every closed set $F \subset S$.*

Remarks.

1^0. If ϱ is a strong lifting of $\mathscr{L}^\infty(\nu)$ then: every continuous function $f \in \mathscr{L}^\infty(\nu)$ is bounded; two continuous functions of $\mathscr{L}^\infty(\nu)$, equal ν-almost everywhere, are equal everywhere; $\int f\, d\nu \neq 0$ for every positive continuous function $f \in \mathscr{L}^\infty(\nu)$; $\nu(U) > 0$ for every ν-integrable open set $U \subset S$.

2°. If $\nu(U) > 0$ for every open set $U \subset S$, then $\|f\| = N_\infty(f, \nu)$, for every continuous function $f \in \mathscr{L}^\infty(\nu)$.

3°. It is not known whether there exists a strong lifting of $\mathscr{L}^\infty(\nu)$, for every positive regular Borel measure $\nu \neq 0$, such that $\nu(U) > 0$ for every open set $U \subset S$.

We give here an example, when the answer is affirmativ.

Proposition 5. *Let ν be a positive regular Borel measure on S such that $\nu(U) > 0$ for every open set $U \in \mathscr{B}(S)$. If S has a countable base of open sets, then there exists a strong lifting of $\mathscr{L}^\infty(\nu)$.*

Consider the space $\mathscr{K}(S)$ of the continuous functions $f: S \to R$ with compact carrier. Since S has a countable base, there exists a countable set $\mathscr{A} \subset \mathscr{K}(S)$ of positive functions such that each function f of $\mathscr{K}(S)$ is the uniform limit of a sequence of $\mathscr{A}$.

Let ϱ be a lifting of $\mathscr{L}^\infty(\nu)$. For every function $f \in \mathscr{A}$ there exists a ν-negligible set $N(f)$ such that

$$\varrho(f)(s) = f(s), \quad \text{for} \quad s \notin N(f).$$

The set $N = \bigcup_{f \in \mathscr{A}} N(f)$ is then ν-negligible and we have

$$\varrho(f)(s) = f(s), \quad \text{for} \quad f \in \mathscr{A} \quad \text{and} \quad s \notin N.$$

We shall prove that the preceding equality remains valid for every $f \in \mathscr{K}(S)$, and $s \notin N$.

In fact, let $f \in \mathscr{K}(S)$ and let (f_n) be a sequence of $\mathscr{A}$ converging uniformly to f. Then

$$\|\varrho(f_n) - \varrho(f)\| = \|\varrho(f_n - f)\| \leqq \|f_n - f\|_\infty = \|f_n - f\|,$$

therefore $\varrho(f_n) \to \varrho(f)$ uniformly. If $s \notin N$, then

$$\varrho(f_n)(s) = f_n(s), \quad \text{for every } n,$$

therefore $\varrho(f)(s) = f(s)$.

For each $s \in N$, let χ_s be a homomorphism of the algebra $\mathscr{L}^\infty(\nu)$ into R such that

$$\chi_s(f) = \chi_s(g) \quad \text{if} \quad f = g,\ \nu\text{-almost everywhere},$$

and

$$\chi_s(f) = f(s), \quad \text{if } f \text{ is continuous}.$$

For every $f \in \mathscr{L}^\infty(\nu)$ define

$$\varrho'(f)(s) = \varrho(f)(s), \quad \text{if} \quad s \notin N,$$

$$\varrho'(f)(s) = \chi_s(f), \quad \text{if} \quad s \in N.$$

It is easy to verify that ϱ' is a lifting of $\mathscr{L}^\infty(\nu)$, and that for every continuous function $f \in \mathscr{L}^\infty(\nu)$ we have $\varrho'(f) = f$, therefore ϱ' is a strong lifting of $\mathscr{L}^\infty(\nu)$.

Remark. The existence of a strong lifting can also be proved if T is a metric locally compact space, or if T is discrete.

3. DISINTEGRATION OF MEASURES

Let T, S be two locally compact spaces and consider the space $M(T)$ of the bounded regular real Borel measures on T. From the Riesz-Kakutani theorem, § 19, it follows that $M(T)$ is the conjugate space of the space $\mathscr{K}(T)$, if we define the norm of a measure $\mu \in M(T)$ by

$$\|\mu\| = |\mu|\,(T).$$

We denote by $M_+(T)$ the set of the positive measures of $M(T)$.

For a measure $\mu \in M(T)$ and a function $g \in \mathscr{K}(T)$ we shall write also $\langle g, \mu \rangle$ or $\mu(g)$ instead of $\int g\, d\mu$.

Let α be a positive regular Borel measure on S, and $\lambda\colon S \to M_+(T)$ a mapping such that for every function $g \in \mathscr{K}(T)$ the mapping $s \to \langle g, \lambda_s \rangle$ (denoted shortly by $\langle g, \lambda \rangle$) is α-integrable.

Then put

$$\mu(g) = \int \langle g, \lambda_s \rangle\, d\alpha(s), \quad \text{for} \quad g \in \mathscr{K}(T).$$

It is easy to see that μ is a positive linear functional on $\mathscr{K}(T)$, therefore by the Riesz-Kakutani theorem, μ can be identified with a measure of $M(T)$. We shall write

$$\mu = \int \lambda_s\, d\alpha(s),$$

and μ will be called the integral of the family $(\lambda_s)_{s \in S}$ of measures.

Conversely, given a positive measure $\mu \in M(T)$, is it possible to "disintegrate" μ, that is, to write μ as an integral of a family of positive measures?

The following theorem gives an answer to this problem.

Theorem 2. *Let μ be a positive regular Borel measure on T, $p\colon T \to S$ a continuous μ-proper function, $\nu = p(\mu)$, $\alpha \neq 0$ a positive regular Borel measure on S such that $\nu = \psi\alpha$ for some locally α-integrable function $\psi \geqq 0$, and ϱ a lifting of $\mathscr{L}^\infty(\alpha)$.*

There exists then a mapping $\lambda\colon S \to M_+(T)$ such that

1. $\varrho[\lambda] = \lambda$;

2. $\|\lambda_s\| = \psi(s)$, *α-almost everywhere;*

3. *$\langle g, \lambda\rangle$ is α-integrable for every $g \in \mathscr{K}(T)$, and*

$$\int g\, d\mu = \int \langle g, \lambda\rangle\, d\alpha, \quad \textit{for} \quad g \in \mathscr{K}(T).$$

4. *If there exists a strong lifting of $\mathscr{L}^\infty(S, \alpha)$, then the measure λ_s is concentrated on the set $\overset{-1}{p}(s)$, for every $s \in S$.*

5. *If $\lambda^i: S \to M_+(T)$, $i = 1, 2$, are two mappings such that λ^i_s is concentrated on $\overset{-1}{p}(s)$, α-almost everywhere, $\varrho[\lambda^i] = \lambda^i$, and*

$$\mu = \int \lambda^i_s\, d\alpha(s),$$

then $\lambda^1_s = \lambda^2_s$, α-almost everywhere.

We shall divide the proof into several parts:

a) For every set $A \in \mathscr{B}(S)$, the set $\overset{-1}{p}(A)$ is μ-integrable, therefore the measure $(\varphi_A \circ p)\, \mu$ is bounded and positive on T, that is, belongs to $M_+(T)$.

Put

$$\boldsymbol{m}(A) = (\varphi_A \circ p)\, \mu, \quad \text{for} \quad A \in \mathscr{B}(S).$$

The mapping $\boldsymbol{m}: \mathscr{B}(S) \to M(T)$ is evidently *additive*. Moreover, for $A \in \mathscr{B}(S)$ we have

$$\|\boldsymbol{m}(A)\| = \|(\varphi_A \circ p)\, \mu\| = \int d(\varphi_A \circ p)\, \mu = \int \varphi_A \circ p\, d\mu = \mu(\overset{-1}{p}(A)) = \nu(A),$$

therefore

$$|\boldsymbol{m}|\,(A) = \sup \sum \|\boldsymbol{m}(A_i)\| = \sup \sum \nu(A_i) = \nu(A),$$

where the supremum is taken for all the finite families (A_i) of disjoint sets of $\mathscr{B}(S)$ with union equal to A.

It follows that $\boldsymbol{m}$ has finite variation and that

$$|\boldsymbol{m}| = \nu,$$

therefore $\boldsymbol{m}$ is countably additive, regular, and absolutely continuous with respect to α. Since α is regular, α has the direct sum property, therefore, by the Lebesgue-Nikodym theorem (see § 13, theorem 5), there exists a function $\lambda: S \to M(T)$ such that $\varrho[\lambda] = \lambda$, the function $s \to \|\lambda_s\|$ is locally α-integrable and

$$\int \varphi\, d|\boldsymbol{m}| = \int \varphi(s)\, \|\lambda_s\|\, d\alpha(s), \quad \text{for} \quad \varphi \in \mathscr{L}^1(|\boldsymbol{m}|);$$

for every $g \in \mathscr{K}(T)$ and every $A \in \mathscr{B}(S)$ the function $\varphi_A\langle g, \lambda\rangle$ is α-integrable and

$$\langle \boldsymbol{m}(A), g\rangle = \int_A \langle g, \lambda_s\rangle\, d\alpha(s).$$

b) We have also $\nu = \psi\alpha$, therefore

$$\int \varphi(s)\,\psi(s)\,d\alpha(s) = \int \varphi(s)\,\|\lambda_s\|\,d\alpha(s), \quad \text{for} \quad \varphi \in \mathscr{L}^1(\nu),$$

therefore $\|\lambda_s\| = \psi(s)$, α-almost everywhere.

c) Since for $A \in \mathscr{B}(S)$ and $g \in \mathscr{K}(T)$ we have

$$\langle \boldsymbol{m}(A), g\rangle = \langle (\varphi_A \circ p)\,\mu, g\rangle = \int g\,d(\varphi_A \circ p)\,\mu = \int g(\varphi_A \circ p)\,d\mu,$$

we deduce that

$$\int_{\overset{-1}{p}(A)} g\,d\mu = \int_A \langle g, \lambda_s\rangle\,d\alpha(s), \quad \text{for} \quad A \in \mathscr{B}(S) \quad \text{and} \quad g \in \mathscr{K}(T).$$

If $g \in \mathscr{K}_+(T)$, then $\int_{\overset{-1}{p}(A)} g\,d\mu \geqq 0$, therefore

$$\int_{\overset{-1}{p}(A)} \langle g, \lambda_s\rangle\,d\alpha(s) \geqq 0, \quad \text{for every} \quad A \in \mathscr{B}(S),$$

consequently $\langle g, \lambda_s\rangle \geqq 0$, α-almost everywhere. Since $\varrho[\lambda] = \lambda$, it follows that $\lambda_s \geqq 0$, α-almost everywhere. We can modify λ on a α-negligible set, to have $\lambda_s \geqq 0$ for every $s \in S$, and the preceding properties remain still valid for the modified function λ.

d) Let $g \in \mathscr{K}_+(T)$ and prove that $\langle g, \lambda\rangle$ is α-integrable. We have

$$(g\mu)\,(\overset{-1}{p}(A)) = \int_{\overset{-1}{p}(A)} g\,d\mu = \int_A \langle g, \lambda\rangle\,d\alpha = (\langle g, \lambda\rangle\,\alpha)\,(A)$$

for every $A \in \mathscr{B}(S)$, therefore

$$p(g\mu) = \langle g, \lambda\rangle\,\alpha.$$

Since the measure $g\mu$ is bounded, the measure $\langle g, \lambda\rangle\,\alpha$ is also bounded, consequently the function $\langle g, \lambda\rangle$ is α-integrable.

Then the function φ_S is integrable with respect to $\langle g, \lambda\rangle\,\alpha$, whence the function $\varphi_S \circ p = \varphi_T$ is integrable with respect to $g\mu$ and we have

$$\int \varphi_T\,d(g\mu) = \int \varphi_S\,d(\langle g, \lambda\rangle\,\alpha),$$

that is

$$\int g\,d\mu = \int \langle g, \lambda\rangle\,d\alpha,$$

and this equality remains valid for every $g \in \mathscr{K}(T)$ (not necessarily $\geqq 0$).

d) Suppose now that ϱ is a strong lifting of $\mathscr{L}^\infty(\alpha)$. Let $s \in S$ and prove that λ_s is concentrated on the closed set $\overset{-1}{p}(s)$. Let $K \subset T$ be a compact set disjoint of $\overset{-1}{p}(s)$. Then $C = p(K)$ is compact in S and $s \notin C$. There exist then two disjoint open sets U and V such that $C \subset U$ and $s \in V$; then $K \subset \overset{-1}{p}(U)$, $\overset{-1}{p}(s) \subset \overset{-1}{p}(V)$, the sets $\overset{-1}{p}(U)$ and $\overset{-1}{p}(V)$ are disjoint and open.

Let $g \in \mathscr{K}(T)$ be such that $g(t) = 1$ for $t \in K$ and $g(t) = 0$ for $t \notin \overset{-1}{p}(U)$. Since $\varphi_{\overset{-1}{p}(V)}\, g = 0$, we have

$$\int_A \varphi_V \langle g, \lambda \rangle \, d\alpha = \int_{\overset{-1}{p}(A)} \varphi_{\overset{-1}{p}(V)}\, g \, d\mu = 0, \quad \text{for every} \quad A \in \mathscr{B}(S),$$

consequently $\varphi_V \langle g, \lambda \rangle = 0$, α-almost everywhere.

We deduce

$$\varphi_{\varrho(V)} \langle g, \lambda \rangle = \varrho(\varphi_V \langle g, \lambda \rangle) = 0 \quad \text{everywhere.}$$

Since ϱ is a strong lifting and V is open we have $\varrho(V) \supset V \ni s$, therefore $\langle g, \lambda_s \rangle = 0$. Then

$$\lambda_s(K) = \int \varphi_K \, d\lambda_s \leqq \int g \, d\lambda_s = \langle g, \lambda_s \rangle = 0,$$

therefore

$$\lambda_s^*(T - \overset{-1}{p}(s)) = \sup \{\lambda_s(K);\, K \subset T - \overset{-1}{p}(s)\} = 0,$$

consequently, λ_s is concentrated on $\overset{-1}{p}(s)$.

e) Finally, let $\lambda^i \colon S \to M(T)$, $i = 1, 2$, be two functions such that λ_s^i is concentrated on $\overset{-1}{p}(s)$, α-almost everywhere, $\varrho[\lambda^i] = \lambda^i$, $\langle g, \lambda^i \rangle$ is α-integrable for every $g \in \mathscr{K}(T)$ and

$$\mu = \int \lambda_s^i \, d\alpha(s),$$

and prove that $\lambda_s^1 = \lambda_s^2$, α-almost everywhere.

We have

$$\int g \, d\mu = \int \langle g, \lambda^1 \rangle \, d\alpha, \quad \text{for every} \quad g \in \mathscr{K}(T).$$

Let now $f \in \mathscr{K}(S)$. Then the function $f \circ p \colon T \to R$ is continuous, therefore $(f \circ p)\, g \in \mathscr{K}(T)$, whence

$$\int (f \circ p)\, g \, d\mu = \int \langle (f \circ p)\, g, \lambda_s^1 \rangle \, d\alpha(s).$$

But for each $s \in S$, λ_s^1 is concentrated on $\overset{-1}{p}(s)$, therefore $f \circ p = f(s)$, λ_s^1-almost everywhere, therefore

$$\int (f \circ p)\, g\, d\mu = \int f(s) \langle g, \lambda_s^1 \rangle\, d\alpha(s), \quad \text{for} \quad f \in \mathcal{K}(S).$$

We deduce in the same way that

$$\int (f \circ p)\, g\, d\mu = \int f(s) \langle g, \lambda_s^2 \rangle\, d\alpha(s), \quad \text{for} \quad f \in \mathcal{K}(S),$$

therefore

$$\int f(s) \langle g, \lambda_s^1 \rangle\, d\alpha = \int f(s) \langle g, \lambda_s^2 \rangle\, d\alpha$$

for each $f \in \mathcal{K}(S)$, and $g \in \mathcal{K}(T)$. It follows that

$$\langle g, \lambda_s^1 \rangle = \langle g, \lambda_s^2 \rangle, \quad \alpha\text{-almost everywhere},$$

for each $g \in \mathcal{K}(T)$, and since $\varrho[\lambda^1] = \lambda^1$ and $\varrho[\lambda^2] = \lambda^2$, we deduce that

$$\lambda_s^1 = \lambda_s^2, \quad \alpha\text{-almost everywhere}$$

and the theorem is completely proved.

Remarks.

1°. If the space S has a countable base, then there exists a strong lifting of $\mathcal{L}^\infty(\alpha)$ (proposition 4), therefore the disintegration of μ is possible without any assumption concerning the strong lifting.

2°. The preceding theorem is valid in the more general situation when, instead of being continuous, p is μ-measurable, that is, for every compact set $K \subset T$ and every $\varepsilon > 0$, there exists a compact subset $K' \subset K$ such that $\mu(K - K') < \varepsilon$ and the restriction of p to K' is continuous.

3°. The existence of a strong lifting of $\mathcal{L}^\infty(\alpha)$ is equivalent to the validity of the preceding theorem whatever be the locally compact space T, the measure μ, and the continuous $p: T \to S$ such that $\nu = p(\mu)$ is absolutely continuous with respect to α.

NOTES AND REMARKS

1. Most of the material included in the paragraphs 1 (classes of sets), 2 (set functions) and 5 (extension of set functions) is standard and can be found in every book devoted to the measure theory. We refer, for example, to Halmos [1]. For the variation and the semi-variation of a set function we refer to Dunford and Schwartz [1] and to M. Nicolescu [3].

2. The semi-tribe was used already by I. Segal [2] (called by him conditional σ-ring).

3. The results of § 2 concerning the Darboux property of a measure are due to S. Marcus [2].

4. The first step of the extension of a positive measure (§ 5) is due to Carathéodory [1]. The second step was already used by I. Segal [2]. The Jordan extension of an additive measure is taken from M. Nicolescu [3]. The extension of an additive set function with finite variation (§ 5, theorems 1 and 5) is due to Arsene and Strătilă [1]. The countably additive case was considered earlier by S. Găină [1] and by N. Dinculeanu [8] (for regular measures). See also M. Métivier [1], I. Kluvanek [2], N. Dinculeanu and I. Kluvanek [1].

5. The uniqueness of the extension given in § 5, theorem 3, is an open problem. It reduces to the following one: let μ be a finite positive measure on a semi tribe $\mathscr{S}$; if a finite positive measure ν on $\Sigma(\mu)$ is equal to 0 on $\mathscr{S}$, does it follow that ν is equal to 0 on $\Sigma(\mu)$? The answer is positive if every μ-negligible set has at most the power of the continuum (see N. Dinculeanu and C. Foiaş [3]).

6. The definition of a measurable real function with respect to a tribe (§ 6) is standard. For the vector functions the measurability with respect to a measure is defined such that in the locally compact case we obtain the definition of Bourbaki [3].

7. For a detailed discussion of the integrability of vector functions with respect to vector measures we refer to Dunford and Schwartz [1], Hildebrandt [2] and R. Bartle [1].

8. *Vector fields.* An integral for vector fields can be constructed as follows:

Let $\mathscr{E} = (E(t))_{t\in T}$ be a family of Banach spaces. A vector field is a function $\boldsymbol{x}$ defined on T such that $\boldsymbol{x}(t) \in E(t)$ for every $t \in T$. The positive function $t \to |\boldsymbol{x}(t)|$ is denoted by $|\boldsymbol{x}|$.

The (totally) measurable, integrable, etc. vector fields are defined not only with respect to some clan or measure, but also with respect to some *fundamental family* of vector fields.

Let $\mathscr{C}$ be a clan. A fundamental family is a vector space $\mathscr{A}$ of vector fields having the following properties:

1) $|\boldsymbol{x}|\,\varphi_A$ is totally $\mathscr{C}$-measurable for every $\boldsymbol{x} \in \mathscr{A}$ and $A \in \mathscr{C}$;

2) $\{\boldsymbol{x}(t);\ \boldsymbol{x} \in \mathscr{A}\}$ is dense in $E(t)$, for every $t \in T$.

For the integration of the vector fields, we need some more conditions:

3) $\|\boldsymbol{x}\|_A = \sup\limits_{t\in A} |\boldsymbol{x}(t)| < \infty$, for every set A of the tribe $\mathscr{T}(\mathscr{C})$;

4) for every vector field $\boldsymbol{x} \in \mathscr{A}$, for every sets $A, B \in \mathscr{C}$ with $A \subset B$ and for every $\varepsilon > 0$, there exists a field $\boldsymbol{y} \in \mathscr{A}$ such that $\varphi_A \boldsymbol{x} = \varphi_A \boldsymbol{y}$ and $\|\boldsymbol{y}\|_B \leqq \|\boldsymbol{x}\|_A + \varepsilon$.

If $E(t) = E$ for every $t \in T$, then a vector field is an usual function $\boldsymbol{x}: T \to E$. In this case we take always $\mathscr{A}$ the space of the constant functions and we identify $\mathscr{A}$ with E. All the definitions and the propositions stated for vector fields have to extend the usual ones, known in this particular case. For example: a step vector field is a vector field of the form $\boldsymbol{x} = \Sigma\varphi_{A_i}\boldsymbol{x}_i$ (finite sum) with $A_i \in \mathscr{C}$ and $\boldsymbol{x}_i \in \mathscr{A}$ and their set is denoted by $\mathscr{E}_{\mathscr{A}}(\mathscr{C})$; then $\mathscr{M}_{\mathscr{A}}(\mathscr{C})$ is the space of the totally measurable vector fields, which vanish outside some set of $\mathscr{C}$ and are uniform limits of step vector fields. A vector field $\boldsymbol{x}$ is measurable with respect to a positive measure μ on $\mathscr{C}$, if on every set of $\mathscr{C}$, $\boldsymbol{x}$ is the limit μ-almost everywhere of a sequence of μ-measurable step vector fields of the form $\sum \varphi \varphi_{A_i} x_i$ with $x_i \in \mathscr{A}$ and A_i μ-measurable. (For the definition of the measurability we can start from a fundamental family $\mathscr{A}$ verifying instead of 1), the following condition: $|x|$ is μ-measurable for every $x \in \mathscr{A}$).

The space $\mathscr{L}^p_{\mathscr{A}}(\mu)$ for $1 \leq p \leq \infty$ is the set of the μ-measurable vector fields x such that $|x| \in \mathscr{L}^p(\mu)$.

Let F be a Banach space. The space $\mathscr{A}$ is endowed with the family of semi-norms $(\|x\|_A)_{A \in \mathscr{C}}$. Then $\mathscr{L}(\mathscr{A}, F)$ is the space of the linear continuous mappings $S: \mathscr{A} \to F$, i.e. such that there exists $A \in \mathscr{C}$ with $|S|_A = \sup \{|Sx|; \|x\|_A \leq 1\} < \infty$.

The set functions $m: \mathscr{C} \to \mathscr{L}(\mathscr{A}, F)$ will be supposed to verify the following condition:

$m(A)\, x = m(A)\, y$, for every set $A \in \mathscr{C}$ and vector fields $x, y \in \mathscr{A}$ such that $\varphi_A x = \varphi_A y$.

We can prove then that for every $A \in \mathscr{C}$ we have $|m(A)|_A < \infty$ and that $|m(A)|_A = |m(A)|_B$ if $A \subset B$, therefore we can write $|m(A)|$ instead of $|m(A)|_A$. If (A_n) is a sequence of sets of $\mathscr{C}$ with union A in $\mathscr{C}$, then the equality $m(A) = \sum m(A_n)$ means that $|m(A) - \sum_{i \leq n} m(A_i)|_B \to 0$ as $n \to \infty$, where B is an arbitrary set of $\mathscr{C}$ containing A.

We can therefore define the measures $m: \mathscr{C} \to \mathscr{L}(\mathscr{A}, F)$ to be countably additive set functions. We can also define the variation

$$\bar{m}(A) = \sup \sum |m(A_i)|$$

and the semi-variation

$$\tilde{m}(A) = \sup |\sum m(A_i)\, x_i|$$

where the supremum is taken for all the finite families $(A_i)_{i \in I}$ of disjoint sets of $\mathscr{C}$ contained in A and all the finite families $(x_i)_{i \in I}$ of $\mathscr{A}$ with $\|x_i\|_{A_i} \leq 1$ for every $i \in I$.

The integral of the step vector fields $x = \sum \varphi_{A_i} x_i$ with respect to an additive set function $m: \mathscr{C} \to \mathscr{L}(\mathscr{A}, F)$ is defined by $\int x\, dm = \sum m(A_i)\, x_i$. If m has finite semi-variation, the integral is extended for totally measurable vector fields. If m is a measure with finite variation μ, then the integral can be extended for the integrable vector fields of $\mathscr{L}^1_{\mathscr{A}}(\mu)$.

We can define the q-variation and the q-semi-variation of a set function and define the integral of the vector fields of $\mathscr{L}^p_{\mathscr{A}}(\mu)$ as in § 13.

For details we refer to R. Godement [1], C. Ionescu Tulcea [1], A. and C. Ionescu Tulcea [1], N. Dinculeanu [1], [3], [4], [14], N. Dinculeanu and C. Foiaş [2], I. Singer [2].

9. The results of § 9 concerning the integral representation of linear operations on totally measurable functions are due to N. Dinculeanu [14] for vector fields. Theorem 1 and corollary 1 of this theorem were proved earlier respectively by M. Gowurin [1] for $T = [a, b]$ and by I. Singer [2] for T compact. The corollaries 2 and 3 of the proposition 12 are taken from Dunford and Schwartz [1].

10. The integration with respect to positive measures defined by densities is adapted from Bourbaki [3]. For vector measures defined by densities see N. Bourbaki [3] and N. Dinculeanu [5].

11. The Lebesgue-Nikodym theorem (known, generally, as the Radon-Nikodym theorem), was proved first by Lebesgue [1] in 1904, in terms of point functions on the real line, then by Radon [1] in 1913, for Borel measures in the Euclidean space, and by Nikodym [1] in the general form.

Usually the theorem is stated for σ-bounded measures, but the proof for the case of the measures with the direct sum property is then immediate. The most general conditions were found by I. Segal [2]. We say that a positive measure μ on a clan $\mathscr{C}$ has the Lebesgue-Nikodym property if every positive measure ν on $\mathscr{C}$, absolutely continuous with respect to μ is of the form $\nu = g\mu$ with g locally μ-integrable. We say that μ is *localizable* if for every family (E_α) of μ-measurable sets there exists a μ-measurable set E such that the equivalence class of φ_E is the least upper bound of the family of the equivalence classes of φ_{E_α}, in the ordered space $L^\infty(\mu)$. If μ has the direct sum property, then μ is localizable. Segal's theorem states that μ has the Lebesgue-Nikodym property if and only if it is localizable. For further discussions on this subject see A. C. Zaanen [5].

Dunford and Pettis [1] extended the Lebesgue-Nikodym theorem for vector measures m with values in a conjugate Banach space X of countable type, absolutely continuous with respect to a positive measure μ, such that $|m(E)| \leq a\mu(E)$ for every $E \in \mathscr{C}$ and some $a > 0$.

Phillips [3] has considered vector measures with values in general Banach spaces X, but such that the set $\left\{\frac{m(E)}{\mu(E)};\quad E \in \Sigma(\mu),\ \mu(E) > 0\right\}$ is weakly compact. M. M. Rao [2] has considered the case where both $\boldsymbol{m}$ and $\boldsymbol{n}$ are vector measures with values in different Banach spaces X and Y, and $\boldsymbol{m}$ is absolutely continuous with respect to $\boldsymbol{n}$, but both $\boldsymbol{m}$ and $\boldsymbol{n}$ verify the preceding two conditions with respect to some positive measure.

In the form stated in § 13 (theorems 4 and 5), the theorem was proved by N. Dinculeanu [13]. Earlier, it was proved for Banach spaces of countable type by Dieudonné [5], N. Dinculeanu [4] and N. Dinculeanu and C. Foiaş [1], [2] for vector measures having values operators on spaces of vector fields.

An extension for positive additive set functions was given by Bochner [3] and Bochner and Phillips [1]. Rickart [3] considered the case where the density is multivalued.

12. *Integral representation of operations on $\mathscr{L}^p$.* We say that a measure μ on a clan $\mathscr{C}$ has the Riesz representation property if every linear continuous functional U on $\mathscr{L}^1(\mu)$ is of the form $U(f) = \int fg\, d\mu$ for some function $g \in \mathscr{L}^\infty(\mu)$. I. Segal [2] proved that μ has the Riesz representation property if and only if μ is localizable, hence if and only if μ has the Lebesgue-Nikodym property.

The integral representation for functionals on $\mathscr{L}^p$ with $1 < p < \infty$ was given by Riesz [4] for $T = [0, 1]$ and by Nikodym [4] and Dunford [3] in the general case. For $\mathscr{L}^1$, the theorem was proved by Steinhaus [1] for $T = [0, 1]$ and by Dunford [3] in the general case.

The form of the functionals on the space $\mathscr{L}_E^p$ was given by Dieudonné [3], [5] and by C. Ionescu Tulcea [2] (for vector fields) in case E is of countable type. R. Godement [1] dropped the countability condition in case E is a Hilbert space (also for vector fields).

The integral form of the operations $U: \mathscr{L}^p \to F$ was given by Dunford [3], Gelfand [2], Dieudonné [3], Dunford and Pettis [1], Phillips [2], Rickart [1] and others for $p = 1$ and by Dunford [3] and Phillips [2] for $1 < p < \infty$.

Finally, the integral representation for operations $U: \mathscr{L}_E^p \to F$ under some countability conditions on E and F was proved first by N. Dinculeanu [1] for $p = 1$, by N. Dinculeanu and C. Foiaş [1], [2] for $1 \leq p < \infty$, and by A. and C. Ionescu Tulcea [1] for $1 \leq p < \infty$ for locally convex spaces (in all these cases there were considered spaces of vector fields).

A. and C. Ionescu Tulcea [3] dropped the countability conditions on E and F. See also N. Dinculeanu [13].

The theorem 1, § 13, was proved by I. Singer [2, II], [5]. For a detailed account on this problem we refer to Dunford and Schwartz [1].

13. The existence of a lifting was proved by J. von Neumann [1] in the case where $T = R$ and μ is the Lebesgue measure, and by D. Maharam [2] for σ-bounded measures. The proof given in § 11 is due to A. and C. Ionescu Tulcea [2]. The non-existence of a lifting of $\mathscr{L}^p$ with $p < \infty$ was proved by A. and C. Ionescu Tulcea [3]. The theorem 2, § 11 was proved by R. Ryan [1].

If T is a locally compact space and if μ is a positive regular Borel measure, then a lifting ϱ of $\mathscr{L}^\infty(\mu)$ is called a strong lifting if $\varrho(f) = f$ for every continuous function $f \in \mathscr{L}^\infty(\mu)$. It is not yet known whether there exists a strong lifting of $\mathscr{L}^\infty(\mu)$. The answer is positive in some particular cases: T is metrizable, μ is atomic, etc. For further details we refer to A. and C. Ionescu Tulcea [6].

14. The part concerning the Borel sets and the Baire sets are taken from Halmos [1]. The definition of the regularity given here is different from that given by Halmos [1] and by Dunford and Schwartz [1]. However, all these definitions agree for Borel measures. The results concerning the regularity of the vector measures are due to N. Dinculeanu [4], [8], [10]. For the extension of the regular measures we refer to N. Bourbaki [3] and Halmos [1]. For the extension of the regular vector measures see N. Dinculeanu [8].

Recently, N. Dinculeanu and I. Kluvanek [1] proved that every Baire measure (not necessarily with finite variation) is regular and can be extended uniquely to a regular Borel measure, and that every additive regular set function defined on $\mathscr{B}$ is countably additive.

The correspondence between vector functions with finite variation on an interval and Stieltjes measures is due to E. Radu [1].

15. *The Riesz representation theorem.* The integral representation of a linear functional on the space $\mathscr{C}(T)$ was given for the first time by Riesz [1] in 1909, for $T = [0, 1]$ and Stieltjes integral.

Successive extensions were given by Radon [1], for a compact subset T of R^n, by Banach in Note II of Saks' book [1] for a metric compact space T, and finally by Kakutani [2] for a compact space T. Other extensions for locally compact spaces are due to Halmos [1], Hewitt [3], Edwards [1] and N. Bourbaki [3]. I. Singer [1], [2] gave an integral representation for functionals on the space $\mathscr{C}_E(T)$ of the vector valued continuous functions. I. Gelfand [1], and Bartle, Dunford and Schwartz [1] considered weakly compact operations $U: \mathscr{C}(T) \to F$. The general case $U: \mathscr{K}_E(T) \to F$ was considered by N. Dinculeanu [2], [4] who introduced the dominated operations and gave an integral representation for this operations even for vector fields. Finally, R. Cristescu [3] has considered the case where E and F are ordered Banach spaces. The characterisation of $|U|$ in theorem 7, § 19 is due to Szász-Felten [1].

Concerning theorem 9, the following problem is open: to give a characterization of the operations U for which the corresponding set function $\boldsymbol{m}$ has one of the following properties:

1) $\boldsymbol{m}$ is countably additive;

2) $\boldsymbol{m}$ is regular (therefore also countably additive);

3) $\boldsymbol{m}$ is regular and has values in $\mathscr{L}(E, F)$.

The operations U for which $\boldsymbol{m}$ has finite variation (therefore is regular, countably additive and has values in $\mathscr{L}(E, F)$) are characterized by the property to be dominated.

If T is compact, the operations $U: \mathscr{C}(T) \to F$ for which $\boldsymbol{m}$ has values in F (not only in F'') are characterized by the property to be weakly compact (Bartle, Dunford and Schwartz [1]); but for operations $U: \mathscr{C}_E(T) \to F$, weakly compactness is only sufficient for $\boldsymbol{m}$ to have values in $\mathscr{L}(E, F)$ (therefore to be also countably additive).

16. For a complete study of images of measures (as well as for induced measures and integration of measures), we refer to N. Bourbaki [3], chap. V. For images of vector measures (and induced vector measures), see N. Dinculeanu [5].

17. The theorem of disintegration is to be found in N. Bourbaki's book on Integration [4], chap. VI, in case both spaces T and S have countable bases. A. Ionescu Tulcea and C. Ionescu Tulcea [6] have dropped the countability hypotheses using the strong lifting property.

BIBLIOGRAPHY

Alexandroff, A. D.

[1] Additive set functions in abstract spaces, I–III, Mat. Sbornik N.S. **8** (50), 307–348 (1940); **9** (51), 563–628 (1941); **13** (55), 169–238 (1943).

Alexiewicz, A.

[1] Linear operations among bounded measurable functions, I, II, Ann. Soc. Pol. Math. **19,** 140–161, 161–164 (1946).

Arsene, G., Strătilă, S.

[1] Prolongement des mesures vectorielles, Revue Roumaine Math. pures et appl. **10**, 333–338 (1965).

Banach, S.

[1] Théorie des opérations linéaires, Warsaw, 1932.

Bartle, R. G.

[1] A general bilinear vector integral, Studia Math. **15**, 337–352 (1956).

Bartle, R. G., Dunford, N., Schwartz, J.

[1] Weak compactness and vector measures, Canad. J. Math. **7**, 289–305 (1955).

Berberian, Sterling, K.

[1] Measure and Integration, New York-London, 1965.

Birkhoff, G.

[1] Integration of functions with values in a Banach space, Trans. Amer. Math. Soc. **38**, 357–378 (1935).

Bochner, S.

[1] Integration von Funktionen, deren Werte die Elemente eines Vectorraumes sind, Fund. Math. **20**, 262–276 (1933).

[2] Absolut-additive abstrakte Mengenfunktionen, Fund. Math. **21**, 211–213 (1933).

[3] Additive set functions on groups, Ann. Math. (2) **40**, 769–799 (1939).

Bochner, S., Phillips, R. S.

[1] Additive set functions and vector lattices, Ann. Math. (2) **42**, 316–324 (1941).

Bochner, S., Taylor, A. E.

[1] Linear functionals on certain spaces of abstractly-valued functions, Ann. Math. (2) **39**, 913–944 (1938).

Bogdanowicz, W. M.

[1] A generalization of the Lebesgue-Bochner-Stieltjes integral and a new approach to the theory of integration, Proc. Nat. Acad. Sci. **53**, 492–498 (1965).

[2] Integral representation of linear continuous operators from the space of Lebesgue-Bochner summable functions into any Banach space, Proc. Nat. Acad. Sci. **54**, 351–354 (1965).

[3] Integral representation of multilinear continuous operators from the space of Lebesgue-Bochner summable functions into any Banach space, Bull. Amer. Math. Soc. **72**, 317–320 (1966).

Bouniakowsky, V.

[1] Sur quelques inéqualités concernant les intégrales ordinaires et les intégrales aux différences finies, Mém. Acad. St. Petersburg (7) **1**, no. 9 (1859).

Bourbaki, N.

[1] Topologie générale, chap. I–X, Hermann, Paris, 1940–1949.

[2] Espaces vectoriels topologiques, chap. I–V, Hermann, Paris, 1953, 1955.

[3] Intégration, chap. I–VI, Hermann, Paris, 1952–1959.

Carathéodory, C.

[1] Vorlesungen über reelle Funktionen, Teubner, Leipzig, 1927.

Colojoară, I., Dinculeanu, N., Marinescu, G.

[1] Measures with values in locally convex spaces, Bull. Math. Soc. Sci. Math. Phys. R.P.R. **5** (53), 167–180 (1961).

Cristescu, R.

[1] La notion d'intégrale dans les espaces sémiordonnés (roumain), Commun. Acad. R.P.R. **2**, 205–208 (1952).

[2] L'intégration dans les espaces semi-ordonnés (roumain), Bul. st. **4**, 291–310 (1952).

[3] Un théoréme sur la représentation des opérations linéaires (roumain), Commun. Acad. R.P.R. **5**, 655–659 (1955).

[4] Espaces linéaires ordonnés (roumain), Ed. Acad. R.P.R., Bucureşti, 1959.

[5] Integrali vettoriali di Stieltjes ed operatori liniari, Rendiconti Accad. Naz. Lincei **27**, 31–34 (1959).

[6] Intégrales vectorielles et représentation de certains opérateurs linéaires, Bull. Math. Soc. Sci. Math. Phys. R.P.R. **3** (51), 7–15 (1959).

[7] Intégrale de Stieltjes dans les espaces semi-ordonnés (Russian), Doklady Akad. Nauk S.S.S.R. **133**, 519–522 (1960).

[8] Sur une intégrale vectorielle (roumain), Commun. Acad. R.P.R. **11**, 1169–1173 (1961).

Császár, A.

[1] Sur la représentation canonique des fonctionelles linéaires, Ann. Univ. Sci. Budapest **2**, 85–92 (1959).

Cuculescu, I.

[1] Généralisation aux groupes quelconques d'un théorème de E. Hille concernant les fonctions facteurs, Rendiconti Accad. Naz. Lincei **24**, 15–19 (1958).

[2] Martingales of sum-functions, Revue Math. pures et appl. **6**, 703–711 (1961).

Daniell, P. J.

[1] A general form of integral, Ann. Math. (2) **19**, 279–294 (1917–1918).

Day, M. M.

[1] The space L^p with $0 < p < 1$, Bull. Amer. Math. Soc. **46**, 816–823 (1940).

[2] Normed linear spaces, Springer-Verlag, Berlin–Göttingen–Heidelberg, 1958.

Deleanu, A.

[1] Sur l'intégration des fonctions d'ensemble, Rendiconti Sem. Mat. Univ. Padova **27**, 27–36 (1957).

Dieudonné, J.

[1] Sur le théorème de Lebesgue-Nikodym, Ann. Math. (2) **42**, 547–555 (1941).

[2] Sur le théorème de Lebesgue-Nikodym II, Bull. Soc. Math. France **72**, 193–239 (1944).

[3] Sur le théorème de Lebesgue-Nikodym III, Ann. Inst. Fourier, Grenoble, **23**, 25–53 (1947–1948).

[4] Sur le théorème de Lebesgue-Nikodym IV, J. Indian Math. Soc. (N.S.) **15**, 77–86 (1951).

[5] Sur le théorème de Lebesgue-Nikodym V, Canad. J. Math. **3**, 129–139 (1951).

[6] Sur la convergence des suites de mesures de Radon, An. Acad. Brasil, Ci., **23**, 21–38, 277–282 (1951).

Dinculeanu, N.

[1] Sur la représentation intégrale de certaines opérations linéaires, C. R. Acad. Sci. Paris **245**, 1203–1205 (1957).

[2] Mesures vectorielles et opérations linéaires, C. R. Acad. Sci. Paris **246**, 2328–2331 (1958).

[3] Sur la représentation intégrale de certaines opérations linéaires II, Compositio Math. **14**, 1–22 (1959).

[4] Sur la représentation intégrale de certaines opérations linéaires III, Proc. Amer. Math. Soc. **10**, 59–68 (1959).

[5] Mesures vectorielles sur les espaces localement compacts, Bull. Math. Soc. Sci. Math. Phys. R.P.R. **2** (50), 137–163 (1958).

[6] Remarks on the integral representation of vector measures and linear operations on L_E^p, Revue Math. pures et appl. **7**, 287–300 (1962).

[7] Sur les seminormes N_p (roumain), An. Univ. Bucureşti **11**, 155–163 (1962).

[8] On the regular vector measures, Acta Sci. Math. Szeged **24**, 236–243 (1963).
[9] Extension of measures, Bull. Math. Soc. Sci. Math. Phys. R.P.R. **7** (55), 151–156 (1963).
[10] Regularity of vector measures, Revue Roumaine Math. pures et appl. **9**, 81–90 (1964).
[11] Théorie de la mesures et fonctions réelles (roumain), Ed. didactică şi pedagogică, Bucureşti, 1964.
[12] Intégration sur les espaces localement compacts (roumain), Ed. Acad. R.P.R., Bucureşti, 1965.
[13] Integral representation of vector measures and linear operations, Studia Math. **25**, 181–205 (1965).
[14] Linear operations on spaces of totally measurable functions, Revue Roumaine Math. pures et appl. **10**, 1493–1524 (1965).
[15] Integral representation of linear operations on spaces of continuous vector fields, Math. Ann. **157** (1966).
[16] Représentation intégrale des opérations linéaires (roumain), I, II, Studii Cercet. Mat. **18**, 349–385, 483–536 (1966).

Dinculeanu, N., Foiaş, C.
[1] Mesures vectorielles et opérations linéaires sur L_E^p, C. R. Acad. Sci. Paris **248**, 1759–1762 (1959).
[2] Sur la représentation intégrale de certaines opérations linéaires IV, Canad. J. Math. **13**, 529–556 (1961).
[3] On the uniqueness of the outer measure, Revue Roumaine Math. pures et appl. **11** (1966).
[4] On the regularity of the semi-variation of set functions, Revue Roumaine Math. pures et appl. **11** (1966).
[5] A universal model for ergodic transformations on separable measure spaces, Michigan Math. J. **13**, 109–117 (1966).

Dinculeanu, N., Kluvanek, I.
[1] On vector measures, Proc. London Math. Soc. (in the press).

Dixmier, J.
[1] Sur certains espaces considérés par M. H. Stone, Summa Brasil. Math. **2**, 151–182 (1951).

Donogue Jr., W. F.
[1] On the lifting property, Proc. Amer. Math. Soc. **16**, 913–914 (1965).

Doob, J. L.
[1] Stochastic processes, Wiley, New York, 1953.

Dunford, N.
[1] Integration in general analysis, Trans. Amer. Math. Soc. **37**, 441–453 (1935).
[2] Integration and linear operations, Trans. Amer. Math. Soc. **40**, 474–494 (1936).
[3] Uniformity in linear spaces, Trans. Amer. Math. Soc. **44**, 305–356 (1938).

Dunford, N., Pettis, B. J.
[1] Linear operations on summable functions, Trans. Amer. Math. Soc. **47**, 323–392 (1940).

Dunford, N., Schwartz, J.
[1] Linear operators, Part I, New York, 1958.

Dunford, N., Stone, M. H.
[1] On the representation theorem for Boolean algebras, Revista Ci. Lima **43**, 447–453 (1941).

Edwards, R. E.
[1] A theory of Radon measures on locally compact spaces, Acta Math. **89**, 133–164 (1953).
[2] Vector-valued measures and bounded variation in Hilbert space, Math. Scandinavica **3**, 90–96 (1955).
[3] On certain algebras of measures, Pacif. J. Math. **5**, 372–389 (1955).
[4] Functional analysis, Holt, Rinehart and Wiston New York, 1965.

Ellis, H. W., Halperin, I.
[1] Function spaces determined by a levelling length function, Canad. J. Math. **5**, 576–592 (1953).

Fichera, G.
[1] Lezioni sulle transformazioni lineari, vol. I, Instituto Matem. Trieste 1954.
[2] Sulla derivazione delle funzioni additive d'insieme, Rendiconti Sem. Mat. Univ. Padova **23**, 366–397 (1954).

Fichtenholz, G.

[1] Sur les opérations linéaires dans l'espace des fonctions continues, Bull. Acad. Roy. Belg. **22**, 26–33 (1936).

Fichtenholz, G., Kantorovitch, L. V.

[1] Sur les opérations linéaires dans l'espace de fonctions bornées, Studia Math. **5**, 69–98 (1934).

Foiaş, C.

[1] Décompositions intégrales des familles spectrales et semi-spectrales en opérateurs qui sortent de l'espace hilbertien, Acta Sci. Math. Szeged **20**, 117–154 (1959).

Foiaş, C., Singer, I.

[1] Some remarks on the representation of linear operators in spaces of vector valued continuous functions, Revue Math. pures et appl. **5**, 729–752 (1960).

Fullerton, R. E.

[1] The representation of linear operators from L^p to L, Proc. Amer. Math. Soc. **5**, 689–696 (1954).

Găină, S.

[1] Extension of vector measures, Revue Math. pures et appl. **8**, 151–154 (1963).

Gelfand, I.

[1] Abstrakte Funktionen und lineare Operatoren, Mat. Sbornik **4** (46), 235–284 (1938).

Gil de Lamadrid, J.

[1] Measures and tensors, Trans. Amer. Math. Soc. **114**, 98–121 (1965).

Godement, R.

[1] Sur la théorie des représentations unitaires, Ann. Math. (2) **53**, 68–124 (1951).

Gowurin, M.

[1] Über die Stieltjessche Integration abstrakter Funktionen, Fund. Math. **27**, 255–268 (1936).

Gomes, R. L.

[1] Mesures vectorielles positives, Portugalia Math. **22**, 101–116 (1963).

Gould, G. G.

[1] Integration over vector-valued measures, Proc. London Math. Soc. **15**, 193–225 (1965).

Grothendieck, A.

[1] Sur les applications linéaires faiblement compactes d'espaces du type $C(K)$, Canad. J. Math. **5**, 129–173 (1953).

[2] Produits tensoriels topologiques et espaces nucléaires, Memoirs Amer. Math. Soc., Providence, 1955.

Haar, A.

[1] Der Maßbegriff in der Theorie der kontinuierlichen Gruppen, Ann. Math. (2) **34**, 174–169 (1933).

Halmos, P. R.

[1] Measure Theory, New York, 1950.

[2] Lectures on ergodic theory, Tokyo, 1956.

Halperin, I.

[1] Function spaces, Canad. J. Math. **5**, 273–288 (1953).

[2] Reflexivity in the L^λ function spaces, Duke Math. J. **21**, 205–208 (1954).

Hewitt, E.

[1] Linear functionals on spaces of continuous functions, Fund. Math. **37**, 161–189 (1950).

[2] Integral representation of certain linear functionals, Ark. för Mat. **2**, 269–282 (1952).

[3] Integration on locally compact spaces I, Univ. of Washington Publ. in Math. **3**, 71–75 (1952).

Hildebrandt, T. H.

[1] Bounded linear functional operations, Trans. Amer. Math. Soc. **36**, 868–875 (1934).

[2] Integration in abstract spaces, Bull. Amer. Math. Soc. **59**, 111–139 (1953).

Hille, E., Phillips, R.

[1] Functional analysis and semi-groups, Amer. Math. Soc. Coll. Publ., 1957.

Ionescu Tulcea, A.

[1] On the lifting property V, Ann. Math. Statist. **36**, 819–828 (1965).

Ionescu Tulcea, A., Ionescu Tulcea, C.
[1] On the decomposition and integral representation of continuous linear operators, Ann. Mat. pura ed appl. **53**, 63–87 (1961).
[2] On the lifting property I, J. Math. Analysis and Appl. **3**, 537–546 (1961).
[3] On the lifting property II, J. Math. Mech. **11**, 773–795 (1962).
[4] Abstract ergodic theorems, Trans. Amer. Math. Soc. **107**, 107–124 (1963).
[5] On the lifting property IV, Disintegration of measures, Ann. Inst. Fourier, Grenoble, **14**, 445–472 (1964).
[6] On the lifting property III, Bull. Amer. Math. Soc. **70**, 193–197 (1964).

Ionescu Tulcea, C.
[1] Deux théorèmes concernant certains espaces de champs de vecteurs, Bull. Sci. Math. **79**, 106–111 (1955).
[2] Espaces hilbertiens (roumain), Ed. Acad. R.P.R., Bucureşti, 1956.
[3] On the lifting property and disintegration of measures, Bull. Amer. Math. Soc. **71**, 829–842 (1965).

Jessen, B.
[1] The theory of integration in a space of an infinite number of dimensions, Acta Math. **63** 249–323 (1934).

Kakutani, S.
[1] Concrete representation of abstract (*L*)-spaces and the mean ergodic theorem, Ann. Math. (2) **42**, 523–537 (1941).
[2] Concrete representation of abstract (*M*)-spaces, Ann. Math. (2) **42**, 994–1024 (1941).

Kluvanek, I.
[1] On vector measures (russian), Mat. Fys. Časopis **8**, 186–192 (1957).
[2] On the theory of vector measures (russian), Mat. Fyz. Časopis, **11**, 173–192 (1961).
[3] On the integral representation of the linear mappings (Russian), Mat. Fys. Časopis **12**, 241–246 (1962).
[4] On some generalisations of the Riesz-Kakutani theorem (Russian), Čehoslov. Mat. J. **23** (88), 89–13 (1963).
[5] Intégrale vectorielle de Daniell, Mat. Fys. Časopis **15**, 146–161 (1965).

Kolmogoroff, A.
[1] Grundbegriffe der Wahrscheinlichkeitsrechnung, Springer, Berlin, 1933.

Kurtz, L. C., Tucker, D. H.
[1] Vector valued summability methods on a linear normed space, Proc. Amer. Math. Soc. **16**, 419–428 (1965).

Lebesgue, H.
[1] Leçons sur l'intégration et la recherche des fonctions primitives, Gauthier-Villars, Paris, 1904.

Loomis, L. H.
[1] An introduction to abstract harmonic analysis, D. von Nostrand Co., New York, 1953.

Lorentz, G. G., Wertheim, D. G.
[1] Representation of linear functionals on Köthe spaces, Canad. J. Math. **5**, 568–575 (1953).

Maharam, D.
[1] The representation of abstract measure functions, Trans. Amer. Math. Soc. **65**, 279–330 (1949).
[2] On a theorem of von Neumann, Proc. Amer. Math. Soc. **9**, 987–994 (1958).

Marcus, S.
[1] La mesure de Jordan et l'intégrale de Riemann dans un espace mesuré topologique, Acta Sci. Math. Szeged **20**, 156–165 (1959).
[2] Atomic measures and Darboux property, Revue Math. pures et appl. **7**, 327–332 (1962).

Marczewski, E.
[1] On compact measures, Fund. Math. **40**, 113–124 (1953).

Marinescu, G.
[1] Espaces vectoriels normés (roumain), Ed. Acad. R.P.R., Bucureşti, 1956.

[2] Espaces vectoriels topologiques et pseudotopologiques (roumain), Ed. Acad. R.P.R., Bucureşti, 1959.
[3] Espaces vectoriels pseudotopologiques et théorie des distributions, VEB Deutscher Verlag der Wissenschaften, Berlin, 1963.

Métivier, M.
[1] Limites projectives de mesures. Martingales. Applications, Ann. Mat. Pura Appl. (4) **63**, 225–352 (1963).

Morse, M.
[1] Bilinear functionals over $C \times C$, Acta Sci. Math. Szeged **12**, 41–48 (1950).
[2] Bimeasures and their integral extensions, Ann. Mat. pura ed appl. **39**, 345–356 (1955).

Morse, M., Transue, V.
[1] Semi normed vector spaces with duals of integral type, J. d'Analyse Math. **4**, 149–186 (1954 — 1955).
[2] C-bimeasures Λ and their superior integrals Λ^*, Rendiconti Circolo Mat. Palermo **4**, 270–300 (1955).
[3] The representation of a C-bimeasure on a general rectangle, Proc. Nat. Acad. Sci. U.S.A. **42**, 89–95 (1956).
[4] C-bimeasures and their integral extensions, Ann. Math. **64**, 480–504 (1956).
[5] Products of a C-measure and a locally integrable mapping, Canad. J. Math. **9**, 475–486 (1957).

Murray, F. J.
[1] Linear transformations in L_p, $p > 1$, Trans. Amer. Math. Soc. **39**, 83–100 (1936).

Naimark, M. A.
[1] On a representation of additive operator set functions (russian), Doklady Akad. Nauk S.S.S.R. (N.S.) **41**, 359–361 (1943).
[2] Normed rings, 2nd ed., P. Noordhoff, Groningen, 1964 (Translation from the russian). German edition: Neumark, M. A., Normierte Algebren, VEB Deutscher Verlag der Wissenschaften, Berlin, 1959.

von Neumann, J.
[1] Algebraische Repräsentanten der Funktionen "bis auf eine Menge vom Maße Null", J. reine angew. Math. **165**, 109–115 (1931).

Nicolescu, M.
[1] Sur quelques propriétés élémentaires de la mesure de Jordan, Bul. Fac., Stiinte, Cernăuţi, **6**, 222–224 (1932).
[2] Sur les fonctions mesurables (J), Bull. Sci. Math. **57**, 276–281 (1933).
[3] Analiza Matematică, vol. I–III, Ed. Tehnică, Bucureşti, 1957, 1958, 1960.
[4] Fonctions réelles et éléments d'analyse fonctionnelle (roumain), Ed. didactică şi pedagogică, Bucureşti, 1962.

Nikodym, O. M.
[1] Sur une généralisation des intégrales de M. J. Radon, Fund. Math. **15**, 131–179 (1930).
[2] Sur les familles bornées de fonctions parfaitement additives d'ensemble abstrait, Monatsh. Math. Phys. **40**, 418–426 (1933).
[3] Sur les suites convergentes de fonctions parfaitement additives d'ensemble abstrait, Monatsh. Math. Phys. **40**, 427–432 (1933).
[4] Contribution à la théorie des fonctionnelles linéaires en connection avec la théorie de la mesure des ensembles abstraits, Mathematica Cluj **5**, 130–141 (1931).

Onicescu, O.
[1] Sur une intégrale et ses applications (roumain), An. Univ. "C. I. Parhon", Bucureşti, **13**, 9–10 (1957).
[2] Sur les champs de vecteurs-somme, C. R. Acad. Sci. Paris **246**, 3574–3576 (1958).
[3] Fonctions sommes sur une b-algèbre, Bull. Math. Soc. Sci. Math. Phys. R.P.R. **3** (51), 77–91 (1959).

Onicescu, O., Mihoc, G., Ionescu Tulcea, C. T.
[1] Calcul des probabilités et applications (roumain), Ed. Acad. R.P.R., Bucureşti, 1956.

Orlicz, W.
[1] Über konjugierte Exponentenfolgen, Studia Math. **3**, 200–211 (1931).
[2] Über eine gewisse Klasse von Räumen vom Typus B, Bull. Int. Acad. Polon. Sci. Sér. A., 207–220 (1932).
[3] Sur les opérations linéaires dans l'espace des fonctions bornées, Studia Math. **10**, 60–89 (1948).

Pál, I. G.
[1] Über die lineare Darstellung der kanonischen Operationen, Ann. Univ. Sci. Budapest **2**, 73–84 (1959).

Pettis, B. J.
[1] On integration in vector spaces, Trans. Amer. Math. Soc. **44**, 277–304 (1938).
[2] Linear functionals and completely additive set functions, Duke Math. J. **4**, 552–565 (1938).
[3] Absolutely continuous functions in vector spaces, Bull. Amer. Math. Soc. **45**, 677 (1939).

Phillips, R. S.
[1] Integration in a convex linear topological space, Trans. Amer. Math. Soc. **47**, 114–145 (1940).
[2] On linear transformations, Trans. Amer. Math. Soc. **48**, 516–541 (1940).
[3] On weakly compact subsets of a Banach space, Amer. J. Math. **65**, 108–136 (1943).

Pitt, H. R.
[1] Integration measure and probability, New York, 1963.

Plancherel, M.
[1] Integral-Darstellung willkürlicher Funktionen, Math. Ann. **67**, 519–534 (1909).

Popescu, V.
[1] Sur la définition des fonctions mesurables (roumain), Studii Cercet. Mat. **17**, 1457–1461 (1965).
[2] Mesures à valeurs dans des espaces vectoriels topologiques quelconques (roumain), Studii Cercet. Mat. **17**, 1515–1528 (1965).

Price, G. B.
[1] The theory of integration, Trans. Amer. Math. Soc. **47**, 1–50 (1940).

Radon, J.
[1] Theorie und Anwendungen der absolut additiven Mengenfunktionen. S.-B. Akad. Wiss. Wien **122**, 1295–1438 (1913).

Radu, E.
[1] Mesures Stieltjes vectorielles, Bull. Math. Soc. Sci. Math. Phys. R.P.R. **6** (54), 79–86 (1962).

Rao, M. M.
[1] Decomposition of vector measures, Proc. Nat. Acad. Sci. U.S.A. **15**, 771–774 (1964).
[2] Radon-Nikodym theorem for vector measures (preprint).

Rickart, C. E.
[1] Integration in a convex linear topological space, Trans. Amer. Math. Soc. **52**, 498–521 (1942).
[2] Decomposition of additive set functions, Duke Math. J. **10**, 653–665 (1943).
[3] An abstract Radon-Nikodym theorem, Trans. Amer. Math. Soc. **56**, 50–66 (1944).

Riesz, F.
[1] Sur les opérations fonctionnelles linéaires, C. R. Acad. Sci. Paris **149**, 974–977 (1909).
[2] Sur la convergence en moyenne, I, II, Acta Sci. Math. Szeged **4**, 58–64, 182–185 (1928–1929).
[3] Sur la représentation des opérations fonctionelles par des intégrales de Stieltjes, Proc. Roy. Physiog. Soc. Lund. **21**, no. 16, 145–151 (1952).
[4] Untersuchungen über Systeme integrierbarer Funktionen, Math. Ann. **69**, 449–497 (1910).

Riesz, F., Sz.-Nagy, B.
[1] Leçons d'analyse fonctionnelle, 4. éd., Akadémiai Kiádó, Budapest, 1965.

Ryan, R.
[1] Representative sets and direct sums, Proc. Amer. Math. Soc. **15**, 387–390 (1964).

Ryll-Nardzewski, C.
[1] On quasi-compact measures, Fund. Math. **40**, 125–130 (1953).

Saks, S.
[1] Theory of the integral, Warsaw, 1937.
[2] Integration in abstract metric space, Duke Math. J. **4**, 408–411 (1938).

Sebastião e Silva, J.

[1] Integration and derivation in Banach spaces, Univ. Lisboa, Revista Fac. Ci. A. Ci. Mat. (2) **1**, 117–166 (1950).

Segal, I. E.

[1] Invariant measures on locally compact spaces, J. Indian Math. Soc. (N.S.) **13**, 105–130 (1949).

[2] Equivalences of measures spaces, Amer. J. Math. **73**, 275–313 (1951).

[3] A non-commutative extension of abstract integration, Ann. Math. **57**, 401–457 (1953).

Sîmboan, G.

[1] Sur les mesures compactes (roumain), Comunic. Acad. R.P.R. **9**, 105–110 (1959).

[2] Mesures dans les espaces topologiques ordonnés (roumain), Comunic. Acad. R.P.R. **9**, 237–243 (1959).

[3] Vectorial measures, Revue Math. pures et appl. **7**, 383–415 (1962).

Singer, I.

[1] Linear functionals on the space of continuous mappings of a compact space into a Banach space (russian), Revue Math. pures et appl. **2**, 301–315 (1957).

[2] Les duals de certains espaces de Banach de champs de vecteurs, I, II, Bull. Sci. Math. **82**, 29–40 (1958); **83**, 73–96 (1959).

[3] Sur les applications linéaires intégrales des espaces de fonctions continues I, Revue Math. pures et appl. **4**, 391–401 (1959).

[4] Sur les applications linéaires majorées des espaces de fonctions continues, Rendiconti Accad. Naz. Lincei, **27**, 35–41 (1959).

[5] Sur la représentation intégrale des applications linéaires continuous des espaces $L_F^p(1 \leqq p < \infty)$, Rendiconti Accad. Naz. Lincei **29**, 28–32 (1960).

[6] Sur une classe d'applications linéaires continues des espaces $L_F^p\,(1 \leqq p < \infty)$, Ann. École Norm. Sup. **77**, 235–256 (1960).

[7] Sur les applications linéaires intégrales des espaces de fonctions continues a valeurs vectorielles, Acta. Sci. Math. Acad. Sci. Hung. **11**, 3–13 (1960).

Steinhaus, H.

[1] Additive und stetige Funktionaloperationen, Math. Z. **5**, 186–221 (1919).

Stieltjes, T. J.

[1] Recherches sur les fractions continues, Ann. Fac. Sci. Toulouse (1) **8**, 1–22 (1894).

Stone, M. H.

[1] The theory of representation of Boolean algebras, Trans. Amer. Math. Soc. **40**, 37–111 (1936).

[2] Applications of the theory of Boolean rings to general topology, Trans. Amer. Math. Soc. **41**, 375–481 (1937).

[3] Notes on integration, I–IV, Proc. Nat. Acad. Sci. U.S.A. **34**, 336–342, 447–445, 483–490 (1948); **35**, 50–58 (1949).

Swong, K.

[1] A representation theory of continuous linear maps, Math. Ann. **155**, 270–291 (1964).

Szász-Felten, I.

[1] Eine unmittelbare Definition des Moduls des vektoriellen Radonschen Maßes, Revue Roumaine Math. **10**, 1385–1389 (1965).

Tucker, D. H.

[1] A note on the Riesz representation theorem, Proc. Amer. Math. Soc. **14**, 354–358 (1963).

[2] A representation theorem for a continuous linear transformation on a space of continuous functions, Proc. Amer. Math. Soc. **16**, 946–953 (1965).

Vasiliu, C.

[1] Sur le théorème de décomposition de Lebesgue (roumain), Comunic. Acad. R.P.R. **13**, 863–869 (1963).

Weil, A.

[1] L'intégration dans les groupes topologiques et ses applications, Paris, 1953.

Zaanen, A. C.

[1] On a certain class of Banach spaces, Ann. Math. (2) **47**, 654–666 (1946).

[2] Note on a certain class of Banach spaces, Nederl. Akad. Wetensch. **52**, 488–499 (1949).

[3] Integral transformations and their resolvents in Orlicz and Lebesgue spaces, Compositio Math. **10**, 56–94 (1952).

[4] Linear Analysis, New York–Amsterdam, 1953.

[5] The Radon-Nikodym theorem, I, II, Indag. Math. **23**, 157–187 (1961).

INDEX OF NOTATIONS

INDEX

OTHER TITLES IN THE SERIES IN PURE AND APPLIED MATHEMATICS

Vol. 1. WALLACE—*An Introduction to Algebraic Topology*
Vol. 2. PEDOE—*Circles*
Vol. 3. SPAIN—*Analytical Conics*
Vol. 4. MIKHLIN—*Integral Equations*
Vol. 5. EGGLESTON—*Problems in Euclidean Space: Application of Convexity*
Vol. 6. WALLACE—*Homology Theory on Algebraic Varieties*
Vol. 7. NOBLE—*Methods Based on the Wiener–Hopf Technique for the Solution of Partial Differential Equations*
Vol. 8. MIKUSIŃSKI—*Operational Calculus*
Vol. 9. HEINE—*Group Theory in Quantum Mechanics*
Vol. 10. BLAND—*The Theory of Linear Viscoelasticity*
Vol. 11. KURTH—*Axiomatics of Classical Statistical Mechanics*
Vol. 12. FUCHS—*Abelian Groups*
Vol. 13. KURATOWSKI—*Introduction to Set Theory and Topology*
Vol. 14. SPAIN—*Analytical Quadrics*
Vol. 15. HARTMAN and MIKUSIŃSKI—*Theory of Lebesgue Measure and Integration*
Vol. 16. KULCZYCKI—*Non-Euclidean Geometry*
Vol. 17. KURATOWSKI—*Introduction to Calculus*
Vol. 18. GERONIMUS—*Polynomials Orthogonal on a Circle and Interval*
Vol. 19. ELSGOLC—*Calculus of Variations*
Vol. 20. ALEXITS—*Convergence Problems of Orthogonal Series*
Vol. 21. FUCHS and LEVIN—*Functions of a Complex Variable, Volume II*
Vol. 22. GOODSTEIN—*Fundamental Concepts of Mathematics*
Vol. 23. KEENE—*Abstracts Sets and Finite Ordinals*
Vol. 24. DITKIN and PRUDNIKOV—*Operational Calculus in Two Variables and its Applications*
Vol. 25. VEKUA—*Generalized Analytic Functions*
Vol. 26. FASS and AMIR-MOÉZ—*Elements of Linear Spaces*
Vol. 27. GRADSHTEIN—*Direct and Converse Theorems*
Vol. 28. FUCHS—*Partially Ordered Algebraic Systems*
Vol. 29. POSTNIKOV—*Foundations of Galois Theory*
Vol. 30. BERMANT—*A Course of Mathematical Analysis, Part II*
Vol. 31. ŁUKASÍEWICZ—*Elements of Mathematical Logic*
Vol. 32. VULIKH—*Introduction to Functional Analysis for Scientists and Technologists*
Vol. 33. PEDOE—*An Introduction to Projective Geometry*
Vol. 34. TIMAN—*Theory of Approximation of Functions of a Real Variable*
Vol. 35. CSÂSZÁR—*Foundations of General Topology*
Vol. 36. BRONSHTEIN and SEMENDYAYEV—*A Guide-Book to Mathematics for Technologists and Engineers*
Vol. 37. MOSTOWSKI and STARK—*Introduction to Higher Algebra*
Vol. 38. GODDARD—*Mathematical Techniques of Operational Research*
Vol. 39. TIKHONOV and SAMARSKII—*Equations of Mathematical Physics*
Vol. 40. MCLEOD—*Introduction to Fluid Dynamics*

Vol. 41. Moisil—*The Algebraic Theory of Switching Circuits*
Vol. 42. Otto—*Nomography*
Vol. 43. Rankin—*An Introduction to Mathematical Analysis*
Vol. 44. Bermant—*A Course of Mathematical Analysis, Part I*
Vol. 44. Bermant—*A Course of Mathematical Analysis, Part I*
Vol. 45. Krasnosel'skii—*Topological Methods in the Theory of Nonlinear Integral Equations*
Vol. 46. Kantorovich and Akilov—*Functional Analysis in Normed Spaces*
Vol. 47. Jones—*The Theory of Electromagnetism*
Vol. 48. Fejes Tóth—*Regular Figures*
Vol. 49. Yano—*Differential Geometry on Complex and Almost Complex Spaces*
Vol. 50. Mikhlin—*Variational Methods in Mathematical Physics*
Vol. 51. Fuchs and Shabat—*Functions of a Complex Variable and Some of their Applications Volume 1*
Vol. 52. Budak, Samarskii and Tikhonov—*A Collection of Problems on Mathematical Physics*
Vol. 53. Giles—*Mathematical Foundations of Thermodynamics*
Vol. 54. Saul'yev—*Integration of Equations of Parabolic Type by the Method of Nets*
Vol. 55. Pontryagin *et al.*—*The Mathematical Theory of Optimal Processes*
Vol. 56. Sobolev—*Partial Differential Equations of Mathematical Physics*
Vol. 57. Smirnov—*A Course of Higher Mathematics, Volume I*
Vol. 58. Smirnov—*A Course of Higher Mathematics, Volume II*
Vol. 59. Smirnov—*A Course of Higher Mathematics, Volume III, Part 1*
Vol. 60. Smirnov—*A Course of Higher Mathematics, Volume III, Part 2*
Vol. 61. Smirnov—*A Course of Higher Mathematics, Volume IV*
Vol. 62. Smirnov—*A Course of Higher Mathematics, Volume V*
Vol. 63. Naimark—*Linear Representations of the Lorentz Group*
Vol. 64. Berman—*A Collection of Problems on a Course of Mathematical Analysis*
Vol. 65. Meshcherskii—*A Collection of Problems of Mechanics*
Vol. 66. Arscott—*Periodic Differential Equations*
Vol. 67. Sansone and Conti—*Non-linear Differential Equations*
Vol. 68. Volkovyskii, Lunts and Aramanovich—*A Collection of Problems on Complex Analysis*
Vol. 69. Lyusternik and Yanpol'skii—*Mathematical Analysis–Functions, Limits, Series, Continued Fractions*
Vol. 70. Kurosh—*Lectures in General Algebra*
Vol. 71. Baston—*Some Properties of Polyhedra in Euclidean Space*
Vol. 72. Fikhtengol'ts—*The Fundamentals of Mathematical Analysis, Volume 1*
Vol. 73. Fikhtengol'ts—*The Fundamentals of Mathematical Analysis, Volume 2*
Vol. 74. Preisendorfer—*Radiative Transfer on Discrete Spaces*
Vol. 75. Faddeyev and Sominskii—*Elementary Algebra*
Vol. 76. Lyusternik, Chervonenkis and Yanpol'skii—*Handbook for Computing Elementary Functions*
Vol. 77. Shilov—*Mathematical Analysis—A Special Course*
Vol. 78. Ditkin and Prudnikov—*Integral Transform and Operational Calculus*
Vol. 79. Polozhii—*The Method of Summary Representations for Numerical Solution of Problems of Mathematical Physics*
Vol. 80. Mishina and Proskuryakov—*Higher Algebra–Linear Algebra, Polynomials, General Algebra*
Vol. 81. Aramanovich *et al.*—*Mathematical Analysis–Differentiation and Integration*
Vol. 82. Redei—*The Theory of Finitely Generated Commutative Semigroups*
Vol. 83. Mikhlin—*Multidimensional Singular Integrals and Integral Equations*
Vol. 84. Lebedev, Skal'skaya and Uflyand—*Problems in Mathematical Physics*
Vol. 85. Gakhov—*Boundary Value Problems*

MADE IN GREAT BRITAIN